# THE CONTINUOUS MAXIMUM PRINCIPLE

*a study of complex*
*systems optimization*

BY THE SAME AUTHORS:

*The Discrete Maximum Principle:*
*A Study of Multistage Systems Optimization*
by Liang-Tseng Fan and Chiu-Sen Wang

# THE CONTINUOUS
# MAXIMUM PRINCIPLE

*a study of complex
systems optimization*

## LIANG-TSENG FAN

*Professor, Department of Chemical Engineering*
*Kansas State University, Manhattan, Kansas*

*In collaboration with*

| | |
|---|---|
| T. C. CHEN | C. S. WANG |
| S. J. CHEN | Y. C. KO |
| Y. K. AHN | L. E. ERICKSON |
| C. L. HWANG | L. S. FAN |

*John Wiley & Sons, Inc., New York · London · Sydney*

SECOND PRINTING, NOVEMBER, 1966

Library of Congress Catalog Card Number: 65-24290

Printed in the United States of America

# Preface

This monograph is a sequel to the earlier volume *The Discrete Maximum Principle* and includes some results that my collaborators and I have obtained in our continuing efforts to apply the maximum principle to the optimization of geometrically simple and complex systems. This work is intended primarily to serve those who are interested in the application of the maximum principle to the design and control of industrial and process engineering systems. As in the preceding volume, there is a strong emphasis on the application of the theory to specific problems, and detailed solutions are presented so that the reader can see how the maximum principle algorithms are used.

Although previous development and applications of the maximum principle dealing primarily with geometrically simple processes are outlined in several of the beginning chapters, the present book emphasizes several versions of the maximum principle algorithm that we have developed which are suitable for optimizing a geometrically complex system containing at least one continuous process within the system. A considerable amount of material related to the discrete form of the maximum principle and to dynamic programming is also included. In industry in general, and in the chemical process industry in particular, one often finds that both continuous and discrete processes are involved within a single system. The discrete version of the maximum principle and dynamic programming can often be advantageously employed in combination with the continuous version of the maximum principle to optimize such a system.

*v*

This book is written in sufficient detail that it can be used both as a text by students who first come into contact with the subject and by practicing "optimizers" and engineers as a self-teaching aid. Although the material is arranged in an increasing degree of complexity, every effort has been made to maintain as elementary a level of mathematics as possible. The approach is informal and no attempt has been made to give a rigorous mathematical treatment to every topic. We did not hesitate to employ a qualitative argument and/or an empirical verification when we could not provide a rigorous one or when the length and complexity of the rigorous treatment appeared to be excessive. We believe that more often than not the invention of a method or a system precedes its rigorous mathematical treatment or description. This should not prevent its use so long as sufficient caution is exerted to verify the result or to examine the product.

Those who wish to learn more about the mathematical foundation of the maximum principle should consult works published by Pontryagin and his coworkers and other sources listed in various chapters of the book.

I am well aware of the fact that other researchers were successful recently in attempting to "generalize" or modify the maximum principle so that it can be used to optimize geometrically complex industrial processes and systems. Some of these results appear to be more rigorous and/or sophisticated than those obtained by our group but we have not tried to include all of these results in this book. To have done so would have broken the continuity and uniformity of presentation and would have required excessive space.

We do not necessarily believe that the maximum principle is the best or the only method of solving every problem treated in the two books. We do believe that every available optimization technique has both strong points and shortcomings. An accumulation of extensive experiences with any method is necessary before one can realize its ultimate capability or limitations. Compared with such established techniques as linear programming and dynamic programming, however, little has been done to exploit the capability of the maximum principle for the design of industrial and process engineering systems.

Our experience has led us to believe that for a specific problem there may be an optimization technique that is superior to the others but that there is no one method that is superior for all problems. The strong emphasis on the maximum principle in this volume therefore should not be construed as evidence that we believe that the maximum principle is always superior to other methods.

A word about the arrangement of the material may be helpful to those reading or teaching the material for the first time. The presentation of the maximum principle algorithms is in Chapters 2, 3, 6, 8, and 10. Most of the applications are presented in Chapters 3, 4, 5, and 7. Chapter 9 deals with the combined use of dynamic programming and the maximum principle and Chapter 11 discusses how dynamic programming, the calculus of variations and the maximum principle are related to each other. The book is written so that it can be used to teach an optimal process design course. However, Chapters 3 and 5 deal more with optimal control than optimal process design, but the material relating to optimal control in these chapters may easily be omitted.

Most books have at least one shortcoming, that of incomplete coverage of the subject, and this book is no exception. Many important topics related to the application of the maximum principle to optimal control are not included. Some other important topics that we have not included are the optimization of distributed systems, the stability problem associated with computation, and the state variable inequality constraint of arbitrary order, to name just a few.

Obviously a monograph of the nature and scope of this could not be written without a great deal of direct or indirect assistance from many persons. I am generally indebted to all the workers in my own field. I also wish to acknowledge the assistance of many of my students and others who read the preliminary form of the manuscript and provided me with many valuable suggestions in revising it.

During the preliminary investigation as well as during the actual writing of this book various comments were relayed directly or indirectly to me by several workers in the field of optimization. Such comments were essential to its successful completion. In this connection I wish to express my sincere appreciation to Professors R. Aris, L. Eagleton, F. Horn, S. Katz, Y. Takahashi, D. Wilde, and to Drs. M. Denn and R. Jackson. Much encouragement and assistance were also received from my colleagues Dean Paul E. Russell, Professors L. Hobson, W. H. Honstead, D. Nesmith and others at Kansas State University.

The material treated in this volume cannot be fully understood without indulging in the pleasure of actual research. My research projects in which the maximum principle has been extensively employed have been financially supported by the *Office of Saline Water, U.S. Department of the Interior*, and the *Engineering Experiment Station of Kansas State University*. All collaborators whose names appear on the inside cover of this monograph participated in the above mentioned projects at one time or another.

The revision of the manuscript and the proof reading of the galleys were done by my collaborators and me during my sabbatical leave which was spent at the Engineering Laboratory of Cambridge University headed by Sir John Baker. This stay during the early part of 1965 was arranged by Mr. J. F. Coales and Dr. H. H. Rosenbrock of the Control Engineering Group of the Laboratory. The author is grateful for the convenience provided by the Laboratory and for its intellectual atmosphere.

Finally I should like to mention those who have been a constant source of encouragement during the most difficult time of my professional career: Mrs. L. T. Fan, Professors H. V. Fairbanks, W. A. Koehler and C. Y. Wen, Dr. S. L. Wang, and the late Professor H. T. Ward.

*Manhattan, Kansas*                                   L. T. FAN
*January 1966*

# Contents

# 1

# *Introduction*

## 1. THE CONCEPT OF OPTIMIZATION

Human wants are ever increasing as technology advances toward obtaining more products from limited natural and human resources. As resources are being further depleted, progress in technology has to be speeded up so that these rapidly expanding demands can be satisfied. The daily activities of individuals, of gigantic enterprises, and, as a matter of fact, of those of the entire economic system have been based on the simple principle of "optimality." The enduring effort to improve the technology has gradually given rise to the notion of optimization. Optimization is the act of obtaining the best result under given (fixed) conditions. To elaborate this point, individuals try to gain maximum satisfaction with their limited budgets (income), and all production of industrial concerns is aimed at attaining maximum profit (minimum cost) under existing technological restrictions (constraints).

The act of optimization frequently presents a mathematical problem of such nature that a certain function of several variables is to be maximized or minimized with some constraints imposed on the variables. Since it is the objective of the optimizer (operator) to operate the system in the best way, such a function representing the performance criterion of a system is called the objective function. It is clear that the maximization or minimization of the objective function leads to the optimization of the system. The optimizer has several variables under his control, which hence are called the decision variables. His problem is to find the values

*1*

of the decision variables within the allowed boundary (constraints) which maximize the value of the objective function, one of the state variables. This sequence of decisions is called an optimal policy.

Optimization is an art that requires the ingenuity and knowledge of the individual involved in carrying it out. However, past experience of human efforts has resulted in many refined mathematical techniques which assist us in attaining goals of optimization.

The common procedure in optimizing a system is divided into five steps by Cochran [1]:

1. Definitions of objective, system boundaries, independent variables, restrictions, and external parameters. This task can be explained briefly. The objective function for business enterprise is usually a profit function that uses capital expenditure as the decision variable. It may also be a cost function when minimization of cost is the objective. All restrictions, boundary conditions, and external parameters should be clearly defined so that the solution for a system is consistent.

2. Analysis and simplification. This step does not need much elaboration. All situations should be analyzed before any calculation is executed because the act of simplification itself may cut down the enormous cost of calculation and it may be a part of the optimal policy. The simplification may apply to the reduction of insignificant variables and of inferior processes. It may also be accomplished by dividing a process of many variables into another with several stages (blocks) of few variables.

3. Simulation or mathematization of the objective (response) function. This task of formulating mathematical equations may be theoretical or empirical. Many statistical or computer techniques will help.

4. Verification or checking. Simulation is useless unless the empirical or theoretical equations are tested against the system which is under consideration in reality. The "goodness" or "badness" of equations determines the success or failure of the last step of actual optimization calculations.

These steps depend largely on the individual in charge of optimization. They are not the main topics of our discussion.

5. Optimization—solutions of functions for extrema. This step usually requires extensive mathematical analysis. Various optimization techniques are discussed briefly in the following section.

As already mentioned, the ceaseless effort of maintaining and improving the welfare of human beings has resulted in the formulation of mathematical techniques of optimization, many of which are applicable to wide fields of human activities.

Many of these activities are stagewise in structure whereas others are continuous. A stagewise (dynamic) process can be described generally by a system of difference equations; a continuous (dynamic) process is, on the other hand, described by a system of differential equations. Our task of optimizing a continuous process is to find the values of the decision variables at each point on its path so that its objective function can be maximized.

A continuous (dynamic) decision process may be considered as an abstract notion by which a large number of human activities can be represented. The process is either deterministic or stochastic. In this book only deterministic cases are treated. A path of the process may represent any real or abstract entity (for example, a space path, a time path, or a sequence of continuing economic activity) in which a certain transformation takes place. Those variables that are transformed along each path are called state variables. The desired transformation is achieved by manipulation of decision variables along the path. The transformation along each path is completely described by a set of performance equations. The process can have more than one initial or final value.

The problem of optimizing a continuous (dynamic) decision process may be called dynamic optimization. The objective function of the process, which is to be maximized or minimized, can be expressed as a function of the state variables leaving the path or paths of the process. Thus a general continuous (dynamic) optimization problem can be stated as follows:

For a process with all the performance equations and the initial and/or final values of some of the state variables given find the values of the decision (control) variables at each point of the path or paths of the process subject to certain constraints in such a way that the objective function is maximized or minimized.

Now, let us consider a few concrete examples of problems of this nature.

The efficiency of a chemical reactor in which a catalytic reaction is carried out gradually decreases as the catalyst becomes older. Eventually a state is reached in which regeneration or replacement of the catalyst is desired. A problem of great significance is to find the best operating conditions (such as temperature and flow rate) at each moment as well as the best time for regenerating or replacing the catalyst in order to obtain the maximum profit. The path in this case is a time path. The operating temperature and the flow rate are the two decision variables. The cumulative flow rate, which characterizes the activity of the catalyst, and the cumulative net profit are considered as the two state variables. The objective function is the total net profit represented by one of the state variables at the end of the single path of the process.

All problems of the classical calculus of variations, such as the brachistochrone problem and the estimation of the optimal trajectory of a rocket, are similar to the catalytic reaction problem already described in that each system or process changes dynamically along a single path.

In the process industries, however, it is not uncommon to find a system that consists of several interconnected and often interacting paths. The composition of a material being processed in the system is transformed (dynamically) along the paths. The optimization problem here is no longer the determination of the values of the decision variables such as temperature and pressure in a single path of the system. Such values of the decision variables in all the interconnected paths must be simultaneously determined.

## 2.  TECHNIQUES OF OPTIMIZATION

There are many techniques of searching for the extremal value of a function. In this section we state briefly some of the most frequently used techniques for solving problems of extrema, commonly called optimization techniques.

*a. Direct Method of Calculation.*  Once a functional relationship is formulated between a decision variable and a state variable (objective function) we can directly calculate the value of the state variable (objective function) for one fixed decision variable. Whenever the value of the function is increased by using another value of the decision variable, we pick the second value instead of the first. This calculation can be repeated until no improvement can be made on the value of the state variable (objective function).

This method is applicable whenever there is a single decision variable or when there are few variables with limited choices. Whenever the domain of the decision variable increases and/or there is more than one extremal value for the state variable (objective function), the task of finding the extremal value becomes inhibitive.

*b. Classical Differential Calculus Method.*  The problem of maxima and minima has been widely treated in conventional differential calculus (see Reference 2). When the objective function $f$ has as its arguments, $x = (x_1, x_2, \ldots, x_n)$ and its first partial derivatives are continuous, we can set the partial derivatives of $f$ with respect to $x_i$ equal to zero.

$$\left(\frac{\partial f}{\partial x_i}\right)_{x_r \text{ for } r \neq i} = 0, \qquad i = 1, 2, \ldots, n.$$

The values of $x_i$ obtained by solving these $n$ equations simultaneously will give the objective function $f$ an extremum. Whether it is maximum or minimum can be determined from the sign and/or magnitude of the second and/or higher derivatives.

When there is no other value greater (smaller) than the value we obtained, we are assured of the maximum (minimum) of the function. The last sentence refers to the unimodality of an extremum.

When the function $f(x_1, x_2, \ldots, x_n) = 0$ is to be solved for extrema under constraints, $g_j(x_1, x_2, \ldots, x_n) = 0$, $(j = 1, 2, \ldots, m; m < n)$, we can solve $m$ equations of $g$ and express variables, $x_{n-m+1}, x_{n-m+2}, \ldots, x_n$, in terms of $x_1, x_2, \ldots, x_{n-m}$. Then the function $f$ is partially differentiated with respect to $x_1, x_2, \ldots, x_{n-m}$, and the $(n - m)$ partial derivatives are set equal to zero and solved for $x_1, x_2, \ldots, x_{n-m}$. The rest of the variables, $x_{n-m+1}, x_{n-m+2}, \ldots, x_n$, are readily obtained from the expression derived from the constraints. The Lagrange multiplier method provides a useful tool in solving problems of constrained extrema.

*c. Lagrange Multiplier Method.* The Lagrange multiplier method introduces $m$ undetermined coefficients (multipliers), $\lambda_1, \lambda_2, \ldots, \lambda_m$, and makes a composite function, $F = f - \lambda_1 g_1 - \lambda_2 g_2 - \cdots - \lambda_m g_m$. The remaining procedure is to form the system of equations by partially differentiating $F$ with respect to $x_1, x_2, \ldots, x_n$:

$$\frac{\partial F}{\partial x_i} = 0, \qquad i = 1, 2, \ldots, n,$$

$$g_j(x_1, x_2, \ldots, x_n) = 0, \qquad j = 1, 2, \ldots, m.$$

With the preceding $(n + m)$ equations we can solve for $n$ unknowns of $x$ and $m$ unknowns of $\lambda$. The set $(x_1, x_2, \ldots, x_n)$ thus obtained is the combination of $x$ which gives the extremal value.

The techniques mentioned apply only to internal extrema. Whenever extrema are located at the boundary points of the region of variation, the property of $\partial f / \partial x_i = 0$ generally does not exist. Thus before any final judgment is passed we have to evaluate $f$ at the boundary points to see whether it is the real maximum (minimum).

*d. The Calculus of Variations.* Another classical analytical method is the calculus of variations. A typical problem treated by this method is that of finding a function $y = y(x)$ such that the integral

$$P = \int_{x_1}^{x_2} F[x, y(x), y'(x)]\, dx$$

is minimized when the two end points $(x_1, y_1)$ and $(x_2, y_2)$ are preassigned. The classical method is to solve the Euler equation

$$\frac{\partial F}{\partial y} - \frac{d}{dx}\left(\frac{\partial F}{\partial y'}\right) = 0$$

for the function $y$.

For the classical treatment readers are referred to Bliss [3].

*e. Experimental Search Method.*    There are various experimental designs for the search of extrema, and we shall list a few of them with brief descriptions. For exhaustive treatments readers are referred to Wilde [4]. *Single Variable Search.* Whenever there is only one decision variable, the interval of search for the value of the variable which gives the extremal value to the objective function can be narrowed down by using either the simultaneous or the sequential method. The effectiveness of various methods is expressed by the ratio of the initial interval of search $I_0$ over the interval after the $n$th trial $I_n$, that is, $I_0/I_n$. The uniform-pairs method divides the interval equally for search, and the effectiveness is shown as $I_0/I_n = (n/2) + 1$. The sequential dichotomous method utilizes past observations in such a way that the interval for search narrows down exponentially, according to the number of observations, and its effectiveness is shown as $I_0/I_n = 2^{n/2}$. The most effective search method is probably the Fibonacci. It utilizes the Fibonacci series to narrow down the interval and has the effectiveness of $I_0/I_n = F_n$; $F_n$ is defined as follows:

$$F_0 = F_1 = 1, \qquad F_n = F_{n-1} + F_{n-2} \quad \text{for} \quad n > 2.$$

Kiefer and Johnson developed this search method in the 1950's. It was shown that of all search methods in the single variable search the Fibonacci method has the minimax property in the sense that the interval by this search is the shortest of all intervals among the longest possible intervals in which the maxima may exist. This was clearly stated by Wilde [4]. The Fibonacci method can narrow down the interval to 1% of the original interval with 11 experiments. There is the golden section method which uses the age-old technique of dividing a section into unequal sections in such a way that the ratio of the whole to the longer section is equal to the ratio of the longer section to the shorter section. *Multivariable Search Method.* When there are more than two decision variables, it is necessary to use highly sophisticated methods to search the region for extrema. The contour tangent method is a technique that eliminates a region by drawing a tangent line to the contour or response surface and then seeks a point in a higher contour area. The tangent line technique is applied repeatedly until the maximum peak is approached. The success of this method presupposes that the response contour is strongly unimodal. The gradient (ascent) method searches a maximum by climbing up a hill to the peak, and it will eventually arrive at the peak (maximum) if the objective function is unimodal. The speed of convergence depends on the scale and also on the technique used to find the steepest way to climb. It does not require that the objective function expressed as a response surface be strongly unimodal. However, if the objective function is strongly unimodal, the tangent method can be combined with the steepest ascent method to speed up the search. Recently, Shah, Buehler, and Kempthorne developed the technique of Partan (parallel tangency), which combines the climbing property of the ascent method and the elimination property of the contour tangent method but most of all utilizes the geometric property of ellipsoidal contours. When two parallel tangent lines touch the ellipsoidal contour, the line that connects two points of tangency passes through the center. This property is easily applied to any ellipsoidal contour, but it can be used for most of the contours after a few steps of either the ascending or the elimination technique are applied.

*f. Linear and Nonlinear Programming.* Whenever an objective function is in linear form with linear constraints on the variables, the maximum (minimum) generally occurs at the boundary so that differential calculus fails to give the maximum (minimum). Linear programming was developed to circumvent this difficulty. It was started during World War II and was well developed in the postwar period. The method can be simply described. The goal of linear programming is to find a combination of $n$ variables $(x_1, x_2, \ldots, x_n)$ to maximize

$$\sum_{i=1}^{n} a_i x_i$$

subject to the following constraints:

$$\sum_{j=1}^{n} B_{1j} x_j \leq C_1,$$

$$\sum_{j=1}^{n} B_{2j} x_j \leq C_2$$

. .

. .

. .

$$\sum_{j=1}^{n} B_{mj} x_j \leq C_m.$$

This solution to the problem is called the simplex method. The works of Dorfman, Samuelson, and Solow and more recently Dantzig [5] are recommended to readers interested in an extensive study of this subject. However, linear objective functions are at most crude approximations, and often objective functions are in quadratic or other nonlinear forms. The method of solving cases of nonlinear objective functions with either nonlinear or linear constraints is called nonlinear programming, but the difficulty in treating the inequality constraints has still to be overcome. An advanced treatment of this subject is found in Arrow, Hurwicz, and Uzawa [6].

*g. Dynamic Programming.*    The founder and the most important propagator of this method is Bellman [7, 8, 9, 37].

Dynamic programming is powerful in treating the optimization of the performance of a process in which the entire procedure can be regarded as a sequence of stages. The number of stages may be numerous, but, if decisions at each stage are few, multistage decision problems can be readily solved with the help of modern computers. A continuous process can be treated in a similar manner by regarding the process as one with a large number of infinitesimal stages. In the field of chemical reactor design, an extensive treatment of optimization problems by dynamic programming has been done by Aris in both continuous and discrete versions [10, 11].

*h. The Maximum Principle.*    The maximum principle was first hypothesized by the Russian mathematician Pontryagin [12] in 1956. The original Pontryagin method is confined to continuous processes, that is, to processes described by a system of first-order differential equations. The development of this method is stated in the following section.

For a comprehensive study of optimization techniques readers are referred to Leitmann [13].

## 3. THE DEVELOPMENT OF THE MAXIMUM PRINCIPLE

Among the numerous attempts to find new dynamic optimization methods in recent years dynamic programming developed by Bellman and the maximum principle derived by Pontryagin are probably the two most successful. The maximum principle was first proposed in 1956 by Pontryagin and his associates [14, 15, 16] for individual types of time-optimizing continuous processes. In the following year Gamkrelidze [17, 18] proved theorems of existence and uniqueness and examined the problem of synthesizing time-optimal controls for linear systems. It was fully proved by Boltyanskii [19] in 1958 that the maximum principle was a necessary condition for time optimality.

In 1958 Gamkrelidze [20] extended the maximum principle to a general case in which an arbitrary functional of an integral function is maximized or minimized. A detailed presentation of the basic results obtained by Pontryagin and his co-workers can be found in References 12, 21, 22, and comprehensive treatment of the essential problems in the theory of automatic control, which are associated with the proof and use of the maximum principle, is given by Rozonoer [23].

The first attempt to extend the maximum principle to the optimization of stagewise processes was made by Rozonoer [23] in 1959 for the processes that are linear in the state variables. In 1960 Chang [24] presented the discrete version of the maximum principle for nonlinear simple processes, which was further explored in his subsequent papers and a book [25, 26, 27]. An algorithm essentially similar to Chang's version was independently obtained by Katz [28, 29], and Denn and Aris extended the derivations of the algorithm to show the weak and strong necessary conditions of the discrete maximum principle [38].

As already indicated, topologically complex processes comprised of a number of stages not interconnected in a simple sequential order are common in the process industries. It is therefore of great interest to modify or "generalize" the maximum principle so that it can be used to optimize these processes. Several successful attempts to "generalize" the discrete version have been reported [30, 31, 32, 33]. A large portion of *The Discrete Maximum Principle—A Study of Multistage Systems Optimization*, which is the companion volume of this book, is also devoted to describe the work that my associates and I have done [34].

We shall emphasize in later chapters a version of the maximum principle applicable to topologically or geometrically complex but continuous processes [35] and several related mathematical methods [33, 36] and their applications.

## REFERENCES

1. Cochran, W. O., "Procedure for Selection of Optimum Conditions," *Chem. Eng. Progr. Symp. Ser.* **31, 56,** 88 (1960).
2. Courant, R., *Differential and Integral Calculus*, Interscience, New York, 1936.
3. Bliss, G. A., *Lectures on the Calculus of Variations*, University of Chicago Press, Chicago, 1946.
4. Wilde, D. J., *Optimum Seeking Methods*, Prentice-Hall, Englewood Cliffs, New Jersey, 1964.
5. Dorfman, R., P. A. Samuelson, and R. M. Solow, *Linear Programming and Economic Analysis*, McGraw-Hill, New York, 1958. See also G. B. Dantzig, *Linear Programming and Extensions*, Princeton University Press, Princeton, New Jersey, 1963.

6. Arrow, K., L. Hurwicz, and H. Uzawa, *Studies in Linear and Nonlinear Programming*, Stanford University Press, Stanford, California, 1958.

7. Bellman, R., *Dynamic Programming, Princeton University Press, Princeton, New Jersey*, 1957.

8. Bellman, R., *Adaptive Control Processes*, Princeton University Press, Princeton, New Jersey, 1961.

9. Bellman, R., and S. E. Dreyfus, *Applied Dynamic Programming*, Princeton University Press, Princeton, New Jersey, 1962.

10. Aris, R., *The Optimal Design of Chemical Reactors. A Study in Dynamic Programming*, Academic Press, New York, 1961.

11. Aris, R., *Discrete Dynamic Programming*, Blaisdell, New York, 1964.

12. Pontryagin, L. S., V. G. Boltyanskii, R. V. Gamkrelidze, and E. F. Mischenko, *The Mathematical Theory of Optimal Processes* (English translation by K. N. Trirogoff), Interscience, New York, 1962.

13. Leitman, G., Ed., *Optimization Techniques with Applications to Aerospace Systems*, Academic Press, New York, 1962.

14. Boltyanskii, V. G., R. V. Gamkrelidze, and L. S. Pontryagin, "On The Theory of Optimum Processes" (in Russian), *Doklady Akad. Nauk SSSR*, **110**, No. 1 (1956).

15. Pontryagin, L. S., "Some Mathematical Problems Arising in Connection with the Theory of Optimum Automatic Control System" (in Russian), Session of the Academy of Sciences of the USSR on Scientific Problems of Automating Industry, October 15–20, 1956.

16. Pontryagin, L. S., "Basic Problems of Automatic Regulation and Control" (in Russian), *Izd-vo. Akad. Nauk SSSR* (1957).

17. Gamkrelidze, R. V., "On the Theory of Optimum Processes in Linear Systems" (in Russian), *Doklady Akad. Nauk SSSR*, **116**, No. 1 (1957).

18. Gamkrelidze, R. V., "The Theory of Time-Optimal Processes in Linear Systems" (in Russian), *Izv. Akad. Nauk SSSR, Ser. Matem.* **22**, No. 4 (1958). English translation in Report No. 61–7, University of California, Department of Engineering, Los Angeles, California.

19. Boltyanskii, V. G., "The Maximum Principle in the Theory of Optimum Processes" (in Russian), *Doklady Akad. Nauk. SSSR*, **119**, No. 6 (1958).

20. Gamkrelidze, R. V., "On the General Theory of Optimum Processes" (in Russian), *Doklady Akad. Nauk SSSR*, **123**, No. 2 (1958). English translation in *Automation Express*, **1**, 37–39 (1959).

21. Pontryagin, L. S., "Optimal Regulation Processes" (in Russian), *Uspekhi Matem, Nauk*, **14**, No. 1, 85 (1959). English translation in *Am. Math. Soc. Trans.*, Ser. 2, **18**, 321–339 (1961).

22. Pontryagin, L. S., *Proc. of First IFAC Conf.*, Vol. 1, p. 454, Butterworths, England, 1961.

23. Rozonoer, L. I., "The Maximum Principle of L. S. Pontryagin in Optimal-system Theory," *Automat. Telemech.*, Moscow, **20**, 1320, 1441, 1561 (1960).

24. Chang, S. S. L., "Digitized Maximum Principle," *Proc. IRE*, **48**, 2030–2031 (1960).

25. Chang, S. S. L., "Computer Optimization of Nonlinear Control Systems by Means of Digitized Maximum Principle," a paper presented at IRE International Convention, New York, March 1961.

26. Chang, S. S. L., "Dynamic Programming and Pontryagin's Maximum Principle," *Proceedings of Dynamic Programming Workshop* (Second Annual Pre-JACC Workshop), pp. 109–183, Boulder, Colorado, June 1961.

27. Chang, S. S. L., *Synthesis of Optimum Control Systems*, McGraw-Hill, New York, 1961.

28. Katz, S., "A Discrete Version of Pontryagin's Maximum Principle," *J. Electron. Control*, **13**, 179 (1962).

29. Katz, S., "Best Operating Points for Staged Systems," *Ind. Eng. Chem., Fundamentals*, **1**, 226 (1962).

30. Wang, C. S., and L. T. Fan, "Multistage Optimization by the Generalized Discrete Maximum Principle," *J. Electron. Control*, **16**, 441 (1964).

31. Jackson, R., "Some Algebraic Properties of Optimization Problems in Complex Chemical Plants," *Chem. Eng. Sci.*, **19**, 19 (1964).

32. Jackson, R., "A Generalized Variational Treatment of Optimization Problems in Complex Chemical Plants," *Chem. Eng. Sci.*, **19**, 253 (1964).

33. Denn, M. M., and R. Aris, "Green's Functions and Optimal Systems I: Necessary Conditions and an Iterative Technique," *Ind. Eng. Chem.*, **4**, No. 1, 7 (1965).

34. Fan, L. T., and C. S. Wang, *The Discrete Maximum Principle—A Study of Multistage Systems Optimization*, Wiley, New York, 1964.

35. Wang, C. S., and L. T. Fan, "The Optimization of Continuous Complex Processes by the Maximum Principle," *J. Electron. Control*, **17**, No. 2, 199 (1964).

36. Fan, L. T., W. S. Hwang, S. J. Chen, and L. S. Fan, "A Sequential Union of the Maximum Principle and Dynamic Programming," *J. Electron. Control* **17**, No. 5, 593 (1964).

37. Roberts, S. M., *Dynamic Programming in Chemical Engineering and Process Control*, Academic Press, New York, 1964.

38. Denn, M. M., and R. Aris, "Second Order Variational Equations and the Strong Maximum Principle," *Chem. Eng. Sci.*, **20**, 373 (1965). (See also M. M. Denn's Ph.D. Dissertation, University of Minnesota, Minneapolis, 1964.)

# 2

# Computational Algorithm for Continuous Simple Processes

In this chapter the basic notion of the original version of Pontryagin's maximum principle is introduced. It can be used to treat a wide variety of optimization problems associated with simple continuous processes. We shall first state the algorithm based on the maximum principle before proceeding to show its application, derivation, and further extension.

## 1. STATEMENT OF THE ALGORITHM

The representation of the continuous simple process is shown schematically in Fig. 2.1. The performance equations of the process have the form [1, 2, 3]

$$\frac{dx_i}{dt} = f_i(x_1(t), x_2(t), \ldots, x_s(t); \theta_1(t), \ldots, \theta_r(t)), \qquad t_0 \leq t \leq T,$$

$$x_i(t_0) = \alpha_i,$$

$$i = 1, 2, \ldots, s,$$

or the vector form

$$\frac{dx}{dt} = f(x(t); \theta(t)), \qquad x(t_0) = \alpha, \tag{1}$$

where $x(t)$ is an $s$-dimensional vector function representing the state of the process at time $t$ and $\theta(t)$ is an $r$-dimensional vector function representing the decision at time $t$. It may be noted that the variable $t$ may represent the distance in a steady-state continuous process in space.

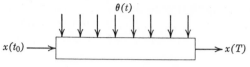

**Fig. 2.1** Simple process.

A typical optimization problem associated with such a process is to find a piecewise continuous decision vector function, $\theta(t)$, subject to the constraints

$$\psi_i[\theta_1(t), \theta_2(t), \ldots, \theta_r(t)] \leq 0, \qquad i = 1, 2, \ldots, m, \tag{2}$$

which makes a function of the final values of the state

$$S = \sum_{i=1}^{s} c_i x_i(T), \qquad c_i = \text{constant}, \tag{3}$$

an extremum when the initial condition $x(t_0) = \alpha^*$ is given. The function $S = \sum_{i=1}^{s} c_i x_i(T)$, which is to be maximized (or minimized), is termed the objective function of the process. The decision vector function so chosen is called an optimal decision vector function or simply an optimal decision and is denoted by $\bar{\theta}(t)$.

When the time interval is fixed, there are two different types of basic problem: a fixed right-end problem and a free right-end problem, depending on whether the final condition is given or not. In this section we shall consider only the free right-end problem.

The procedure for solving the problem is to introduce an $s$-dimensional adjoint vector $z(t)$ and a Hamiltonian function $H$ which satisfy the following relations:

$$H(z(t), x(t), \theta(t)) = \sum_{i=1}^{s} z_i f_i(x(t); \theta(t)), \tag{4}$$

$$\frac{dz_i}{dt} = -\frac{\partial H}{\partial x_i} = -\sum_{j=1}^{s} z_j \frac{\partial f_j}{\partial x_i}, \qquad i = 1, 2, \ldots, s, \tag{5}$$

$$z_i(T) = c_i, \qquad i = 1, 2, \ldots, s. \tag{6}$$

The optimal decision vector function $\bar{\theta}(t)$, which makes $S$ an extremum (maximum or minimum), is the decision vector function $\theta(t)$, which renders the Hamiltonian function $H$ extremum for almost every $t$,†

---

* $x(t_0) = \alpha$ is a vector representation of a collection of $x_1(t_0) = \alpha_1$, $x_2(t_0) = \alpha_2$, ..., $x_s(t_0) = \alpha_s$.

† It is proved that if the decision vector function $\theta(t)$ is piecewise continuous then the extremum value of $H$ is constant for every $t$ as stated in the theorem given in this section [2].

$t_0 \leq t \leq T$. If the optimal decision vector function $\bar{\theta}(t)$ is interior to the set of admissible decisions $\theta(t)$ [the set given by equation (2)], a necessary condition for $S$ to be an extremum with respect to $\theta(t)$ is

$$\frac{\partial H}{\partial \theta} = 0. \tag{7}$$

If $\theta(t)$ is constrained, the optimal decision vector function $\bar{\theta}(t)$ is determined either by solving equation (7) for $\theta(t)$ or by searching the boundary of the set.

Once the decision vector function $\theta(t)$ is chosen the adjoint vector function $z(t)$ is uniquely determined by equations (5) and (6) and the initial condition at $t = t_0$, $x(t_0) = \alpha$. It may be noted that the performance equation (1) can be written in terms of the Hamiltonian function as

$$\frac{dx_i}{dt} = \frac{\partial H}{\partial z_i}, \qquad i = 1, 2, \ldots, s. \tag{8}$$

Pontryagin's maximum principle can be summarized in the following theorem.

**Theorem.**   *Let $\theta(t)$, $t_0 \leq t \leq T$ be a piecewise continuous vector function satisfying the constraints given in equation (2). In order that the scalar function S given in equation (3) may be a maximum (or minimum) for a process described by equation (1), with the initial condition at $t = t_0$, $x(t_0) = \alpha$, given, it is necessary that there exist a nonzero continuous vector function $z(t)$ satisfying equations (5) and (6) and that the vector function $\theta(t)$ be so chosen that $H(z(t), x(t), \theta(t))$ is a maximum (or minimum) for every t, $t_0 \leq t \leq T$. Furthermore, the maximum (or minimum) value of H is a constant for every t.*

## 2.   A SIMPLE EXAMPLE

We shall illustrate in this section the use of the maximum principle by considering a simple example in detail [2, 3]. Let the performance equation of a simple process be

$$\frac{dx_1}{dt} = -ax_1 + \theta, \qquad x_1(0) = \alpha_1, \qquad 0 \leq t \leq T. \tag{9}$$

We want to minimize the integral

$$S = \frac{1}{2} \int_0^T [(x_1)^2 + (\theta)^2] \, dt.$$

To solve this problem we introduce an additional state variable

$$x_2(t) = \frac{1}{2} \int_0^t [(x_1)^2 + (\theta)^2] \, dt.$$

It follows that the performance equation for $x_2$ is

$$\frac{dx_2}{dt} = \tfrac{1}{2}(x_1)^2 + \tfrac{1}{2}(\theta)^2, \qquad x_2(0) = 0. \tag{10}$$

The problem is thus transformed into that of minimizing $S = x_2(T)$ or, equivalently, equation (3) for the case in which $c_1 = 0$ and $c_2 = 1$. According to equations (4) through (6), we have

$$H(z, x, \theta) = -az_1 x_1 + \tfrac{1}{2}z_2(x_1)^2 + z_1\theta + \tfrac{1}{2}z_2(\theta)^2, \tag{11}$$

$$\frac{dz_1}{dt} = -\frac{\partial H}{\partial x_1} = az_1 - z_2 x_1, \qquad z_1(T) = 0, \tag{12}$$

$$\frac{dz_2}{dt} = -\frac{\partial H}{\partial x_2} = 0, \qquad\qquad z_2(T) = 1. \tag{13}$$

Solving equation (13) for $z_2$ gives

$$z_2 = 1$$

for every $t$, $0 \le t \le T$. Hence the Hamiltonian function can be rewritten as

$$H(z, x, \theta) = -az_1 x_1 + \tfrac{1}{2}(x_1)^2 + z_1\theta + \tfrac{1}{2}(\theta)^2. \tag{14}$$

According to the maximum principle, $H$ must be a minimum in $\theta$ with the values of $x$ and $z$ considered as fixed. Putting

$$\frac{\partial H}{\partial \theta} = 0,$$

we have

$$\frac{\partial H}{\partial \theta} = z_1 + \theta = 0$$

or

$$z_1(t) = -\theta(t) = -\bar{\theta}(t). \tag{15}$$

Substitution of equation (15) and $z_2 = 1$ into equations (9) and (12), respectively, gives

$$\frac{dx_1}{dt} = -ax_1 - z_1 \tag{16}$$

and

$$\frac{dz_1}{dt} = -x_1 + az_1. \tag{17}$$

The system of differential equations, equations (16) and (17), is solved simultaneously. From equation (16) we have

$$z_1 = -\frac{dx_1}{dt} - ax_1. \tag{18}$$

Differentiation of equation (18) with respect to $t$ yields

$$\frac{dz_1}{dt} = -\frac{d^2x_1}{dt^2} - a\frac{dx_1}{dt}. \tag{19}$$

By substituting equations (18) and (19) into equation (17) we obtain

$$\frac{d^2x_1}{dt^2} + a\frac{dx_1}{dt} = x_1 + a\left(\frac{dx_1}{dt} + ax_1\right)$$

or

$$\frac{d^2x_1}{dt^2} - (a^2 + 1)x_1 = 0. \tag{20}$$

The solution of equation (20) is

$$x_1(t) = A_1 e^{\lambda t} + A_2 e^{-\lambda t}, \tag{21}$$

where

$$\lambda = \sqrt{a^2 + 1}.$$

By differentiating equation (21) with respect to $t$ and substituting the result, together with equation (21), into equation (18), we obtain

$$z_1(t) = -A_1(\lambda + a)e^{\lambda t} + A_2(\lambda - a)e^{-\lambda t}. \tag{22}$$

Application of the boundary conditions

$$x_1(0) = \alpha_1$$

and

$$z_1(T) = 0$$

to equations (21) and (22), respectively, gives

$$x_1(0) = A_1 + A_2 = \alpha_1, \tag{23}$$

$$z_1(T) = -A_1(\lambda + a)e^{\lambda T} + A_2(\lambda - a)e^{-\lambda T} = 0. \tag{24}$$

The solution of equations (23) and (24) for $A_1$ and $A_2$ is

$$A_1 = \frac{\alpha_1(\lambda - a)e^{-\lambda T}}{(\lambda + a)e^{\lambda T} + (\lambda - a)e^{-\lambda T}} \tag{25}$$

and

$$A_2 = \frac{\alpha_1(\lambda + a)e^{\lambda T}}{(\lambda + a)e^{\lambda T} + (\lambda - a)e^{-\lambda T}}. \tag{26}$$

The optimal policy $\bar{\theta}(t)$, which may be obtained by the substitution of equations (15), (25), (26) and the relation $\lambda^2 - a^2 = 1$ into equation (22), is

$$\bar{\theta}(t) = \frac{\alpha_1[e^{-\lambda(T-t)} - e^{\lambda(T-t)}]}{(\lambda + a)e^{\lambda T} + (\lambda - a)e^{-\lambda T}} .$$ (27)

The objective function $S = x_2(T)$ becomes

$$S = x_2(T) = \frac{1}{2} \int_0^T [(x_1)^2 + (\theta)^2] \, dt$$

$$= \frac{1}{2} \int_0^T \{(A_1 e^{\lambda t} + A_2 e^{-\lambda t})^2 + [(\lambda + a)A_1 e^{\lambda t} - (\lambda - a)A_2 e^{-\lambda t}]^2\} \, dt$$

$$= \tfrac{1}{2}[A_1^2(\lambda + a)(e^{2\lambda T} - 1) - A_2^2(\lambda - a)(e^{-2\lambda T} - 1)].$$ (28)

Further simplification of equation (28) gives

$$x_2(T) = \frac{\alpha_1}{2} [A_2(\lambda - a) - A_1(\lambda + a)]$$

$$= \frac{(\alpha_1)^2}{2} \frac{(e^{\lambda T} - e^{-\lambda T})}{(\lambda + a)e^{\lambda T} + (\lambda - a)e^{-\lambda T}} .$$ (29)

## 3. DERIVATION OF THE ALGORITHM

In this section we shall present a simplified derivation of the algorithm stated in the preceding section for maximizing the objective function. The algorithm for minimizing the objective function can be derived by reversing the direction of the inequality signs.

Let $\bar{\theta}(t)$ be the optimal decision vector function and $\bar{x}(t)$, the corresponding optimal state vector function; then

$$\frac{d\bar{x}(t)}{dt} = f(\bar{x}; \bar{\theta}).$$ (30)

Assume that the function $f(x(t); \theta(t))$ is continuous in its arguments, that its first partial derivatives exist and are continuous in their arguments, and that the function $f(x(t); \theta(t))$, its partial derivatives, and $\theta(t)$ are bounded. If the decision vector is perturbed arbitrarily but slightly from the optimal value at every point of the process, that is,

$$\theta(t, \epsilon) = \bar{\theta}(t) + \epsilon\varphi(t) + 0(\epsilon^2),$$ (31)

the resulting perturbation of the state vector function is

$$x(t, \epsilon) = \bar{x}(t) + \epsilon y(t) + 0(\epsilon^2),$$ (32)

where $\varphi(t)$ and $y(t)$ are bounded vector functions of $t$ with the same dimensions and order of magnitude as $\theta(t)$ and $x(t)$, respectively, $\epsilon$ represents a very small number, and $0(\epsilon^2)$ denotes the term including $\epsilon^2$ and those of higher order.

A variational equation can be obtained from equations (1) and (30) as

$$\epsilon \frac{dy_i}{dt} = [f_i(x; \theta) - f_i(\bar{x}; \bar{\theta})] + 0(\epsilon^2). \tag{33}$$

The bracketed quantity may be expanded in a Taylor series around $\bar{x}(t)$ and $\bar{\theta}(t)$ to give

$$[f_i(x; \theta) - f_i(\bar{x}; \bar{\theta})] = \sum_{j=1}^{s} \epsilon y_j \frac{\partial f_i(\bar{x}; \bar{\theta})}{\partial \bar{x}_j} + \sum_{j=1}^{r} \epsilon \varphi_j \frac{\partial f_i(\bar{x}; \bar{\theta})}{\partial \bar{\theta}_j} + 0(\epsilon^2). \tag{34}$$

Combining equations (33) and (34) gives

$$\epsilon \frac{dy_i}{dt} = \sum_{j=1}^{s} \epsilon y_j \frac{\partial f_i(\bar{x}; \bar{\theta})}{\partial \bar{x}_j} + \sum_{j=1}^{r} \epsilon \varphi_j \frac{\partial f_i(\bar{x}; \bar{\theta})}{\partial \bar{\theta}_j} + 0(\epsilon^2). \tag{35}$$

If equations (5) and (35) are substituted into the expression

$$\frac{d}{dt} \sum_{i=1}^{s} \epsilon y_i z_i = \sum_{i=1}^{s} \epsilon z_i \frac{dy_i}{dt} + \sum_{i=1}^{s} \epsilon y_i \frac{dz_i}{dt}, \tag{36}$$

we obtain

$$\frac{d}{dt} \sum_{i=1}^{s} \epsilon y_i z_i = \sum_{i=1}^{s} z_i \left[ \sum_{j=1}^{s} \epsilon y_j \frac{\partial f_i(\bar{x}; \bar{\theta})}{\partial \bar{x}_j} + \sum_{j=1}^{r} \epsilon \varphi_j \frac{\partial f_i(\bar{x}; \bar{\theta})}{\partial \bar{\theta}_j} \right]$$
$$+ \sum_{i=1}^{s} \epsilon y_i \left( -\frac{\partial H}{\partial x_i} \right) + 0(\epsilon^2). \tag{37}$$

Making use of equation (5) after expanding it in a Taylor series around $\bar{x}(t)$ and $\bar{\theta}(t)$, we have

$$\frac{d}{dt} \sum_{i=1}^{s} \epsilon y_i z_i = \sum_{i=1}^{s} z_i \left[ \sum_{j=1}^{s} \epsilon y_j \frac{\partial f_i(\bar{x}; \bar{\theta})}{\partial \bar{x}_j} + \sum_{j=1}^{r} \epsilon \varphi_j \frac{\partial f_i(\bar{x}; \bar{\theta})}{\partial \bar{\theta}_j} \right]$$
$$- \sum_{i=1}^{s} \epsilon y_i \sum_{j=1}^{s} \frac{\partial f_i(\bar{x}; \bar{\theta})}{\partial \bar{x}_i} z_j + 0(\epsilon^2) \tag{38}$$

or

$$\frac{d}{dt} \sum_{i=1}^{s} \epsilon y_i z_i = \sum_{i=1}^{s} \sum_{j=1}^{r} z_i \frac{\partial f_i(\bar{x}; \bar{\theta})}{\partial \bar{\theta}_j} \epsilon \varphi_j + 0(\epsilon^2). \tag{39}$$

Considering the linear terms in equation (39) and integrating from $t = 0$ to $t = T$, we obtain

$$\sum_{i=1}^{s} \epsilon[y_i(T)z_i(T) - y_i(0)z_i(0)] = \int_0^T \sum_{i=1}^{s} \sum_{j=1}^{r} z_i \frac{\partial f_i}{\partial \bar{\theta}_j} \epsilon\varphi_j \, dt. \tag{40}$$

Since the initial values of $x(t)$ are given and fixed, we have

$$y_i(0) = 0, \qquad i = 1, 2, \ldots, s. \tag{41}$$

Substitution of equations (6) and (41) into equation (40) and use of the definition of the Hamiltonian give

$$\sum_{i=1}^{s} \epsilon c_i \, y_i(T) = \int_0^T \sum_{j=1}^{r} \frac{\partial H}{\partial \bar{\theta}_j} \epsilon\varphi_j \, dt. \tag{42}$$

The quantity on the left-hand side of equation (42) is the variation of the objective function $S$, which must be zero along the optimal trajectory for free variations (unconstrained variations) and negative for variations at the boundary of the constraints, that is,

$$\sum_{i=1}^{s} \epsilon c_i \, y_i(T) \leq 0. \tag{43}$$

Thus from equation (42) we conclude that for arbitrary $\epsilon\varphi$ the necessary conditions for $S$ to be a maximum are

$$\frac{\partial H}{\partial \theta_j} = 0 \quad \text{at} \quad \theta_j(t) = \bar{\theta}_j(t), \qquad j = 1, 2, \ldots, r, \qquad 0 \leq t \leq T, \tag{44}$$

when $\bar{\theta}_j(t)$ lies in the interior of the region of $\theta(t)$ or

$$H = \max \quad \text{at} \quad \theta_j(t) = \bar{\theta}_j(t), \qquad j = 1, 2, \ldots, r, \qquad 0 \leq t \leq T, \tag{45}$$

when $\bar{\theta}_j(t)$ lies at a boundary of the constraints.

The simplified derivations given here do not show the equivalence of equations (44) and (45) as stated in the theorem. For rigorous mathematical proof readers are referred to Reference 2. The derivations of the algorithm can also be obtained by using Green's identity [8, 9, 10]. Further treatment and additional references are given in Chapter 11.

Under the optimal condition, we have

$$\bar{\theta} = \bar{\theta}(t, \bar{x}(t), \bar{z}(t)). \tag{46}$$

Therefore, the corresponding $H$ given by equation (45), which we may designate as $\bar{H}$, is a function of $\bar{z}(t)$, $\bar{x}(t)$, and $t$; that is,

$$\bar{H} = \bar{H}(\bar{z}(t), \bar{x}(t), t). \tag{47}$$

By differentiating this with respect to $t$, we have

$$\frac{d\bar{H}(\bar{z}(t), \bar{x}(t), t)}{dt} = \frac{\partial \bar{H}(\bar{z}(t), \bar{x}(t), t)}{\partial t} + \sum_{i=1}^{s} \frac{\partial \bar{x}_i(t)}{\partial t} \frac{\partial \bar{H}(\bar{z}(t), \bar{x}(t), t)}{\partial \bar{x}_i}$$

$$+ \sum_{i=1}^{s} \frac{\partial \bar{z}_i(t)}{\partial t} \frac{\partial \bar{H}(\bar{z}(t), \bar{x}(t), t)}{\partial \bar{z}_i}.$$

By substituting equations (5) and (8) into this equation, we obtain

$$\frac{d\bar{H}(\bar{z}(t), \bar{x}(t), t)}{dt} = \frac{\partial \bar{H}(\bar{z}(t), \bar{x}(t), t)}{\partial t} - \sum_{i=1}^{s} \frac{\partial \bar{x}_i(t)}{\partial t} \frac{\partial \bar{z}_i(t)}{\partial t} + \sum_{i=1}^{s} \frac{\partial \bar{z}_i(t)}{\partial t} \frac{\partial \bar{x}_i(t)}{\partial t}$$

$$= \frac{\partial \bar{H}(\bar{z}(t), \bar{x}(t), t)}{\partial t}. \tag{48}$$

If $\bar{H}$ is not a function of $t$ explicitly, this derivative will be equal to zero. Therefore, as stated in the basic theorem, the maximum value of $H$ is constant at every point in a continuous simple process described by equation (1) [2, 4].

## 4.  EXTENSIONS OF THE ALGORITHM

The algorithm presented in Section 2.1 can be extended to handle a variety of problems usually encountered in practice.  Most of the following examples of the extensions are basically similar to those made by Katz [5] for a discrete version of the maximum principle.

*a. Processes with Fixed End Points.*    For the optimization (maximization or minimization) problem in which some of $x_i(T)$, say $x_a(T)$, $x_b(T)$, are preassigned and the objective function is specified as

$$\sum_{\substack{i=1 \\ i \neq a \\ i \neq b}}^{s} c_i x_i(T),$$

the basic algorithm represented by equations (1) through (8) is still applicable except that equation (6) should be replaced by

$$z_i(T) = c_i, \qquad i = 1, 2, \ldots, s, \tag{49}$$

$$i \neq a, b.$$

This modification is verified by noting that $y_a(T) = y_b(T) = 0$, and thus the conditions $z_i(T) = c_i$ for $i = a, b$ included in equation (6) are redundant in obtaining equation (42) from equation (40).

The interested reader may wish to rework the example in Section 2 for the case in which $x_1(T)$ is fixed.

**b. Processes with Choice of Initial Values.**  Suppose that $m$ of the initial values of $x$ are not preassigned and we wish to choose these missing initial values as well as the decision vector function so that $S = \sum_{i=1}^{s} c_i x_i(T)$ is an extremum. In addition to the extremum condition of the Hamiltonian we need a condition for the initial values of $x$ which are not preassigned.

This can be shown by making a small perturbation of $x_i(0)$ as

$$x_i(0) = \bar{x}_i(0) + \epsilon y_i(0), \qquad i = 1, 2, \ldots, m \leq s. \tag{50}$$

The corresponding decision vector function $\theta$, which makes $S$ an extremum, is perturbed to

$$\theta(t, \epsilon) = \bar{\theta}(t) + \epsilon \varphi(t) + 0(\epsilon^2) \tag{51}$$

and the state vector $x$, to

$$x(t, \epsilon) = \bar{x}(t) + \epsilon y(t) + 0(\epsilon^2). \tag{52}$$

Equation (41) becomes

$$y_i(0) \neq 0, \qquad i = 1, 2, \ldots, m \leq s. \tag{53}$$
$$y_i(0) = 0, \qquad i = m+1, m+2, \ldots, s.$$

Therefore equation (40) is reduced to

$$\epsilon \sum_{i=1}^{s} y_i(T) z_i(T) = \epsilon \sum_{i=1}^{m} y_i(0) z_i(0) + \int_0^T \sum_{j=1}^{r} \frac{\partial H}{\partial \bar{\theta}_j} \epsilon \varphi_j \, dt \tag{54}$$

or

$$\epsilon \sum_{i=1}^{s} c_i y_i(T) = \epsilon \sum_{i=1}^{m} y_i(0) z_i(0) + \int_0^T \sum_{j=1}^{r} \frac{\partial H}{\partial \bar{\theta}_j} \epsilon \varphi_j \, dt. \tag{55}$$

For the maximizing case inequality (43) must be satisfied. Hence from equation (55) we may conclude that

$$\frac{\partial H}{\partial \theta_j} = 0 \quad \text{at} \quad \theta_j(t) = \bar{\theta}_j(t), \qquad j = 1, 2, \ldots, r, \tag{56}$$

and

$$z_i(0) = 0, \qquad i = 1, 2, \ldots, m, \tag{57}$$

when $\bar{\theta}_j(t)$ lies in the interior of the region of $\theta(t)$ or that

$$H = \max \quad \text{at} \quad \theta_j(t) = \bar{\theta}_j(t), \qquad j = 1, 2, \ldots, r, \tag{58}$$

and

$$\sum_{i=1}^{m} x_i(0)\, z_i(0) = \max \tag{59}$$

when $\bar{\theta}_j(t)$ lies at a boundary of the constraints.

**c. Nonautonomous Systems.**    A system is called nonautonomous if the right-hand side of the performance equation depends explicitly on time $t$. The performance equation is in the form of

$$\frac{dx}{dt} = f(x; t; \theta). \tag{60}$$

This can be transformed to the standard form of equation (1) by introducing a new state variable $x_{s+1}$ to satisfy

$$x_{s+1}(t) = t, \qquad t_0 \leq t \leq T. \tag{61}$$

Hence the corresponding component of the adjoint vector can also be written in the form

$$\frac{dz_{s+1}}{dt} = -\frac{\partial H}{\partial t}.$$

Then equation (60) becomes

$$\frac{d\underline{x}}{dt} = f(\underline{x}; \theta), \tag{62}$$

where $\underline{x}$ represents an $(s + 1)$-dimensional vector, $(x_1, x_2, \ldots, x_s, x_{s+1})$. The new state variable satisfies the differential equation

$$\frac{dx_{s+1}}{dt} = 1, \qquad t_0 \leq t \leq T, \tag{63}$$

and the initial condition

$$x_{s+1}(t_0) = t_0. \tag{64}$$

Equation (62), which includes equation (63), is the performance equation of an enlarged system in the form of equation (1) with initial conditions given by $x(t_0) = \alpha$ and equation (64).

The example in Section 2 may now be reworked for the case in which the performance equation is

$$\frac{dx_1}{dt} = -ax_1 + \theta + t. \tag{65}$$

Problems involving nonautonomous systems can also be solved without introducing an additional state variable. The basic theorem, with the exception of the condition that the maximum value of $H$ is a constant for every $t$ [2, 4], is valid.

***d. Processes with Choice of Extra Parameters.*** When the performance of a process depends not only on the choice of the decision vector but also on an additional parameter $\sigma$, we have to choose the decision variables as well as the parameter $\sigma$ such that the objective function of the process is an extremum. The performance equation for such a process can be written

$$\frac{dx}{dt} = f(x; \sigma; \theta). \tag{66}$$

If a new state variable $x_{s+1}$ which satisfies the equations

$$x_{s+1}(t) = \sigma, \qquad t_0 \leq t \leq T, \tag{67}$$

and

$$\frac{dx_{s+1}}{dt} = 0, \qquad t_0 \leq t \leq T, \tag{68}$$

is introduced, the new performance equation then becomes

$$\frac{d\underline{x}}{dt} = f(\underline{x}; \theta), \tag{69}$$

where $\underline{x}$ is an $(s + 1)$-dimensional vector, $(x_1, \ldots, x_s, x_{s+1})$. Thus we have obtained an enlarged process, which is described by a set of $(s + 1)$ performance equations represented by equation (69). The original problem is now transformed into one in which we seek a decision vector function $\theta$ and the initial value of the state variable $x_{s+1}$ such that the objective function is an extremum.

The example in Section 2 may now be reworked for the case in which the performance equation is

$$\frac{dx_1}{dt} = -ax_1 + \theta + \sigma. \tag{70}$$

***e. Processes with Memory in Decisions.*** If the transformation at a point in a process is not only a function of the decision variable $\theta$ but also of $d\theta/dt$, that is, the slope of the decision vector function has an effect on the process, we may write the performance equation of the system as

$$\frac{dx}{dt} = f\left(x; \theta, \frac{d\theta}{dt}\right), \tag{71}$$

where the initial values of $x$ are given by $x(t_0) = \alpha$, the initial values of $\theta$ are given by

$$\theta(t_0) = \eta$$

and we are to choose $\theta$ to extremize (maximize or minimize) the objective function of the process. We reduce this type of problem to the standard form by introducing new state variables $x_{s+j}$ in which

$$x_{s+j}(t) = \theta_j(t), \qquad t_0 \le t \le T, \qquad j = 1, 2, \ldots, r, \tag{72}$$

and by introducing a new decision vector $\omega$ to satisfy

$$\omega(t) = \frac{d\theta(t)}{dt}, \qquad t_0 \le t \le T. \tag{73}$$

We then have

$$\frac{d\underline{x}}{dt} = f(\underline{x}; \omega), \tag{74}$$

where $\underline{x}$ represents an $(s + r)$-dimensional vector $(x_1, x_2, \ldots, x_s, x_{s+1}, x_{s+2}, \ldots, x_{s+r})$ and

$$\frac{dx_{s+j}}{dt} = \omega_j(t), \qquad t_0 \le t \le T. \tag{75}$$

Equation (74) is the performance equation of the enlarged system, with the initial conditions given by

$$x_{s+j}(t_0) = \eta_j, \tag{76}$$

where $\eta_j$ is a $j$th component of $\eta$ and

$$x(t_0) = \alpha. \tag{77}$$

It should be noted that $\theta(t)$ in equation (71) may not be constrained.

*f. Processes with Arbitrary Final Measures as the Objective Function.*
Suppose that we are to extremize (maximize or minimize) $h[x(T)]$, an arbitrary continuous function of $x(T)$, rather than a certain component of $x(T)$.

Problems of this kind can be reduced to the standard form by introducing a new state variable $x_{s+1}$ for the function $h[x(t)]$

$$x_{s+1}(t) = h[x(t)], \qquad t_0 \le t \le T. \tag{78}$$

By differentiating equation (78) with respect to $t$, we then have

$$\frac{dx_{s+1}}{dt} = \sum_{i=1}^{s} \frac{\partial h[x(t)]}{\partial x_i} \frac{dx_i}{dt}$$

$$= \sum_{i=1}^{s} \frac{\partial h[x(t)]}{\partial x_i} f_i(x(t); \theta(t)), \qquad t_0 \le t \le T. \tag{79}$$

The initial condition is

$$x_{s+1}(t_0) = h[x(t_0)] = h[\alpha]. \tag{80}$$

Equations (1) and (79) are thus the performance equations of the enlarged system with the initial conditions given by equations (77) and (80).

**g. Processes with Cumulated Measures as the Objective Function.** Suppose that we are to extremize (maximize or minimize) $\int_0^T \psi[x(t); \theta(t)] \, dt$ for the system defined by equation (1) and the initial conditions. We shall transform this problem by introducing a new state variable $x_{s+1}(t)$ defined as

$$x_{s+1}(t) = \int_{t_0}^t \psi[x(t); \theta(t)] \, dt, \qquad t_0 \leq t \leq T, \tag{81}$$

$$x_{s+1}(t_0) = 0. \tag{82}$$

It follows that the new state variable $x_{s+1}(t)$ satisfies the differential equation

$$\frac{dx_{s+1}}{dt} = \psi[x(t); \theta(t)], \qquad t_0 \leq t \leq T. \tag{83}$$

Equations (1) and (83) with the initial conditions in (77) and (82) completely specify the new enlarged system. This extension has been illustrated in the example in Section 2.

**h. Processes Described by a Second-Order Differential Equation with Constant Coefficients.** One of the performance equations of a system may be a second-order differential equation of the form

$$a \frac{d^2 x_i}{dt^2} + b \frac{dx_i}{dt} + c x_i = f(\theta), \tag{84}$$

where $a$, $b$, and $c$ are constants. The initial conditions may be

$$x_i(t_0) = \alpha_i \quad \text{and} \quad \frac{dx_i}{dt}\bigg|_{t=t_0} = \beta_i.$$

Let

$$\frac{dx_i}{dt} = x_{s+1}, \qquad x_{s+1}(t_0) = \beta_i. \tag{85}$$

Equation (84) is then transformed into

$$\frac{dx_{s+1}}{dt} = -\frac{b}{a} x_{s+1} - \frac{c}{a} x_i + f(\theta). \tag{86}$$

A set of the performance equations comprised of equations (85) and (86) are now in the standard form; that is, the problem is now transformed into one in which the performance equation is an $(s + 1)$-dimensional vector equation of the form

$$\frac{dx}{dt} = f(x; \theta). \tag{87}$$

It is worth noting that the performance equation of a system described by an $n$th order differential equation with constant coefficients can also be reduced to the standard form in a similar manner [2].

The example in Section 2 may now be reconsidered for the case in which the performance equation is of the form

$$\frac{d^2x_1}{dt^2} = -ax_1 + \theta, \qquad x_1(0) = \alpha_1, \qquad \frac{dx_1}{dt}\bigg|_{t=0} = \beta_1.$$

### i. Processes with Constraints Imposed on the Final State Variables. Suppose that the constraining conditions can be specified as

$$g_\alpha[x(T)] = 0, \qquad \alpha = 1, 2, \ldots, m, \quad m < s. \tag{88}$$

The function to be minimized (or maximized) then may be defined as [6]

$$S = \sum_{i=1}^{s} c_i x_i(T) + \sum_{\alpha=1}^{m} \lambda_\alpha g_\alpha[x(T)], \tag{89}$$

where $\lambda_\alpha$ are unknown multipliers.

Boundary conditions on the adjoint vector are specified as

$$z_i(T) = \left[ c_i + \sum_{\alpha=1}^{m} \lambda_\alpha \frac{\partial g_\alpha}{\partial x_i(T)} \right], \qquad i = 1, 2, \ldots, s. \tag{90}$$

By substituting equation (90) into equation (40) we obtain

$$\sum_{i=1}^{s} \epsilon y_i(T) \left[ c_i + \sum_{\alpha=1}^{m} \lambda_\alpha \frac{\partial g_\alpha}{\partial x_i(T)} \right] = \int_0^T \sum_{j=1}^{r} \frac{\partial H}{\partial \theta_j} \epsilon \varphi_j \, dt. \tag{91}$$

The bracketed quantity on the left-hand side of equation (91) is the variation of $S$ in equation (89). Hence the necessary conditions for $S$ to be a maximum or minimum are

$$\frac{\partial H}{\partial \theta_j} = 0 \quad \text{at} \quad \theta_j(t) = \bar{\theta}_j(t) \quad \text{in the interior of the region of } \theta(t),$$

or

$$H(z(t), x(t), \theta(t))$$

$$= \text{maximum (or minimum) at a boundary of the constraints.} \tag{92}$$

The $m$ unknowns $\lambda_\alpha$, $\alpha = 1, 2, \ldots, m$, can be obtained from the additional conditions

$$g_\alpha[\bar{x}(T)] = 0.$$

Similar results can be obtained for $t = t_0$.

A different formulation of the necessary condition is given by Denn and Aris [10].

*j. Processes with Constraints on State Variables* [7]. If, in addition to the performance equation, equation (1), and the initial conditions, a constraint on the state variables is given in the form

$$g(x(t); \theta(t)) \geq 0, \tag{93}$$

the necessary condition for the optimum can be obtained by defining the basic algorithm:

$$H = \sum_{i=1}^{s} z_i f_i(x; \theta), \tag{94}$$

$$\frac{dz_i}{dt} = -\left( \sum_{j=1}^{s} z_j \frac{\partial f_j}{\partial x_i} + \lambda \frac{\partial g}{\partial x_i} \right), \tag{95}$$

where $\lambda = 0$ if $\bar{x}(t)$ is an interior point within the constraint. If $\bar{x}(t)$ lies on the boundary, the value of $\lambda$ is to be determined by the condition

$$g(\bar{x}(t); \bar{\theta}(t)) = 0. \tag{96}$$

A more extensive treatment of this case can be found in References 8 and 11.

In conclusion the variations of optimization problems can be classified into three general types: (1) variation in the specification of initial and final conditions, such as parts a and b, (2) variation in the form of performance equations, such as parts c through e and parts h through j, (3) variation in the form of objective functions, such as parts f and g. The first type of variation is solved by adding or deleting the initial and final conditions for the corresponding components of $z$. The second and third types of variation can generally be reduced to the standard form of optimization problem by introducing new state variables.

We now see that although the optimization problem posed in the foregoing sections seems to be somewhat narrow it actually can cover a wide variety of problems if the modifications presented are employed.

## REFERENCES

1. Fan, L. T., and C. S. Wang, *The Discrete Maximum Principle*, Wiley, New York, 1964.
2. Pontryagin, L. S., V. G. Boltyanskii, R. V. Gamkrelidze, and E. F. Mischenko, *The Mathematical Theory of Optimal Processes* (English translation by K. N. Trirogoff), Interscience, New York, 1962.
3. Rozonoer, L. I., "L. S. Pontryagin's Maximum Principle in the Theory of Optimum System I," *Automation and Remote Control*, **20**, 1288 (1959).

4. Rozonoer, L. I., "L. S. Pontryagin's Maximum Principle in the Theory of Optimum System II," *Automation and Remote Control*, **20,** 1405 (1959).
5. Katz, S., "Best Operating Points for Staged Systems," *Ind. Eng. Chem.*, *Fundamentals*, **1,** 226 (1962).
6. Kopp, R. E., "Pontryagin Maximum Principle," in *Optimization Techniques*, A. Leitmann, Ed., Academic Press, New York, 1962.
7. Dahlin, E. B., and J. M. Nelson, "Simulation and Optimal Control of Chemical Processes," *Chem. Eng. Progr.*, **60,** No. 3 (1964).
8. Denn, M. M., The Optimization of Complex Systems, Ph.D. Thesis, University of Minnesota, 1964.
9. Denn, M. M., "On 'The Optimization of Continuous Complex Systems by the Maximum Principle'," *Int. J. Control*, **1,** 497 (1965).
10. Denn, M. M., and R. Aris, "An Elementary Derivation of the Maximum Principle," *A.I.Ch.E.J.*, **11,** 367 (1965).
11. Bryson, A. E., Jr., W. F. Denham, and S. E. Dreyfus, "Optimal Programming Problems with Inequality Constraints I, II," *AIAA J.*, **1,** 11 (1963); **2,** 1 (1964).

# 3

# *Optimal Control*

In this chapter the application of the maximum principle to control problems is presented, and several relatively simple examples show how the maximum principle may be employed in the analysis and design of optimal control systems. These examples illustrate some of the advantages of the maximum principle over other classical methods in solving the problems in which the variables are constrained.

In this introductory section an additional algorithm based on the maximum principle, which is used frequently in the examples, is described first. It is applied when the time interval is not fixed. This algorithm enables us to consider a class of optimization problems in which the initial and final values of the state vector function $x(t_0)$ and $x(T)$ are fixed but in which the final time $T$ is to be determined.

The performance equations and boundary conditions of a process can be represented in vector form as

$$\frac{dx}{dt} = f(x; \theta), \qquad x(t_0) = \alpha, \qquad x(T) = \beta, \tag{1}$$

where $x(t)$ is an $s$-dimensional state vector function and $\theta(t)$ is an $r$-dimensional decision vector function. The optimization problem is to choose the decision vector function $\theta(t)$ subject to the $m$ constraints

$$\varphi_i[\theta(t)] \leq 0, \qquad i = 1, 2, \ldots, m, \tag{2}$$

such that the objective function

$$S = \int_{t_0}^{T} g(x; \theta) \, dt \tag{3}$$

is minimum.

In order to solve this problem, we let

$$x_{s+1} = \int_{t_0}^{t} g(x; \theta) \, dt,$$

according to a technique suggested in Chapter 2, and we introduce an $s + 1$-dimensional adjoint vector $z(t)$ and a Hamiltonian function $H$ which satisfy the following relations

$$H(z(t), x(t), \theta(t)) = \sum_{i=1}^{s+1} z_i f_i(x(t); \theta(t)), \tag{4}$$

$$\frac{dz_i}{dt} = -\frac{\partial H}{\partial x_i}, \qquad i = 1, 2, \ldots, s, s + 1, \tag{5}$$

$$z_{s+1}(T) = 1. \tag{6}$$

The optimal decision vector function $\bar{\theta}(t)$ which makes $S$ minimum causes $H$ to be minimum and fixed at zero; that is

$$\min H = 0, \qquad t_0 \le t \le T. \tag{7}$$

$\bar{\theta}(t)$ therefore is determined either by solving the equation

$$\frac{\partial H}{\partial \theta} = 0$$

for $\theta(t)$ or by searching the boundaries of the set of decision variables.

The condition that $H$ must equal zero may be used as a boundary condition (usually at $t = t_0$) along with other already known boundary conditions at $t_0$ and $T$ in the solution of the system of differential equations, equations (1) and (5). One of the boundary conditions at $T$ is generally used to evaluate the final time $T$. The following theorem summarizes this algorithm [1].

**Theorem.** *Let $\theta(t)$, $t_0 \le t \le T$ be a piecewise continuous vector function that satisfies the constraints given in equation (2). In order that the scalar function $S$ in equation (3) may be a minimum for a process described by equation (1) with the given initial conditions at $t = t_0$,*

$$x_i(t_0) = \alpha_i, \qquad i = 1, 2, \ldots, s, s + 1,$$

*and the given final conditions at some undetermined time, $t = T$,*

$$x_i(T) = \beta_i, \qquad i = 1, 2, \ldots, s,$$

*it is necessary that there be a nonzero continuous vector function $z(t)$ that satisfies equations (5) and (6) and that the vector function $\theta(t)$ be chosen so that $H(z(t), x(t), \theta(t))$ is zero and minimum at every $t$, $t_0 \le t \le T$.*

We present the following discussion in order to show that the minimum of $H$ is zero for every $t$. Let us assume that the optimal trajectory $\bar{x}(t)$

and the optimal decision vector $\bar{\theta}(t)$ have been found. Let us further assume that the corresponding final time is equal to $\bar{T}$. We may now consider this case as a fixed time problem with final time fixed at $\bar{T}$ and with the given initial conditions. Therefore the objective function already defined for a fixed time problem [see equation (3) of Chapter 2] now becomes

$$S = \sum_{i=1}^{s+1} c_i x_i(\bar{T})$$

and correspondingly the components of the adjoint vector take the value of $c_i$ at $t = \bar{T}$; that is

$$z_i(\bar{T}) = c_i, \qquad i = 1, 2, \ldots, s, s+1.$$

Consider now a variation of the objective function $S$ resulting from a very small change of time, from $\bar{T}$ to $\bar{T} + \delta T$, along the optimal trajectory $\bar{x}(t)$. We have

$$\delta S = \sum_{i=1}^{s+1} [c_i \bar{x}_i(\bar{T} + \delta T) - c_i \bar{x}_i(\bar{T})]$$

$$= \sum_{i=1}^{s+1} c_i \frac{d\bar{x}_i}{dt}\bigg|_{t=\bar{T}} \delta T$$

$$= \sum_{i=1}^{s+1} z_i(\bar{T}) \frac{d\bar{x}_i}{dt}\bigg|_{t=\bar{T}} \delta T$$

$$= H\big|_{t=\bar{T}} \delta T.$$

Since $\delta S$ must be greater than or equal to zero for a minimum of $S$ (or $\delta S$ must be less than or equal to zero for a maximum of $S$) and $\delta T$ may be positive or negative, we may conclude that

$$\delta S = 0;$$

that is,

$$H\big|_{t=\bar{T}} = 0.$$

From the theorem in Chapter 2 we already know that the extremum of $H$ is constant for every $t$, $t_0 \le t \le \bar{T}$. It follows that

$$\min H = 0, \quad \text{for} \quad t_0 \le t \le \bar{T}.$$

A different derivation of this result was also obtained [12].

An important special case of this algorithm occurs when the time interval is to be minimized; that is

$$S = \int_{t_0}^{T} dt.$$

When the objective function for a control problem takes this form, we refer to it as a time-optimal control problem.

## 1. CONTROL AND CONTROL SYSTEMS

To facilitate the presentation a number of terms and the basic notions employed in the analyses and syntheses of control systems are introduced.

A general schematic representation of a feedback control system is shown in Fig. 3.1. The elements in the control system may be classified into the following three categories [2]:

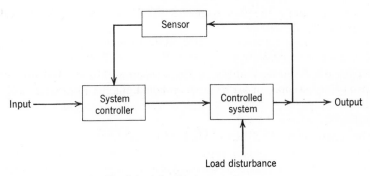

*Fig. 3.1* A feedback control system.

1. The controlled system, which may also be called the plant, the process, or the fixed component.

2. The sensors or measuring devices.

3. The system controller.

Since the first two items are usually given or specified by plant designers or engineers, a control-system designer's job is essentially to design the system controller itself.

In this chapter we are concerned primarily with the optimization of the control action because this information is the basis for the design of an optimal control system.

Control problems may be classified as stabilizing problems and maneuvering problems. For example, stabilizing problems are those arising in process industries in which the control forces are used primarily to counteract load disturbances in the controlled systems or processes. For such problems the desired states of the systems are either fixed or changing slowly. A maneuvering problem is characterized by a change in the desired state of the system. The control system for such a process is used to bring the controlled system to the new desired state. The load disturbances are often neglected in the designing of a control system for maneuvering.

A controlled dynamic system, such as an aircraft or a chemical process, can often be described by a system of first-order differential equations which can be represented in vector form for an autonomous system as

$$\frac{dx}{dt} = f(x; \theta) \tag{8}$$

or for a nonautonomous system as

$$\frac{dx}{dt} = f(x; t; \theta). \tag{9}$$

In the equations $x$ represents a set of state variables $x_i$, $i = 1, 2, \ldots, s$ and $\theta$, a set of control forces $\theta_j$, $j = 1, 2, \ldots, r$ which we can employ to effectuate the desired changes in the dynamic state of the controlled system. For a second- or higher-order system a change of variables may be made to reduce the system to a set of first-order differential equations, as described in Section 2.4.

The phase-plane and phase-space concepts* are very useful in the analysis of optimal control systems. The $s$-dimensional space with $x_i$ as its coordinates is called the phase-space or, if $s = 2$, the phase-plane. Each point in the phase-space is given by a set of values $x_i$ and represents the dynamic state of the system at some time $t$. As time increases, the point $x$ traces out a locus (path or curve) in the phase-space. The locus is often called the trajectory of the system.

In many problems of control-system design the performance specifications are given in terms of damping ratio and natural frequency. Any linear second-order system can be described in the form

$$\frac{d^2x}{dt^2} + 2\,\delta\omega_n \frac{dx}{dt} + \omega_n{}^2 x = 0, \tag{10}$$

where $\delta$ = damping ratio,

$\delta < 1$, underdamped case,

$\delta = 1$, critically damped case,

$\delta > 1$, overdamped case,

$\delta = 0$, undamped case,

$\omega_n$ = natural frequency, that is, frequency of oscillation, when damping is zero ($\delta = 0$),

$\delta\omega_n = \eta$, damping constant, that is, actual damping.

---

* See Shinner [3] for additional information on the phase-plane and phase-space concepts.

Generally speaking, the most desirable system response (optimal response) may be the one with the shortest rise time and adequate damping. But this is not always true. In a practical system various factors enter into the control problems, and the optimum performance that the system may achieve is limited not only by factors in the controlled system and in the environment of the control, such as load disturbance and noise, but also by the unpredictable changes and interrelations of these factors.

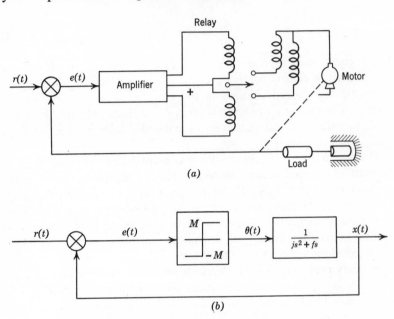

*Fig. 3.2* A position servo with a bang-bang controller [4]: (*a*) schematic diagram; (*b*) block diagram. (Benjamin C. Kuo, *Automatic Control Systems*, Copyright 1962. Reprinted by permission of Prentice-Hall, Inc., Englewood Cliffs, New Jersey.)

There is a class of control systems in which the motor applies full power to the output member whenever the error signal exceeds some predetermined value; this constant power is maintained until the error is reduced to some insignificant value. Since switching relays are often used to accomplish this on-off control of power, a system of this type is referred to as a "relay-type," "on-off," or "bang-bang" control (servo) [4]. Bang-bang control is often considered to be an optimal control because for many systems the response time is minimized when bang-bang control is used. A simple example of a control system (servo) with a bang-bang controller is shown in Fig. 3.2, in which the control signal $\theta(t)$ is considered as an exciting voltage and the response signal $x(t)$ is defined as a shaft position. The desired response signal $r(t)$ is the desired shaft position, and the difference between $r(t)$ and $x(t)$ is the error signal; $j$ is the moment of inertia and $f$ is the friction coefficient.

Since one of the most common problems of optimal controller design is associated with the bang-bang type control, we shall discuss it again in considerably more detail in a later section.

## 2. APPLICATIONS

In this section we shall show by means of simple examples how the maximum principle may be used to find an optimal control policy. Examples are chosen to include a wide variety of problems.

In addition to the stabilizing and maneuvering categories, control problems can be classified in many other ways; for instance, according to the forms of the functional $S$ (or the objective function in general), the specifications of the initial and final state, and the types of controller. Some typical forms are listed below.

### a. Functional (objective function) S

1. Minimal time control, in which $S = \int_0^T dt^*$.

2. Minimal integrated error, in which $S = \int_0^T f(x_i)\, dt$,

   $f(x_i)$ is of the form, $|x_i|, (x_i)^2, \ldots$

3. Minimal integrated effort, in which $S = \int_0^T f(\theta_i)\, dt$,

   $f(\theta_i)$ is of the form, $|\theta_i|, (\theta_i)^2, \ldots$

4. Minimal terminal error, in which

$$S = [x_1(T)]^2 + [x_2(T)]^2 + \cdots + [x_s(T)]^2.$$

### b. Specifications of the Initial and Final State

1. End points fixed; that is, $x_1(0), x_2(0), \ldots, x_s(0)$ and $x_1(T), x_2(T), \ldots, x_s(T)$ are completely specified.

2. End points partly fixed; that is, only some of the $x_i(0)$ and $x_i(T)$, $i = 1, 2, \ldots, s$ are specified.

3. Final point not fixed; that is, $x_1(T), x_2(T), \ldots, x_s(T)$ are not specified.

Different combinations of the functional and the terminal state are possible in practical control problems.

---

*The initial time $t_0$ is considered as zero time in the remainder of this chapter.

*c. Types of Control.*    In extremizing the Hamiltonian $H$ with respect to $\theta$ we can disregard the terms that do not involve $\theta$. For convenience we can therefore divide $H$ into two parts as

$H =$ (groups of terms in which $\theta$ appears explicitly) + (other terms which do not involve $\theta$) = $H^* +$ remainder.

Then, for a constrained control variable, $\theta_{min} \leq \theta \leq \theta_{max}$, the following three typical types of optimal control may be considered [5]:

1. Bang-bang.    This is the case in which the functional (objective function) does not include $\theta$ or has a term that is proportional to $\theta$, and $H^*$ is of the form

$$H^* = h\theta, \tag{11}$$

where $h$ may be a function of time. The conditions for $H^*$ to be minimum are

$$\theta = \theta_{min} \quad \text{if} \quad h > 0,$$
$$\theta = \theta_{max} \quad \text{if} \quad h < 0.$$

2. Bang-bang with coasting (bang-coast-bang, bang-off-bang).    This is the case in which the functional (objective function) involves $|\theta|$ and $H^*$ is of the form

$$H^* = w\,|\theta| + h\theta, \tag{12}$$

where $w$ is a positive constant and $h$ involves $z_i(t)$. For the control variable constrained in the form

$$\theta_{min} \leq \theta \leq \theta_{max}$$

the function $H^*$ attains its minimum when

$$\theta = \theta_{min} \quad \text{if} \quad w < h,$$
$$\theta = 0 \quad\quad \text{if} \quad -w < h < w,$$
$$\theta = \theta_{max} \quad \text{if} \quad h < -w.$$

3. Continuous with or without saturation.    This is the case in which the functional involves $(\theta)^2$. If $H^*$ is of the form

$$H^* = w(\theta)^2 + h\theta, \tag{13}$$

then $H^*$ attains its extremum value only if

$$\frac{\partial H^*}{\partial \theta} = 0$$

or

$$\theta = -\frac{h}{2w},$$

which is the optimal control if it is in the range of admissible control. Therefore $\theta$ can take any value between the two limits, $\theta_{min}$ and $\theta_{max}$.

**Example 1.** Consider the first-order linear dynamic system shown in Fig. 3.3. Let $x_1(t)$ represent the deviation of the state of the system from the desired value (steady-state value) of the output variable and let $\theta(t)$ be the control action. We are required to find an optimal control that will bring the system from its initial state $x_1(0) = 2$, which deviates from the desirable operating state, to its final operating state $x_1(T) = 0$. At the same time we are to minimize the functional (objective function)

$$S = \int_0^T \left[ 1 + (\theta)^2 \right] dt = \int_0^T dt + \int_0^T (\theta)^2 \, dt.$$

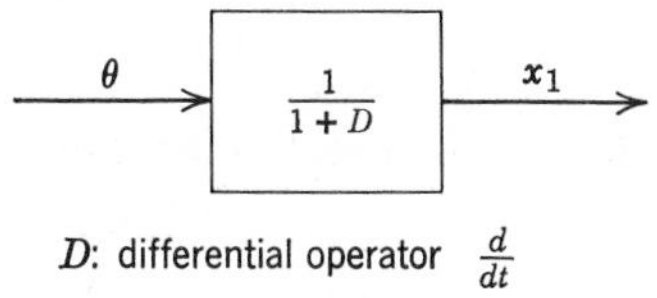

Assume that no constraint is imposed on the control variable $\theta$.

*D*: differential operator $\frac{d}{dt}$

**Fig. 3.3** Block diagram of the dynamic system in Example 1.

This problem as stated may be considered as a stabilizing problem in which a load disturbance has caused a sudden deviation from the desired operating state. The objective function is obtained by combining the minimal time control function $\int_0^T dt$ with a function representing the minimal integrated control effort $\int_0^T (\theta)^2 \, dt$. The final time is not specified, but both end points (state variables) are fixed.

From Fig. 3.3 we have

$$\theta = (1 + D)x_1,$$

which is identical to

$$\frac{dx_1}{dt} = -x_1 + \theta. \tag{14}$$

To solve this problem we introduce an additional state variable

$$x_2(t) = \int_0^t [1 + (\theta)^2] \, dt.$$

It follows that

$$\frac{dx_2}{dt} = 1 + (\theta)^2, \qquad x_2(0) = 0. \tag{15}$$

The problem is thus transformed into that of minimizing $x_2(T)$.

The Hamiltonian is

$$H(z, x, \theta) = z_1(\theta - x_1) + z_2[1 + (\theta)^2].$$

According to the definition of the adjoint vector, we have

$$\frac{dz_1}{dt} = -\frac{\partial H}{\partial x_1} = z_1, \tag{16}$$

$$\frac{dz_2}{dt} = -\frac{\partial H}{\partial x_2} = 0, \qquad z_2(T) = 1. \tag{17}$$

Solution of equations (16) and (17) for $z_1(t)$ and $z_2(t)$ gives

$$z_1(t) = A_1 e^t, \tag{18}$$

$$z_2(t) = 1. \tag{19}$$

Hence the Hamiltonian can be rewritten as

$$H = z_1\theta - z_1 x_1 + 1 + (\theta)^2.$$

Therefore $H^*$, the portion of $H$ which depends on $\theta$, is as follows:

$$H^* = z_1\theta + (\theta)^2. \tag{20}$$

Inspection of $H^*$ shows that the optimal controller should be a continuous type [cf. equation (13)].

It is worth recalling that in minimizing the functional (objective function) the Hamiltonian must be minimized. Since the control (decison) variable is not constrained, the optimal control for this type is found from the condition

$$\frac{\partial H^*}{\partial \theta} = 2\theta + z_1 = 0 \tag{21}$$

or

$$z_1 = -2\theta. \tag{22}$$

Combining this condition with equation (18), we have

$$\theta(t) = -\frac{z_1}{2} = -\frac{A_1}{2} e^t. \tag{23}$$

From the theorem presented at the beginning of this chapter we know that the minimum value of $H$ is

$$H = 1 + (\theta)^2 - 2(\theta)^2 + 2\theta x_1$$
$$= -(\theta)^2 + 2\theta x_1 + 1 = 0, \qquad 0 \le t \le T. \tag{24}$$

Application of the boundary condition at $t = 0$, that is, $x_1(0) = 2$, to equation (24) gives

$$[\theta(0)]^2 - 4\theta(0) - 1 = 0. \tag{25}$$

The roots of this quadratic equation are $\theta(0) = 4.236$ and $\theta(0) = -0.236$. For

$$\theta(0) = -0.236$$

equation (23) becomes

$$\theta(0) = -\frac{A_1}{2} = -0.236 \quad \text{or} \quad A_1 = 0.472.$$

Hence

$$\theta(t) = -0.236e^t, \tag{26}$$

$$z_1(t) = 0.472e^t. \tag{27}$$

By substituting equation (26) into equation (14) and solving the resulting differential equation we obtain

$$x_1(t) = -0.118e^t + A_2e^{-t}. \tag{28}$$

Application of the boundary condition at $t = 0$ gives

$$x_1(0) = 2 = -0.118 + A_2.$$

Thus

$$A_2 = 2.118$$

and

$$x_1(t) = -0.118e^t + 2.118e^{-t}. \tag{29}$$

The final time is found by applying the second boundary condition on equation (29) as

$$x_1(T) = 0 = -0.118e^T + 2.118e^{-T},$$

$$T = 1.45.$$

For

$$\theta(0) = 4.236$$

we obtain

$$\theta(t) = 4.236e^t,$$

$$z_1(t) = -8.472e^t,$$

$$x_1(t) = 2.118e^t - 0.118e^{-t},$$

$$x_1(T) = 0 = 2.118e^T - 0.118e^{-T}$$

by following the same procedure. However, the final equation produces negative $T$ which is not physically feasible. Therefore equation (26) represents the desired optimal control, and from this solution we may conclude generally that the control force is in the direction opposite to the direction of deviation.

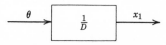

**Fig. 3.4** Block diagram of the linear system in Example 2.

**Example 2** [13]. Consider the simple dynamic system shown in Fig. 3.4 in which $x_1(t)$ represents the deviation of the desired value of the output variable and $\theta(t)$ represents the control action. The boundary conditions are $x_1(0) = 2$, corresponding to the original deviation from the desirable state, and $x_1(T) = 0$, signifying the cancellation of such deviation because of the control action applied. The constraint is imposed on $\theta$ so that $|\theta| \leq 1$. We are to find the control action that minimizes the objective function

$$S = \int_0^T [(x_1)^2 + (\theta)^2]\, dt.$$

This may again be considered as a stabilizing problem in which we are to minimize a combination of the integrated deviation from the steady-state output (characterized by the first term in the bracket) and the integrated effort (characterized by the second term in the bracket) during the control action. Furthermore, the end points are fixed but the final time is unspecified.

From the block diagram in Fig. 3.4 we know that the performance equation of the system is

$$Dx_1 = \theta$$

or

$$\frac{dx_1}{dt} = \theta. \tag{30}$$

By introducing an additional variable $x_2(t)$ in which

$$x_2(t) = \int_0^t [(x_1)^2 + (\theta)^2]\, dt$$

we have

$$\frac{dx_2}{dt} = (x_1)^2 + (\theta)^2, \qquad x_2(0) = 0, \tag{31}$$

and

$$S = x_2(T). \tag{32}$$

The Hamiltonian is

$$H = z_1\theta + z_2[(x_1)^2 + (\theta)^2]. \tag{33}$$

The components of the adjoint vector are defined by

$$\frac{dz_1}{dt} = -\frac{\partial H}{\partial x_1} = -2z_2 x_1, \tag{34}$$

$$\frac{dz_2}{dt} = -\frac{\partial H}{\partial x_2} = 0, \qquad z_2(T) = 1. \tag{35}$$

Solving for $z_2(t)$ from equation (35) yields

$$z_2(t) = 1, \qquad 0 \leq t \leq T. \tag{36}$$

Hence the Hamiltonian becomes

$$H = z_1\theta + (x_1)^2 + (\theta)^2 \tag{37}$$

and

$$H^* = z_1\theta + (\theta)^2. \tag{38}$$

This shows that the optimal control is continuous as in the first example. The control action for this problem, however, is constrained in such a manner that

$$|\theta| \leq 1,$$

whereas there are no constraints imposed on it in the first problem.

First we shall determine whether the optimal control may be determined from the condition that

$$\frac{\partial H^*}{\partial \theta} = 0 = z_1 + 2\theta;$$

that is

$$\theta = -\frac{z_1}{2}$$

Applying the theorem, we have the minimum value of $H$ at $t = 0$ as

$$H = 0 = -[\theta(0)]^2 + [x_1(0)]^2 = -[\theta(0)]^2 + 4. \tag{39}$$

It follows that

$$\theta(0) = \pm 2,$$

which lie outside the constraint, that is, the saturation limit. Therefore the condition

$$\frac{\partial H^*}{\partial \theta} = 0$$

does not yield the admissible control action.

The optimal control for $0 \leq t \leq t_1$ is either

$$\theta = -1,$$

or

$$\theta = +1, \tag{40}$$

where $t_1$ is the time when the saturation period ends, which is still to be determined. Use of equations (36) and (40) (assuming that $\theta = -1$) and solution of equations (30) and (34) for $x_1(t)$ and $z_1(t)$ yields

$$x_1(t) = -t + A_1, \qquad 0 \leq t \leq t_1, \tag{41}$$

$$z_1(t) = (t)^2 - 2A_1t + A_2, \qquad 0 \leq t \leq t_1. \tag{42}$$

Using the boundary conditions at $t = 0$, we have

$$x_1(0) = 2 = A_1,$$
$$H = 0 = z_1(0)(-1) + [x_1(0)]^2 + (-1)^2$$
$$= -z_1(0) + 4 + 1.$$

Thus we have

$$z_1(0) = 5 = A_2.$$

Equations (41) and (42) then become

$$x_1(t) = -t + 2, \qquad 0 \le t \le t_1, \tag{43}$$
$$z_1(t) = (t)^2 - 4t + 5, \qquad 0 \le t \le t_1. \tag{44}$$

At $t_1$ (actually right after $t_1$) the control action will no longer be saturated and thus the condition

$$\frac{\partial H^*}{\partial \theta} = 0$$

can be used to determine the optimal condition as already stated. Therefore we can write

$$\theta(t_1) = -\frac{z_1(t_1)}{2}$$

or

$$z_1(t_1) = -2\theta(t_1) = +2. \tag{45}$$

Solving equations (44) and (45) for $t_1$, we have

$$t_1 = 3 \quad \text{or} \quad 1.$$

For

$$t_1 = 3,$$
$$x_1(t_1) = -3 + 2 = -1.$$

This condition can be attained only by a drastic change from the original state of $x_1 = 2$. In addition, this state still deviates considerably from the desired operating state at which $x_1 = 0$. We shall therefore use

$$t_1 = 1$$

for which

$$x_1(t_1) = -1 + 2 = 1.$$

After this period of saturation the optimal control can be determined from the condition that

$$\frac{\partial H^*}{\partial \theta} = 0.$$

For the period $t_1 \leq t \leq T$ we can consider that

$$\frac{dx_1}{dt} = \theta = -\tfrac{1}{2}z_1,$$

$$\frac{dz_1}{dt} = -2x_1.$$

Solving for $x_1(t)$ and $\theta(t)$ from this set of equations, we obtain

$$x_1(t) = A_1'e^t + A_2'e^{-t},$$

$$\theta(t) = \frac{dx_1}{dt} = A_1'e^t - A_2'e^{-t}.$$

Application of the boundary conditions of $x_1(t)$ and $\theta(t)$ at $t_1$ yields

$$A_1' = 0,$$
$$A_2' = e.$$

Therefore, we have

$$x_1(t) = e^{1-t}, \qquad t_1 \leq t \leq T,$$
$$\theta = -e^{1-t}, \qquad t_1 \leq t \leq T.$$

Consequently

$$x_1(T) = 0 = e^{1-T} = e(e^{-T}),$$

from which we can conclude that

$$T \to \infty.$$

For $\theta = 1$, $0 \leq t \leq t_1$, the values of $t_1$ are negative and thus may be neglected. Hence the assumption that $\theta = -1$ gives the optimal control for $0 \leq t \leq t_1$ is correct.

**Example 3.**  Consider the dynamic system treated in Example 1. The boundary conditions, however, are changed to

$$x_1(0) = 2,$$
$$x_1(T) = x_1(2) = 0,$$

and the control force is constrained as

$$|\theta| \leq 1.$$

We are to minimize the integrated control effort

$$S = \int_0^2 |\theta| \, dt.$$

Since this is the case in which both end points and time are fixed, the first extension of the basic algorithm given in Chapter 2 can be used to obtain the solution. The performance equation for the system is, as already given,

$$\frac{dx_1}{dt} = -x_1 + \theta. \tag{46}$$

The objective function $S$ is the final value of a new state variable $x_2$ defined by the following performance equation

$$\frac{dx_2}{dt} = |\theta|, \qquad x_2(0) = 0. \tag{47}$$

The Hamiltonian is

$$H = -z_1 x_1 + z_1 \theta + z_2 |\theta|. \tag{48}$$

The components of the adjoint vector are defined by

$$\frac{dz_1}{dt} = z_1, \tag{49}$$

$$\frac{dz_2}{dt} = 0, \qquad z_2(T) = z_2(2) = 1. \tag{50}$$

It follows from equation (50) that

$$z_2(t) = 1.$$

The Hamiltonian then becomes

$$H = -z_1 x_1 + z_1 \theta + |\theta|. \tag{51}$$

Therefore we see that

$$H^* = |\theta| + z_1 \theta. \tag{52}$$

Comparing this equation with equation (12), we know that the bang-bang control with coasting probably must be used and that the value of $H^*$ attains its minimum when

$$\begin{aligned}
\theta &= -1, && \text{if } z_1 > 1, \\
\theta &= 0, && \text{if } 1 > z_1 > -1, \\
\theta &= 1, && \text{if } -1 > z_1.
\end{aligned} \tag{53}$$

In order to bring the initial deviated state $x_1(0) = 2$ to the final desired operating state $x_1(2) = 0$, we reject the control $\theta = 1$ as we did in the two preceding examples.

Starting with the control

$$\theta = 0, \qquad 1 > z_1 > -1,$$

we obtain $x_1(t)$ from equation (46) as

$$x_1(t) = A_1 e^{-t}.$$

Application of the first boundary condition

$$x_1(0) = 2$$

to this equation gives

$$A_1 = 2$$

and

$$x_1(t) = 2e^{-t}. \tag{54}$$

Let $t_s$ be the time for switching from

$$\theta = 0$$

to

$$\theta = -1.$$

Then, for $t_s \leq t \leq T$, $x_1(t)$ is solved from equation (46) as

$$x_1(t) = A_2 e^{-t} - 1. \tag{55}$$

Because of the continuity of $x_1$ with respect to $t$, we have from equations (54) and (55)

$$2e^{-t_s} = A_2 e^{-t_s} - 1. \tag{56}$$

This gives

$$A_2 = 2 + e^{t_s}.$$

Therefore

$$x_1(t) = (2 + e^{t_s})e^{-t} - 1, \qquad t_s \leq t \leq T. \tag{57}$$

From equation (57) and the boundary condition

$$x_1(2) = 0$$

$t_s$ is found as

$$t_s = 1.685.$$

Thus, from equation (55) and the condition $x_1(2) = 0$, we have

$$x_1(t) = e^{2-t} - 1, \qquad 1.685 \leq t \leq 2. \tag{58}$$

It is worth noting that the minimum value of $H$ is a constant but that in this case it is not zero as it was in the two preceding examples. As mentioned in Chapter 2, the minimum (or maximum) value of $H$ is a constant but not zero over the fixed time interval considered. We shall show that this is true for this example.

At the point of switching we know from equation (53) that

$$z_1(t_s) = 1.$$

By solving equation (49) for $z_1(t)$ and employing the foregoing condition and equation (57) at $t = 2$ we obtain

$$z_1(t) = \frac{e^t}{(e)^2 - 2}, \qquad 0 \leq t \leq 2.$$

The values of the Hamiltonians are checked as follows:  for

$$0 \leq t \leq t_s, \qquad \theta = 0,$$

we have

$$
\begin{aligned}
H &= -z_1 x_1 + z_1 \theta + |\theta| \\
&= -z_1 x_1 \\
&= -\frac{e^t}{(e)^2 - 2} 2e^{-t} \\
&= \frac{-2}{(e)^2 - 2} = \text{constant.}
\end{aligned}
$$

For

$$t_s \leq t \leq 2, \qquad \theta = -1,$$

we have

$$
\begin{aligned}
H &= -z_1 x_1 + z_1 \theta + |\theta| \\
&= 1 - (x_1 + 1)z_1 \\
&= 1 - (e^{2-t} - 1 + 1)\left(\frac{e^t}{(e)^2 - 2}\right) \\
&= \frac{-2}{(e)^2 - 2} = \text{constant.}
\end{aligned}
$$

We have thus confirmed that the minimum value of $H$ is a constant at every point of this continuous simple process, as stated in the basic theorem.

**Example 4.**    Consider the feedback control system shown in Fig. 3.5. We wish to change the output of the system $x_1(t)$ from the original operating condition of

$$x_1 = 0 \quad \text{at} \quad t = 0$$

to the final condition of

$$x_1 = 2 \quad \text{at} \quad t = T = 5$$

and at the same time to minimize the integrated squared error given by

$$S = \int_0^T [e(t)]^2 \, dt.$$

This is the case in which time and end points are fixed. However, we are to manipulate the input $r(t)$ instead of the control action $q(t)$ which results from the comparison of the input $r(t)$ and the measured output $x_1(t)$, that is, from the error signal $e(t)$. We shall do this by minimizing the integrated error while the system goes from the initial state to the desired final state in a given period of time. This class of problem is usually called maneuvering in contrast to the stabilizing problems treated in the

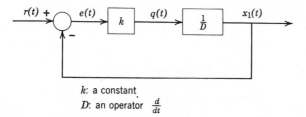

k: a constant
D: an operator $\frac{d}{dt}$

**Fig. 3.5** Block diagram of the feedback control system with a proportional controller in Example 4.

preceding examples. It is worth noting at this point that for this problem the input $r(t)$ instead of the control action $q(t)$ is the decision vector (variable) of the process usually designated as $\theta(t)$ in our algorithm.

The error signal $e(t)$ is defined as

$$e(t) = r(t) - x_1(t). \tag{59}$$

From the block diagram we obtain the performance equation of the plant being controlled as

$$\frac{dx_1}{dt} = q \tag{60}$$

and that of the controller (a proportional controller) as

$$q(t) = ke(t), \qquad k = a \text{ proportional constant.} \tag{61}$$

Combination of equations (59), (60), and (61) gives the performance equation of the complete system as

$$\frac{dx_1}{dt} = k[r(t) - x_1(t)]. \tag{62}$$

The objective function to be minimized can now be rewritten as

$$S = \int_0^5 [r(t) - x_1(t)]^2 \, dt \tag{63}$$

or, in the form of a differential equation, as

$$\frac{dx_2}{dt} = [r(t) - x_1(t)]^2, \qquad x_2(0) = 0. \tag{64}$$

By employing the algorithm in Chapter 2 we have

$$H = k[r(t) - x_1(t)]z_1 + [r(t) - x_1(t)]^2 z_2, \tag{65}$$

$$\frac{dz_1}{dt} = kz_1 + 2[r(t) - x_1(t)]z_2, \tag{66}$$

$$\frac{dz_2}{dt} = 0, \qquad z_2(T) = 1. \tag{67}$$

It follows from equation (67) that

$$z_2(t) = 1.$$

Thus equations (65) and (66) become

$$H = k[r(t) - x_1(t)]z_1 + [r(t) - x_1(t)]^2, \tag{68}$$

$$\frac{dz_1}{dt} = kz_1 + 2[r(t) - x_1(t)]. \tag{69}$$

The necessary condition for the optimal control is that $H$ attain its minimum in minimizing the objective function, or

$$\frac{\partial H}{\partial r} = kz_1 + 2[r(t) - x_1(t)] = 0;$$

that is,

$$r(t) = \tfrac{1}{2}[-z_1 k + 2x_1(t)]. \tag{70}$$

Substitution of this equation into equation (69) yields

$$\frac{dz_1}{dt} = 0;$$

that is

$$z_1(t) = A_1 = -\frac{2}{k}[r(t) - x_1(t)]. \tag{71}$$

By combining this equation with equation (62) we obtain

$$\frac{dx_1}{dt} = -\frac{1}{2}A_1 k^2$$

and solving for $x_1(t)$ we have

$$x_1(t) = -\tfrac{1}{2}A_1 k^2 t + A_2. \tag{72}$$

The initial and final conditions applied to equation (72) give

$$A_2 = 0 \quad \text{and} \quad A_1 = -\frac{4}{5k^2}.$$

Therefore we have

$$x_1(t) = \frac{2t}{5}, \tag{73}$$

$$z_1(t) = -\frac{4}{5k^2}. \tag{74}$$

From equations (71), (73), and (74) we obtain

$$\frac{4}{5k^2} = \frac{2}{k}\left(r(t) - \frac{2t}{5}\right),$$

$$r(t) = \frac{2}{5k} + \frac{2t}{5}.$$

The corresponding control action is

$$q(t) = ke(t)$$
$$= k[r(t) - x_1(t)]$$
$$= \tfrac{2}{5}.$$

Readers may note that the frequency-domain (Laplace transform or Fourier transform) approach (Nyquist, Bode, or Nichols) conventionally used for this type of problem has not been employed in the solution of

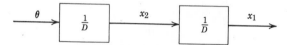

*Fig. 3.6*   Block diagram for the inertial system in Example 5.

any of the examples. Solutions have been completely carried out in the real time domain. In other words, the state-space (or phase-space) approach mentioned in the preceding section has been used.

**Example 5.**   An inertial system, one whose state changes with acceleration, is represented by the block diagram in Fig. 3.6. The state variables $x_1(t)$ and $x_2(t)$ denote position and velocity, respectively. We wish to change the state of the system from

$$x_1(0) = 2$$
$$x_2(0) = 0$$

to a final state which is confined to lie on a unit circle in the phase plane; that is

$$[x_1(T)]^2 + [x_2(T)]^2 = 1$$

at $t = T$, where $T$ is unspecified. The control variable is constrained as

$$|\theta| \leq 1.$$

We are to find an optimal control in which

$$S = \int_0^T (|\theta| + \tfrac{1}{2}) \, dt$$

is minimized.

The performance equations of the system, which are given in the block diagram, are

$$\frac{dx_1}{dt} = x_2, \tag{75}$$

$$\frac{dx_2}{dt} = \theta. \tag{76}$$

Let

$$\frac{dx_3}{dt} = |\theta| + \frac{1}{2}, \qquad x_3(0) = 0. \tag{77}$$

Then we have

$$H = z_1 x_2 + z_2 \theta + z_3 |\theta| + \frac{z_3}{2}, \tag{78}$$

$$\frac{dz_1}{dt} = 0, \tag{79}$$

$$\frac{dz_2}{dt} = -z_1, \tag{80}$$

$$\frac{dz_3}{dt} = 0, \qquad z_3(T) = 1. \tag{81}$$

It follows from equations (79), (80), and (81) that

$$z_1(t) = A_1, \tag{82}$$

$$z_2(t) = -A_1 t + A_2, \tag{83}$$

$$z_3(t) = 1. \tag{84}$$

Thus the Hamiltonian becomes

$$H = A_1 x_2 + z_2 \theta + |\theta| + \tfrac{1}{2} \tag{85}$$

and

$$H^* = |\theta| + z_2 \theta. \tag{86}$$

This corresponds to bang-bang control with coasting. Equation (86) indicates that the optimal control action which minimizes $H^*$ should be as follows [also compare with equation (12)]:

$$\begin{aligned}
\theta &= -1 \quad \text{if} \quad z_2 > 1, \\
\theta &= 0 \quad \text{if} \quad 1 > z_2 > -1, \\
\theta &= 1 \quad \text{if} \quad -1 > z_2.
\end{aligned} \tag{87}$$

From equations (85) and (87) we know that the optimal control at $t = 0$ is either $\theta = -1$ or $\theta = 1$ because the condition $H = 0$ at $t = 0$ is not satisfied if $\theta = 0$. Let us assume for the time being that the optimal control action at $t = 0$ is $\theta = -1$. We start with the control

$$\theta = -1 \quad \text{for} \quad 0 \le t \le t_s$$

and switch to

$$\theta = 0$$

after the time $t_s$.

First, by applying the condition given in the theorem specifically at $t = 0$ we obtain from equation (85)

$$H = 0 = -z_2(0) + \tfrac{3}{2}$$

or

$$z_2(0) = \tfrac{3}{2}.$$

Therefore, from equation (83), we have

$$A_2 = \tfrac{3}{2}$$

and equation (83) becomes

$$z_2(t) = -A_1 t + \tfrac{3}{2}. \tag{88}$$

From equation (87) we know that

$$z_2(t_s) = 1. \tag{89}$$

Therefore $A_1$ is determined from equations (88) and (89) as

$$A_1 = \frac{1}{2t_s},$$

and $z_1(t)$ and $z_2(t)$ may be rewritten from equations (82) and (83) as

$$z_1(t) = \frac{1}{2t_s}, \qquad 0 \le t \le T, \tag{90}$$

$$z_2(t) = \frac{3}{2} - \frac{1}{2t_s} t, \qquad 0 \le t \le T. \tag{91}$$

For $\theta = -1$, $x_1(t)$ and $x_2(t)$ are solved from equations (75) and (76) with the initial conditions. The results are

$$x_1(t) = 2 - \tfrac{1}{2}(t)^2, \quad 0 \le t \le t_s, \tag{92}$$
$$x_2(t) = -t, \qquad\qquad 0 \le t \le t_s. \tag{93}$$

For $\theta = 0$ we obtain similarly

$$x_1(t) = A_3 t + A_4, \qquad t_s \le t \le T, \tag{94}$$
$$x_2(t) = A_3, \qquad\qquad t_s \le t \le T. \tag{95}$$

Because of the continuity of $x$ with respect to $t$, we have from the last four equations at $t = t_s$

$$x_1 = 2 - \tfrac{1}{2}(t_s)^2 = A_3 t_s + A_4, \tag{96}$$

$$x_2 = -t_s = A_3, \tag{97}$$

which on solving for $A_3$ and $A_4$ give

$$A_3 = -t_s,$$
$$A_4 = 2 + \tfrac{1}{2}(t_s)^2.$$

Hence

$$x_1(t) = 2 + \tfrac{1}{2}(t_s)^2 - t_s t, \qquad t_s \leq t \leq T, \tag{98}$$

$$x_2(t) = -t_s, \qquad\qquad\qquad t_s \leq t \leq T. \tag{99}$$

The values of $t_s$ and $T$ must be determined by the transversality condition, a subject that is treated more extensively in Chapter 11. The transversality condition for this problem is

$$z_1(T)a_1 + z_2(T)a_2 = 0, \tag{100}$$

where $a_1$ and $a_2$ are components of the tangent vector to the circle, that is,

$$(a_1, a_2) = [-x_2(T), x_1(T)]. \tag{101}$$

Then equation (100) becomes

$$-z_1(T)\,x_2(T) + z_2(T)\,x_1(T) = 0$$

or

$$z_1(T)\,x_2(T) = z_2(T)\,x_1(T). \tag{102}$$

The simultaneous solution of equations (90), (91), (98), (99), (102) and the given equation

$$[x_1(T)]^2 + [x_2(T)]^2 = 1$$

gives

$$t_s = 0.56$$

and

$$T = 2.38.$$

It is worth noting that the optimal trajectory ends during the second period in this example. If, at the end of the second period, the optimal trajectory does not reach the circle, we have to consider the third period which corresponds to the control $\theta = 1$ and so on. If we start with the control $\theta = 1$, it can be shown that the trajectory deviates away from the given circle; hence the assumed optimal control action at $t = 0$ is correct. This example was originally treated by Takahashi [5].

**Example 6** [1]. Consider a dynamic system described by the following differential equation:

$$\frac{d^2x}{dt^2} = \theta,$$

where $\theta$ is constrained by the condition that

$$|\theta| \leq 1.$$

In the phase-space defined by the two coordinates

$$x_1 = x \quad \text{and} \quad x_2 = \frac{dx}{dt}$$

the differential equation of the system may be rewritten as

$$\frac{dx_1}{dt} = x_2, \tag{103}$$

$$\frac{dx_2}{dt} = \theta. \tag{104}$$

This set of equations is the same as that in Example 5.

The system is required to change from the initial state

$$x_1(0) = 1, \qquad x_2(0) = 1,$$

to the final state

$$x_1(T) = 0, \qquad x_2(T) = 0,$$

in the shortest time. In other words, we are considering the time-optimal (minimum) problem for the case in which the origin of the phase-space is the final state.

The objective function for the problem to be minimized is then

$$S = \int_0^T dt,$$

where $T$ is the unspecified final time.

If a new variable $x_3$ is introduced as

$$x_3(t) = \int_0^t dt \tag{105}$$

or

$$\frac{dx_3(t)}{dt} = 1, \qquad x_3(0) = 0,$$

the Hamiltonian becomes

$$H = z_1 x_2 + z_2 \theta + z_3. \tag{106}$$

From equations (5) and (6) we obtain

$$\frac{dz_1}{dt} = 0,$$

$$\frac{dz_2}{dt} = -z_1, \tag{107}$$

$$\frac{dz_3}{dt} = 0, \qquad z_3(T) = 1.$$

Therefore, we have

$$H^* = z_2 \theta. \tag{108}$$

An optimal control corresponding to this case should be the bang-bang type described in Section 2c. Thus the conditions for optimal control (minimum $H^*$) are

$$\theta = -1, \quad \text{if} \quad z_2 > 0,$$
$$\theta = \phantom{-}1, \quad \text{if} \quad z_2 < 0. \tag{109}$$

In order to bring the initial operating state $x(0) = 1$ to the final desired state $x(T) = 0$, we shall first apply the control $\theta = -1$ as we have done in Examples 1, 2, and 3.

Therefore, for the time interval $0 \leq t \leq t_s$ on which $\theta = -1$, we have from equations (103) and (104) and the initial values of $x$

$$x_2(t) = -t + 1, \qquad\qquad 0 \leq t \leq t_s, \tag{110}$$
$$x_1(t) = -\tfrac{1}{2}(t)^2 + t + 1, \qquad 0 \leq t \leq t_s. \tag{111}$$

For the control $\theta = 1$ we have, again from equations (103) and (104) and the boundary conditions,

$$x_2(t) = t + A_1, \qquad\qquad\quad t_s \leq t \leq T,$$
$$x_1(t) = \tfrac{1}{2}(t)^2 + A_1 t + A_2, \qquad t_s \leq t \leq T.$$

Following the computational procedures employed in Examples 2 and 3, we obtain

$$t_s = 2.225$$

and

$$T = 3.45.$$

**Example 7** [5]. Consider the system represented by the block diagram in Fig. 3.7 in which $g(t)$ represents a load disturbance varying with respect to time. The initial state of the system is

$$x_1(0) = 0.$$

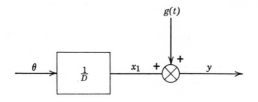

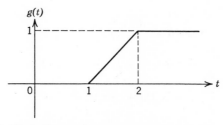

**Fig. 3.7** Block diagram for the control system in Example 7.

It is desired to find an optimal control to minimize

$$S = \int_0^T [(y)^2 + (\theta)^2] \, dt \quad \text{for } T = 2,$$

where $y$ is the output of the system. From Fig. 3.7 we see that

$$y(t) = x_1(t) + g(t) \tag{112}$$

and that

$$g(t) = \begin{cases} 0 & \text{if } 0 \le t \le 1, \\ t - 1 & \text{if } 1 \le t \le 2, \\ 1 & \text{if } 2 \le t. \end{cases} \tag{113}$$

Hence this is a nonautonomous system in which time $t$ appears explicitly in the objective function. We treat this problem, as discussed in Section 2.4c, by introducing an additional state variable $x_2(t)$ in which

$$x_2(t) = t, \qquad x_2(0) = 0. \tag{114}$$

Thus we have

$$\frac{dx_2}{dt} = 1. \tag{115}$$

From the block diagram we know that the performance equation of the system is

$$\frac{dx_1}{dt} = \theta. \tag{116}$$

Let

$$x_3(t) = \int_0^t [(y)^2 + (\theta)^2]\, dt.$$

Then

$$\frac{dx_3}{dt} = (y)^2 + (\theta)^2$$
$$= [x_1 + g(t)]^2 + (\theta)^2, \qquad x_3(0) = 0. \tag{117}$$

Hence we have

$$H = z_1\theta + z_2 + z_3[x_1 + g(t)]^2 + z_3(\theta)^2$$
$$= z_1\theta + z_2 + z_3[x_1 + g(x_2)]^2 + z_3(\theta)^2, \tag{118}$$

$$\frac{dz_1}{dt} = -2z_3[x_1 + g(t)], \qquad z_1(T) = 0, \tag{119}$$

$$\frac{dz_2}{dt} = -2z_3[x_1 + g(x_2)]\frac{dg}{dx_2}$$
$$= -2z_3[x_1 + g(t)]\frac{dg}{dt}, \qquad z_2(T) = 0, \tag{120}$$

$$\frac{dz_3}{dt} = 0, \qquad z_3(T) = 1. \tag{121}$$

It follows from equation (121) that

$$z_3(t) = 1.$$

Equations (118), (119), and (120) can then be rewritten as

$$H = z_1\theta + z_2 + (\theta)^2 + [x_1 + g(t)]^2, \tag{122}$$

$$\frac{dz_1}{dt} = -2[x_1 + g(t)], \tag{123}$$

$$\frac{dz_2}{dt} = -2[x_1 + g(t)]\frac{dg}{dt}, \tag{124}$$

and

$$H^* = (\theta)^2 + z_1\theta. \tag{125}$$

The optimal control is found from the necessary condition for optimality as

$$\frac{\partial H}{\partial \theta} = \frac{\partial H^*}{\partial \theta} = 0 = 2\theta + z_1,$$

that is,

$$2\theta = -z_1. \tag{126}$$

From equation (113) we have

$$g(t) = 0, \qquad 0 \le t \le 1. \tag{127}$$

Solution of equations (116), (123), and (126) for $x_1(t)$ and $\theta(t)$ yields

$$x_1(t) = A_1 e^t + A_2 e^{-t}, \qquad 0 \le t \le 1, \tag{128}$$
$$\theta(t) = A_1 e^t - A_2 e^{-t}, \qquad 0 \le t \le 1. \tag{129}$$

By using the initial value of $x_1$, we obtain

$$x_1(t) = A_1(e^t - e^{-t}), \qquad 0 \le t \le 1, \tag{130}$$
$$\theta(t) = A_1(e^t + e^{-t}), \qquad 0 \le t \le 1. \tag{131}$$

In the second period we are given

$$g(t) = t - 1, \qquad 1 \le t \le 2. \tag{132}$$

Therefore we obtain

$$x_1(t) = A_3 e^t + A_4 e^{-t} - t + 1, \tag{133}$$
$$\theta(t) = A_3 e^t - A_4 e^{-t} - 1, \tag{134}$$

by following the same procedure as in the first period. Because of the continuity of $x_1$ and $\theta$ with respect to $t$ we have from equations (130), (131), (133), and (134) at $t = 1$

$$A_1(e - e^{-1}) = A_3 e + A_4 e^{-1},$$
$$A_1(e + e^{-1}) = A_3 e - A_4 e^{-1} - 1.$$

Thus from these two equations we obtain

$$A_3 = \tfrac{1}{2} e^{-1} + A_1,$$
$$A_4 = -\tfrac{1}{2} e - A_1. \tag{135}$$

Equations (133) and (134) then become

$$x_1(t) = (\tfrac{1}{2} e^{-1} + A_1) e^t - (\tfrac{1}{2} e + A_1) e^{-t} - t + 1, \qquad 1 \le t \le 2, \tag{136}$$
$$\theta(t) = (\tfrac{1}{2} e^{-1} + A_1) e^t + (\tfrac{1}{2} e + A_1) e^{-t} - 1. \qquad 1 \le t \le 2. \tag{137}$$

Application of the boundary condition of equation (119) to equation (126) gives

$$\theta(T) = \theta(2) = 0.$$

Therefore $A_1$ is solved from equation (137) as

$$A_1 = -0.0728.$$

From equation (135) we have

$$A_3 = 0.112,$$
$$A_4 = -1.28.$$

Thus the optimal control and trajectory are

$$\theta(t) = -0.0728(e^t + e^{-t}), \qquad 0 \le t \le 1,$$
$$x_1(t) = -0.0728(e^t - e^{-t}), \qquad 0 \le t \le 1,$$

and
$$\theta(t) = 0.112e^t + 1.28e^{-t} - 1, \qquad 1 \le t \le 2,$$
$$x_1(t) = 0.112e^t - 1.28e^{-t} - t + 1, \qquad 1 \le t \le 2.$$

**Example 8** [13].   Consider another nonautonomous system represented by the block diagram shown in Fig. 3.8.  We are to find the optimal control

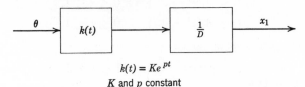

$$k(t) = Ke^{pt}$$
$$K \text{ and } p \text{ constant}$$

*Fig. 3.8*   Block diagram for the control system in Example 8.

in which the integrated effort
$$S = \int_0^T (\theta)^2 \, dt, \qquad \text{for } T = 2,$$

is minimized.  The initial and final states are
$$x_1(0) = 0, \qquad x_1(2) = 2.$$

From the block diagram the performance equation is
$$\frac{dx_1}{dt} = Ke^{pt}\theta. \tag{138}$$

Let
$$x_2(t) = t, \tag{139}$$
$$x_3(t) = \int_0^t (\theta)^2 \, dt. \tag{140}$$

Then we have
$$\frac{dx_2}{dt} = 1, \qquad x_2(0) = 0, \qquad x_2(2) = 2, \tag{141}$$
$$\frac{dx_3}{dt} = (\theta)^2, \qquad x_3(0) = 0, \tag{142}$$

and thus
$$H = z_1 Ke^{pt}\theta + z_2 + z_3(\theta)^2 \tag{143}$$
$$= z_1 Ke^{px_2}\theta + z_2 + z_3(\theta)^2,$$
$$\frac{dz_1}{dt} = 0, \tag{144}$$
$$\frac{dz_2}{dt} = -Kpe^{pt}z_1\theta, \tag{145}$$
$$\frac{dz_3}{dt} = 0, \qquad z_3(T) = 1. \tag{146}$$

From equation (146) we have $z_3(t) = 1$; hence

$$H = z_1 K e^{pt}\theta + z_2 + (\theta)^2. \tag{147}$$

The optimal control is found from the condition

$$\frac{\partial H}{\partial \theta} = 0 = z_1 K e^{pt} + 2\theta$$

to be

$$\theta = -\tfrac{1}{2} K z_1 e^{pt}. \tag{148}$$

It is worth noting that the final state is fixed; therefore the final value for the adjoint vector is not completely specified in contrast to Example 7. It follows from equation (144) that

$$z_1(t) = A_1.$$

Thus

$$\theta(t) = -\tfrac{1}{2} K A_1 e^{pt}. \tag{149}$$

From equations (138) and (149) we obtain

$$\frac{dx_1}{dt} = -\tfrac{1}{2}(K)^2 A_1 e^{2pt} \tag{150}$$

and

$$x_1(t) = -\frac{(K)^2}{4p} A_1 e^{2pt} + A_2. \tag{151}$$

Application of the boundary conditions of $x_1$ yields

$$A_1 = \frac{-8p}{(K)^2(e^{4p} - 1)},$$

$$A_2 = -\frac{2}{e^{4p} - 1}.$$

Hence from equations (149) and (151) we have the optimal control and trajectory as

$$\theta(t) = \frac{4p}{K(e^{4p} - 1)} e^{pt},$$

$$x_1(t) = \frac{2(e^{2pt} - 1)}{e^{4p} - 1}.$$

**Example 9** [5].  The inertial system considered in Example 5 is to take off and land on a target whose position and velocity are changing according to the following set of equations:

$$y_1 = \frac{(t)^2}{2},$$

$$y_2 = \frac{dy_1}{dt} = t.$$

The final time for landing on the target is not specified. We are to find an optimal control in which the objective function

$$S = \int_0^T [(\theta)^2 + 3]\, dt$$

is minimized. This is a problem in which the system equations are nonautonomous, and a transversality condition must be applied because the final conditions are specified by a set of equations which are functions of time. The initial conditions are given in Example 5 as

$$x_1(0) = 2,$$
$$x_2(0) = 0.$$

The performance equations are

$$\frac{dx_1}{dt} = x_2, \tag{152}$$

$$\frac{dx_2}{dt} = \theta. \tag{153}$$

Let

$$x_3(t) = t$$

and

$$x_4(t) = \int_0^t [(\theta)^2 + 3]\, dt.$$

Then we have

$$\frac{dx_3}{dt} = 1, \qquad\qquad x_3(0) = 0, \tag{154}$$

$$\frac{dx_4}{dt} = (\theta)^2 + 3, \qquad x_4(0) = 0, \tag{155}$$

and

$$H = z_1 x_2 + z_2 \theta + z_3 + z_4(\theta)^2 + 3z_4, \tag{156}$$

$$\frac{dz_1}{dt} = 0, \tag{157}$$

$$\frac{dz_2}{dt} = -z_1, \tag{158}$$

$$\frac{dz_3}{dt} = 0, \tag{159}$$

$$\frac{dz_4}{dt} = 0, \qquad z_4(T) = 1. \tag{160}$$

Equation (156), rewritten by using the solution of equation (160), $z_4 = 1$, yields

$$H = z_1 x_2 + z_2 \theta + z_3 + (\theta)^2 + 3.$$

The optimal control is found from the condition that

$$\frac{\partial H}{\partial \theta} = 0 = z_2 + 2\theta;$$

that is

$$\theta = -\frac{z_2}{2}. \tag{161}$$

Applying the theorem, we have, at $t = 0$,

$$H = z_1(0)\, x_2(0) + z_2(0)\, \theta(0) + z_3(0) + [\theta(0)]^2 + 3 = 0. \tag{162}$$

By employing the initial conditions of $x$ and substituting equation (161) into equation (162) we obtain

$$H = 0 = -[\theta(0)]^2 + z_3(0) + 3$$

or

$$z_3(0) = -3 + [\theta(0)]^2. \tag{163}$$

Solution of equations (157), (158), and (159) yields

$$z_1(t) = A_1, \tag{164}$$
$$z_2(t) = -A_1 t + A_2, \tag{165}$$
$$z_3(t) = A_3 = z_3(0) = -3 + [\theta(0)]^2. \tag{166}$$

From equations (161), (165), and (166) we have

$$\theta(t) = -\frac{z_2(t)}{2} = \tfrac{1}{2} A_1 t - \tfrac{1}{2} A_2, \tag{167}$$
$$z_3(t) = -3 + \tfrac{1}{4}(A_2)^2. \tag{168}$$

Solution of equations (152), (153), and (154) and use of the initial conditions of $x_1$, $x_2$, $x_3$ result in

$$x_1(t) = \tfrac{1}{12} A_1(t)^3 - \tfrac{1}{4} A_2(t)^2 + 2, \tag{169}$$
$$x_2(t) = \tfrac{1}{4} A_1(t)^2 - \tfrac{1}{2} A_2 t, \tag{170}$$
$$x_3(t) = t. \tag{171}$$

Assuming that the system hits the target at $t = T$, we have

$$y_1(T) = x_1(T),$$
$$y_2(T) = x_2(T),$$

or

$$\frac{(T)^2}{2} = \frac{1}{12} A_1(T)^3 - \frac{1}{4} A_2(T)^2 + 2, \tag{172}$$

$$T = \frac{1}{4} A_1(T)^2 - \frac{1}{2} A_2 T. \tag{173}$$

The tangent vector of the target at $t = T$ in the phase-space of the coordinates $x_1$, $x_2$, and $x_3$ is

$$(a_1, a_2, a_3) = (T, 1, 1).$$

By applying the transversality condition at $t = T$, that is,

$$a_1 z_1(T) + a_2 z_2(T) + a_3 z_3(T) = 0,$$

and employing equations (164), (165), and (168) we have

$$A_1 T - A_1 T + A_2 - 3 + \tfrac{1}{4}(A_2)^2 = 0. \tag{174}$$

$A_2$ is solved from this equation to be

$$A_2 = 2 \quad \text{or} \quad -6.$$

Thus by substitution of $A_2 = 2$ into equations (172) and (173) and solving for $T$ and $A_1$ we obtain

$$T = \sqrt{6},$$

$$A_1 = \frac{8}{\sqrt{6}}.$$

The use of $A_2 = -6$ gives a negative $T$. Therefore the optimal control and trajectory are

$$\theta(t) = \frac{4}{\sqrt{6}} t - 1,$$

$$x_1(t) = \frac{2}{3\sqrt{6}} (t)^3 - \tfrac{1}{2}(t)^2 + 2,$$

$$x_2(t) = \frac{2}{\sqrt{6}} (t)^2 - t.$$

**Example 10.**   Consider a minimum integrated effort control of an under-damped second-order system which is described by the differential equation

$$\frac{d^2 x}{dt^2} + 3 \frac{dx}{dt} + 2x = \theta. \tag{175}$$

We are to minimize the functional

$$S = \int_0^T |\theta| \, dt \tag{176}$$

for unspecified $T$ and $|\theta| \leq 1$ while bringing the system from the initial state

$$\frac{dx}{dt}\bigg|_{t=0} = \eta_1,$$
$$x(0) = \eta_2, \tag{177}$$

where $\eta_1$ and $\eta_2$ are given constants to a final state that will be specified later.

First let us define new variables, $x_1$, $x_2$ and $x_3$, in which

$$x_1(t) = 2x(t) + \frac{dx(t)}{dt}, \tag{178}$$

$$x_2(t) = -x(t) - \frac{dx(t)}{dt}, \tag{179}$$

$$x_3(t) = \int_0^t |\theta|\, dt. \tag{180}$$

Next, we rewrite equation (175) as

$$\left(\frac{d^2x}{dt^2} + 2\frac{dx}{dt}\right) + \left(\frac{dx}{dt} + 2x\right) = \theta \tag{181}$$

and

$$\left(\frac{d^2x}{dt^2} + \frac{dx}{dt}\right) + 2\left(\frac{dx}{dt} + x\right) = \theta. \tag{182}$$

Substitution of equations (178) and (179) into equations (181) and (182), respectively, yields

$$\frac{dx_1}{dt} = -x_1 + \theta, \tag{183}$$

$$\frac{dx_2}{dt} = -2x_2 - \theta, \tag{184}$$

and

$$\frac{dx_3}{dt} = |\theta|. \tag{185}$$

Equations (183), (184), and (185) are now to be solved with the initial conditions

$$x_1(0) = \xi_1 = \eta_1 + 2\eta_2,$$
$$x_2(0) = \xi_2 = -\eta_1 - \eta_2, \tag{186}$$
$$x_3(0) = \xi_3 = 0,$$

and $x_3(T)$ is to be minimized. It follows that the Hamiltonian and adjoint system (the set of adjoint functions) for this problem is

$$H = -z_1 x_1 + z_1 \theta - 2z_2 x_2 - z_2 \theta + z_3 |\theta|,$$

$$\frac{dz_1}{dt} = z_1, \tag{187}$$

$$\frac{dz_2}{dt} = 2z_2, \tag{188}$$

$$\frac{dz_3}{dt} = 0, \qquad z_3(T) = 1. \tag{189}$$

The solutions of equations (187), (188), and (189) are obtained as

$$z_1(t) = z_1(0)e^t, \tag{190}$$

$$z_2(t) = z_2(0)e^{2t}, \tag{191}$$

$$z_3(t) = 1; \tag{192}$$

hence the Hamiltonian is

$$H = -z_1 x_1 - 2z_2 x_2 + \theta(z_1 - z_2) + |\theta| \tag{193}$$

or

$$H^* = |\theta| + h(t)\theta, \tag{193}$$

where $h(t) = z_1 - z_2 = z_1(0)e^t - z_2(0)e^{2t}$. This implies that a set of optimal control must be of the form (see Example 6)

$$\begin{aligned}
\theta &= -1 \quad \text{if} \quad h(t) \geq 1, \\
\theta &= 0 \quad\;\; \text{if} \quad\;\; 1 > h(t) > -1, \\
\theta &= 1 \quad\;\; \text{if} \quad -1 \geq h(t);
\end{aligned} \tag{194}$$

that is,

$$\theta(t) = 0 \quad \text{or} \quad \theta(t) = \Delta = \pm 1.$$

However, the fact that $h(t)$ is a nonlinear function makes the further analysis somewhat complicated. Examination of the function $h(t)$ indicates that the following control sequences are allowable for minimum effort operation: $\{0\}$, $\{\Delta\}$, $\{0, \Delta\}$, $\{\Delta, 0\}$, $\{\Delta, 0, \Delta\}$, $\{\Delta, 0, -\Delta\}$, $\{0, \Delta, 0\}$, and $\{0, \Delta, 0, -\Delta\}$. Further discussion is given in reference 8 and 10.

Substituting $\theta(t) = 0$ or $\theta(t) = \Delta$ into equations (183) and (184) and solving, we obtain

$$\begin{aligned}
x_1(t) &= \xi_1 e^{-t}, \\
x_2(t) &= \xi_2 e^{-2t},
\end{aligned} \quad \text{if} \quad \theta(t) = 0, \tag{195}$$

or

$$\begin{aligned}
x_1(t) &= (\xi_1 - \Delta)e^{-t} + \Delta, \\
x_2(t) &= (\xi_2 + 0.5\Delta)e^{-2t} - 0.5\Delta,
\end{aligned} \quad \text{if} \quad \theta(t) = \Delta. \tag{196}$$

By eliminating the time $t$ from equation (195) we obtain the equations of the free (without control action) trajectories

$$x_2(t) = \frac{\xi_2}{(\xi_1)^2} [x_1(t)]^2. \tag{197}$$

Similarly, from equation (196) we obtain the equations for the forced (with control action) trajectories

$$x_2(t) = -0.5\Delta + (\xi_2 + 0.5\Delta)\left(\frac{x_1 - \Delta}{\xi_1 - \Delta}\right)^2. \tag{198}$$

The problem of reaching the origin $x_1(T) = 0$, $x_2(T) = 0$ from any initial state is a trivial one. From equation (195) we see that after an infinite time theoretically $x_1 = 0$ and $x_2 = 0$. The effort required is zero, since $\theta(t)$ is identically zero for all time $t$. Therefore let us consider a specific terminal state $P$ other than the origin, say $x_1(T) = 0.4$ and $x_2(T) = -0.2$.

First we construct three curves $\gamma_0$, $\gamma_+$, and $\gamma_-$, as shown in Fig. 3.9. The $\gamma_0$ is the locus of all states in the plane among which any state may be forced to $P$, using $\theta(t) = 0$. Its equation, using equation (197), is

$$x_2 = \frac{-0.2}{(0.4)^2}(x_1)^2 = -1.25(x_1)^2, \qquad x_1 \geq 0.4, \qquad x_2 \leq -0.2. \tag{199}$$

The $\gamma_+(\gamma_-)$ curve is the locus of all states in the plane among which any state may be forced to $P$, using $\theta(t) = 1$ $(\theta(t) = -1)$. The equations, from equation (198), are

$$\gamma_+: \ x_2 = -0.5 + 0.834(x_1 - 1)^2, \qquad x_1 \leq 0.4; \qquad x_2 \geq -0.2. \tag{200}$$

$$\gamma_-: \ x_2 = 0.5 - 0.357(x_1 + 1)^2, \qquad x_1 \geq 0.4; \qquad x_2 \leq -0.2. \tag{201}$$

The next step is to establish the minimum-effort path from the origin $(0, 0)$ to $T$. We can show that the control $\{1, 0\}$ must be used; that is, at $(0, 0)$ we apply $\theta(t) = 1$ until $\gamma_0$ is reached and then apply $\theta(t) = 0$.

The effort required to reach $P$ from $(0, 0)$ is $F_m = 0.84$ unit. Since every state may be taken to $(0, 0)$ with zero effort, the maximum effort required to reach $P$ from any initial state is 0.84 unit.

Next, let us construct the so-called $(1, 0)$ iso-effort curves. Consider all the states $(\hat{\xi}_1, \hat{\xi}_2)$ which may be forced to the $\gamma_0$ curve, using $\theta(t) = 1$, and which require the same amount of effort $F$. Since, along the forced trajectories, the time elapsed equals the effort consumed, we have from

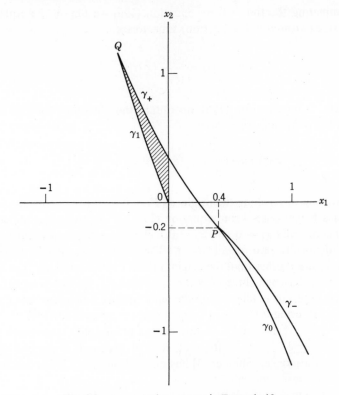

*Fig. 3.9*   $\gamma_0$, $\gamma_+$, and $\gamma_-$ curves in Example 10.

equation (196)

$$x_1 = 1 + (\hat{\xi}_1 - 1)e^{-F},$$
$$x_2 = -0.5 + (\hat{\xi}_2 + 0.5)e^{-2F}. \qquad (202)$$

By substituting equation (202) into equation (199) we find that

$$-0.5 + (\hat{\xi}_2 + 0.5)e^{-2F} = -1.25[1 + (\hat{\xi}_1 - 1)e^{-F}]^2 \qquad (203)$$

or

$$\hat{\xi}_2 = -0.5 + 0.5e^{2F} - 1.25(\hat{\xi}_1 - 1 + e^F)^2.$$

Equation (203) defines a family of curves, with $F$ as the parameter, which are called iso-effort curves. The curve with $F = T_m = 0.84$ passes through the origin (see Fig. 3.9).

Consider now an initial state $(\xi_1, \xi_2)$ which is in the shaded area of Fig. 3.9. This state belongs to a particular $(1, 0)$ iso-effort curve, say with $F = F^*$. Suppose that $\theta(t) = 0$ is applied. The resulting free trajectory will move toward the origin of the phase-plane. During the motion the trajectory will intersect other iso-effort curves with $F > F^*$. If at $(\xi_1, \xi_2)$ the control $\theta(t) = -1$ is applied, the resulting forced trajectory will move toward the point $(-1, 0.5)^*$ and it will intersect iso-effort curve with $F > F^*$. If we examine the allowable sequences of control, we conclude that, in order to reach to $P$, $\theta(t) = +1$ is the initial control that forces the state to the $\gamma_0$ curve from which $P$ can be reached by $\theta(t) = 0$.

For other initial states that are not in the shaded area more extensive analysis is required. Interested readers are referred to References 8, 9, and 10.

We have not treated the optimal control theory thoroughly in this chapter. What we have done is to try to illustrate some of the typical methods and procedures used in many applications of the maximum principle to control problems. Additional examples are available in published literature [1, 2, 5, 6, 11].

The maximum principle only supplies the necessary conditions for optimality, except for special cases [1]. Strictly speaking, the maximum principle provides candidates for optimal control policies. In actual systems, however, we often know that minima (or maxima) exist on physical grounds and thus the necessary conditions provide us with the optimal solutions.

We have shown that the state-space or phase-space concept plays an important role in the solution of control problems by means of the maximum principle. Shinner [3] has pointed out some of the advantages of the state-space concept.

1. The solution to a set of first-order differential equations is much easier to obtain than the solution to higher-order differential equations.

2. The state-space concept can greatly simplify the mathematical notation by utilizing vector matrix notation for the set of first-order equations.

3. Although the inclusion of initial conditions in the analysis of control systems based on conventional techniques is quite difficult, the state-space approach readily lends itself to the inclusion of the system's initial conditions as part of the solution.

4. The state-space approach can be readily applied to the solution of certain nonlinear and time-varying systems.

It should be pointed out that the maximum principle only provides a method for determining an optimal control system. There are other methods, such as dynamic programming, which probably are just as powerful as the maximum principle. The success of any of these so-called

---

* Let $t \to \infty$ and $\Delta = -1$ in equation (196); then $x_1(\infty) = -1$, $x_2(\infty) = +0.5$.

"modern"* approaches to the optimal control depends on several important factors [3]:

1. The derivation of an adequate mathematical model of the controlled system or plant.
2. The definition of an optimal control objective (the objective function and the constraints).
3. The computation of the optimal control policy.
4. The design or realization of a stable control system which realizes the optimal control policy.

A mathematical model [equation (1)], which is used to describe the dynamics of a controlled system, is usually an approximation of the actual physical situation. Because of the complexity of many processes, the derivation of equation (1) is often difficult and sometimes impossible. When the mathematical model cannot be derived theoretically, it must be developed by using experimental data. The ability to obtain a simple mathematical model which adequately describes the dynamics of the controlled system is very important in determining an optimal control system.

The definition of an optimal control objective, as it is used here, includes the definition of an objective function, equation (3), and the constraints which must be considered in minimizing the objective function. In many control problems the definition of a realistic and proper optimal control objective is a difficult task which takes considerable time and effort.

After an adequate model of the controlled system and an optimal control objective have been obtained, the maximum principle (or other equivalent methods) may be used to determine the optimal control policy.

The design of a stable control system which realizes the optimal control policy determined by using the maximum principle is often a design goal rather than a reality. Often the additional cost of a control system which actually realizes the optimal control policy must be considered in determining whether this is actually the optimal control system.

Those who are interested in further study of optimal control should consult available books and monographs on the subject [1, 2, 3, 4, 7, 11].

## REFERENCES

1. Pontryagin, L. S., V. G. Boltyanskii, R. V. Gamkrelidze, and E. F. Mishchenko, *The Mathematical Theory of Optimal Processes* (English translation by K. N. Trirogoff), Interscience, New York, 1962.

---

* In contrast, the so-called frequency domain approach (Nyguist, Bode, and Nichols) is considered "classical". It is more or less empirical, and many persons working in the field of control systems design feel that it has somewhat reached its peak.

2. Chang, S. S. L., *Synthesis of Optimum Control Systems*, McGraw-Hill, New York, 1961.
3. Shinner, S. M., *Control System Design*, Wiley, New York, 1964.
4. Kuo, B. C., Automatic Control Systems, Prentice-Hall, Englewood Cliffs, New Jersey, 1962.
5. Takahashi, Y., "The Maximum Principle and its Applications," ASME. *Paper* 63-*WA*-333 (1963).
6. Boyadjieff, C., D. Eggleston, M. Jacques, H. Sutakutra, and Y. Takahashi, "Some Applications of the Maximum Principle to Second-order Systems, Subject to Input Saturation, Minimizing Error, and Effort," *Trans. ASME, J. Basic Eng.*, **86**, Series D, No. 1, 11 (1964).
7. Merrian, C. W., III, *Optimization Theory and the Design of Feedback Control Systems*, McGraw-Hill, New York, 1964.
8. Athans, M., "Minimum-Fuel Feedback Control Systems: Second Order Case," *AIEE Trans. Applications and Industry*, **82**, 65, 8 (1963).
9. Ladd, H. O., and B. Friedland, "Minimum Fuel Control of a Second Order Linear Process with a Constraint on Time-to-Run," *Trans. ASME, J. Basic Eng.*, **86**, Series D, No. 1, 160 (1964).
10. Athans, M., "Minimum-Fuel Control of Second-Order Systems with Real Poles," *AIEE Trans. Applications and Industry*, **83**, 72, 148 (1964).
11. Tou, J. T., *Modern Control Theory*, McGraw-Hill, New York, 1964.
12. Denn, M. M., and R. Aris, "An Elementary Derivation of the Maximum Principle," *A.I.Ch.E. J.*, **11**, 367 (1965).
13. Takahashi, Y., private communication, 1964.

# 4

# *Applications of the Algorithm for Simple Processes to Industrial Process Systems*

## 1. INTRODUCTION

In this chapter we apply the basic algorithm of the maximum principle given in Chapter 2 to simple continuous processes commonly found in the chemical and process industries. Design parameters and operating conditions of process systems, which maximize (or minimize) certain objective functions (performance criterion, yield, and profit), are determined by using the maximum principle.

A number of practical but relatively simple examples taken from various process systems are solved in detail to illustrate the use of the algorithm and the handling of the so-called two-point boundary value problems (split-type boundary value problems) which result from the use of the maximum principle. Even though this principle leads to two-point boundary value problems which are often difficult to solve, it still provides a practical approach to process-systems optimization. The twofold purpose of this chapter is to illustrate how the maximum principle may be used to obtain a system of differential equations that leads to the optimum solution and how analog, digital, and hybrid computers may be employed to obtain the numerical solution.

Several computational procedures for solving two-point boundary value problems are presented in this chapter and in Appendix I. We feel that for the maximum principle to be of any practical value to the process design engineer solutions of the two-point boundary value problems encountered must be obtained.

## 2. OPTIMIZATION OF CHEMICAL REACTIONS IN A TUBULAR REACTOR

*a. Optimal Temperature Profile for the First-Order Reversible Reaction*
[1, 2, 3, 4]. In an exothermic reversible reaction,* as the temperature increases, the equilibrium conversion decreases exponentially, and the specific reaction rate increases, as shown in Fig. 4.1. Thus an increase in

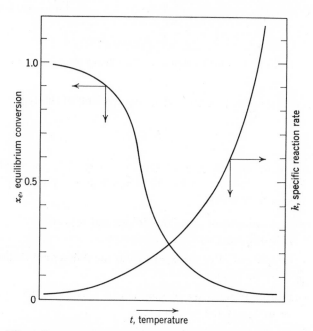

**Fig. 4.1** Effect of temperature on equilibrium conversion and specific reaction rate for an exothermic reaction [1].

temperature increases the rate of forward reaction but it decreases the maximum attainable conversion. Hence near the inlet of a tubular reactor (plug-flow or slug-flow-reactor), in which the reacting fluid is far from equilibrium, it is advantageous to use a high temperature. Near the reactor outlet, in which the equilibrium condition is approached, the temperature should be lowered so that the equilibrium will shift to the more favorable values for higher conversion. This suggests that optimum processing is achieved with the use of a varying temperature progression

---

\* For an endothermic reversible single reaction the best policy is to operate at as high a temperature as possible. We are not interested in this reaction here.

[4]. We shall show the correctness of this suggestion by using the maximum principle to determine the optimal temperature profile (temperature gradient) along the length of the reactor, that is, the temperature profile that will maximize the conversion.

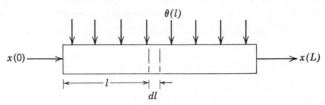

**Fig. 4.2**  Simple process showing a chemical reaction taking place in a tubular reactor.

Consider a first-order reversible chemical reaction of the type

$$A \underset{k_2}{\overset{k_1}{\rightleftharpoons}} B$$

taking place in the tubular reactor shown in Fig. 4.2. A steady-state differential material balance for the $i$th component in a plug-flow tubular reactor is generally given by

{rate of input of component $i$ into the differential section $dl$ of the reactor}

— {rate of exit of component $i$ from the differential section $dl$ of the reactor}

+ {rate of production of component $i$ in the differential section $dl$ of the reactor}

= 0

or

$$\{Gx_i\} - \left\{G\left(x_i + \frac{dx_i}{dl} dl\right)\right\} + \{R_i\} dl = 0$$

or

$$G \frac{dx_i}{dl} = R_i, \tag{1}$$

where $x_i$ = mass fraction of component $i$, dimensionless,

$\quad\quad R_i$ = mass reaction rate, that is, the rate at which the $i$th component, component $A$ or $B$, is formed per unit volume, lb/ft$^3$-hr,

$\quad\quad l$ = axial position in the tubular reactor (measured from the inlet), ft,

$\quad\quad G$ = mass velocity of feed, lb/ft$^2$-hr.

For the reaction under consideration we may denote the mass fraction of $B$ as $x_1$. Then the mass fraction of $A$ is $(1 - x_1)$, and we have [3, 4]

$$G \frac{dx_1}{dl} = k_1(1 - x_1) - k_2 x_1$$

or

$$\frac{dx_1}{dl} = -\frac{1}{G}[(k_1 + k_2)x_1 - k_1]. \tag{2}$$

We assume that the specific reaction rate $k_i$ follows Arrhenius' law, that is,

$$k_1 = \rho k_{10} e^{-E_1/RT}, \tag{3}$$

$$k_2 = \rho k_{20} e^{-E_2/RT}, \tag{4}$$

where $\rho =$ density of fluid, assumed to be constant, lb/ft³,
  $k_{i0} =$ frequency factor, hr⁻¹,
  $E =$ activation energy, Btu/lb-mole,
  $T =$ temperature of reaction, °R,
  $R =$ gas constant, Btu/(lb-mole)(°R).

We introduce $\rho$ in the Arrhenius temperature-dependence equations to account for the material balance in terms of the mass fraction.

The problem now is to find the optimal temperature along the reactor that will maximize the concentration of product $B$ at the outlet of the reactor with the initial concentration of $B$ given. We define the mass fraction of $B$, denoted by $x_1$, as the state variable of the system and the temperature of the reaction as the decision variable $\theta$. From equation (2) the performance equation is

$$\frac{dx_1}{dl} = -\frac{1}{G}\{[k_1(\theta) + k_2(\theta)]x_1 - k_1(\theta)\}, \qquad x_1(0) = \alpha_1. \tag{5}$$

According to the maximum principle, the Hamiltonian for this problem becomes

$$H = z_1 \frac{dx_1}{dl} = -\frac{z_1}{G}\{[k_1(\theta) + k_2(\theta)]x_1 - k_1(\theta)\}, \tag{6}$$

where the adjoint variable $z_1$ satisfies

$$\frac{dz_1}{dl} = -\frac{\partial H}{\partial x_1} = \frac{z_1}{G}[k_1(\theta) + k_2(\theta)]. \tag{7}$$

Since the objective is to maximize $x_1(L)$ (the concentration in terms of mass fraction of $B$ at the end of the reactor), the boundary condition for $z_1(l)$ is

$$z_1(L) = 1.$$

Because the maximum of $H$ occurs at the stationary point ($\theta$ is not constrained), we can determine the optimal $\theta$ by taking the partial derivative of $H$ with respect to $\theta$ and setting it equal to zero. Thus, from equation (6), we obtain

$$\frac{\partial H}{\partial \theta} = -\frac{z_1}{G}\left[\left(\frac{dk_1}{d\theta} + \frac{dk_2}{d\theta}\right)x_1 - \frac{dk_1}{d\theta}\right] = 0. \tag{8}$$

From equations (3) and (4) we have

$$\begin{aligned}
\frac{dk_1}{d\theta} &= \rho\left(\frac{k_{10}E_1}{R(\theta)^2}\right)e^{-E_1/R\theta}, \\
\frac{dk_2}{d\theta} &= \rho\left(\frac{k_{20}E_2}{R(\theta)^2}\right)e^{-E_2/R\theta}.
\end{aligned} \tag{9}$$

Substituting equation (9) into equation (8) yields

$$-\frac{z_1}{G}\rho\,\frac{1}{R(\theta)^2}\left[(k_{10}E_1e^{-E_1/R\theta} + k_{20}E_2e^{-E_2/R\theta})x_1 - k_{10}E_1e^{-E_1/R\theta}\right] = 0. \tag{10}$$

Assuming that $\theta$ is not equal to infinity, we obtain from this equation

$$(k_{10}E_1e^{-E_1/R\theta} + k_{20}E_2e^{-E_2/R\theta})x_1 - k_{10}E_1e^{-E_1/R\theta} = 0. \tag{11}$$

By solving equation (11) for $\theta$ we have

$$\bar{\theta}(l) = \frac{E_2 - E_1}{R\ln\{\xi[x_1/(1-x_1)]\}}, \tag{12}$$

where

$$\xi = \frac{k_{20}E_2}{k_{10}E_1}.$$

Equation (12) shows the optimal temperature for maximizing the exit concentration of $B$ as a function of position $l$ inside the reactor.

By substituting equation (12) into equations (3) and (4), we obtain

$$\begin{aligned}
k_1(\theta) &= \rho k_{10}\exp\left\{-\frac{E_1}{R}\left[\left(\frac{R}{E_2 - E_1}\right)\ln\left(\xi\frac{x_1}{1-x_1}\right)\right]\right\} \\
&= \rho k_{10}\exp\left[-\frac{E_1}{E_2 - E_1}\ln\left(\xi\frac{x_1}{1-x_1}\right)\right], \\
k_2(\theta) &= \rho k_{20}\exp\left[-\frac{E_2}{E_2 - E_1}\ln\left(\xi\frac{x_1}{1-x_1}\right)\right],
\end{aligned}$$

or

$$k_1(\theta) = \rho k_{10}\left(\xi\frac{x_1}{1-x_1}\right)^{-\lambda_1}, \tag{13}$$

$$k_2(\theta) = \rho k_{20}\left(\xi\frac{x_1}{1-x_1}\right)^{-\lambda_2}, \tag{14}$$

where

$$\lambda_1 = \frac{E_1}{E_2 - E_1} \quad \text{and} \quad \lambda_2 = \frac{E_2}{E_2 - E_1}. \tag{15}$$

By substituting equations (13) and (14) into equation (5) we obtain

$$\begin{aligned}
\frac{dx_1}{dl} &= -\frac{\rho}{G}\left\{ \left[ k_{10}\left( \xi\,\frac{x_1}{1 - x_1} \right)^{-\lambda_1} + k_{20}\left( \xi\,\frac{x_1}{1 - x_1} \right)^{-\lambda_2} \right] x_1 \right. \\
&\qquad\qquad\qquad\qquad \left. - k_{10}\left( \xi\,\frac{x_1}{1 - x_1} \right)^{-\lambda_1} \right\} \\
&= \frac{\rho}{G}\left[ k_{10}\left( \xi\,\frac{x_1}{1 - x_1} \right)^{-\lambda_1}(1 - x_1) - k_{20}x_1\left( \xi\,\frac{x_1}{1 - x_1} \right)^{-\lambda_2} \right] \\
&= \frac{\rho}{G}\,\frac{k_{10}\xi^{-\lambda_1}(1 - x_1)^{\lambda_1+1}(x_1)^{\lambda_2-1} - k_{20}\xi^{-\lambda_2}(1 - x_1)^{\lambda_2}(x_1)^{\lambda_1}}{(x_1)^{\lambda_1+\lambda_2-1}}. \tag{16}
\end{aligned}$$

Separating variables and integrating, we have

$$\frac{G}{\rho}\int_{\alpha_1}^{x_1} \frac{(x_1)^{\lambda_1+\lambda_2-1}\,dx_1}{k_{10}\xi^{-\lambda_1}(1 - x_1)^{\lambda_1+1}(x_1)^{\lambda_2-1} - k_{20}\xi^{-\lambda_2}(1 - x_1)^{\lambda_2}(x_1)^{\lambda_1}} = \int_0^l dl = l. \tag{17}$$

Consider the integration of equation (17) for a specific case for which the activation energies of the forward and backward reactions are chosen such that

$$\frac{E_2}{E_1} = 2$$

or

$$\lambda_1 = \frac{E_1}{E_2 - E_1} = 1 \quad \text{and} \quad \lambda_2 = \frac{E_2}{E_2 - E_1} = 2. \tag{18}$$

By substituting these values of $\lambda$ into equation (17), we obtain

$$\frac{G}{\rho}\int_{\alpha_1}^{x_1} \frac{(x_1)^2\,dx_1}{k_{10}\xi^{-1}(1 - x_1)^2 x_1 - k_{20}\xi^{-2}(1 - x_1)^2 x_1} = l. \tag{19}$$

Simplification of equation (19) yields

$$\frac{G}{\rho(k_{10}\xi^{-1} - k_{20}\xi^{-2})}\int_{\alpha_1}^{x_1} \frac{x_1\,dx_1}{(1 - x_1)^2} = l$$

or

$$\frac{G}{\rho(k_{10}\xi^{-1} - k_{20}\xi^{-2})}\left[ \frac{1}{1 - x_1} + \ln\,(1 - x_1) \right]\Bigg|_{\alpha_1}^{x_1} = l. \tag{20}$$

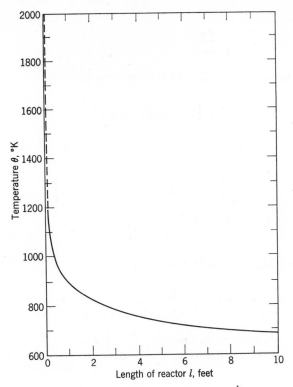

**Fig. 4.3** Optimal temperature profile for the reaction $A \underset{k_2}{\overset{k_1}{\rightleftharpoons}} B$ in a plug-flow tubular reactor.

By substituting the limits of integration into equation (20) we obtain

$$\frac{G}{\rho(k_{10}\xi^{-1} - k_{20}\xi^{-1})}\left[\frac{1}{1 - x_1} - \frac{1}{1 - \alpha_1} + \ln\frac{1 - x_1}{1 - \alpha_1}\right] = l \qquad (21)$$

Equation (21) gives the concentration of $B$ along the reactor length under the optimal condition. It can be seen that a combination of equations (12) and (21) will yield the optimal temperature profile along the reactor length.

It should be noted that equation (17) can be integrated for any value of activation energies as long as $E_2 > E_1$; $E_2 > E_1$ indicates that the reaction is exothermic. The specific values employed here are purely for the purpose of simplifying mathematical manipulation. It may also be noted that because of the simplicity of this problem, which involves only one state variable and one unconstrained decision variable, it can be solved by the classical variational calculus and dynamic programming [4]. It appears, however, that the use of the maximum principle leads to a more straightforward formulation and a more concise solution.

The numerical computations of the optimal conditions from equations (12) and (21) are illustrated by the use of the following data:

$$\frac{G}{\rho} = 1000 \text{ ft/hr,}$$

$$k_{10} = 2.51 \times 10^5 / \text{hr,}$$

$$k_{20} = 1.995 \times 10^7 / \text{hr,}$$

$$E_1 = 10,000 \text{ Btu/lb-mole,}$$

$$E_2 = 20,000 \text{ Btu/lb-mole,}$$

$$R = 1.987 \text{ Btu/(lb-mole)}^\circ \text{R,}$$

$$\alpha_1 = 0,$$

$$L = 10 \text{ ft.}$$

The resulting optimal temperature profile and the corresponding optimal concentration profile of $B$ are plotted in Figs. 4.3 and 4.4 as a function of distance at the reactor. It can be seen from Fig. 4.3 that the qualitative suggestion stated at the beginning of this section is correct. Similar optimal temperature and concentration profiles have been reported by Aris [4].

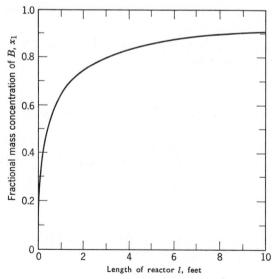

*Fig. 4.4* Optimal concentration profile for the reaction $A \underset{k_2}{\overset{k_1}{\rightleftharpoons}} B$ in a plug-flow tubular reactor.

*b. Optimal Temperature Profile in a Tubular Reactor for the First-Order Irreversible Consecutive Reaction.*  In this section we take up a plug-flow tubular reactor in which the chemical reactions

$$A \xrightarrow{k_1} B \xrightarrow{k_2} C$$

(where $B$ is the desired product) take place. Both reactions are of the first order. This problem has been solved by Bilous and Amundson [5] who used functional differentiation and then by Aris [4] who employed dynamic programming. Katz [6] discussed the solution of this problem by using the calculus of variations. More recently Lee [7] treated this problem by the combined use of the maximum principle and a maximum (or minimum) seeking technique on the analog computer.

This general problem has also been studied in detail in References 25, 26, 28. The specific problem of one second-order reaction has been treated in Reference 27.

If we designate $x_1(t)$ and $x_2(t)$ as the state variables which represent the concentrations of $A$ and $B$, respectively, the kinetics of the reactions and the flow conditions (plug or slug flow) will lead to the performance equations of the reactor representing the material balance of component $i$ ($A$ or $B$) as follows:

{rate of input of component $i$ into the differential section
      $dl$ of the reactor}

    $-$ {rate of output of component $i$ from the differential section
        $dl$ of the reactor}

    $+$ {rate of production of component $i$ in the differential section
        $dl$ of the reactor}

    $= 0$

or

$$\{Aux_i\} - \left\{Au\left(x_i + \frac{dx_i}{dl}\,dl\right)\right\} + A\,dl\{R_i\} = 0, \qquad (22a)$$

where $A$ is the cross sectional area of the reactor, $u$ is the average bulk velocity and $R_i$ is the rate of production of component $i$. By simplifying equation (22a) we have

$$u\frac{dx_i}{dl} = R_i. \qquad (22b)$$

The rates of production for component 1 (component A) and component 2 (component B) can be written as

$$R_1 = -k_1x_1, \qquad (22c)$$

$$R_2 = k_1x_1 - k_2x_2. \qquad (22d)$$

By substituting equations (22c) and (22d) into (22b), we have

$$\frac{dx_1}{d(l/u)} = -k_1 x_1, \tag{22e}$$

$$\frac{dx_2}{d(l/u)} = k_1 x_1 - k_2 x_2. \tag{22f}$$

If we write equations (22e) and (22f) in terms of holding time, $t = l/u$, we obtain

$$\frac{dx_1}{dt} = -k_1 x_1, \tag{23}$$

$$\frac{dx_2}{dt} = k_1 x_1 - k_2 x_2, \tag{24}$$

where $k_1$ and $k_2$ are the specific rate constants of the reactions and

$$k_1 = k_{10} e^{-E_1/R\theta}, \qquad k_2 = k_{20} e^{-E_2/R\theta}. \tag{25}$$

As in the problem in part $a$, $t$ is proportional to the position measured from the inlet of the reactor and is often called the holding time of the reactor up to a given point; $\theta(t)$ is the absolute temperature at the corresponding position. The yield of $B$ (component 2) over the prescribed total holding time $t = T$ of the reactor is to be maximized. Now the problem becomes that of finding the optimal choice of $\theta(t)$ which maximizes $x_2(T)$ for a system described by equations (23) and (24). The objective function is

$$S = c_1 x_1(T) + c_2 x_2(T) = x_2(T), \tag{26}$$

where

$$c_1 = 0, \qquad c_2 = 1. \tag{27}$$

According to the basic algorithm of the maximum principle given in Section 2.1, the Hamiltonian function is

$$H(x_1, z_1, \theta) = z_1 \frac{dx_1}{dt} + z_2 \frac{dx_2}{dt}$$

$$= z_1(-k_1 x_1) + z_2(k_1 x_1 - k_2 x_2), \tag{28}$$

where $z_1$ and $z_2$ are the adjoint variables and

$$\frac{dz_1}{dt} = -\frac{\partial H}{\partial x_1} = k_1 z_1 - k_1 z_2, \tag{29}$$

$$\frac{dz_2}{dt} = -\frac{\partial H}{\partial x_2} = k_2 z_2. \tag{30}$$

The boundary conditions are

$$x_1(0) = \alpha_1, \qquad x_2(0) = \alpha_2,$$

and

$$z_1(T) = c_1 = 0, \qquad z_2(T) = c_2 = 1. \tag{31}$$

The optimal temperature $\theta(t)$ is determined so that $H$ is a maximum for all values of $t$, $0 \leq t \leq T$. Assuming that no constraint is imposed on $\theta(t)$, the maximum of $H$ occurs at the stationary point. We have, therefore,

$$\frac{\partial H}{\partial \theta} = -x_1 z_1 \frac{dk_1}{d\theta} + x_1 z_2 \frac{dk_1}{d\theta} - x_2 z_2 \frac{dk_2}{d\theta} = 0$$

or

$$\frac{1}{R(\theta)^2} [(z_2 x_1 - z_1 x_1)k_{10}E_1 e^{-E_1/R\theta} - z_2 x_2 k_{20}E_2 e^{-E_2/R\theta}] = 0.$$

For finite and positive values of $\theta$ we have

$$(z_2 x_1 - z_1 x_1)k_{10}E_1 e^{-E_1/R\theta} - z_2 x_2 k_{20}E_2 e^{-E_2/R\theta} = 0. \tag{32}$$

By solving this equation for $\theta$ we obtain

$$\bar{\theta}(t) = \left(\frac{E_1 - E_2}{R}\right)\left\{ \ln\left[ \frac{k_{10}E_1}{k_{20}E_2} \frac{x_1(z_2 - z_1)}{x_2 z_2} \right] \right\}^{-1}$$

or

$$\bar{\theta}(t) = \frac{E_1 - E_2}{R \ln \{\xi[x_1(z_2 - z_1)/x_2 z_2]\}}, \tag{33}$$

where

$$\xi = \frac{k_{10}E_1}{k_{20}E_2}.$$

Equation (33) gives the optimal temperature at a certain holding time as a function of the corresponding state vector $x$ and the adjoint vector $z$. The system of equations (23), (24), (29), (30), and (33) now defines what may be called the optimal solution to this problem. By substituting equation (33) into equations (23), (24), (29), and (30) and recalling the boundary conditions given in equation (31), we obtain

$$\frac{dx_1}{dt} = -k_{10}\left[ \xi \frac{x_1}{x_2}\left(\frac{z_2 - z_1}{z_2}\right) \right]^{\lambda_1} x_1, \qquad x_1(0) = \alpha_1, \tag{34}$$

$$\frac{dx_2}{dt} = k_{10}\left[ \xi \frac{x_1}{x_2}\left(\frac{z_2 - z_1}{z_2}\right) \right]^{\lambda_1} x_1$$

$$\qquad\qquad - k_{20}\left[ \xi \frac{x_1}{x_2}\left(\frac{z_2 - z_1}{z_2}\right) \right]^{\lambda_2} x_2, \qquad x_2(0) = \alpha_2, \tag{35}$$

$$\frac{dz_1}{dt} = k_{10}\left[ \xi \frac{x_1}{x_2}\left(\frac{z_2 - z_1}{z_2}\right) \right]^{\lambda_1}(z_1 - z_2), \qquad z_1(T) = 0, \tag{36}$$

$$\frac{dz_2}{dt} = k_{20}\left[ \xi \frac{x_1}{x_2}\left(\frac{z_2 - z_1}{z_2}\right) \right]^{\lambda_2} z_2, \qquad z_2(T) = 1, \tag{37}$$

where

$$\lambda_1 = \frac{E_1}{E_2 - E_1}, \qquad \lambda_2 = \frac{E_2}{E_2 - E_1}.$$

It can be seen that in order to obtain the solution of this system of simultaneous differential equations, equations (34) through (37), which determine the optimal solution of this system, a two-point boundary value problem must be solved.

In Appendix I several techniques that may be used to treat two-point (or split) boundary value problems are presented in general form. We shall illustrate the use of several of the techniques by employing them to obtain the solution of the problem considered here.

Lee [7] (see Appendix I) combined the use of the maximum principle and a maximum- (or minimum-) seeking technique on an analog computer to obtain the solution of this problem. In this method the original set of equations, equations (23) through (31), is used. The procedure, which divides the $t$ coordinate into $n$ intervals, is as follows:

1. Assume a set of initial values for the adjoint vector; that is, assume values for $z_1(0)$ and $z_2(0)$.
2. At $t = 0$ the value of $\theta$, that is, $\theta(0)$, is obtained by maximizing $H$ with the known initial conditions for $x$ [$x_1(0) = \alpha_1$ and $x_2(0) = \alpha_2$] and the assumed initial conditions for $z$, that is, $z_1(0)$ and $z_2(0)$.
3. At $t = t_1$ assume a value for $\theta$, say $\theta(t_1)$.
4. Connect $\theta(0)$ and $\theta(t_1)$ by a straight line. Integrate equations (23), (24), (29), and (30) along this straight line. A set of values [$x_1(t_1)$, $x_2(t_1)$, $z_1(t_1)$, and $z_2(t_1)$] is obtained at $t_1$.
5. Substitute this set of values into equation (28) and obtain an improved $\theta(t_1)$ by maximizing $H$.
6. Using this improved $\theta(t_1)$, steps 4 and 5 are repeated until no further change occurs in the improved $\theta(t_1)$.
7. At $t = t_2$ assume a value for $\theta$, say $\theta(t_2)$, and repeat steps 4 to 6. The integration must now be performed along the two-line segments, $\theta(0) - \theta(t_1)$ and $\theta(t_1) - \theta(t_2)$. The set of values obtained for $x$ and $z$ are $x_1(t_2)$, $x_2(t_2)$, $z_1(t_2)$, and $z_2(t_2)$.
8. Similarly, we can obtain $\theta(t_3), \ldots, \theta(T)$.
9. At $t = T$ the calculated values for $z_1(T)$ and $z_2(T)$ are compared with the final values for $z(T)$ which are $z_1(T) = 0$ and $z_2(T) = 1$. If they are different, appropriate adjustment is made to obtain a new set of initial values for $z$, and steps 2 to 8 are repeated until the given final values for $z$ are the same as those calculated for $z$.

Lee [7] used the random search technique to determine the maximum value of $H$ in steps 2 and 5.

The numerical values chosen are [7]

$$k_{10} = 0.535 \times 10^{11}/\text{min},$$
$$k_{20} = 0.461 \times 10^{18}/\text{min},$$
$$E_1 = 18,000 \text{ cal/mole},$$
$$E_2 = 30,000 \text{ cal/mole},$$
$$R = 2 \text{ cal/mole-K}^\circ,$$
$$T = 8 \text{ min},$$
$$\alpha_1 = 0.53 \text{ mole/liter},$$
$$\alpha_2 = 0.43 \text{ mole/liter}.$$

It should be noted that a fairly large value of $\alpha_2$ is chosen. This is done to avoid rescaling the problems on the analog computer during calculations. The foregoing numerical values are the same as those used by Bilous and Amundson [5] in their example A, except for the values of $T$ and the initial conditions. The results are given in Reference 7 by Lee in graphical form, in which the optimal values of $x$, $z$, and $\theta$ are plotted against $t$. Since we have only one decision variable to investigate, a simple plot of $H$ against $\theta$ at any value of $t$ can also be used to obtain the maximum of $H$. The results of Bilous and Amundson, which were estimated from their plots, compared favorably with Lee's results.

The approximate iterative Runge-Kutta method (see Appendix I) may also be used to obtain a numerical solution of a problem of this kind. This method may be combined with a backward integration procedure to obtain a numerical solution of the two-point boundary value problem characterized by equations (34) through (37). These equations may be rewritten using dimensionless time:

$$\frac{dx_1}{d\eta} = -m_1 \left[ \xi \frac{x_1}{x_2} \left( \frac{z_2 - z_1}{z_2} \right) \right]^{\lambda_1} x_1, \tag{38}$$

$$\frac{dx_2}{d\eta} = m_1 \left[ \xi \frac{x_1}{x_2} \left( \frac{z_2 - z_1}{z_2} \right) \right]^{\lambda_1} x_1 - m_2 \left[ \xi \frac{x_1}{x_2} \left( \frac{z_2 - z_1}{z_2} \right) \right]^{\lambda_2} x_2, \tag{39}$$

$$\frac{dz_1}{d\eta} = m_1 \left[ \xi \frac{x_1}{x_2} \left( \frac{z_2 - z_1}{z_2} \right) \right]^{\lambda_1} (z_1 - z_2), \tag{40}$$

$$\frac{dz_2}{d\eta} = m_2 \left[ \xi \frac{x_1}{x_2} \left( \frac{z_2 - z_1}{z_2} \right) \right]^{\lambda_2} z_2, \tag{41}$$

where $\eta = t/T$,

$m_1 = k_{10}T$,

$m_2 = k_{20}T$.

To employ the approximate iterative Runge-Kutta method, equations (38) and (39) are differentiated with respect to $x_1(1)$ and $x_2(1)$, as follows:

$$\frac{dG_1}{d\eta} = \frac{d(dx_1/d\eta)}{dx_1(1)} = -m_1(\lambda_1 + 1)\left[\xi\frac{x_1}{x_2}\left(\frac{z_2 - z_1}{z_2}\right)\right]^{\lambda_1} G_1, \tag{42}$$

$$\frac{dG_2}{d\eta} = \frac{d(dx_2/d\eta)}{dx_2(1)} = -m_1\lambda_1\left[\xi\frac{x_1}{x_2}\left(\frac{z_2 - z_1}{z_2}\right)\right]^{\lambda_1}\left(\frac{x_1}{x_2}\right) G_2$$

$$+ m_2(\lambda_2 - 1)\left[\xi\frac{x_1}{x_2}\left(\frac{z_2 - z_1}{z_2}\right)\right]^{\lambda_2} G_2. \tag{43}$$

In these approximate equations

$$G_1 = \frac{dx_1}{dx_1(1)}, \qquad G_2 = \frac{dx_2}{dx_2(1)}.$$

The boundary conditions for $G_1$ and $G_2$ are

$$G_1(1) = \frac{dx_1}{dx_1(1)}\bigg|_{\eta=1} = 1,$$

$$G_2(1) = \frac{dx_2}{dx_2(1)}\bigg|_{\eta=1} = 1.$$

Thus for the six differential equations, equations (38) through (43), we have six boundary conditions

$$
\begin{aligned}
x_1(0) &= \alpha_1, \\
x_2(0) &= \alpha_2, \\
z_1(1) &= 0, \\
z_2(1) &= 1, \\
G_1(1) &= 1, \\
G_2(1) &= 1,
\end{aligned}
\tag{44}
$$

Since the Runge-Kutta method requires $x_1(1)$ and $x_2(1)$ to begin the backward integration, we assume two additional boundary conditions

$$
\begin{aligned}
x_1(1) &= \beta_1, \\
x_2(1) &= \beta_2.
\end{aligned}
$$

Equations (38) through (43) may now be integrated by the Runge-Kutta method and with the six boundary conditions at $\eta = 1$. From the integration we obtain $x_1(0)$, $x_2(0)$, $G_1(0)$, and $G_2(0)$. The approximate equations

$$G_1(0) = \frac{dx_1}{dx_1(1)}\bigg|_{\eta=0} = \frac{x_1(0) - \alpha_1}{\beta_1 - x_1(1)}, \tag{45}$$

$$G_2(0) = \frac{dx_2}{dx_2(1)}\bigg|_{\eta=0} = \frac{x_2(0) - \alpha_2}{\beta_2 - x_2(1)}; \tag{46}$$

may be employed to determine better approximations for $x_1(1)$ and $x_2(1)$. By using the improved approximation of $x_1(1)$ and $x_2(1)$ and repeating the Runge-Kutta integration, we obtain values for $x_1(0)$, $x_2(0)$, $G_1(0)$, and $G_2(0)$, which may be used again in equations (45) and (46) to arrive at a better approximation for $x_1(1)$ and $x_2(1)$. This process should be repeated until the computed values of $x_1(0)$ and $x_2(0)$ are approximately equal to $\alpha_1$ and $\alpha_2$, respectively.

*Table 4.1*    Computational Results for the Problem $A \to B \to C$

| $\eta$ | $x_1$ (mole/liter) | $x_2$ (mole/liter) | $z_1$ | $z_2$ | $\theta$ (°K) |
|---|---|---|---|---|---|
| 1.0 | 0.17045 | 0.67984 | 0.00000 | 1.00000 | 335.88 |
| 0.9 | 0.18828 | 0.67218 | 0.09398 | 0.98506 | 336.08 |
| 0.8 | 0.20834 | 0.66246 | 0.17901 | 0.96994 | 336.31 |
| 0.7 | 0.23098 | 0.65031 | 0.25577 | 0.95456 | 336.56 |
| 0.6 | 0.25668 | 0.63528 | 0.32493 | 0.93886 | 336.87 |
| 0.5 | 0.28603 | 0.61677 | 0.38708 | 0.92274 | 357.22 |
| 0.4 | 0.31981 | 0.59403 | 0.44277 | 0.90606 | 337.64 |
| 0.3 | 0.35909 | 0.56601 | 0.49247 | 0.88867 | 338.16 |
| 0.2 | 0.40536 | 0.53121 | 0.53663 | 0.87028 | 338.81 |
| 0.1 | 0.46089 | 0.48741 | 0.57562 | 0.85048 | 339.64 |
| 0.0 | 0.52941 | 0.43092 | 0.60974 | 0.82853 | 340.79 |

This computational procedure was programmed for an IBM 1620 computer and the solution of equations (38) through (41) was obtained by using the same numerical values as before. For the arbitrarily chosen values $x_1(1) = 0.20$ and $x_2(1) = 0.70$ approximately 65 minutes of computer time was needed to obtain the final solution. About three minutes of computer time were consumed for each trial calculation. The results of the computation, which are tabulated in Table 4.1 and shown in Fig. 4.5, compare very well with Lee's results [7].

It is worthwhile to note, however, that for almost any design problem we are not only interested in a specified set of initial conditions but also in the vicinity of these conditions. Moreover we would like to investigate the effects of various sets of initial conditions on the optimal performances and the final yields. The following method meets this purpose. As in the preceding iteration solution, a fourth-order Runge-Kutta method is employed and a backward integration procedure is carried out, but this time without iteration.

If values for $x_1(1)$ and $x_2(1)$ are assumed, equations (38) through (41) may be integrated by using these assumed values with the given final

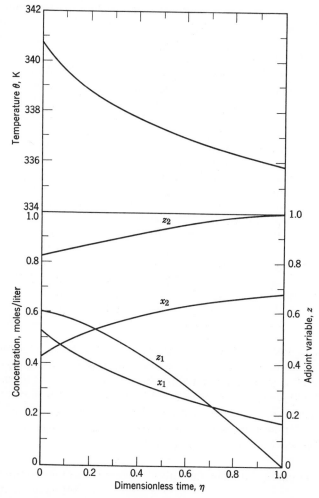

**Fig. 4.5** Optimal concentration and temperature profiles in a plug-flow reactor with reaction $A \to B \to C$.

values for $z_1(1)$ and $z_2(1)$. By integrating backward with a fourth-order Runge-Kutta method, we obtain certain values of $x_1(0)$ and $x_2(0)$. Each backward integration gives the optimal path corresponding to the initial conditions thus computed.

An IBM 1620 computer carried out the calculations. Table 4.2 lists a number of sets of initial conditions and their corresponding optimum yields. Figure 4.6 shows several optimal concentration profiles corresponding to sets 2, 6, 10, and 13 in Table 4.2. The corresponding optimal

**Table 4.2**    The Effects of Initial Conditions on the Optimum
Yields of the $A \to B \to C$ Reaction

| No. | $x_1(0)$ | $x_2(0)$ | $x_1(T)$ | $x_2(T)$ |
|-----|----------|----------|----------|----------|
| 1. | 0.350 | 0.575 | 0.15 | 0.70 |
| 2. | 0.397 | 0.488 | 0.15 | 0.65 |
| 3. | 0.470 | 0.449 | 0.16 | 0.66 |
| 4. | 0.488 | 0.425 | 0.16 | 0.65 |
| 5. | 0.502 | 0.474 | 0.17 | 0.70 |
| 6. | 0.540 | 0.424 | 0.17 | 0.68 |
| 7. | 0.562 | 0.394 | 0.17 | 0.67 |
| 8. | 0.571 | 0.448 | 0.18 | 0.72 |
| 9. | 0.594 | 0.419 | 0.18 | 0.71 |
| 10. | 0.620 | 0.387 | 0.18 | 0.70 |
| 11. | 0.650 | 0.351 | 0.17 | 0.69 |
| 12. | 0.686 | 0.309 | 0.18 | 0.68 |
| 13. | 0.716 | 0.335 | 0.19 | 0.72 |
| 14. | 0.719 | 0.287 | 0.19 | 0.71 |
| 15. | 0.732 | 0.258 | 0.18 | 0.67 |
| 16. | 0.793 | 0.193 | 0.18 | 0.66 |
| 17. | 0.816 | 0.226 | 0.19 | 0.70 |

temperature profiles, of course, can be recovered from equation (33). The initial conditions for set No. 6 are $x_1(0) = 0.540$, $x_2(0) = 0.424$, which are close to the given initial conditions. The optimal concentration profiles for this case compare favorably with that given in Fig. 4.5.

The maximum principle provides the necessary conditions for an extremum. Only if there exists an extremum of the objective function can we find the optimal solution from the condition

$H$ = maximum or minimum (and also constant for simple, continuous,
autonomous systems)

For the first-order irreversible consecutive reaction under consideration we have chosen the numerical values of the activation energies in which $E_2 > E_1$, because under such a condition there is a maximum value of $x_2(T)$. This value is obtained if the optimal temperature profile is used. If $E_1 > E_2$, the end-point product concentration $x_2(T)$ or, alternatively, the Hamiltonian function $H$ defined over the space of possible temperature profiles has in general a saddle point at the extremal temperature profile given by equation (33) [6]. As a matter of fact, if $E_1 > E_2$, which is similar to the endothermic reversible reaction considered in part a of this section, the optimal policy is to maintain the temperature at the highest permissible

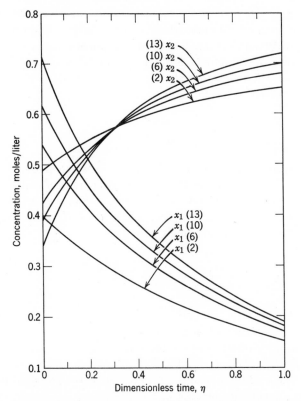

**Fig. 4.6** Some optimal concentration profiles in a tubular reactor for the problem, $A \rightarrow B \rightarrow C$. (Numbers in parentheses correspond to case numbers in Table 4.2.)

level [4]. If $E_1 = E_2$, for which temperature has no effect on the relative rates of the two reactions, there will be no unique optimal temperature profile. Actually there should be more than one temperature profile leading to the same best yield of $x_2(T)$.

*c. Optimal Pressure Profile for Gaseous Reactions.* Pressure as well as temperature often plays an important role in determining the system design and operating parameters of a process system. The effect of pressure, however, is of particular interest in gas phase reactions in which the number of moles increases as the reaction takes place (e.g., dehydrogenation reactions). For reactions of this type low pressure favors the conversion of the gaseous reactants but high pressure increases the concentrations of the reactants and therefore increases the reaction rate. Thus we have a problem of optimization similar to that treated in Section 2a for the exothermic reversible reaction. High pressure will be favorable in the first part of the tubular reactor, in which the reaction mixture is far from equilibrium, whereas low pressure is favorable in the last part, in which equilibrium concentrations are approached. We shall find such a decreasing optimal pressure profile so that the yield of the desired product will be maximized.

Consider a reversible reaction

$$A \underset{k_2}{\overset{k_1}{\rightleftharpoons}} 2B$$

carried out isothermally in a tubular reactor in which $B$ is the desired product [11]. The forward reaction of $A$ being transformed to $B$ is a first-order reaction and the backward reaction of $B$ being transformed to $A$ is a second-order reaction. In other words, the performance equation of the reactor system can then be given by

$$G \frac{dx_1}{dl} = -k_1 p_1 + k_2 (p_2)^2, \qquad (47)$$

where $G$ = mass flow rate, gm/min,
  $x_1$ = concentration of $A$, gm-moles/gm,
  $l$ = length parameter of the reactor, liters,
  $p_1, p_2$ = partial pressure of $A$ and $B$, respectively, atm,
  $k_1, k_2$ = reaction rate constants (proportional constants) of the forward and backward reactions, respectively.

For ideal gases for which Dalton's law is valid we have

$$p_1 = P \frac{n_1}{N} = P \frac{x_1}{x_1 + x_2}, \qquad (48)$$

$$p_2 = P \frac{n_2}{N} = P \frac{x_2}{x_1 + x_2}, \qquad (49)$$

where $P$ = total pressure, atm,
  $n_1, n_2$ = moles of $A$ and $B$, respectively,
  $N$ = total moles,
  $x_2$ = concentration of $B$, gm-moles/gm.

If we assume that the feed to the reactor contains only $A$, the material balance at a position $l$ along the reactor will give

$$x_1 + x_2 = x_1 + 2(x_1(0) - x_1) = 2\alpha_1 - x_1, \qquad (50)$$

where $\alpha_1$ = initial concentration of $A$.

Substitution of equations (48), (49), and (50) into equation (47) yields the performance equation of the system as

$$\frac{dx_1}{dt} = -k_1\theta \frac{x_1}{2\alpha_1 - x_1} + k_2(\theta)^2 \frac{4(\alpha_1 - x_1)^2}{(2\alpha_1 - x_1)^2}, \tag{51}$$

where $t = l/G$, the length parameter, liters-min/gm,
    $\theta = P$, the total pressure, atm.

Now the problem is transformed into one of finding the optimal total pressure $\theta$, which is the decision variable, along the reactor so that the final concentration of $A$, $x_1(T)$, will be minimum; that is, the outlet concentration of the product $B$ will be maximum for a process described by equation (51). The Hamiltonian function is

$$H = -\left[\frac{k_1 x_1}{2\alpha_1 - x_1}\theta - \frac{4k_2(\alpha_1 - x_1)^2}{(2\alpha_1 - x_1)^2}(\theta)^2\right]z_1. \tag{52}$$

The optimal decision $\bar{\theta}(t)$ is determined from

$$\frac{\partial H}{\partial \theta} = 0$$

because the minimum of $H$ occurs at a stationary point. Therefore we have

$$\frac{\partial H}{\partial \theta} = \frac{k_1 x_1}{2\alpha_1 - x_1} - \frac{8k_2(\alpha_1 - x_1)^2}{(2\alpha_1 - x_1)^2}\theta = 0. \tag{53}$$

Thus we obtain

$$\bar{\theta}(t) = \frac{k_1 x_1(2\alpha_1 - x_1)}{8k_2(\alpha_1 - x_1)^2}. \tag{54}$$

An examination of equation (54) indicates that for the optimal pressure profile to be realized $\theta$ has to be infinite for $x_1 = \alpha_1$, that is, at the reactor inlet. Because of physical limitations, this optimal pressure obviously cannot be maintained. But the deviation from it can be minimized if the pressure in the first part of the tube is taken as high as possible; that is, it should be equal to the inlet pressure up to the point at which the concentration $x_1$ has become so low that the pressure corresponds to the pressure calculated in equation (54). From here on the pressure can be chosen in agreement with that equation.

By substituting equation (54) into equation (51) we obtain

$$\frac{dx_1}{dt} = -\frac{(k_1)^2(x_1)^2}{16k_2(\alpha_1 - x_1)^2}, \tag{55}$$

and by integrating this equation we obtain

$$\frac{(k_1)^2}{16k_2}\, t = \frac{(\alpha_1)^2}{x_1} + 2\alpha_1 \ln x_1 - x_1 + C. \tag{56}$$

The integration constant is evaluated by the initial condition $x_1(0) = \alpha_1$. Thus we finally have

$$\frac{(k_1)^2}{16k_2}\, t = 2\alpha_1 \ln \left(\frac{x_1}{\alpha_1}\right) + \frac{(\alpha_1)^2}{x_1} - x_1. \tag{57}$$

A combination of equations (54) and (57) yields the optimal pressure profile along the reactor. Van de Vusse [11] obtained the same results expressed by equations (54) and (57) by using a classical approach.

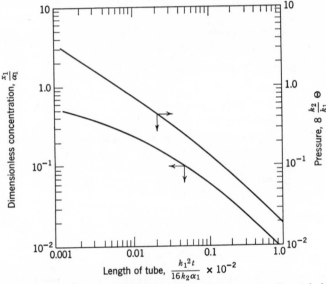

*Fig. 4.7*  Optimal pressure and concentration profiles in a plug-flow tubular reactor for a gas phase reaction $A \underset{k_2}{\overset{k_1}{\rightleftharpoons}} 2B$ [11].

But, again, the use of the maximum principle appears to lead to a more straightforward and easily understood formulation of the optimal solution. It may be noted that because of the simplicity of this problem, in which the objective function is the end-point value of the state variable, the adjoint variable can actually be eliminated in the process of obtaining the optimal solution. This is generally true, as we can also see from part a, Section 2, in which we have dealt with the optimal temperature profile of the reversible exothermic reaction. In Fig. 4.7 the optimal pressure and concentration profiles according to equations (54) and (57) are given.

If the pressure remains constant along the reactor and is equal to the outlet pressure, rather than to an optimal pressure profile, the reactor volume needed at constant pressure is two to three times as high as that with optimum pressure if the comparison is made on the basis of equal conversion [11].

For our second example [7], we shall take up the reaction scheme

$$A \xrightarrow{k_1} 2B \xrightarrow{k_2} C$$

carried out isothermally in a tubular reactor; $B$ is the desired product. $A$ transformed to give $B$ is a first-order reaction, and the desired product $B$ is transformed into $C$ according to a second-order reaction. The kinetic equations for the reactions representing the rates of production are given by

$$G\frac{dx_1}{dl} = -k_1 p_1, \tag{58}$$

$$G\frac{dx_2}{dl} = 2k_1 p_1 - k_2(p_2)^2, \tag{59}$$

where $G$ = mass flow rate, gm/min,

$x_1, x_2$ = concentrations of $A$ and $B$, respectively, gm-moles/gm,

$l$ = length parameter of the reactor, that is, the unit cross-sectional area $\times$ distance, liters,

$p_1, p_2$ = partial pressure of $A$ and $B$, respectively, atm,

$k_1, k_2$ = reaction rate constants of the first and second reactions, respectively.

For ideal gases in which Dalton's law is obeyed

$$p_1 = P\frac{n_1}{N} = P\frac{x_1}{x_1 + x_2 + x_3},$$

$$p_2 = P\frac{n_2}{N} = P\frac{x_2}{x_1 + x_2 + x_3}, \tag{60}$$

where $P$ = total pressure, atm,

$n_1, n_2$ = moles of $A$ and $B$, respectively,

$N$ = total moles,

$x_3$ = concentration of $C$.

Assuming that only $A$ and $B$ are present in the feed at the entrance of the reactor, a material balance at a position $l$ along the reactor gives

$$(\alpha_1 - x_1) + \tfrac{1}{2}(\alpha_2 - x_2) = x_3, \tag{61}$$

where $\alpha_1, \alpha_2$ = concentration of $A$ and B, respectively, at the entrance of the reactor.

Because of equations (60) and (61), equations (58) and (59), which are the performance equations of the system, become

$$\frac{dx_1}{dt} = -2k_1\theta \frac{x_1}{\beta + x_2}, \tag{62}$$

$$\frac{dx_2}{dt} = 4k_1\theta \frac{x_1}{\beta + x_2} - 4k_2(\theta)^2 \frac{(x_2)^2}{(\beta + x_2)^2}, \tag{63}$$

where $t = l/G$, the length parameter, liter-min/gm,

$\theta = P$, the total pressure, atm,

$\beta = 2\alpha_1 + \alpha_2$.

Now the optimization problem is transformed into one of finding the optimal total pressure $\theta$, the decision variable, along a reactor in which the final concentration of $B$, $x_2(T)$, is maximum for a process described by equations (62) and (63). The Hamiltonian function for the present problem is

$$H(z, x, \theta) = -2z_1k_1 \frac{\theta x_1}{\beta + x_2} + 4z_2k_1 \frac{\theta x_1}{\beta + x_2} - 4z_2k_2(\theta)^2 \frac{(x_2)^2}{(\beta + x_2)^2}, \tag{64}$$

where the adjoint vector function $z$ is defined by

$$\frac{dz_1}{dt} = 2z_1k_1 \frac{\theta}{\beta + x_2} - 4z_2k_1 \frac{\theta}{\beta + x_2}, \tag{65}$$

$$\frac{dz_2}{dt} = -2z_1k_1\theta \frac{x_1}{(\beta + x_2)^2} + 4z_2k_1\theta \frac{x_1}{(\beta + x_2)^2}$$

$$+ 8z_2k_2(\theta)^2 \frac{x_2}{(\beta + x_2)^2} - 8z_2k_2(\theta)^2 \frac{(x_2)^2}{(\beta + x_2)^3}. \tag{66}$$

The objective function to be maximized is $x_2(T)$, which is equivalent to equation (2-3) for $c_1 = 0$ and $c_2 = 1$. Hence we have the following boundary conditions:

$$x_1(0) = \alpha_1, \qquad x_2(0) = \alpha_2,$$

$$z_1(T) = 0, \qquad z_2(T) = 1. \tag{67}$$

If we assume that no constraints are imposed on $\theta(t)$, the optimal decision $\bar{\theta}(t)$ is determined from the condition

$$\frac{\partial H}{\partial \theta} = 0,$$

that is,

$$-z_1k_1 \frac{x_1}{\beta + x_2} + 2z_2k_1 \frac{x_1}{\beta + x_2} - 4z_2k_2\theta \frac{(x_2)^2}{(\beta + x_2)^2} = 0. \tag{68}$$

By solving equation (68) for $\theta$ we obtain

$$\bar{\theta}(t) = \frac{x_1(\beta + x_2)(2z_2k_1 - z_1k_1)}{4z_2k_2(x_2)^2}. \tag{69}$$

Substituting equation (69) into equations (62), (63), (65), and (66) and noting the boundary conditions in equation (67), we have

$$\frac{dx_1}{dt} = -\frac{k_1(x_1)^2(2k_1z_2 - k_1z_1)}{2k_2z_2(x_2)^2}, \qquad x_1(0) = \alpha_1, \tag{70}$$

$$\frac{dx_2}{dt} = \frac{k_1(x_1)^2}{k_2z_2(x_2)^2}(2k_1z_2 - k_1z_1)$$

$$-\frac{(x_1)^2}{4(z_2)^2k_2(x_2)^2}(2k_1z_2 - k_1z_1)^2, \qquad x_2^{(0)} = \alpha_2, \tag{71}$$

$$\frac{dz_1}{dt} = \frac{k_1x_1(z_1 - 2z_2)(2k_1z_2 - k_1z_1)}{2k_2z_2(x_2)^2}, \qquad z_1(T) = 0, \tag{72}$$

$$\frac{dz_2}{dt} = \frac{k_1(x_1)^2(2z_2 - z_1)(2k_1z_2 - k_1z_1)}{2k_2z_2(x_2)^2(\beta + x_2)}$$

$$+\frac{\beta(x_1)^2(2k_1z_2 - k_1z_1)^2}{2k_2z_2(x_2)^3(\beta + x_2)}, \qquad z_2(T) = 1. \tag{73}$$

Again we have in our hands a two-point boundary value problem. Simultaneous solution of equations (70) through (73) will yield the optimal solution of this problem, but, instead, we shall solve this problem by using Lee's computational scheme discussed in the preceding section (see Appendix I). The numerical values chosen are [7]

$$k_{10} = 0.2 \times 10^9 \text{ gm-moles/liter-min-atm,}$$
$$k_{20} = 0.63 \times 10^{16} \text{ gm-moles/liter-min-atm}^2,$$
$$E_1 = 18,000 \text{ cal/mole,}$$
$$E_2 = 30,000 \text{ cal/mole,}$$
$$k_1 = k_{10}e^{-E_1/RT'},$$
$$k_2 = k_{20}e^{-E_2/RT'},$$
$$R = 2 \text{ cal/mole-}°\text{K,}$$
$$T' = 380°\text{K,}$$
$$T = 8 \text{ liter-min/gm,}$$
$$\alpha_1 = 0.0105 \text{ gm-moles/gm,}$$
$$\alpha_2 = 0.0085 \text{ gm-moles/gm,}$$
$$\alpha_3 = 0$$

The results given by Lee [7] are shown in Fig. 4.8.

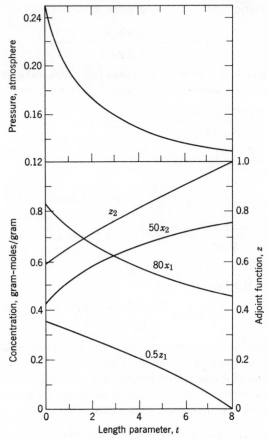

**Fig. 4.8**  Optimal pressure and concentration profiles for a gas phase reaction $A \to 2B \to C$ in a plug flow tubular reactor [7].

It may be noted that for the opposite case, a gas reaction in which the number of moles decreases, the best policy is to keep the pressure as high as possible.

**d. Optimal Temperature Profile for a First-Order Reversible Reaction with Accompanying Diffusion (Axial Dispersion).**   So far we have investigated the optimal performance of a tubular reactor in which the flow is assumed to be plug flow; that is, we have assumed that the velocity gradient in the radial direction and the diffusion in the radial and in the axial directions do not exist in the reactor.

In this section we consider the effect of axial dispersion on the optimum performance of a reactor. The formulation of this problem gives rise to a second-order linear differential equation which can be solved by applying the extension of the basic algorithm for simple processes described in Section 2.4h.

According to the axial diffusion model* of a flow reactor, a steady state material balance with respect to a reactant $i$ is given by the following equation of mass conservation:

{rate of input of component $i$ into the differential section $dl$ of the reactor due to bulk flow}

+ {rate of input of component $i$ into the differential section $dl$ of the reactor due to diffusion}

− {rate of output of component $i$ from the differential section $dl$ of the reactor due to bulk flow}

− {rate of output of component $i$ from the differential section $dl$ of the reactor due to diffusion}

+ {rate of production of component $i$ in the differential section $dl$ of the reactor}

= 0,

$$\{Gx_i\} + \left\{-D\rho \frac{dx_i}{dl}\right\} - \left\{+Gx_i + G\frac{dx_i}{dl} dl\right\}$$
$$- \left\{-D\rho \frac{dx_i}{dl} - D\rho \frac{d^2 x_i}{dl^2} dl\right\} + \{R_i\} dl = 0,$$

or

$$D\rho \frac{d^2 x_i}{dl^2} - G\frac{dx_i}{dl} + R_i = 0, \tag{74}$$

where $D$ = mass diffusion (dispersion) coefficient, ft²/hr,
$G$ = mass flow rate, lb/(ft²)(hr),
$x_i$ = fractional mass concentration of component $i$,
$R_i$ = reaction rate with respect to component $i$ based on the production of component $i$, lb/(ft³)(hr),
$\rho$ = mass density, lb/ft³,
$l$ = length of reactor, ft.

In the derivation of equation (74) it has been assumed that only the dispersion (diffusion) in the axial direction is significant and that the coefficient $D$ is independent of position in the reactor.

For a first-order reversible reaction

$$A \underset{k_2}{\overset{k_1}{\rightleftharpoons}} B$$

---

* A model of a tubular reactor in which the effect of axial diffusion is considered.

the reaction rate (the rate of production of $A$) is given, as mentioned earlier, by

$$R_A = -k_1 x_A + k_2 x_B, \tag{75}$$

where $x_A$ and $x_B$ represent the fractional mass concentration of $A$ and $B$, respectively, and

$$k_1 = \rho k_{10} e^{-E_1/RT}, \tag{76}$$

$$k_2 = \rho k_{20} e^{-E_2/RT}. \tag{77}$$

Substitution of equations (75), (76), and (77) into equation (74) gives

$$D\rho \frac{d^2 x_A}{dl^2} - G \frac{dx_A}{dl} = \rho(k_{10} e^{-E_1/RT} x_A - k_{20} e^{-E_2/RT} x_B). \tag{78}$$

Since only the reactants $A$ and $B$ are involved, we have

$$x_B = 1 - x_A.$$

Hence equation (78) becomes

$$D\rho \frac{d^2 x_A}{dl^2} - G \frac{dx_A}{dl} = \rho[(k_{10} e^{-E_1/RT} + k_{20} e^{-E_2/RT}) x_A - k_{20} e^{-E_2/RT}]. \tag{79}$$

Various boundary conditions have been suggested for use in equation (79). Danckwerts [12], for instance, introduced a set of intuitive boundary conditions based on the equation of continuity. This set has been quantitatively justified by the works of several authors [13, 14, 15] and is expressed mathematically as

$$\frac{dx_A}{dl} = \frac{(G/\rho)}{D} [x_A(0^+) - 1], \qquad l = 0, \tag{80}$$

$$\frac{dx_A}{dl} = 0, \qquad\qquad\qquad l = L. \tag{81}$$

The following transformation of variables,

$$\eta = \frac{l}{L},$$

$$M = \frac{(G/\rho)L}{2D},$$

$$F_1 = \frac{2k_{10}L}{G/\rho}, \tag{82}$$

$$F_2 = \frac{2k_{20}L}{G/\rho},$$

leads to the dimensionless form of equation (79) as

$$\frac{d^2x_1}{d\eta^2} - 2M\frac{dx_1}{d\eta} - M[(F_1e^{-E_1/R\theta} + F_2e^{-E_2/R\theta})x_1 - F_2e^{-E_2/R\theta}] = 0, \quad (83)$$

where $x_1$, the fractional mass concentration of component $A$, is the state variable and $\theta$, the temperature, is the decision variable. The corresponding dimensionless boundary conditions are

$$\frac{dx_1}{d\eta} = 2M[x_1(0^+) - 1], \qquad \eta = 0,$$
$$\frac{dx_1}{d\eta} = 0, \qquad\qquad\qquad \eta = 1. \tag{84}$$

To solve this problem we introduce a new state variable $x_2$ in which

$$\frac{dx_1}{d\eta} = x_2. \tag{85}$$

Equation (83) then becomes

$$\frac{dx_2}{d\eta} = 2Mx_2 + M(F_1e^{-E_1/R\theta} + F_2e^{-E_2/R\theta})x_1 - MF_2e^{-E_2/R\theta}. \tag{86}$$

The boundary conditions are then transformed into

$$x_2(0^+) = 2M[x_1(0^+) - 1], \tag{87}$$
$$x_2(1) = 0. \tag{88}$$

The problem is now transformed into one in which the end value of one of the state variables, $x_1(1)$, is to be minimized. This is equivalent to maximizing the end concentration of product $B$ for a process defined by equations (85) through (88).

The Hamiltonian is

$$H = x_2z_1 + [2Mx_2 + M(F_1e^{-E_1/R\theta} + F_2e^{-E_2/R\theta})x_1 - MF_2e^{-E_2/R\theta}]z_2,$$
$$\tag{89}$$

and the adjoint variables are defined by

$$\frac{dz_1}{d\eta} = -M(F_1e^{-E_1/R\theta} + F_2e^{-E_2/R\theta})z_2, \tag{90}$$

$$\frac{dz_2}{d\eta} = -z_1 - 2Mz_2. \tag{91}$$

The objective function to be minimized is

$$S = c_1x_1(1)$$

with

$$c_1 = 1.$$

The final boundary condition then becomes

$$z_1(1) = c_1 = 1. \tag{92}$$

It should be noted that the final condition of $z_2(1)$ is not preassigned, for the end point of $x_2$ is fixed as given by equation (88) (see Section 2.4a).

The optimal decision $\theta(\eta)$ can be determined from

$$\frac{\partial H}{\partial \theta} = 0$$

because the maximum of $H$ occurs at the stationary point. Thus we have

$$\frac{\partial H}{\partial \theta} = z_2 \left\{ M x_1 \left[ \frac{F_1 E_1}{R(\theta)^2} e^{-E_1/R\theta} + \frac{F_2 E_2}{R(\theta)^2} e^{-E_2/R\theta} \right] - M \left( \frac{F_2 E_2}{R(\theta)^2} \right) e^{-E_2/R\theta} \right\} = 0. \tag{93}$$

Solving this equation for $\theta$, we have

$$\bar{\theta}(\eta) = - \frac{E_2 - E_1}{R \ln \left[ \xi(x_1/1 - x_1) \right]}, \tag{94}$$

where

$$\xi = \frac{F_1 E_1}{F_2 E_2}.$$

Equation (94) gives the optimal temperature as a function of the fractional mass concentration of component $A$. By comparing this result to the optimal temperature for the reactor without diffusion effect, given by equation (12), we can see that the optimal temperature with respect to the concentration of the reactant is the same for both. Substituting equation (94) into equations (76) and (77), we have

$$k_1(\theta) = \rho k_{10} \left[ \xi \left( \frac{x_1}{1 - x_1} \right) \right]^{\lambda_1},$$

$$k_2(\theta) = \rho k_{20} \left[ \xi \left( \frac{x_1}{1 - x_1} \right) \right]^{\lambda_2}, \tag{95}$$

where

$$\lambda_1 = \frac{E_1}{E_2 - E_1} \quad \text{and} \quad \lambda_2 = \frac{E_2}{E_2 - E_1}.$$

Substituting equation (95) into equation (83), we obtain

$$\frac{d^2 x_1}{d\eta^2} = 2M \frac{dx_1}{d\eta} + M \left\{ F_1 \left[ \xi \left( \frac{x_1}{1 - x_1} \right) \right]^{\lambda_1} x_1 - F_2 \left[ \xi \left( \frac{x_1}{1 - x_1} \right) \right]^{\lambda_2} (1 - x_1) \right\}. \tag{96}$$

Equation (96), together with the boundary conditions expressed in equation (84), contain the optimal solution. To perform the integration the activation energies of the forward and backward reactions again have been chosen so that

$$\frac{E_2}{E_1} = 2 \quad \text{or} \quad \lambda_1 = 1 \quad \text{and} \quad \lambda_2 = 2. \tag{97}$$

Substitution of equation (97) into equation (96) yields

$$\frac{d^2 x_1}{d\eta^2} = 2M \frac{dx_1}{d\eta} + M\xi(F_1 - F_2\xi)\left[\frac{(x_1)^2}{1 - x_1}\right]. \tag{98}$$

Equation (98) together with the boundary condition, equation (84), forms a boundary value problem characterized by a second-order nonlinear differential equation which cannot be solved analytically.

The numerical values chosen are the same as those for the problem without diffusion given in part a, Section 2; that is,

$$\frac{G}{\rho} = 1000 \text{ ft/hr,}$$

$$k_{10} = 2.51 \times 10^5/\text{hr,}$$

$$k_{20} = 1.995 \times 10^7/\text{hr,}$$

$$E_1 = 10,000 \text{ Btu/lb-mole,}$$

$$E_2 = 20,000 \text{ Btu/lb-mole,}$$

$$R = 1.987 \text{ Btu/lb-mole-°R.}$$

The corresponding values of $F_1$, $F_2$, and $\xi$ are obtained as

$$F_1 = 5.02 \times 10^3,$$

$$F_2 = 3.99 \times 10^5,$$

$$\xi = 6.29 \times 10^{-3},$$

By substituting these values into equation (98) we have

$$\frac{d^2 x_1}{d\eta^2} = 2M \frac{dx_1}{d\eta} + 15.804M\left(\frac{(x_1)^2}{1 - x_1}\right). \tag{99}$$

A digital computer was employed to solve this equation. Computations were carried out for various values of the parameter $M$. The results are shown in Fig. 4.9. The optimal temperature profile is obtained by substituting the corresponding optimal concentration into equation (94) and the results are shown in Fig. 4.10.

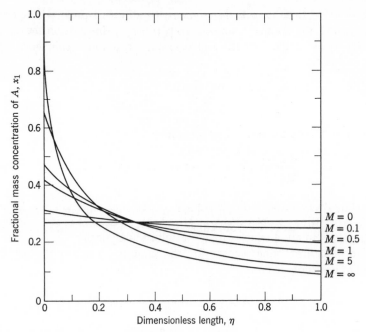

*Fig. 4.9* Optimal concentration profiles in a tubular reactor with axial diffusion (dispersion) for a reaction $A \underset{k_2}{\overset{k_1}{\rightleftharpoons}} B$.

Two limiting cases, $M = \infty$ and $M = 0$, are also shown in Figs. 4.9 and 4.10 for comparison. From equation (82) we see that $M = \infty$ is equivalent to zero diffusion or pure convection (plug flow) in a tubular reactor. This is the case we treated in part a, Section 2, in which we have assumed plug flow in the reactor. The optimal temperature and concentration profiles shown in Figs. 4.9 and 4.10 for $M = \infty$ are plotted according to equations (12) and (21).

$M = 0$ indicates infinite diffusion (complete mixing) in a tubular reactor, which is equivalent to a continuous-flow stirred tank reactor (CSTR) with the same volume. The optimal temperature and outlet concentration of a CSTR are easily determined.

According to the discrete maximum principle [1], the performance equation, which is derived from the material balance, and the Hamiltonian can be written as follows for a single stirred tank reactor:

$$x_1^{\,1} = \frac{\alpha_1 + tk_2}{1 + t(k_1 + k_2)} \tag{100a}*$$

---

* The superscript refers to the stage number.

and

$$H^1 = \frac{\alpha_1 + tk_2}{1 + t(k_1 + k_2)} z_1^{\;1},$$

where $t$ is the residence time which equals $10^{-2}$ hour for this problem. The optimal temperature for this reactor is obtained by setting

$$\frac{\partial H^1}{\partial \theta^1} = 0.$$

This gives

$$\bar{\theta}^1 = - \frac{E_2}{R \ln (\lambda_1/tk_{20})}.  \qquad (100b)$$

The corresponding optimal outlet concentration is recovered from equation (100a). The optimal temperature for the one-stage reactor, of course, can be evaluated from equation (100a) directly by the use of any

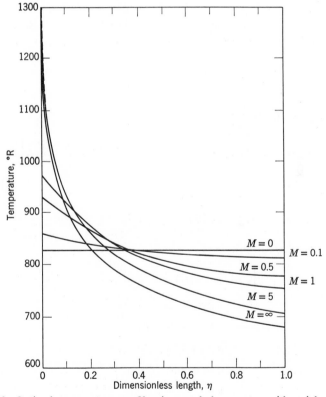

**Fig. 4.10** Optimal temperature profiles in a tubular reactor with axial diffusion (dispersion) for a reaction $A \underset{k_2}{\overset{k_1}{\rightleftharpoons}} B$.

classical method, but it is more convenient to use the discrete maximum principle when we have a series of stirred tank reactors [1].

Adler [3] reported the same results we have here. He used a classical variational method in which he introduced a Lagrange multiplier to take care of the optimal solution. In his report the Bodenstein number Bo is equal to $2M$. He represented the optimal solutions for fixed values of the Damhohler number $D_A$ and used Bo as the parameter. The Damhohler number is determined by the reactor length $L$, the flow rate $G$, and the frequency factor $k_{10}$ and is defined as $D_A = Lk_{10}/G$.

In what follows we present in detail the numerical solution of equation (99) with the boundary conditions, equation (84). The fourth-order Runge-Kutta method is employed in this calculation. To do so equation (99) is transformed by substituting equation (85):

$$\frac{dx_2}{d\eta} = 2Mx_2 + 15.804M\left[\frac{(x_1)^2}{1 - x_1}\right]. \tag{101}$$

The steps taken to calculate and solve equations (85) and (101) by means of the fourth-order Runge-Kutta method (see Appendix I) are given in the following way:

$$m_1 = hx_{2,n}, \qquad q_1 = h\left\{2M(x_{2,n}) + 15.8M\left[\frac{(x_{1,n})^2}{1 - x_{1,n}}\right]\right\},$$

$$m_2 = h\left(x_{2,n} + \frac{q_1}{2}\right),$$

$$q_2 = h\left\{2M\left(x_{2,n} + \frac{q_1}{2}\right) + 15.8M\left[\frac{(x_{1,n} + m_1/2)^2}{1 - (x_{1,n} + m_1/2)}\right]\right\},$$

$$m_3 = h\left(x_{2,n} + \frac{q_2}{2}\right),$$

$$q_3 = h\left\{2M\left(x_{2,n} + \frac{q_2}{2}\right) + 15.8M\left[\frac{(x_{1,n} + m_2/2)^2}{1 - (x_{1,n} + m_2/2)}\right]\right\},$$

$$m_4 = h(x_{2,n} + q_3),$$

$$q_4 = h\left\{2M(x_{2,n} + q_3) + 15.8M\left[\frac{(x_{1,n} + m_3)^2}{1 - (x_{1,n} + m_3)}\right]\right\},$$

$$x_{1,n+1} = x_{1,n} + \tfrac{1}{6}(m_1 + 2m_2 + 2m_3 + m_4),$$

$$x_{2,n+1} = x_{2,n} + \tfrac{1}{6}(q_1 + 2q_2 + 2q_3 + q_4).$$

(102)*

The procedure of calculation is as follows:

1. Calculate the extreme values of $x_1(1)$ for $M = 0$ and $M = \infty$.
2. Assume a value for $x_1(1)$, remembering that $x_2(1) = 0$ [equation (88)].

---

* The second subscript, $n$, indicates a point of division in the finite difference calculation by means of the Runge-Kutta method (see Appendix I).

3. Use the Runge-Kutta method given by equation (102) to integrate equations (85) and (101) from $\eta = 1$ to $\eta = 0$.

4. Check to see if equation (87) is satisfied, that is, to determine if

$$|x_2(0) - 2M[x_1(0^+) - 1]| \leq \epsilon.$$

5. If this inequality is satisfied, calculate $\bar{\theta}$ according to equation (94); if it is not satisfied, assume a new value for $x_1(1)$ and repeat steps 2 to 5.

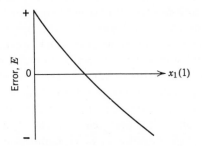

**Fig. 4.11**   The form of error curve.

The assumption of values for $x_1(1)$ need not be done arbitrarily. Several numerical techniques are available. If we write an equation for the error as

$$E = x_2(0) - 2M[x_1(0^+) - 1], \tag{103}$$

we can compute the error associated with each assumed value of $x_1(1)$. The form of the error curve, which can be determined by computing several values of $E$, is given in Fig. 4.11.

For an error curve of this form the Regula Falsi method [16] or the method of Bolzano [16] may be employed to obtain the next trial value of $x_1(1)$. A modified combination of these two forms, employed to obtain the results of this section, is as follows: let the values of $x_1(1)_{M=\infty}$ and $x_1(1)_{M=0}$ be $\alpha$ and $\beta$, respectively. Since the values of $x_1(1)$ for $0 < M < \infty$ have to lie between the two extreme values of $\alpha$ and $\beta$, we divide them into five equal parts. For each point of division, $n$, we write

$$x_{1,n}(1) = \left[\alpha + \frac{\beta - \alpha}{5}(n)\right], \qquad n = 1, 2, \ldots, 5.$$

According to the steps given in equation (102), calculate $x_1(0)$ and $x_2(0)$ for these five points. If these values do not satisfy equation (87), we locate the point at which the error changes its sign (see Fig. 4.11) and designate the values of $x_{1,n}(1)$ on each side of this point as $\alpha'$ and $\beta'$. We then calculate $x_1(1)$ by straight-line interpolation between the two points as

$$x_1(1) = \frac{|E(\beta')\alpha'| + |E(\alpha')\beta'|}{|E(\alpha')| + |E(\beta')|}.$$

where $E(\alpha')$ and $E(\beta')$ are the values of the error at $\alpha'$ and $\beta'$, respectively. Again, according to the steps in equation (102) and using this value of $x_1(1)$, we calculate $x_1(0)$ and $x_2(0)$ to determine whether these two values satisfy equation (87). If they do not, repeat the calculation by again dividing $\alpha'$ and $\beta'$ into five equal parts until equation (87) is satisfied.

It would be desirable to recognize that the optimal temperature or pressure profile along a tubular reactor which we have found in this section may often be quite difficult to realize in practice.

For example, the temperature gradients may be so steep that they will be outside the capabilities of conventional heat transfer equipment. The chief value of this investigation, however, is to furnish the designer with an objective figure for the best yield theoretically attainable, together with an indication of the direction in which temperature must be tailored to approach this theoretical maximum. The designer will then be in a position to rate his system for each configuration of heat transfer equipment that may occur to his educated intuition, keeping at every trial a firm grasp on the amount of theoretically attainable yield he is sacrificing [6]. It may be noted that good approximations to the maximum yield can often be obtained by dividing the reactor into a small number of isothermal stages.

Instead of using temperature and pressure as the decision variables in the study of the optimal performance of a tubular reactor, we can also manipulate the heat input along the reactor as in thermal cracking of vapor phase reactions, in which the material balance, pressure gradient, and heat balance should be considered. Roberts [17] treated this problem by dynamic programming with finite difference approximations.

### 3. OPTIMIZATION OF A DISTILLATION COLUMN—OPTIMAL DISTILLATE-RATE IN BATCH DISTILLATION

A batch distillation with rectification differs from continuous distillation in that it involves normally charging the still with the total amount of material to be separated and carrying out the fractionation (separation by means of distillation) until the desired amount has been distilled. A schematic diagram of a batch distillation system is shown in Fig. 4.12. The methods of operation and the equipment employed are similar for both continuous and batch distillation, but in the latter the mathematical analysis must be on a differential basis because of the changing composition and quantity of material that has not been withdrawn overhead; that is, unsteady state conditions prevail in the column throughout the operation.

The two especially well known methods of operating batch distillation columns are constant reflux ratio operation and operation at constant overhead composition. These methods are appealing because of the relative ease of controlling the column rather than the ability to yield the

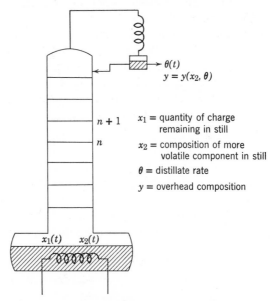

*Fig. 4.12*   Schematic diagram of a batch distillation system.

most profitable operation. By contrast, our interests here are in determining the optimal operation method, specifically the optimal distillate-rate policy, to meet a certain performance criterion of the operation.

A specific problem treated here may be stated as follows [18]:

Given the time of operation and the feed condition and assuming constant boil-up rate, how can we control the distillate rate in a batch distillation so that the maximum amount of overhead product will be collected and at the same time the product purity specification will be met?

Generally speaking, we need to know the optimal distillate rate as well as the optimal duration of operation. This consideration renders the problem more general. It can, however, be divided into two parts. First, we can determine the optimal distillate-rate policy for a specified duration of operation. Once this is solved, the over-all problem can be solved by repeating the first step for various durations. In this manner functional relationships can be developed between the optimal distillate-rate policy (and the resulting amount of product) and the duration of operation. Then by introducing a penalty for longer operation to account for the increased operating cost an optimal duration and corresponding distillate-rate policy can be determined. We shall point out that the essence of the problem lies in the first step, the determination of the optimal distillate-rate policy for a specified duration of operation.

The batch distillation with rectification (recycle) is generally considered (1) without liquid holdup in the column and (2) with holdup. We shall begin by dealing with the case without holdup for the binary mixture; the solution of the case with holdup is discussed in a later part.

Consider the system shown in Fig. 4.12. If we assume that the distillation is carried out under constant boil-up rate, an over-all differential material balance over a differential time $dt$ gives

$$\theta \, dt = -dx_1$$

or

$$\frac{dx_1}{dt} = -\theta, \qquad x_1(0) = \alpha_1, \tag{104}$$

where $\alpha_1$ is the given initial condition of $x_1(t)$. A material balance for the more volatile component over the differential time $dt$ gives

$$y\theta \, dt = -d(x_1 x_2)$$
$$= -x_1 \, dx_2 - x_2 \, dx_1.$$

Substitution of equation (104) into the preceding equation yields

$$y\theta \, dt = -x_1 \, dx_2 + x_2 \theta \, dt$$

or

$$\frac{dx_2}{dt} = \frac{\theta}{x_1}(x_2 - y), \qquad x_2(0) = \alpha_2, \tag{105}$$

where $\alpha_2$ is the given initial condition of $x_2(t)$. In equations (104) and (105)

$x_1$ = quantity of charge remaining in the still—moles,

$x_2$ = composition of more volatile component in the still—mole fraction,

$\theta$ = distillate withdrawal rate—moles/hr.

$y$ = overhead composition of more volatile component—mole fraction,

$t$ = time of operation—hr.

The two state variables are $x_1$ and $x_2$ and the decision variable is $\theta$. The overhead composition $y$ depends on both the distillate rate and the composition in the still; that is,

$$y = y(x_2; \theta).$$

Now the optimization problem at hand can be stated as follows: maximize

$$J = \int_0^T \theta(t) \, dt, \tag{106}$$

subject to the constraint

$$\bar{y} = \frac{\displaystyle\int_0^T y\theta \, dt}{\displaystyle\int_0^T \theta \, dt} = y^* \tag{107}$$

by a proper choice of

$$\theta(t), \qquad 0 \le t \le T,$$

that is, collect the largest possible amount of distillate of the specified average composition $y^*$ over a given time of operation $T$. The constraint on product purity is removed by employing the method of Lagrange multipliers [20].

A combination of equations (106) and (107) yields

$$S = \int_0^T \theta[1 - \lambda(y^* - y)] \, dt, \tag{108}$$

where $\lambda$ is the Lagrange multiplier which assures satisfaction of the constraint (107). Now $S$ instead of $J$ must be maximized; that is, $S$ is the objective function of the process.

To solve this problem we introduce an additional state variable $x_3(t)$ defined as

$$x_3(t) = \int_0^t \theta[1 - \lambda(y^* - y)] \, dt. \tag{109}$$

It follows that

$$\frac{dx_3}{dt} = \theta[1 - \lambda(y^* - y)], \qquad x_3(0) = 0. \tag{110}$$

The problem is thus transformed into one of maximizing $x_3(T)$ for a system described by equations (104), (105), and (110) by a proper choice of $\theta(t)$ which must not be greater than the boil-up rate. The Hamiltonian function, which should be maximized, is

$$H = -z_1\theta + z_2 \frac{\theta}{x_1} (x_2 - y) + z_3\theta[1 - \lambda(y^* - y)]. \tag{111}$$

Recalling that the objective function is $x_3(T)$, or, equivalently, $c_1 = c_2 = 0$ and $c_3 = 1$ in the general form of the objective function

$$S = \sum_{i=1}^{3} c_i x_i(T),$$

we have the final conditions for $z_i$ as

$$z_1(T) = z_2(T) = 0$$

and    (112)

$$z_3(T) = c_3 = 1.$$

The corresponding three adjoint vector functions, noting that $y = y(x_2; \theta)$, are

$$\frac{dz_1}{dt} = z_2 \frac{\theta(x_2 - y)}{(x_1)^2}, \qquad\qquad z_1(T) = 0, \qquad (113)$$

$$\frac{dz_2}{dt} = -z_2 \frac{\theta}{x_1}\left[1 - \left(\frac{\partial y}{\partial x_2}\right)\right] - \lambda z_3 \theta\left(\frac{\partial y}{\partial x_2}\right), \qquad z_2(T) = 0, \qquad (114)$$

$$\frac{dz_3}{dt} = 0, \qquad\qquad z_3(T) = 1. \qquad (115)$$

Solution of equation (115) for $z_3$ gives

$$z_3(t) = 1.$$

Hence the Hamiltonian function and equation (114) can be rewritten as

$$H = -z_1 \theta + z_2 \frac{\theta}{x_1}(x_2 - y) + \theta[1 - \lambda(y^* - y)] \qquad (116)$$

and

$$\frac{dz_2}{dt} = -z_2 \frac{\theta}{x_1}\left[1 - \left(\frac{\partial y}{\partial x_2}\right)\right] - \lambda\theta\left(\frac{\partial y}{\partial x_2}\right). \qquad (117)$$

If we assume first that the maximum of $H$ occurs at a stationary point with respect to $\theta$, the optimal decision $\theta(t)$ can be found from the condition

$$\frac{\partial H}{\partial \theta} = -z_1 + \frac{z_2}{x_1}\left[(x_2 - y) - \theta\left(\frac{\partial y}{\partial \theta}\right)\right]$$

$$+ \left\{[1 - \lambda(y^* - y)] + \lambda\theta\left(\frac{\partial y}{\partial \theta}\right)\right\} = 0. \quad (118)$$

Solving equation (118) for $\theta$, we obtain

$$\bar{\theta}(t) = \frac{(z_2/x_1)(x_2 - y) - z_1 - \lambda(y^* - y) + 1}{(\partial y/\partial \theta)[z_2/x_1 - \lambda]}, \qquad (119)$$

The simultaneous solution of equations (104), (105), (110), (113), (117), and (119) will give the optimal distillate-rate policy and the resulting product will be specified.

Converse and Gross [18] have considered the problem of determining the Lagrange multiplier, $\lambda$, which must have a numerical value that satisfies the constraint equation (107). This means that the solution involves a trial and error on the multiplier $\lambda$. If the duration of operation $T$ is not set, the situation alters considerably. For any given duration of operation $T$, $\lambda$ has a constant value throughout the operation. Yet, when the duration is changed, $\lambda$ must take on a new constant value. This means that equations (104), (105), (110), (113), (117) and (119) must be reintegrated with a new value of $\lambda$. The resulting solutions are valid at only one value of $T$. Hence, when both the optimal distillate-rate policy and optimal duration of operation are desired, the computer time required will be considerably larger. This problem has been solved by Gross [20] with dynamic programming and the method of characteristics; he obtained a set of ordinary differential equations and the optimal distillate-rate equation in a lengthy derivation. These equations are exactly the same as the set consisting of the performance equations, the adjoint vector functions, and the optimal distillate-rate equation presented previously.

The derivation in which the maximum principle is used is quite straightforward and simple. The advantages of the maximum principle over dynamic programming in dealing with continuous processes can now be recognized, at least for this particular problem. It can be seen that its solution also involves a two-point boundary value problem. Gross [20] obtained several simultaneous solutions of equations (104), (105), (110), (113), (117), and (119) by assuming values of $x_1(T)$ and $x_2(T)$ and then performing a backward integration with Euler's method without any modification [22] (see Appendix I). By employing the backward integration procedure we obtain an optimal solution as soon as the trial and error search for the correct Lagrange multiplier is completed. This optimal solution, however, is for the values of $x_1(0)$ and $x_2(0)$ which result from the backward integration. The computer flow diagram given by Gross [20] is shown in Fig. 4.13.

Examination of equations (117) and (119) indicates that the computation of $(\partial y/\partial \theta)$ and $(\partial y/\partial x_2)$ is necessary. According to Converse and Gross [18], the function $y = y(x_2; \theta)$, that is, the functional dependence of overhead composition with respect to the still composition and distillate rate, must in general be constructed numerically from the material balance and equilibrium relationships because the resulting equations are nonlinear. An implicit analytical expression involving $y$, $x_2$, and $\theta$ can

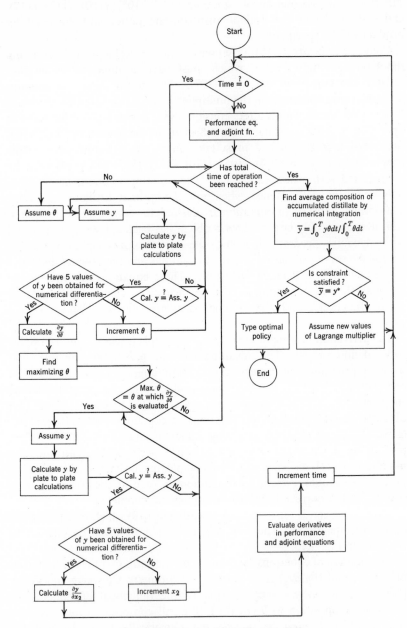

*Fig. 4.13*   Computer flow diagram [20].

be obtained, but for the foregoing derivatives it is a cumbersome process. Furthermore, as the number of plates varies, the form of the expression changes, rendering a general equation for the derivatives unfeasible. Therefore the function $y(x_2; \theta)$ was generated numerically by the use of a digital computer at each point in the integration and the derivatives evaluated by Newton's well-known five-point central difference formulas [21]. In evaluating $(\partial y/\partial x_2)$ the increment on $x_2$ was 0.0001, whereas $\theta$ was incremented by 0.01 mole/hr in evaluating $(\partial y/\partial \theta)$. This computer simulation produces a rather general algorithm which is good for any number of plates and, with slight change, any vapor-liquid equilibrium relationship. These derivatives are required at each point in time. It is to be noted that the value of $\theta$ at which they are evaluated must be identical to the $\bar{\theta}(t)$ calculated from equation (119). This requirement leads to an iterative procedure.

In this batch-distillation calculation the following assumptions are made to simplify the computations [18]:

1. No liquid or vapor holdup.
2. Constant molal overflow and equal latent heats of vaporization (McCabe-Thiele assumptions).
3. Perfect plates (three plates and a still).
4. Binary system with relative volatility independent of composition.
5. Constant boil-up rate.
6. Total condenser.
7. Start-up transients neglected.

With the exception of the first, they could be removed without changing the basic structure of the procedure developed.

The numerical data chosen for illustration are [20]

| | |
|---|---|
| number of plates | 4 |
| product purity | $y^* = 0.9$ |
| boil-up rate | 110 moles/hr |
| relative volatility | 2 |
| duration of operation | 1 hr |
| initial conditions of $x_1, x_2$ | $\alpha_1, \alpha_2$ (various cases investigated) |

The constraint of equation (107) is checked by a numerical integration with Simpson's method [21]. Using the Bendix G-20 digital computer, Gross [20] found that for the simplified model considered an optimal policy can be generated in about 15 minutes of machine time, the most important consideration being the trial and error required on $\lambda$. Also of major importance is the number of points in time at which a policy is calculated. Of secondary importance are such items as number of trays and the convergence criteria.

The optimal distillate-rate policies and resulting distillate production were found by Converse and Gross [18] for various cases, that is, different values of the initial amount of charge, $\alpha_1$, and the initial composition in the still, $\alpha_2$. The amount of product in each case was compared with the

**Table 4.3**  Comparisons of Total Distillate Accumulated by
Various Distillate-Rate Policies [20]

| Case No. | Initial Composition of Charge, $\alpha_2$, Mole Fraction | Initial Amount of Charge, $\alpha_1$, Moles | Total Distillate Accumulation, Moles | | |
|---|---|---|---|---|---|
| | | | by Optimum Policy | by Constant Overhead Composition | by Constant Reflux Ratio |
| 1. | 0.303 | 93.9 | 13.87 | 13.22 | 13.50 |
| 2. | 0.362 | 78.0 | 18.01 | 17.30 | 17.97 |
| 3. | 0.487 | 116.1 | 36.10 | 35.67 | 35.63 |
| 4. | 0.498 | 69.5 | 29.52 | 28.46 | 29.06 |
| 5. | 0.545 | 101.3 | 41.26 | 40.72 | 40.63 |
| 6. | 0.600 | 133.0 | 52.97 | 52.63 | 52.19 |
| 7. | 0.636 | 90.3 | 50.27 | 49.90 | 49.19 |
| 8. | 0.646 | 117.9 | 57.94 | 57.55 | 56.93 |
| 9. | 0.685 | 148.6 | 68.63 | 68.31 | 67.50 |
| 10. | 0.713 | 106.1 | 66.24 | 66.18 | 64.69 |
| 11. | 0.715 | 74.3 | 54.33 | 53.93 | 53.28 |
| 12. | 0.721 | 133.0 | 73.02 | 72.16 | 72.00 |
| 13. | 0.770 | 121.9 | 81.89 | 81.30 | 79.87 |
| 14. | 0.772 | 91.4 | 71.51 | 70.73 | 69.75 |
| 15. | 0.809 | 107.1 | 87.86 | 87.21 | 84.38 |
| 16. | 0.836 | 120.8 | 100.75 | 99.13 | 98.44 |

amount of product that would be obtained from constant-overhead-composition and constant-distillate-rate policies, as shown in Table 4.3. The maximum improvement in product yield was 5 per cent over the constant-overhead-composition policy and 4 per cent over the constant-distillate-rate policy. The distillate-rate and overhead-composition functions are presented in Fig. 4.14 for cases 11, 8, and 13. The improvement that the optimal policy affords over the two conventional methods of operation discussed is seen to depend on both the amount and the composition of the feed. In Fig. 4.14a and b the distillate policies do not meet the boil-up-rate boundary. In Fig. 4.14a a relatively large difference exists between the optimal policy and conventional policies, whereas in

Fig. 4.14*b* there is only a small difference. In Fig. 4.14*c* the boil-up-rate limit is encountered and the overhead composition goes through a mininium [18].

If we consider the effect of liquid hold-up in this batch distillation, the problem would be much more complicated. Converse et al. [23] has investigated this effect on the optimal distillate-rate policy.

## 4. OPTIMIZATION OF FLUX-STATE CHANGES IN NUCLEAR REACTORS [24]

In this section we consider the optimization of control-rod movement for a one-delayed-neutron group reactor with temperature feedback proportional to flux [24]. Figure 4.15 is a block diagram of part of this system. More sophisticated models can probably be treated in a similar manner [24].

The kinetic equations which are the performance equations of this system are given by

$$\frac{dn}{dt} = \frac{1}{\Lambda}[\rho n - \alpha(n)^2 - \beta n] + \lambda c, \tag{120}$$

$$\frac{dc}{dt} = \frac{\beta}{\Lambda}n - \lambda c, \tag{121}$$

where the neutron density $n$ and the precursor concentration $c$ are the state variables, the reactivity $\rho$ is the decision (control) variable, and

$\Lambda$ = neutron generation time, the average time before one neutron generates one prompt neutron or one precursor, a constant,

$\lambda$ = equivalent decay constant for the one-delay-group case, a constant,

$\alpha$ = power coefficient of reactivity,

$\beta$ = fraction of the neutrons given off in the fission that are delayed and are not emitted instantaneously.

The system is at steady state for time $t < 0$ and has the initial conditions

$$n(0) = n_0, \qquad c(0) = c_0.$$

The problem is to change the flux level (or neutron density) from $n_0$ to $an_0$, in which $a$ is a constant, in a fixed time $T$ by controlling the reactivity function so that the integral square input will be a minimum; in other words, to minimize

$$S = \int_0^T [\rho(t)]^2 \, dt. \tag{122}$$

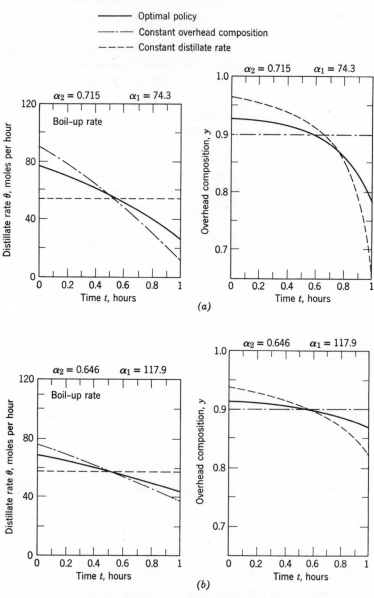

*Fig. 4.14* Optimal distillate rate policy and overhead composition [20].

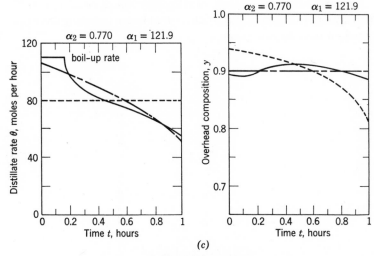

Fig. 4.14 (continued).

Further, we wish the new power level $an_0$ to remain at this value for $t > T$. This requires the slope of the neutron density to be zero at time $t = T$. Thus we have the final conditions

$$n(T) = an_0, \qquad \left.\frac{dn}{dt}\right|_{t=T} = 0. \tag{123}$$

It may be noted that the objective function, equation (122), can be interpreted as an optimization of the control-rod movement [24]; if $y(t)$ denotes the control-rod position, then

$$S = \int_0^T y \, dt$$

is the performance criterion for minimum control-rod movement. If we assume that the control rod is originally at the center of the reactor, the reactivity of the control rod decreases with increasing values of $|y|$. If this is taken into account by selecting $y = \rho^2$, the objective function is given by equation (122).

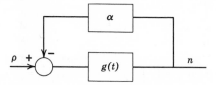

**Fig. 4.15**  Block diagram of one delayed-neutron-group reactor [24].

For nuclear-reactor control we usually have the limitation that the maximum available reactivity is restricted; that is, the following constraint is imposed on the decision variable:

$$|\rho(t)| < \rho_{max} \tag{124}$$

To be consistent with our previous notations we make the substitutions $x_1 = n$, $x_2 = c$, and $\rho(t) = \theta(t)$ and define a new state variable

$$x_3 = \int_0^t (\theta)^2 \, dt. \tag{125}$$

The problem now becomes that of minimizing $x_3(T)$.

The Hamiltonian function is

$$H = z_1\left[\frac{1}{\Lambda}\left[\theta x_1 - \alpha(x_1)^2 - \beta x_1\right] + \lambda x_2\right] + z_2\left(\frac{\beta}{\Lambda} x_1 - \lambda x_2\right) + z_3(\theta)^2. \tag{126}$$

The corresponding performance equations and adjoint functions are

$$\frac{dx_1}{dt} = \frac{1}{\Lambda}\left[\theta x_1 - \alpha(x_1)^2 - \beta x_1\right] + \lambda x_2,$$

$$x_1(0) = \alpha_1, \ x_1(T) = a\alpha_1 \quad \text{and} \quad \left.\frac{dx_1}{dt}\right|_{t=T} = 0, \tag{127}$$

$$\frac{dx_2}{dt} = \frac{\beta}{\Lambda} x_1 - \lambda x_2, \qquad x_2(0) = \alpha_2, \tag{128}$$

$$\frac{dx_3}{dt} = (\theta)^2, \qquad\qquad x_3(0) = 0, \tag{129}$$

$$\frac{dz_1}{dt} = -\frac{1}{\Lambda}(\theta - 2\alpha x_1 - \beta)z_1 - \frac{\beta}{\Lambda} z_2, \tag{130}$$

$$\frac{dz_2}{dt} = -\lambda z_1 + \lambda z_2, \tag{131}$$

$$\frac{dz_3}{dt} = 0. \tag{132}$$

The objective function is $x_3(T)$ or, equivalently, $c_3 = 1$ in

$$S = c_3 x_3(T).$$

The final condition for the adjoint variable $z_3$ is thus

$$z_3(T) = c_3 = 1. \tag{133}$$

$z_1(T)$ and $z_2(T)$ are left undefined because two end conditions of $x_1$ are fixed. According to equations (132) and (133) it can be seen that

$$z_3(t) = 1 \quad \text{for} \quad 0 \le t \le T. \tag{134}$$

If we assume that the maximum value of the Hamiltonian occurs at a stationary point and that the optimal decision function thus found lies inside the constraints, that is, $|\bar{\theta}(t)| < \theta_{\max}$, then $\bar{\theta}(t)$ can be determined from the condition [note that $z_3(t) = 1$]

$$\frac{\partial H}{\partial \theta} = \frac{z_1}{\Lambda} x_1 + 2\theta = 0,$$

or

$$\bar{\theta}(t) = -\frac{z_1}{2\Lambda} x_1. \tag{135}$$

Thus equation (135), together with equations (127) through (132), determines an optimal solution of this problem. If we substitute for $\theta(t)$ in equations (127), (128), (130) and (131), it can be seen that we shall end up with four simultaneous differential equations with split-type boundary values.

A repetitive analog computer is especially suitable for this system of equations, for its memory capability makes possible an automatic iterative solution of the split boundary value problem [24].

The numerical values chosen are [24]

$$\lambda = 0.1 \text{ sec} \qquad \alpha_1 = 10 \text{ kw}$$
$$\alpha = 10^{-5} \text{ kw} \qquad \beta = 0.0064$$
$$\Lambda = 10^{-3} \text{ sec} \qquad T = 1 \text{ sec}$$

The analog computer flow diagram for this problem is given in Fig. 4.16 [24] and representative results appear in Figs. 4.17 and 4.18. Figure 4.17 shows a family of optimal reactivity functions for final values of the power level (neutron density) which vary from $x_1(T) = 2\alpha_1$ to $x_1(T) = 10\alpha_1$. Figure 4.18 gives the corresponding optimal power levels.

The boundary condition

$$\left. \frac{dx_1}{dt} \right|_{t=T} = 0$$

brings the flux to the required level with a zero slope, but this alone does not guarantee that the power level will stay at this value. Further changes in the power level depend on the control of the reactivity function, that is,

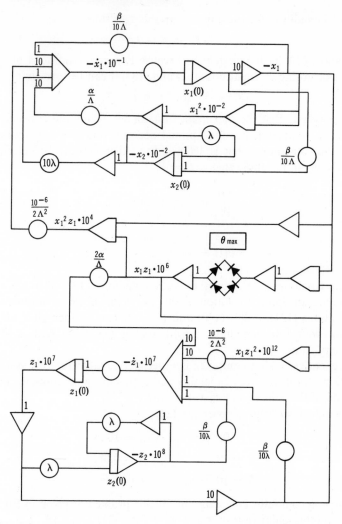

**Fig. 4.16**  Analog computer block diagram [24].

on the reactivity program after time $t = T$. The required reactivity input, which can be calculated easily from the kinetic equations, is given by [24]

$$\rho(t) = \alpha n(T) + [\rho(T) - \alpha n(T)]e^{-\lambda(t-T)}, \qquad t > T.$$

This part of the reactivity function and power level are indicated in Figs. 4.17 and 4.18 by dashed lines.

When the optimal reactivity function $\bar{\theta}(t)$ calculated from equation (135) is outside the constraint indicated by equation (124), $\bar{\theta}(t)$ given by

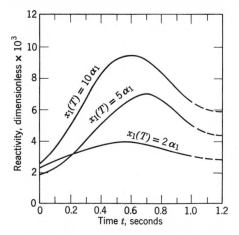

*Fig. 4.17*   Optimal reactivity as a function of time [24].

equation (135) is no longer valid. The control should operate on its boundary. Figure 4.19 shows the optimal reactivity profile obtained for different values of $\theta_{max}$.

The maximum principle has many important applications in nuclear processes and engineering. The calculation of an optimal fuel distribution in reactors in which the critical size will be a minimum and the determination of a reactor shutdown program which will result in the smallest xenon buildup are problems that can be treated by this method. Another example is the optimization of the start-up of nuclear space systems with respect to the consumption of auxiliary power or the optimal control for

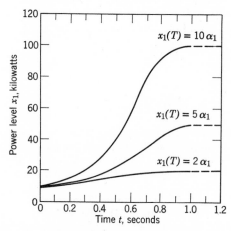

*Fig. 4.18*   Optimal power level as a function of time [24].

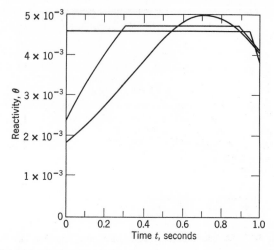

*Fig. 4.19*    Optimal reactivity versus time with constrained reactivity [24].

nuclear reactor start-up according to various performance indices such as the minimizing of certain error criterion [24].

In this chapter the maximum principle has been used to optimize several process systems. The two-point boundary value problems which result from the application of the maximum principle have been solved in a variety of ways. The examples treated should serve as a guide to those who wish to apply the maximum principle to other process systems.

It should be pointed out that the maximum principle only gives the necessary conditions for an extremum of a process. However, for the design engineer who has a sufficient qualitative understanding of the process, sufficiency conditions often may not be needed to obtain the optimal solution of the process.

## REFERENCES

1. Fan, L. T., and C. S. Wang, *The Discrete Maximum Principle*, Wiley, New York, 1964.
2. Levenspiel, O., *Chemical Reaction Engineering*, Wiley, New York, 1962.
3. Adler, J., and D. Vortmyer, "The Effect of Axial Diffusion Processes on the Optimum Yield of Tubular Reactors—I," *Chem. Eng. Sci.*, **18**, 99–108 (1963).
4. Aris, R., *The Optimal Design of Chemical Reactions*, Academic Press, New York, 1961.
5. Bilous, O., and N. P. Amundson, "Optimum Temperature Gradients in Tubular Reactors," *Chem. Eng. Sci.*, **5** (I and II), 81, 115 (1956).
6. Katz, S., "Best Temperature Profiles in Plug-flow Reactors: Methods of the Calculus of Variations," *Ann. N.Y. Acad. Sci.*, **84**, Art. 12, 441–478 (1960).

7. Lee, E. S., "Optimization by Pontryagin's Maximum Principle on the Analog Computer," *A.I.Ch.E. J.* **10**, 3, 309–315 (1964); also presented at JACC, Minneapolis, Minnesota, 1963.

8. Favreau, R. R., and R. Franks, "Random Optimization by Analog Techniques," presented at the Second International Conference for Analog Computation, Strasbourg, September 1958.

9. Munson, J. E., and A. I. Rubin, "Optimization by Random Search on the Analog Computer," presented at the National Simulation Conference, Dallas, Texas (1958).

10. Satterthwarts, F. E., "Random Evolutionary Operation," Report No. 10/10/59, Statistical Engineering Institute, Wellesley, Massachusetts.

11. Van de Vusse, J. G., and H. Voetter, "Optimum Pressure and Concentration Gradient in Tubular Reactors," *Chem. Eng. Sci.*, **14**, 901 (1961).

12. Danckwerts, P. V., "Continuous Flow System," *Chem. Eng. Sci.*, **1**, 1 (1953).

13. Wehener, J. F., and R. H. Wilhelm, "Boundary Conditions of Continuous Flow Systems," *Chem. Eng. Sci.*, **6**, 89 (1956).

14. Van der Laan, E. Th., "Notes on the Diffusion-type Model for the Longitudinal Mixing of Fluid in Flow," *Chem. Eng. Sci.*, **7**, 187 (1958).

15. Fan, L. T., and Y. K. Ahn, "Critical Evaluations of Boundary Conditions for Tubular Flow Reactors," *Ind. Eng. Chem., Process Design Develop.*, **1**, 90 (1962).

16. Stanton, R. G., *Numerical Methods for Science and Engineering*, Prentice-Hall, Englewood Cliffs, New Jersey, 1961.

17. Roberts, S. M., *Dynamic Programming in Chemical Engineering and Process Control*, Academic Press, New York, 1964.

18. Converse, A. O., and G. D. Gross, "Optimal Distillate-Rate Policy in Batch Distillation," *Ind. Eng. Chem. Fundamentals*, **2**, 217 (1963).

19. Bliss, G. A., *Lectures on the Calculus of Variations*, University of Chicago Press, Chicago, 1946.

20. Gross, G. D., "Optimal Distillate-Rate Policy in Batch Distillation," M. S. Thesis, Carnegie Institute of Technology, 1962.

21. Milne, W. E., *Numerical Calculus*, Princeton University Press, Princeton, N.J., 1949.

22. Sangren, W. C., *Digital Computers and Nuclear Reactor Calculations*, Wiley, New York, 1960.

23. Converse, A. O., C. I. Huber, and B. F. Rothenberger, "Application of Dynamic Optimization Methods to Batch and Transient Continuous Distillation," unpublished communications, 1962.

24. Rosztoczy, Z. R., A. P. Sage, and L. E. Weaver, "Application of Pontryagin's Maximum Principle to Flux-State Changes in Nuclear Reactors," Division of USAEC TID 7662 "Reactor Kinetics and Control," *2nd AEC Symposium Series*.

25. Denn, M. M., "The Optimization of Complex Systems," Ph.D. Thesis, University of Minnesota, 1964.

26. Horn, F., "Optimale Temperatur-und Konzentrationsverläufe," *Chem. Eng. Sci.*, **14**, 77–89 (1961).

27. Denn, M. M., and R. Aris, "Green's Functions and Optimal Systems I: Necessary Conditions and an Iterative Technique," *Ind. Eng. Chem. Fundamentals*, **4**, 7 (1965).

28. Denn, M. M., and R. Aris, "Generalized Euler Equations," *Z. Angew. Math. Phys.*, **16**, 290 (1965).

# 5

# *Application of the Algorithm*
# *for Simple Processes*
# *to Aerospace Systems*

The design and operation of aerospace systems give rise to many optimization problems. The optimum shapes of aircraft and missile components and the optimum trajectories of aircrafts, missiles, and spaceships are some of the examples.

This chapter is designed to show the readers how the maximum principle may be applied to the solution of some of the optimization problems of aerospace systems. Four specific examples which may be considered representative of aerospace systems optimization problems are treated in considerable detail.

This chapter is by no means intended to cover all phases of optimization that relate to aerospace systems. Readers who are interested in a more complete coverage of the subject are referred to the work edited by Leitmann [1].

## 1. LUNAR SOFT LANDING [3]

In this section we shall consider an optimal (minimum fuel) thrust program for the terminal phase of a lunar soft-landing mission, a problem that has been treated by some investigators [1, 2, 3]. A space vehicle in the terminal phase of a lunar soft-landing mission is shown in Fig. 5.1. In the development that follows it is assumed that (a) the space vehicle is in vertical motion, (b) aerodynamic forces are negligible, (c) the thrust is tangent to the descent trajectory, (d) the moon surface is flat in the vicinity of the desired landing site, (e) the acceleration of gravity is constant, and (f) the velocity of the exhaust gases with respect to the vehicle is constant.

Under these assumptions the motion of the vehicle can be expressed by [1]

$$\frac{d^2x_1}{dt^2} = -\frac{k(dm/dt)}{m} - g, \qquad (1)$$

where

$$k > 0, \qquad \frac{dm}{dt} \le 0;$$

$x_1$ is the altitude, $m$, the total mass, $dm/dt$, the mass flow rate, $k$, the velocity of the exhaust gases with respect to the vehicle, and $g$, the acceleration of gravity of the moon.

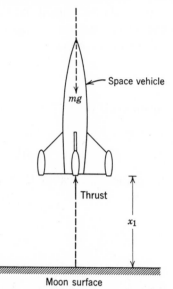

Fig. 5.1  Schematic diagram of lunar landing [3].

It is further assumed that the ratio of the maximum thrust to the initial mass is greater than the acceleration of gravity and that the propulsion system is capable of stopping the vehicle above or just at the surface of the moon. The altitude and altitude rate can be measured, for instance, by using a radar altimeter and doppler radar.

Since the vehicle is in the terminal descent phase of the mission and must arrive at the surface of the moon with zero velocity to achieve a soft landing, we have initial conditions of the form

$$x_1(0) > 0, \qquad \frac{dx_1}{dt}\bigg|_{t=0} < 0$$

and final conditions which are

$$x_1(T) = 0, \qquad \frac{dx_1}{dt}\bigg|_{t=T} = 0.$$

We are to find an optimal thrust program which minimizes the objective function

$$S = -\int_0^T \frac{dm(t)}{dt}\,dt = m(0) - m(T), \qquad 0 \le t \le T, \qquad (2)$$

where $T$ is not specified. The optimal thrust program thus obtained must satisfy the following conditions:

1. $\dfrac{dm(t)}{dt}$ is a measurable function.

2. $-a \le \dfrac{dm(t)}{dt} \le 0$, where $a$ is a positive constant.

It should be pointed out that the value of equation (2) is simply the change in mass during the mission and is therefore equal to the fuel consumption. Since

$$\frac{1}{m}\frac{dm}{dt} = \frac{d}{dt}(\ln m),$$

equation (1) can be rewritten as

$$\frac{d^2x_1}{dt^2} = -k\frac{d}{dt}(\ln m) - g. \tag{3}$$

Integration of equation (3) between the limits of 0 and $t$ yields

$$\frac{dx_1(t)}{dt} = -k\ln\frac{m(t)}{m(0)} - gt + \frac{dx_1}{dt}\bigg|_{t=0}. \tag{4}$$

By setting

$$\frac{dx_1}{dt}\bigg|_{t=T} = 0$$

we have

$$k\ln\frac{m(T)}{m(0)} = \frac{dx_1}{dt}\bigg|_{t=0} - gT.$$

Solving for $m(T)$, we obtain

$$m(T) = m(0)\exp\left(\frac{\dfrac{dx_1}{dt}\bigg|_{t=0} - gT}{k}\right). \tag{5}$$

Substitution of equation (5) into equation (2) produces the objective function

$$S = m(0)\left[1 - \exp\left(\frac{\dfrac{dx_1}{dt}\bigg|_{t=0} - gT}{k}\right)\right].$$

Thus for a given set of $m(0)$, $\dfrac{dx_1}{dt}\bigg|_{t=0}$, $g$ and $k$ the amount of fuel required to stop the vehicle is a strictly monotonic increasing function of the terminal time $T$. It follows that minimizing the terminal time $T$ is equivalent to minimizing the fuel consumption. This is the reason for letting $T$ be free in the problem formulation.

To solve this problem, we set

$$\frac{dx_1}{dt} = x_2, \qquad x_3 = m, \qquad \theta = \frac{dm}{dt}, \quad \text{and} \quad x_4(t) = \int_0^t dt.$$

Equation (1) can then be replaced by the following set of equations:

$$\frac{dx_1}{dt} = x_2,$$

$$\frac{dx_2}{dt} = -\frac{k}{x_3}\theta - g,$$

(6)

$$\frac{dx_3}{dt} = \theta,$$

$$\frac{dx_4}{dt} = 1,$$

with the constraint

$$-a \le \theta(t) \le 0$$

and the boundary conditions

$$x_1(0) = x_1(0),$$

$$x_2(0) = \frac{dx_1}{dt}\bigg|_{t=0},$$

$$x_3(0) = m(0),$$

$$x_4(0) = 0,$$

$$x_1(T) = 0,$$

$$x_2(T) = 0,$$

$$x_3(T) = m(T),$$

$$x_4(T) = T.$$

The Hamiltonian then becomes

$$H = z_1 x_2 - z_2\frac{k}{x_3}\theta - z_2 g + z_3\theta + z_4 = z_1 x_2 - z_2 g + \left(z_3 - \frac{k}{x_3}z_2\right)\theta + z_4.$$

(7)

The components of the adjoint vector are given by

$$\frac{dz_1}{dt} = 0,$$

$$\frac{dz_2}{dt} = -z_1,$$

(8)

$$\frac{dz_3}{dt} = -z_2\frac{k}{(x_3)^2}\theta,$$

$$\frac{dz_4}{dt} = 0.$$

Noting that equation (7) is linear with respect to $\theta(t)$ and recalling the constraint already mentioned, we see that the Hamiltonian is a minimum if $\theta(t)$ is chosen as

$$\theta(t) = \begin{cases} -a & \text{if } \left[ z_3(t) - \dfrac{k}{x_3(t)} z_2(t) \right] > 0, \\[3mm] 0 & \text{if } \left[ z_3(t) - \dfrac{k}{x_3(t)} z_2(t) \right] < 0; \end{cases}$$

that is, the optimal control pattern has the following form:

$$\theta(t) = \begin{cases} -a & \text{if } z_2(t) < \dfrac{x_3(t)}{k} z_3(t), \\[3mm] 0 & \text{if } z_2(t) > \dfrac{x_3(t)}{k} z_3(t). \end{cases} \tag{9}$$

Note that $\theta(t)$ is indeterminate whenever

$$z_3(t) - \frac{k}{x_3(t)} z_2(t) = 0.$$

The condition expressed by this relation is called the singularity condition. It is shown in the work of Meditch [3] that the singularity condition cannot be maintained for any finite closed interval $[0, T]$. It is also shown that there is at most one switching in $[0, T]$ and that the optimal control consists of either full thrust until touchdown or a period of zero thrust (free fall), followed by full thrust until touchdown.

The optimal thrust program can be synthesized by determining an appropriate switching function, which can be obtained by integrating the equation of motion under the assumption of full thrust, $\theta(t) = -a$, and determining the relation that must exist between the initial altitude and altitude rate. If we denote the time from the initiation of full thrust to touchdown by $t_1$ and let $t'$ be such that $0 \le t' \le t_1$, we obtain from equations (4) and (6)

$$x_3(t') = m(0) - at',$$

$$x_2(t') = -k \ln \left( 1 - \frac{a}{m(0)} t' \right) - gt' + x_2(0), \tag{10}$$

$$\begin{aligned} x_1(t') &= \int_0^{t'} x_2(s) \, ds + x_1(0) \\ &= \frac{km(0)}{a} \left( 1 - \frac{a}{m(0)} t' \right) \ln \left( 1 - \frac{a}{m(0)} t' \right) + kt' \\ &\quad - \frac{1}{2} g(t')^2 + x_2(0)t' + x_1(0). \end{aligned} \tag{11}$$

Since    $x_1(t_1) = x_2(t_1) = 0$, equations (10) and (11) become at $t' = t_1$,

$$0 = -k \ln \left(1 - \frac{a}{m(0)} t_1\right) - g t_1 + x_2(0), \tag{12}$$

and

$$0 = \frac{km(0)}{a}\left(1 - \frac{a}{m(0)} t_1\right) \ln \left(1 - \frac{a}{m(0)} t_1\right) + k t_1$$

$$- \frac{1}{2} g(t_1)^2 + x_2(0)t_1 + x_1(0), \tag{13}$$

respectively. It follows from the above two equations that the relationship that determines the initial state from which a soft landing can be achieved in time $t_1$, using full thrust, is given by

$$x_1(0) = - \frac{km(0)}{a} \ln \left(1 - \frac{a}{m(0)} t_1\right) - k t_1 - \frac{1}{2} g(t_1)^2 \tag{14}$$

and

$$x_2(0) = k \ln \left(1 - \frac{a}{m(0)} t_1\right) + g t_1. \tag{15}$$

An exact expression $f(x_1(0), x_2(0)) = 0$ for the switching function can be obtained by eliminating $t_1$ from equations (14) and (15), but we shall proceed to derive an approximate relation that is adequate for a large number of cases.

It is worth noting that $a t_1/m(0)$ is the fraction of the initial mass consumed during thrusting. Suppose that the mission is to be accomplished with no more than 25 per cent of the initial mass as propellant; then we may utilize the following approximation obtained by truncating the Taylor's series expansion of the logarithmic function

$$\ln \left(1 - \frac{a}{m(0)} t_1\right) = - \frac{a t_1}{m(0)} - \frac{1}{2}\left(\frac{a t_1}{m(0)}\right)^2.$$

The maximum error in this approximation is 2.23 per cent. If we substitute it into equations (14) and (15), we obtain, after simplification,

$$x_1(0) = A(t_1)^2 \tag{16}$$

$$x_2(0) = -2A t_1 - B(t_1)^2, \tag{17}$$

respectively, where

$$A = \frac{1}{2}\left[\frac{ka - g\, m(0)}{m(0)}\right] \tag{18}$$

and

$$B = \frac{k(a)^2}{2[m(0)]^2} .$$ (19)

Since we have assumed that the ratio of the maximum thrust to the initial mass is greater than $g$, it follows that $ka > gm(0)$ and $A > 0$. The initial altitude, $x_1(0)$, is also positive. Thus the value of $t_1$, which satisfies equation (16) and which is physically meaningful, is

$$t_1 = \sqrt{\frac{x_1(0)}{A}} .$$ (20)

By substituting equation (20) into equation (17) and simplifying we obtain

$$f(x_1(0), x_2(0)) = \frac{B}{A} x_1(0) + 2A\sqrt{\frac{x_1(0)}{A}} + x_2(0) = 0,$$ (21)

which is the desired switching function. The set of all initial states from which it is possible to reach the origin (the landing site) by using full thrust is comprised of those states $(x_1(0), x_2(0))$ that satisfy equation (21). For physical reasons, however, equation (21) is of interest only for a particular region of the fourth quadrant of the $x_1$, $x_2$ plane. This can be seen by noting the existence of a relation

$$0 \le t_1 \le 0.25 \frac{m(0)}{a} .$$

The lower bound results when the vehicle is initially at the landing site, that is, $x_1(0) = x_2(0) = 0$; the upper bound results when 25 per cent of the initial mass is used for the mission. It follows from equations (16) and (17) that the region of the $x_1$, $x_2$ plane in which we are interested is defined by the relations

$$0 \le x_1 \le 0.0625A\left(\frac{m(0)}{a}\right)^2$$

and                                                                                            (22)

$$\left[-0.5A\left(\frac{m(0)}{a}\right) - 0.0625B\left(\frac{m(0)}{a}\right)^2\right] \le x_2 \le 0.$$

A plot of the switching function defined by equation (21) with constraints expressed by equation (22) is shown in Fig. 5.2.

For a given initial altitude $\alpha$ and initial altitude rate $\beta$ the free-fall trajectory of the space vehicle can be obtained as

$$x_1 = \alpha - \frac{1}{2g}[(x_2)^2 - (\beta)^2].$$

The free-fall trajectory for a given initial state $(\alpha, \beta)$ in the fourth quadrant of the $x_1$, $x_2$ plane is shown in Fig. 5.2. It can be seen that the curves of the switching function and the free-fall trajectory cannot intersect more than once in the fourth quadrant. If the point $(\alpha, \beta)$ lies above the switching function curve, the optimal thrust program will be such that the vehicle will be allowed to free fall until its altitude and altitude

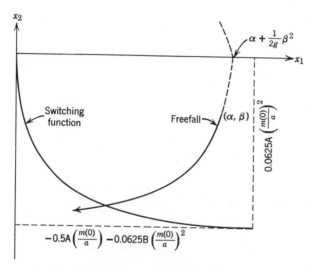

**Fig. 5.2**   Phase trajectory of the vehicle [3].

rate satisfy the switching function $f(x_1, x_2) = 0$, at which time full thrust will be initiated and will continue until touchdown. Since the free-fall trajectory and the switching curve intersect only once, it follows that the switching time is unique, and therefore it must be the optimal one. This optimal thrust program can be realized in practice by measuring altitude and altitude rate taken during free fall and substituting them into the relation

$$f(x_1, x_2) = \frac{B}{A} x_1 + 2A \sqrt{\frac{x_1}{A}} + x_2.$$

As long as $f(x_1, x_2) > 0$, the vehicle will be allowed to free fall, and thrust is initiated as soon as $f(x_1, x_2) = 0$. A block diagram of the optimal system is given in Fig. 5.3. If the altitude and altitude rate at the initiation of the mission are such that $f(\alpha, \beta) = 0$, thrust is initiated immediately; but, if $f(\alpha, \beta) < 0$, a soft landing is beyond the capability of the assumed propulsion system and a higher thrust level is required.

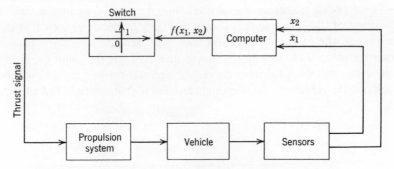

**Fig. 5.3**   Block diagram of optimal lunar landing system [3].

For further discussion of this problem the reader is referred to Meditch [3] and Leondes [13].

## 2.  ATTITUDE CONTROL [5]

For many spacecrafts designed to orbit the earth there are some requirements on the attitude orientation of the vehicle. Gravity-gradient torques are used to provide attitude control about the pitch axis (the axis normal to the plane of the orbit) by properly choosing the principal moments of inertia of the vehicle. In addition to gravity-gradient torques, two sets of gas nozzles are often used to obtain control for the roll and yaw axes.

Craig and Flügge-Lotz [5] have shown that the small-angle attitude variations of a satellite in circular orbit about the earth can be expressed by the following equations:

$$\text{Yaw:} \quad \ddot{\psi} + \frac{I_3 - I_2}{I_1}(n)^2\psi - \left(1 - \frac{I_3 - I_2}{I_1}\right)n\dot{\Phi} = \frac{T_{c\psi}}{I_1}, \quad (23)$$

$$\text{Roll:} \quad \ddot{\Phi} + 4\frac{I_3 - I_1}{I_2}(n)^2\Phi + \left(1 - \frac{I_3 - I_1}{I_2}\right)n\dot{\psi} = \frac{T_{c\Phi}}{I_2}, \quad (24)$$

where a dot indicates differentiation with respect to time. $I_1$, $I_2$, and $I_3$ are the moments of inertia about the yaw, roll, and pitch axes, respectively, $n$ is the orbital angular frequency, $\psi$ is a yaw angle, $\Phi$ is a roll angle, $T_{c\psi}$ is the yaw component of the control torque, and $T_{c\Phi}$ is the roll component of the control torque (see Fig. 5.4).

The equation for the pitch motion is not listed here, for pitch motions are independent of roll and yaw motions, and control of pitch attitude is

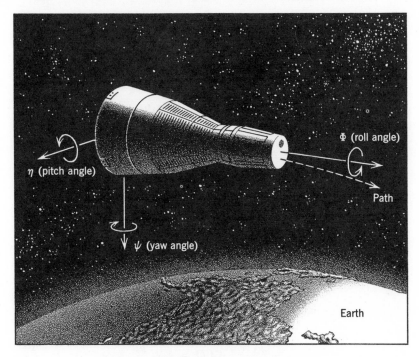

**Fig. 5.4** Attitude orientation of a satellite [5].

a separate and simpler problem. The forcing functions on the right-hand side of equation (23) are the components of the control torque produced by regulating the flow through the gas nozzles.

It is convenient to normalize the equations by setting

$$\tau = nt \quad \text{so that} \quad \frac{d}{dt} = n\frac{d}{d\tau}$$

$$\frac{T_{c\psi}}{(n)^2 I_1} = \theta_1, \qquad \frac{T_{c\Phi}}{(n)^2 I_2} = \theta_2, \tag{25}$$

$$\frac{I_3 - I_2}{I_1} = A_1, \qquad \frac{I_3 - I_1}{I_2} = A_2;$$

$\theta_1$ and $\theta_2$ are considered the decision variables of the system. The normalized equations are

$$\ddot{\psi} = -A_1\psi + (1 - A_1)\dot{\Phi} + \theta_1, \tag{26}$$

$$\ddot{\Phi} = (A_2 - 1)\dot{\psi} - 4A_2\Phi + \theta_2, \tag{27}$$

where the dot now indicates differentiation with respect to $\tau$. Letting

$$y_1 = \psi, \qquad y_3 = \Phi,$$
$$y_2 = \frac{d\psi}{d\tau}, \qquad y_4 = \frac{d\Phi}{d\tau}, \tag{28}$$

we may replace equations (26) and (27) by the following set of four equations:

$$\frac{dy_1}{d\tau} = y_2, \tag{29}$$

$$\frac{dy_2}{d\tau} = -A_1 y_1 + (1 - A_1)y_4 + \theta_1, \tag{30}$$

$$\frac{dy_3}{d\tau} = y_4, \tag{31}$$

$$\frac{dy_4}{d\tau} = (A_2 - 1)y_2 - 4A_2 y_3 + \theta_2. \tag{32}$$

A linear transformation in which we introduce the following new variables,

$$x_1 = \frac{A_1}{w_1} y_1 + \frac{w_1[(w_2)^2 - 4A_2]}{4A_2(1 - A_2)} y_4, \tag{33}$$

$$x_2 = y_2 + \frac{4A_2 - (w_2)^2}{1 - A_2} y_3, \tag{34}$$

$$x_3 = \frac{w_2[A_1 - (w_1)^2]}{A_1(1 - A_1)} y_2 + \frac{4A_2}{w_2} y_3, \tag{35}$$

$$x_4 = \frac{(w_1)^2 - A_1}{1 - A_1} y_1 + y_4, \tag{36}$$

uncouples the modes of motion to give

$$\frac{dx_1}{d\tau} = w_1 x_2 + B_1 \theta_2, \tag{37}$$

$$\frac{dx_2}{d\tau} = -w_1 x_1 + \theta_1, \tag{38}$$

$$\frac{dx_3}{d\tau} = w_2 x_4 + B_2 \theta_1, \tag{39}$$

$$\frac{dx_4}{d\tau} = -w_2 x_3 + \theta_2. \tag{40}$$

where

$$B_1 = \frac{w_1[4A_2 - (w_2)^2]}{4A_2(A_2 - 1)}, \tag{41}$$

$$B_2 = \frac{w_2[A_1 - (w_1)^2]}{A_1(1 - A_1)}, \tag{42}$$

and $w_1$ and $w_2$ are the roots of the equation

$$(S)^4 + [(1 - A_1)(1 - A_2) + A_1 + 4A_2](S)^2 + 4A_1A_2 = 0. \tag{43}$$

Equations (37) through (40) are the performance equations of the system.

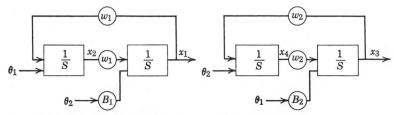

**Fig. 5.5** Block diagram of the two uncoupled second-order systems [5].

A block-diagram representation of the uncoupled equations is shown in Fig. 5.5. Values of the moments of inertia, which produce satisfactory pitch attitude performance, serve to bound $B_i$ and $w_i$. For this problem these bounds are assumed to be

$$0 < B_1 < 1,$$
$$0 < B_2 < 1,$$

where $B_1$ and $B_2$ cannot both be equal to one at the same time and

$$\frac{w_2}{w_1} \le 10,$$

where

$$w_2 > w_1.$$

For the minimum fuel consumption control it is generally desired to select control variables $\theta_1$ and $\theta_2$, with constraints $|\theta_1| \le M_1$ and $|\theta_2| \le M_2$, which will bring a state vector $x$ from some initial condition $x(0)$ to a final condition $x(\tau_f)$ in some unspecified time $\tau_f$, with the least amount of fuel consumption. The objective function of the problem may be expressed as

$$S = \int_0^{\tau_f} \sum_{i=1}^{2} |\theta_i| \, d\tau. \tag{44}$$

If we let

$$x_5(\tau) = \int_0^\tau \sum_{i=1}^2 |\theta_i| \, d\tau, \tag{45}$$

our problem becomes one of minimizing $x_5(\tau_f)$. Equation (45) may be written in the form

$$\frac{dx_5(\tau)}{d\tau} = \sum_{i=1}^2 |\theta_i|. \tag{46}$$

The Hamiltonian function of the system is

$$H = z_1(w_1 x_2 + B_1 \theta_2) + z_2(-w_1 x_1 + \theta_1)$$
$$+ z_3(w_2 x_4 + B_2 \theta_1) + z_4(-w_2 x_3 + \theta_2) + z_5(|\theta_1| + |\theta_2|). \tag{47}$$

If we let $H^*$ denote that portion of $H$ which involves the decision variables $\theta_1$ and $\theta_2$, we may write

$$H^* = z_1 B_1 \theta_2 + z_2 \theta_1 + z_3 B_2 \theta_1 + z_4 \theta_2 + z_5(|\theta_1| + |\theta_2|). \tag{48}$$

The differential equations for the components of the adjoint vector $z$ are

$$\frac{dz_1}{d\tau} = +w_1 z_2, \tag{49}$$

$$\frac{dz_2}{d\tau} = -w_1 z_1, \tag{50}$$

$$\frac{dz_3}{d\tau} = +w_2 z_4, \tag{51}$$

$$\frac{dz_4}{d\tau} = -w_2 z_3, \tag{52}$$

$$\frac{dz_5}{d\tau} = 0. \tag{53}$$

The boundary conditions are

$$x_i(0) = \alpha_i, \quad x_i(\tau_f) = \beta_i; \quad i = 1, 2, 3, 4, \tag{54}$$
$$x_5(0) = 0, \quad z_5(\tau_f) = 1, \tag{55}$$

and

$$H_{\min} = 0, \quad 0 \le \tau \le \tau_f. \tag{56}$$

Equation (53) may be integrated to give

$$z_5(\tau) = 1 \tag{57}$$

By substituting this result into equation (48) and letting

$$g_1 = z_2 + B_2 z_3, \tag{58}$$

$$g_2 = B_1 z_1 + z_4,$$

we obtain

$$H^* = g_1 \theta_1 + g_2 \theta_2 + |\theta_1| + |\theta_2|. \tag{59}$$

From equation (59) and the constraints

$$|\theta_1| \le M_1 \quad \text{and} \quad |\theta_2| \le M_2 \tag{60}$$

we see that $H^*$ is a minimum when

$$
\begin{aligned}
\theta_1 &= -M_1 \operatorname{sgn} g_1, && \text{if} \quad M_1 |g_1| \ge M_1, \\
\theta_1 &= 0, && \text{if} \quad M_1 |g_1| < M_1, \\
\theta_2 &= -M_2 \operatorname{sgn} g_2, && \text{if} \quad M_2 |g_2| \ge M_2, \\
\theta_2 &= 0, && \text{if} \quad M_2 |g_2| < M_2,
\end{aligned}
\tag{61}
$$

where

$$
\operatorname{sgn} g = 
\begin{cases}
\dfrac{g}{|g|} & \text{if } g \ne 0, \\[2mm]
0 & \text{if } g = 0.
\end{cases}
\tag{62}
$$

Equation (61) contains the conditions that give an optimal control of the bang-coast-bang type (see Chapter 3) which is characteristic of minimum fuel problems.

Equations (49) and (50) may be combined to give

$$\frac{d^2 z_2}{d\tau^2} + (w_1)^2 z_2 = 0. \tag{63}$$

Similarly, from equations (51) and (52), we obtain

$$\frac{d^2 z_4}{d\tau^2} + (w_2)^2 z_4 = 0. \tag{64}$$

It is clear that the $z_i$, $i = 1, 2, 3, 4$ are harmonic functions of time. Assuming the maximum amplitude $P_i$ and the phase angle as constants in the solution for $z_i$, $i = 1, 2, 3, 4$, the functions $g_1$ and $g_2$ may be written as follows:

$$g_1 = P_2 \cos(w_1 \tau + \delta_1) + B_2 P_4 \sin(w_2 \tau + \delta_2), \tag{65}$$

$$g_2 = P_4 \cos(w_2 \tau + \delta_2) + B_1 P_2 \sin(w_1 \tau + \delta_1). \tag{66}$$

Figure 5.6 illustrates a sketch of $g_2$ plotted as a function of $g_1$ for visualization of the control action and the control time history of an arbitrarily chosen problem.

Since the desired control action is expressed in terms of the adjoint vector $z$ rather than the state vector $x$, relationships must be found between $z$ and $x$.

Theoretically, the optimal time $\tau_f$ may be determined from the condition given by equation (56). An alternative method of finding the optimal

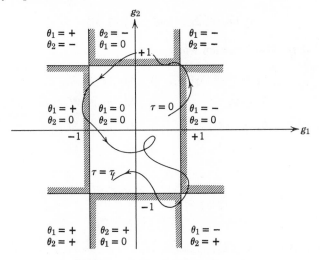

*Fig. 5.6* A control law trajectory [5].

value of $\tau_f$ is to consider $\tau_f$ as a parameter and to obtain a family of solutions, each of which is a true minimal fuel solution for that value of $\tau_f$. An examination of these solutions enables us to determine the optimal value of $\tau_f$.

Numerical solutions of this minimum fuel problem were obtained by using a repetitive analog computer and backward time by Craig and Flügge-Lotz [5]. Two oscilloscopes were employed by them to view the two-state space planes $x_1 x_2$ and $x_3 x_4$. By use of the repetitive operation the problem was solved many times per second and the solutions were displayed on the oscilloscopes. A graphic picture of the effect of parameter changes was thus obtained on the two oscilloscopes. If $\tau^* = \tau_f - \tau$, then $z(\tau^* = 0)$ corresponds to the initial value of $z$ for the backward time integration. By varying the four components of $z(\tau^* = 0)$, the two trajectories (one on each oscilloscope) were changed until the curves passed through the chosen values of $x(\tau^* = \tau_f)$. A block diagram of the simulation is shown in Fig. 5.7.

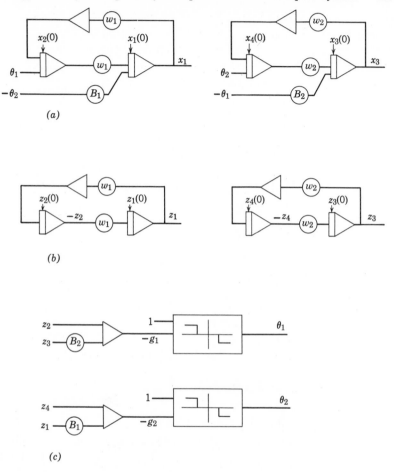

**Fig. 5.7** Block diagram of the uncoupled system [5]: (*a*) plant; (*b*) adjoint; (*c*) control law synthesis.

The numerical results are presented and discussed in detail by Craig and Flügge-Lotz [5]. An efficient suboptimal control is also described.

## 3.  ORBITAL TRANSFER [6]

The optimal transfer of a thrust-limited vehicle with steering and throttling capability between coplanar circular orbits is now considered. It is assumed that the orbits are close; that is, the ratio of the final orbital radius to the initial orbital radius is of the order $1 + \epsilon$, in which $\epsilon$ is a small parameter. Under the assumption that the orbits are close, the governing equations take on a linear form that is particularly amenable to numerical calculation. Two different optimization problems are discussed, namely, minimum angle transfer and minimum fuel transfer.

McIntyre and Crocco [6] have shown that under these assumptions the equations of the system can be written in the form

$$\frac{dx_1}{dr} = \frac{(x_1)^2 x_3}{x_2},$$

$$\frac{dx_2}{dr} = \frac{(x_1)^3}{x_2 x_4} M\theta_1 \cos\theta_2,$$

$$\frac{dx_3}{dr} = \frac{(x_1)^2}{x_2 x_4} M\theta_1 \sin\theta_2 + \frac{x_2}{x_1} - \frac{1}{x_2},$$

$$\frac{dx_4}{dr} = \frac{-(x_1)^2}{x_2 N} M\theta_1,$$

(67)

where $x_1$ = distance from the center of attraction,

$x_2$ = angular momentum,

$x_3$ = radial velocity,

$x_4$ = mass of the vehicle,

$\theta_1$ = throttle setting ($0 \leq \theta_1 \leq 1$),

$\theta_2$ = steering angle,

$M$ = maximum thrust value per $g$ of the initial orbit,

$N$ = exhaust velocity,

$r$ = central range angle.

The units of measurement are

length—the initial orbital radius,

velocity—the initial orbital velocity,

time—the initial orbital period over $2\pi$,

mass—the initial mass of the vehicle.

It is further assumed that the central range angle $r$ is a monotonic function of time $t$, $dr/dt$ is always positive, and $r$ is related to $t$ by the relation

$$\frac{d}{dt} = \frac{x_2}{(x_1)^2} \frac{d}{dr}.$$

At the start, the vehicle is in the given circular orbit with boundary conditions

$$\begin{aligned} x_1 &= 1, \\ x_2 &= 1, \\ x_3 &= 0, \\ x_4 &= 1, \end{aligned} \quad \text{at} \quad r = 0.$$

(68)

If the radius of the final orbit is required to be

$$x_1 = 1 + \epsilon \quad \text{at} \quad r = r_f,$$

where $\epsilon$ is a small number, and we use the relation [7]

$$\frac{1}{x_1} = \frac{1}{(x_2)^2},$$

we obtain

$$x_2 = \sqrt{1 + \epsilon} \quad \text{at} \quad r = r_f.$$

Thus we have the following boundary conditions for the final orbit:

$$
\begin{aligned}
x_1 &= 1 + \epsilon, \\
x_2 &= \sqrt{1 + \epsilon} = 1 + \frac{\epsilon}{2} + \cdots, \\
x_3 &= 0, \qquad\qquad\qquad\qquad \text{at } r = r_f, \qquad (69)\\
x_4 &= \text{(unspecified)},
\end{aligned}
$$

where $r_f$ may or may not be specified.

***a. Minimum Range Angle Transfer.***   We wish to find the control action that will minimize the final value of the range angle $r_f$ for the system of equations and boundary conditions given by equations (67), (68), and (69).

Since equation (67) is nonlinear, it may be desirable to linearize it. Inspection of equations (68) and (69) suggests that the solution may be represented as a power series in the parameter $\epsilon$ with the first-order terms representing a linearized version of the actual system. Since the throttle is on full swing during the entire maneuver for minimum-range angle transfer, the variable $\theta_1$ can be removed from the equations by replacing it by its maximum value of unity.

It can be seen that a thrust level that is independent of $\epsilon$ will lead to an impulsive maneuver with decreasing $\epsilon$. On the contrary, if the thrust level is taken as

$$M = A\epsilon, \qquad (70)$$

where $A =$ "thrust level" of the vehicle, the duration of the thrust application will not vanish with decreasing $\epsilon$, and we can obtain interesting information for the case of continuous burning, even at $\epsilon = 0$.

Let us assume that the solution to equation (67) takes the form

$$
\begin{aligned}
x_1 &= x_{10} + \epsilon x_{11} + \epsilon^2 x_{12} + \cdots, \\
x_2 &= x_{20} + \epsilon x_{21} + \epsilon^2 x_{22} + \cdots, \\
x_3 &= x_{30} + \epsilon x_{31} + \epsilon^2 x_{32} + \cdots, \qquad (71)\\
x_4 &= x_{40} + \epsilon x_{41} + \epsilon^2 x_{42} + \cdots, \\
\theta_2 &= \theta_{20} + \epsilon \theta_{21} + \epsilon^2 \theta_{22} + \cdots.
\end{aligned}
$$

By substituting equations (70) and (71) into equation (67) and noting the boundary conditions, equation (68), we obtain the zeroth-order approximations to the state equations as

$$x_{10} = 1,$$
$$x_{20} = 1,$$
$$x_{30} = 0,$$
$$x_{40} = 1,$$

which indicate that, in the limit as $\epsilon \to 0$, the thrust becomes zero and the vehicle remains in the initial orbit.

The first-order state equations are given by

$$\frac{dx_{11}}{dr} = x_{31},$$

$$\frac{dx_{21}}{dr} = A \cos \theta_{20},$$

$$\frac{dx_{31}}{dr} = A \sin \theta_{20} + 2x_{21} - x_{11},$$

$$\frac{dx_{41}}{dr} = -\frac{A}{N},$$

$$(72)$$

with the boundary conditions

$$x_{11} = 0,$$
$$x_{21} = 0,$$
$$x_{31} = 0, \quad \text{at} \quad r = 0, \qquad (73)$$
$$x_{41} = 0,$$

and

$$x_{11} = 1,$$
$$x_{21} = 0.5,$$
$$x_{31} = 0, \quad \text{at} \quad r = r_f. \qquad (74)$$
$$x_{41} = \text{unspecified}.$$

For small values of $\epsilon$, minimizing $r_f$, subject to the linearized first-order equations, equation (72), with their boundary conditions, equations (73) and (74), should provide results accurate to the order of $\epsilon^2$, and thus equations (72), (73), and (74) can be regarded as representing the actual system. It is to this linearized system that we shall apply the maximum principle.

The objective function that will cause the final value of the range angle to be a minimum is

$$S = \int_0^{r_f} dr.$$

If we let

$$x_{51}(r) = \int_0^r dr,$$

we have

$$\frac{dx_{51}}{dr} = 1, \qquad x_{51}(0) = 0.$$

The Hamiltonian function is

$$H = z_1 x_{31} + z_2 A \cos \theta_{20} + z_3 [A \sin \theta_{20} + 2x_{21} - x_{11}] - z_4 \frac{A}{N} + z_5, \quad (75)$$

where the components of the adjoint vector $z$ are given by

$$\frac{dz_1}{dr} = -\frac{\partial H}{\partial x_{11}} = z_3,$$

$$\frac{dz_2}{dr} = -\frac{\partial H}{\partial x_{21}} = -2z_3,$$

$$\frac{dz_3}{dr} = -\frac{\partial H}{\partial x_{31}} = -z_1, \qquad (76)$$

$$\frac{dz_4}{dr} = -\frac{\partial H}{\partial x_{41}} = 0,$$

$$\frac{dz_5}{dr} = -\frac{\partial H}{\partial x_{51}} = 0.$$

We have the boundary conditions

$$z_4 = 0 \quad \text{at} \quad r = r_f,$$
$$z_5 = 1 \quad \text{at} \quad r = r_f, \qquad (77)$$

and the condition

$$H_{\min} = 0, \qquad 0 \le r \le r_f.$$

By differentiating equation (75) with respect to $\theta_{20}$ and setting the derivative equal to zero, we obtain the optimal control as

$$\sin \theta_{20} = \frac{z_3}{\sqrt{(z_2)^2 + (z_3)^2}},$$

$$\cos \theta_{20} = \frac{z_2}{\sqrt{(z_2)^2 + (z_3)^2}}, \qquad (78)$$

where the $z_i$ are determined from equations (76) and (77). They are

$$z_1(r) = z_1(0) \cos r + z_3(0) \sin r,$$
$$z_2(r) = -2z_1(r) + z_2(0) + 2z_1(0),$$
$$z_3(r) = z_3(0) \cos r - z_1(0) \sin r, \tag{79}$$
$$z_4(r) = 0,$$
$$z_5(r) = 1,$$

where $z_1(0)$, $z_2(0)$, and $z_3(0)$ represent the initial values of $z_1$, $z_2$, and $z_3$, respectively. The solution of the optimum transfer depends only on the initial value of the $z$ vector. Despite the simple forms of the governing equations, this vector cannot be determined analytically. We must resort, therefore, to an iterative numerical process.

A numerical process devised by Neustadt [8, 9, 10] and modified by Paiewonsky and Woodrow [11] was used by McIntyre and Crocco [6] to generate the numerical solutions to this first-order transfer problem.

It should be pointed out that the minimum value of $r_f$ corresponding to the solution of the first-order system, equations (72) and (76) will likely not be equal to the minimum $r_f$ corresponding to a solution of the actual nonlinear problem. This indicates that the final value of the range angle should also be expanded in a power series in $\epsilon$ as

$$r_f = r_{f0} + \epsilon r_{f1} + \epsilon^2 r_{f2} + \cdots , \tag{80}$$

where $r_{f0}$ corresponds to the minimum $r_f$ solution of the first-order system with the boundary conditions, equation (74), satisfied at $r_f = r_{f0}$.

*b. Minimum Fuel Transfer.* As before, the thrust level is taken as

$$M = A\epsilon,$$

but in this case it is not on full throttle during the entire maneuver. Since $r_f$ is large enough, there may be one or more coasting periods in which the throttle is set at zero. Thus the linearized equations (72) now contain the throttle control $\theta_1$, $0 \leq \theta_1 \leq 1$ and we have

$$\frac{dx_{11}}{dr} = x_{31},$$

$$\frac{dx_{21}}{dr} = A\theta_1 \cos \theta_{20},$$

$$\frac{dx_{31}}{dr} = A\theta_1 \sin \theta_{20} + 2x_{21} - x_{11}, \tag{81}$$

$$\frac{dx_{41}}{dr} = -\frac{A\theta_1}{N}.$$

It should be noted that $\theta_1$ is not expanded in a power series. The boundary conditions are given by

$$
\begin{aligned}
x_{11} &= 0, \\
x_{21} &= 0, \\
x_{31} &= 0, \\
x_{41} &= 0,
\end{aligned}
\qquad \text{at} \quad r = 0,
\tag{82}
$$

and

$$
\begin{aligned}
x_{11} &= 1, \\
x_{21} &= 0.5, \\
x_{31} &= 0, \\
x_{41} &= \text{maximum},
\end{aligned}
\qquad \text{at} \quad r = r_f,
\tag{83}
$$

where the variable $r_f$ is specified. Note that we are assuming again that maximizing the final value of $x_{41}$ will give results valid to the order of $\epsilon^2$ of the actual nonlinear problem of maximizing the final mass.

According to the maximum principle, the Hamiltonian function is

$$
H = z_1 x_{31} + z_2 A\theta_1 \cos \theta_{20} + z_3 A\theta_1 \sin \theta_{20}
$$
$$
+ 2z_3 x_{21} - z_3 x_{11} - z_4 \frac{A\theta_1}{N}, \tag{84}
$$

and the components of the adjoint vector $z$ are given by

$$
\frac{dz_1}{dt} = z_3,
$$

$$
\frac{dz_2}{dt} = -2z_3,
$$

$$
\frac{dz_3}{dt} = -z_1,
$$

$$
\frac{dz_4}{dt} = 0.
$$

Since $x_{41}$ is to be a maximum at $r = r_f$, we have the boundary condition

$$
z_4 = 1 \quad \text{at} \quad r = r_f.
$$

Differentiating the Hamiltonian function with respect to $\theta_{20}$ and setting the derivative equal to zero, we obtain the optimal values of $\theta_{20}$ as

$$
\sin \theta_{20} = \frac{z_3}{\sqrt{(z_2)^2 + (z_3)^2}},
$$

$$
\cos \theta_{20} = \frac{z_2}{\sqrt{(z_2)^2 + (z_3)^2}}.
$$

Substituting the optimal values of $\theta_{20}$ into equation (84), we find that the values of $\theta_1$ which cause the Hamiltonian function to be a maximum are

$$
\theta_1 = \begin{cases} 1.0 & \text{if} \quad \sqrt{(z_2)^2 + (z_3)^2} - \dfrac{1}{N} > 0, \\[3mm] 0 & \text{if} \quad \sqrt{(z_2)^2 + (z_3)^2} - \dfrac{1}{N} < 0, \end{cases}
$$

with $z_i$, $i = 1, 2, 3, 4$ given by

$$
\begin{aligned}
z_1(r) &= z_1(0) \cos r + z_3(0) \sin r, \\
z_2(r) &= -2z_1(r) + z_2(0) + 2z_1(0), \\
z_3(r) &= z_3(0) \cos r - z_1(0) \sin r, \\
z_4(r) &= 1.0.
\end{aligned}
\tag{85}
$$

When the initial values of $z_i$, $i = 1, 2, 3, 4$ are known, the minimum fuel transfer problem is solved. The results of the numerical solution of the first-order equations indicate that the minimum fuel trajectory consists of a two-burn maneuver similar to the Hohmann transfer, provided that the thrust level is greater than a certain minimum value. For thrust levels below the minimum value the optimal maneuver consists of three or more burns in which the number of burning periods increases without limit as the thrust level decreases to zero. For certain cases the maximum principle becomes degenerate with two or more different control programs which yield the same minimum value for the fuel required.

The numerical solution and analysis of this problem are given in detail by McIntyre and Crocco [6].

## 4. ROCKET THRUST [12]

We shall now be concerned with the optimal programming of the magnitude and direction of rocket thrust. It is assumed that the rocket is a point of variable mass, that is, $m(t) = m(0) x_3(t)$, in which $x_3(t)$ is the dimensionless mass, and that the rocket is in plane motion in the homogeneous gravitational field of the earth in the absence of aerodynamic forces. In Fig. 5.8 $x_1(t)$ and $x_2(t)$ represent the horizontal and vertical velocity components, $x_4(t)$ and $x_5(t)$, the range and height, $\theta_1(t) = M(t)/M_{\max}$, the dimensionless thrust based on the magnitude of the maximum value $M_{\max}$, and $\theta_2(t)$, the inclination of the thrust vector to the horizontal.

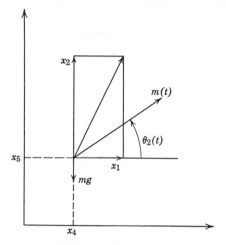

*Fig. 5.8* Rocket thrust [12].

Assuming that the effective outflow velocity is constant ($W_e = C$), we obtain

$$\frac{dx_1}{dt} = \frac{A\theta_1 \cos \theta_2}{x_3},$$

$$\frac{dx_2}{dt} = \frac{A\theta_1 \sin \theta_2}{x_3} - g,$$

$$\frac{dx_3}{dt} = -\alpha\theta_1, \qquad (86)$$

$$\frac{dx_4}{dt} = x_1,$$

$$\frac{dx_5}{dt} = x_2,$$

where $\alpha = M_{\max}/[m(0)C]$, $A = \alpha C$, and the magnitude of the thrust is bounded by the relation

$$0 \le \theta_1(t) \le 1. \qquad (87)$$

In this problem we wish to find the optimal control $\theta = (\theta_1, \theta_2)$ which takes the system represented by equation (86) from a fixed initial position $x(0) = \{x_1(0), x_2(0), \ldots, x_5(0)\}$ to a final position in a fixed amount of time $T$, where

$$x_1(T) = \text{unspecified},$$
$$x_2(T) = 0,$$
$$x_3(T) = \beta_3,$$
$$x_4(T) = \text{maximum},$$
$$x_5(T) = \beta_5;$$

that is, we wish to maximize the range $x_4(T)$ when the height and dimensionless mass are specified and the rocket is in horizontal motion at time $T$. Since $x_3(0)$ is always equal to 1, it is necessary to assume that $m(0)$ is given. This should be borne in mind whenever the set of initial values $x(0)$ is being described.

In accordance with the procedure of the maximum principle, we obtain

$$H = H(x, z, \theta)$$

$$= \theta_1 \left[ \frac{A}{x_3} (z_1 \cos \theta_2 + z_2 \sin \theta_2) - \alpha z_3 \right] - z_2 g + z_4 x_1 + z_5 x_2, \quad (88)$$

$$\frac{dz_1}{dt} = -z_4,$$

$$\frac{dz_2}{dt} = -z_5,$$

$$\left. \frac{dz_3}{dt} = \frac{A\theta_1}{(x_3)^2} (z_1 \cos \theta_2 + z_2 \sin \theta_2), \right\} \quad (89)$$

$$\frac{dz_4}{dt} = 0,$$

$$\frac{dz_5}{dt} = 0,$$

and

$$H^* = A\theta_1 \left[ \frac{1}{x_3} (z_1 \cos \theta_2 + z_2 \sin \theta_2) - \frac{z_3}{C} \right]. \quad (90)$$

Differentiating equation (90) with respect to $\theta_2$ and setting the derivative equal to zero, we obtain

$$\sin \theta_2 = \frac{z_2}{\sqrt{(z_1)^2 + (z_2)^2}},$$

$$\cos \theta_2 = \frac{z_1}{\sqrt{(z_1)^2 + (z_2)^2}}. \quad (91)$$

The value of $H^*$ in equation (90) attains an absolute maximum under the conditions

$$\theta_1 = \text{sgn} \, f(z, x),$$

$$\theta_2 = \arctan \frac{z_2}{z_1}, \quad (92)$$

where

$$\operatorname{sgn} f = \begin{cases} 1 & \text{for } f > 0, \\ 0 & \text{for } f < 0, \end{cases}$$

$$f(z, x) = \frac{\sqrt{(z_1)^2 + (z_2)^2}}{x_3} - \frac{z_3}{C}.$$

These relations, equation (92), are the desired optimal conditions. Substituting equation (92) into equations (86) and (89), we obtain

$$\frac{dx_1}{dt} = \frac{A \operatorname{sgn} f}{x_3} \frac{z_1}{\sqrt{(z_1)^2 + (z_2)^2}},$$

$$\frac{dx_2}{dt} = \frac{A \operatorname{sgn} f}{x_3} \frac{z_2}{\sqrt{(z_1)^2 + (z_2)^2}} - g,$$

$$\frac{dx_3}{dt} = -\alpha \operatorname{sgn} f,$$

$$\frac{dx_4}{dt} = x_1,$$

$$\frac{dx_5}{dt} = x_2,$$

$$\frac{dz_1}{dt} = -z_4, \tag{93}$$

$$\frac{dz_2}{dt} = -z_5,$$

$$\frac{dz_3}{dt} = \frac{A \operatorname{sgn} f}{(x_3)^2} \sqrt{(z_1)^2 + (z_2)^2},$$

$$\frac{dz_4}{dt} = 0,$$

$$\frac{dz_5}{dt} = 0,$$

which are nonlinear differential equations describing the optimal motion of the system given by equation (86). The boundary conditions are

$$x_1(0) = \alpha_1,$$
$$x_2(0) = \alpha_2,$$
$$x_3(0) = 1, \tag{94}$$
$$x_4(0) = \alpha_4,$$
$$x_5(0) = \alpha_5,$$

and

$$z_1(T) = 0,$$

$$x_2(T) = 0,$$

$$x_3(T) = \beta_3, \tag{95}$$

$$z_4(T) = 1,$$

$$x_5(T) = \beta_5.$$

Integrating the adjoint vector equations involving $z_1$, $z_2$, $z_4$, and $z_5$ and employing the boundary conditions $z_1(T) = 0$ and $z_4(T) = 1$, we obtain

$$z_4(t) = z_4(T) = 1, \tag{96}$$

$$z_5(t) = z_5(0), \tag{97}$$

$$z_1(t) = -t + T, \tag{98}$$

$$z_2(t) = -z_5(0)t + z_2(0). \tag{99}$$

This enables us to write equation (92) in the form

$$\tan \theta_2(t) = \frac{z_2(0) - z_5(0)t}{-t + T}, \tag{100}$$

which shows that the tangent of the angle formed by the axis of the moving object and the horizontal is a linear fractional function of time.

The magnitude of the thrust $\theta_1(t)$ is either zero or one, depending on the sign of the switching function

$$f(z, x) = \frac{\sqrt{(z_1)^2 + (z_2)^2}}{x_3} - \frac{z_3}{C}. \tag{101}$$

Isaev [12] showed that if the switching function is written in the form

$$f(z, x) = \Phi(z, x) - P(z, x)$$

it may be analyzed geometrically by using $z_1$, $z_2$, and $P$ as axes [see Fig. 5.9].

Equations (98) and (99) may be combined to give

$$z_2 = z_5(0)z_1 - z_5(0)\, z_1(0) + z_2(0), \tag{102}$$

which shows that $z_2$ and $z_1$ may be related by a straight line in the $z_1 z_2$ plane. The results of the analysis by Isaev [12] are the following:

1. The optimal control is the boundary type.
2. There are not more than two active portions, the control on which is $\theta_1(t) = 1$.

3. When there are two active portions present in the composition of the control ($t_i'$ denotes the time when the $i$th portion of active control is initiated and $t_i''$ denotes the time when the $i$th active portion is terminated), the following is true: (a) $t_1' = 0$, and (b) the switching times $t_2'$ and $t_1''$ of the optimal control $\theta$, corresponding to some $z$-trajectory, are symmetric with respect to the point $[z_1(t_0), z_2(t_0)]$ lying on the given $z$-trajectory and occurring at a minimal distance from the origin [see Fig. 5.9].

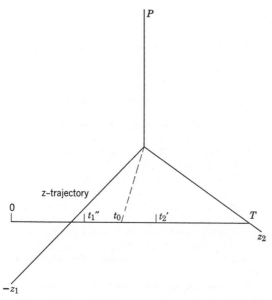

*Fig. 5.9* The optimal switching times for a given $z$-trajectory with two active portions [12].

Isaev [12] used this information on the magnitude and direction of the thrust to integrate equation (93). The result takes the form

$$x_i(t) = F_i(z_2(0), z_5(0), \xi, t) + \alpha_i, \qquad i = 1, \ldots, 5,$$

which depends on the initial values $z_2(0)$, $z_5(0)$ and the switching position $\xi$. The boundary conditions $x_2(T) = 0$, $x_3(T) = \beta_3$, and $x_5(T) = \beta_5$ may now be applied to determine $z_2(0)$, $z_5(0)$, and $\xi$. An appropriate iterative technique can be used to obtain the solution.

A solution to this problem can also be obtained with an analog computer which has the repetitive operation feature. If the switching function is included as a part of the analog computer program, the solution may be obtained by varying $z_2(0)$, $z_3(0)$, and $z_5(0)$ until the desired values of

$x_2(T)$, $x_3(T)$, and $x_5(T)$ are obtained. A procedure similar to that used by Craig and Flügge-Lotz [5] may also be employed.

In this chapter we have considered four examples that illustrate the use of the maximum principle as it is applied to optimization problems associated with aerospace systems. We hope that these examples show clearly that the maximum principle is a useful tool in the design of aerospace systems.

## REFERENCES

1. Leitmann, G. ed., *Optimization Techniques: with Applications to Aerospace Systems*, Academic Press, New York, 1962.
2. Hull, D. G., "Thrust Programs for Minimum Propellant Consumption During Vertical Take-Off and Landing Maneuvers of a Rocket Vehicle in a Vacuum," Boeing Scientific Research Laboratories, *Flight Science Laboratory TR No. 59*, July 1962.
3. Meditch, J. S., "On the Problem of Optimal Thrust Programming For a Lunar Soft Landing," JACC 1964 preprints, pp. 233–238.
4. Flügge-Lotz, I. and Craig, A., "The Choice of Time for Zeroing a Disturbance in a Minimum Fuel Consumption Problem," *ASME, Paper 63-WA*33.
5. Craig, A. J. and Flügge-Lotz, I., "Investigation of Optimal Control with a Minimum-Fuel Consumption Criterion for a Fourth-Order Plant with Two Control Inputs: Synthesis of an Efficient Sub-Optimal Control," JACC 1964, preprints, pp. 207–221.
6. McIntyre, J. E. and Crocco, L., "Optimal Transfer between Close Circular Orbits Using the Pontryagin Maximum Principle," AIAA preprint No. 64-29 Aerospace Science Meeting, New York, January 1964.
7. Nelson, W. C. and E. E. Loft, *Space Mechanics*, Prentice-Hall, Englewood Cliffs, New Jersey, 1962.
8. Neustadt, L. W., "Synthesizing Time Optimal Control Systems," *J. Math. Anal. Applic.*, **1**, No. 4 (1960).
9. Neustadt, L. W., "Minimum Effort Control Systems," *J. Soc. Ind. Appl. Math. Control*, **1**, No. 1 (1962).
10. Neustadt, L. W. and Paiewonsky, B., "On Synthesizing Optimal Controls," Paper presented at IFAC Conference, Basle, Switzerland, September 1963.
11. Paiewonsky, B. and Woodrow, P., "The Synthesis of Optimal Controls for a Class of Rocket Steering Problems," Paper No. 63-22A presented at the AIAA Summer Meeting, Los Angeles, California, June 1963.
12. Isaev, V. K., "L. S. Pontryagin's Maximum Principle and Optimal Programming of Rocket Thrust," *Automat. Telemech.*, **22**, No. 8, 986–1001 (August 1961).
13. Leondes, C. T. ed., *Advances in Control Systems: Theory and Applications*, Vol. 1, Academic Press, New York, 1964.

# 6

# Computational Algorithm for Complex Continuous Processes

In this chapter a generalized algorithm for the optimization of continuous processes of complex topology is presented. Many of the processes encountered in practice, especially in the chemical industry, are complex, and, although the optimal policy for a complex process often can be obtained by dissecting it into several simpler subprocesses, independently optimizing each subprocess, and then combining the optimal policies for all the subprocesses, it is desirable to derive an algorithm capable of obtaining directly the optimal policy for the entire process without decomposing it.

First some of the basic notions and definitions associated with continuous processes presented in the preceding chapters are briefly reviewed. A process refers to the dynamical change of the state of a system with respect to time or space, depending on whether the change of the state is along the time or the space coordinate. Since these two types of process are mathematically identical, the coordinate $t$ is used to denote either time or space in the following discussion.

For a deterministic process the state of a system at a certain time or position $t$ is completely described by the state vector $x(t)$. The change of the state is a result of the action of the decision vector $\theta(t)$ which can be manipulated independently. In a simple continuous process (see Fig. 6.1) the change of the state can be described by the following performance equations [1]:

$$\frac{dx_i}{dt} = f_i(x_1, \ldots, x_s; \theta_1, \ldots, \theta_r), \qquad i = 1, 2, \ldots, s, 0 \leq t \leq T,$$

or, in vector form,

$$\frac{dx}{dt} = f(x; \theta), \qquad 0 \le t \le T, \tag{1}$$

where $s$ and $r$ are the dimensions of $x$ and $\theta$, respectively. The length of the process is specified and denoted by $T$, which is the distance between the two end points in the $t$-coordinate.

All of the complex continuous processes are composed of several interconnected branches. The point at which two or more branches

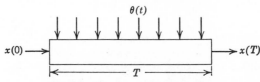

**Fig. 6.1**  Simple continuous process.

connect is called a junction point. There may be, as shown in Fig. 6.2, three different types of junction point: (a) separating, (b) combining, and (c) crossing. A separating point represents a point at which one branch of the path splits into several branches; a combining point is a point at which several branches combine into a single branch; and a junction point, at which several branches combine and then split again into several branches, is called a crossing point.

Each branch in a complex process is described by a performance equation of the type categorized by equation (1), although the form of the function $f(x; \theta)$ and the length $T$ may differ for different branches. A number may be arbitrarily assigned to each branch for convenience. The superscripts in $f^{(k)}(x^{(k)}; \theta^{(k)})$ and the subscript of $T_k$ represent the branch number.

The arrows at the junction point show the direction of the flow of the process streams. The relationships between the state vectors of different branches at the junction points are described by the junction equations [2]. They are

(a) *separating points*

$$x^{(2)}(0) = g^{(2)}(x^{(1)}(T_1))$$
$$x^{(3)}(0) = g^{(3)}(x^{(1)}(T_1))$$
$$\dots\dots\dots\dots\dots\dots \tag{2}$$
$$\dots\dots\dots\dots\dots\dots$$
$$x^{(n)}(0) = g^{(n)}(x^{(1)}(T_1));$$

(b) *combining points*

$$x^{(n)}(0) = g^{(n)}(x^{(1)}(T_1), x^{(2)}(T_2), \ldots, x^{(n-1)}(T_{n-1}));$$    (3)

(c) *crossing points*

$$x^{(m+1)}(0) = g^{(m+1)}(x^{(1)}(T_1), x^{(2)}(T_2), \ldots, x^{(m)}(T_m))$$

$$x^{(m+2)}(0) = g^{(m+2)}(x^{(1)}(T_1), x^{(2)}(T_2), \ldots, x^{(m)}(T_m))$$

$$\cdots\cdots\cdots\cdots\cdots\cdots\cdots\cdots\cdots\cdots\cdots\cdots\cdots\cdots\cdots\cdots$$    (4)

$$\cdots\cdots\cdots\cdots\cdots\cdots\cdots\cdots\cdots\cdots\cdots\cdots\cdots$$

$$x^{(n)}(0) = g^{(n)}(x^{(1)}(T_1), x^{(2)}(T_2), \ldots\ldots\ldots, x^{(m)}(T_m)),$$

where the function $g^{(n)}(x^{(k)}(T_k))$ is the vector form of $g^{(n)}(x_1^{(k)}(T_k),$ $x_2^{(k)}(T_k), \ldots, x_{s^{(k)}}^{(k)}(T_k))$. It may be noted that the dimensions of the state vector may differ from branch to branch. Superscripts, such as $(k)$ appearing in $s^{(k)}$, are used to indicate the difference.

In a complex process there may be some branches that do not possess the decision vector, such as the upper branch of the simple feedback loop shown in Fig. 6.3. The performance equation for such a nondecision branch is

$$\frac{dx}{dt} = f(x),$$    (5)

or for the special case in which the state vector remains constant equation (5) reduces to

$$\frac{dx}{dt} = 0.$$

A complex process may have several initial points and final points at which the values of the state vectors are called initial states and final states, respectively.

The optimization problem under considerations may be stated as follows [2].

Given all of the performance equations, junction equations, lengths, and initial states of a complex process consisting of a path with $n$ branches, $b$ initial points, and $f$ final points, find the decision vector function of each branch to maximize a certain linear function of the final states of the process, such as

$$\sum_{k=1}^{f} \sum_{i=1}^{s^{(k)}} c_i^{(k)} x_i^{(k)}(T_k),$$

in which $c_i$ are constants; the summations are taken over all the components of the state vectors and over all the final states.

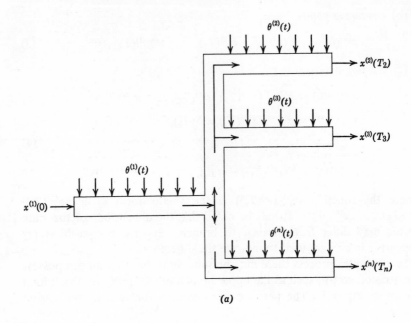

(a)

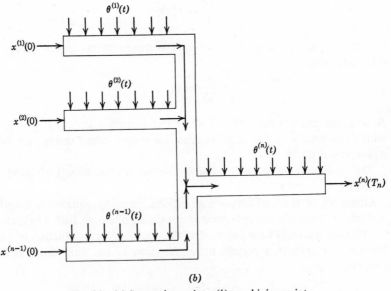

(b)

**Fig. 6.2** (a) Separating point; (b) combining point.

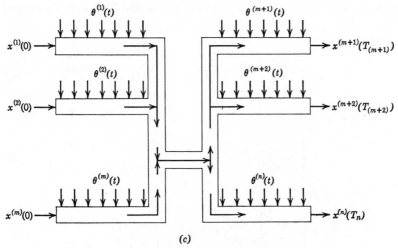

(c)

***Fig. 6.2*** (c) Crossing point.

The set of the decision vector functions $\theta^{(k)}(t)$, $k = 1, 2, \ldots, n$ thus found is called the optimal policy. The function to be maximized is called the objective function.

## 1. OPTIMIZATION PROCEDURE [2]

The procedure to find the optimal policy for a complex process can be divided into two steps.

*Step* 1. Introduce an adjoint vector $z^{(k)}(t)$ and a Hamiltonian function $H^{(k)}(x, z, \theta)$ for each branch satisfying*

$$H^{(k)}(x, z, \theta) = \sum_{i=1}^{s^{(k)}} z_i^{(k)} f_i^{(k)}(x_1^{(k)}, \ldots, x_{s^{(k)}}^{(k)}; \theta_1^{(k)}, \ldots, \theta_{r^{(k)}}^{(k)}) \tag{6}$$

or, in vector form,

$$H^{(k)}(x, z, \theta) = z^{(k)} \cdot f^{(k)}$$

and

$$\frac{dz_i^{(k)}(t)}{dt} = -\frac{\partial H^{(k)}(x, z, \theta)}{\partial x_i^{(k)}} = -\sum_{j=1}^{s} z_j \frac{\partial f_j^{(k)}(x; \theta)}{\partial x_i^{(k)}}, \qquad i = 1, 2, \ldots, s^{(k)}, \tag{7}$$

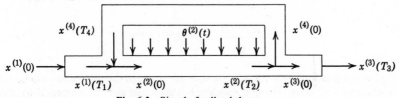

***Fig. 6.3*** Simple feedback loop.

* For simplicity, we write $H^{(k)}(x^{(k)}, z^{(k)}, \theta^{(k)})$ as $H^{(k)}(x, z, \theta)$.

with the values of $z_i^{(k)}$ at the junction points and final points satisfying

(a) *separating points*

$$z_i^{(1)}(T_1) = \sum_{k=2}^{n} \sum_{j=1}^{s^{(k)}} \frac{\partial g_j^{(k)}}{\partial x_i^{(1)}} z_j^{(k)}(0), \qquad i = 1, 2, \ldots, s^{(1)}; \qquad (8)^*$$

(b) *combining points*

$$z_i^{(k)}(T_k) = \sum_{j=1}^{s^{(n)}} \frac{\partial g_j^{(n)}}{\partial x_i^{(k)}} z_j^{(n)}(0), \qquad \begin{array}{l} i = 1, 2, \ldots, s^{(k)}, \\ k = 1, 2, \ldots, n-1; \end{array} \qquad (9)$$

(c) *crossing points*

$$z_i^{(p)}(T_p) = \sum_{k=m+1}^{n} \sum_{j=1}^{s^{(k)}} \frac{\partial g_j^{(k)}}{\partial x_i^{(p)}} z_j^{(k)}(0), \qquad \begin{array}{l} i = 1, 2, \ldots, s^{(k)}, \\ p = 1, 2, \ldots, m; \end{array} \qquad (10)$$

(d) *final points*

$$z_i^{(k)}(T_k) = c_i^{(k)}, \qquad \begin{array}{l} i = 1, 2, \ldots, s^{(k)}, \\ k = 1, 2, \ldots, f. \end{array} \qquad (11)$$

*Step* 2.   For each branch find the decision vector function $\theta^{(k)}$ from the following necessary condition:

$$H^{(k)}(x, z, \theta) = \text{maximum at every point } t, k = 1, 2, \ldots, n. \quad (12)$$

In other words, the functions $\bar{\theta}^{(k)}$ are obtained by varying $\theta^{(k)}$ until the maximum value of $H^{(k)}$ is attained at each point.

## 2.   DERIVATION OF THE ALGORITHM [2]

The assumptions made in Chapter 2 concerning the continuity and boundedness of the function and the derivatives apply to each branch of the process. Let $\bar{\theta}^{(k)}(t)$ be the optimal decision vector function and let $\bar{x}^{(k)}(t)$ be the optimal state vector function of the $k$th branch. Then

$$\frac{d\bar{x}^{(k)}(t)}{dt} = f^{(k)}(\bar{x}^{(k)}; \bar{\theta}^{(k)}). \qquad (13)$$

---

* $g$ is a function of the final values of the state variables and the differentiation indicated in equations (8), (9), and (10) and elsewhere is with respect to $x_i^{(k)}(T_k)$, where $T_k$ denotes the final time for branch $k$.

If a small independent perturbation of the decision vector is made at every point of the process so that

$$\theta^{(k)}(t, \epsilon) = \bar{\theta}^{(k)}(t) + \epsilon\varphi^{(k)}(t) + 0(\epsilon^2),  \tag{14}$$

the state vector function will be perturbed to

$$x^{(k)}(t, \epsilon) = \bar{x}^{(k)}(t) + \epsilon y^{(k)}(t) + 0(\epsilon^2),  \tag{15}$$

where $\varphi^{(k)}(t)$ and $y^{(k)}(t)$ are functions of $t$ with the same dimensions and order of magnitude as $\theta^{(k)}$ and $x^{(k)}$, respectively: $\epsilon$ represents a very small number; $0(\epsilon^2)$ denotes the terms of order $\epsilon^2$ and those of higher order.

From equation (15) we have

$$\epsilon y^{(k)}(t) = x^{(k)}(t) - \bar{x}^{(k)}(t) + 0(\epsilon^2).$$

By differentiating this equation with respect to $t$ and substituting equations (1) and (13) into the resulting equation we obtain for each component of the state vector

$$\epsilon \frac{dy_i^{(k)}(t)}{dt} = \frac{dx_i^{(k)}(t)}{dt} - \frac{d\bar{x}_i^{(k)}(t)}{dt} + 0(\epsilon^2)$$

$$= [f_i^{(k)}(x^{(k)}; \theta^{(k)}) - f_i^{(k)}(\bar{x}^{(k)}; \bar{\theta}^{(k)})] + 0(\epsilon^2).$$

By expanding the right-hand side in a Taylor series we obtain

$$\epsilon \frac{dy_i^{(k)}}{dt} = \sum_{j=1}^{s^{(k)}} \epsilon y_j^{(k)} \frac{\partial f_i^{(k)}(\bar{x}^{(k)}; \bar{\theta}^{(k)})}{\partial \bar{x}_j^{(k)}} + \sum_{j=1}^{r^{(k)}} \epsilon \varphi_j^{(k)} \frac{\partial f_i^{(k)}(\bar{x}^{(k)}; \bar{\theta}^{(k)})}{\partial \bar{\theta}_j^{(k)}} + 0(\epsilon^2). \tag{16}$$

The relationships between the variations of the state vectors of different branches at the junction points are obtained by expanding the junction equations in powers of $\epsilon y_i$:

1. *Separating Points.* We have under the optimal condition, from equation (2),

$$\bar{x}_i^{(k)}(0) = g_i^{(k)}(\bar{x}_1^{(1)}(T_1), \bar{x}_2^{(1)}(T_1), \ldots, \bar{x}_{s^{(1)}}^{(1)}(T_1)), \qquad \begin{matrix} i = 1, 2, \ldots, s^{(k)}, \\ k = 2, 3, \ldots, n. \end{matrix}$$

If a small independent perturbation of the decision variable is made, the state variable will be perturbed to

$$x_i^{(k)}(0) = \bar{x}_i^{(k)}(0) + \epsilon y_i^{(k)}(0) + 0(\epsilon^2).$$

By means of Taylor's expansions we obtain

$$\epsilon y_i^{(k)}(0) = x_i^{(k)}(0) - \bar{x}_i^{(k)}(0) + 0(\epsilon^2)$$

$$= \bar{x}_i^{(k)}(0) + \sum_{j=1}^{s^{(1)}} \epsilon y_j^{(1)}(T_1) \frac{\partial g_i^{(k)}(\bar{x}_1^{(1)}(T_1), \ldots, \bar{x}_{s^{(1)}}^{(1)}(T_1))}{\partial \bar{x}_j^{(1)}} - \bar{x}_i^{(k)}(0) + 0(\epsilon^2)$$

$$= \sum_{j=1}^{s^{(1)}} \epsilon y_j^{(1)}(T_1) \frac{\partial g_i^{(k)}(\bar{x}_1^{(1)}(T_1), \ldots, \bar{x}_{s^{(1)}}^{(1)}(T_1))}{\partial \bar{x}_j^{(1)}} + 0(\epsilon^2).$$

By dropping the upper lines of the state variables with the understanding that the perturbation will be made around the optimal point we obtain

$$\epsilon y_i^{(k)}(0) = \sum_{j=1}^{s^{(1)}} \epsilon y_j^{(1)}(T_1) \frac{\partial g_i^{(k)}(x_1^{(1)}(T_1), \ldots, x_{s^{(1)}}^{(1)}(T_1))}{\partial x_j^{(1)}} + 0(\epsilon^2),$$

$$\begin{aligned} &i = 1, 2, \ldots, s^{(k)}, \\ &k = 2, 3, \ldots, n. \end{aligned} \quad (17)$$

Similarly, we can obtain the following variational equations:

2. *Combining points*

$$\epsilon y_i^{(n)}(0) = \sum_{k=1}^{n-1} \sum_{j=1}^{s^{(k)}} \epsilon y_j^{(k)}(T_k) \frac{\partial g_i^{(n)}(x^{(1)}(T_1), \ldots, x^{(n-1)}(T_{n-1}))}{\partial x_j^{(k)}} + 0(\epsilon^2),$$

$$i = 1, 2, \ldots, s^{(n)}. \quad (18)$$

3. *Crossing Points*

$$\epsilon y_i^{(p)}(0) = \sum_{k=1}^{m} \sum_{j=1}^{s^{(k)}} \epsilon y_j^{(k)}(T_k) \frac{\partial g_i^{(p)}(x^{(1)}(T_1), \ldots, x^{(m)}(T_m))}{\partial x_j^{(k)}} + 0(\epsilon^2),$$

$$\begin{aligned} &i = 1, 2, \ldots, s^{(p)}, \\ &p = m + 1, m + 2, \ldots, n. \end{aligned} \quad (19)$$

Since all the initial states of the process are given and fixed, we have

$$y_i^{(k)}(0) = 0, \quad \begin{aligned} &i = 1, 2, \ldots, s^{(k)}, \\ &k = 1, 2, \ldots, b. \end{aligned} \quad (20)$$

Now, if we substitute the expression for $dz_i^{(k)}/dt$ from equation (7) and that for $dy_i^{(k)}/dt$ from equation (16) into the following equation,

$$\frac{d}{dt} \sum_{i=1}^{s^{(k)}} \epsilon y_i^{(k)} z_i^{(k)} = \sum_{i=1}^{s^{(k)}} \epsilon z_i^{(k)} \frac{dy_i^{(k)}}{dt} + \sum_{i=1}^{s^{(k)}} \epsilon y_i^{(k)} \frac{dz_i^{(k)}}{dt},$$

we obtain [see equations (2.37) and (2.38)]

$$\frac{d}{dt} \sum_{i=1}^{s^{(k)}} \epsilon y_i^{(k)} z_i^{(k)} = \sum_{i=1}^{s^{(k)}} z_i^{(k)} \sum_{j=1}^{r^{(k)}} \epsilon \varphi_j^{(k)} \frac{\partial f_i^{(k)}(\bar{x}^{(k)}; \bar{\theta}^{(k)})}{\partial \bar{\theta}_j^{(k)}} + 0(\epsilon^2),$$

$$k = 1, 2, \ldots, n.$$

Integrating the above equations from $t = 0$ to $t = T_k$ and summing over all branches give

$$\sum_{k=1}^{n} \sum_{i=1}^{s^{(k)}} \epsilon[y_i^{(k)}(T_k)\, z_i^{(k)}(T_k) - y_i^{(k)}(0)\, z_i^{(k)}(0)]$$

$$= \sum_{k=1}^{n} \int_0^{T_k} \sum_{i=1}^{s^{(k)}} z_i^{(k)} \left[ \sum_{j=1}^{r^{(k)}} \epsilon \varphi_j^{(k)} \frac{\partial f_i^{(k)}(\bar{x}^{(k)}; \bar{\theta}^{(k)})}{\partial \bar{\theta}_j^{(k)}} \right] dt + 0(\epsilon^2). \quad (21)$$

For the branches containing the initial points or states, that is, for $k = 1, 2, \ldots, b$, we have in the left-hand side of equation (21)

$$\epsilon y_i^{(k)}(0)\, z_i^{(k)}(0) = 0.$$

This is because of equation (20).

For those branches connected to a separating point, as shown in Fig. 6.2*a*, we have, by using equations (8) and (17) and neglecting second-order terms,

$$\sum_{k=2}^{n} \sum_{i=1}^{s^{(k)}} \epsilon y_i^{(k)}(0)\, z_i^{(k)}(0) = \sum_{k=2}^{n} \sum_{i=1}^{s^{(k)}} \sum_{j=1}^{s^{(1)}} \epsilon y_j^{(1)}(T_1)\ \frac{\partial g_i^{(k)}}{\partial x_j^{(1)}}\, z_i^{(k)}(0)$$

$$= \sum_{j=1}^{s^{(1)}} \epsilon y_j^{(1)}(T_1) \sum_{k=2}^{n} \sum_{i=1}^{s^{(k)}} \frac{\partial g_i^{(k)}}{\partial x_j^{(1)}}\, z_i^{(k)}(0)$$

$$= \sum_{j=1}^{s^{(1)}} \epsilon y_j^{(1)}(T_1)\, z_j^{(1)}(T_1)$$

$$= \sum_{i=1}^{s^{(1)}} \epsilon y_i^{(1)}(T_1)\, z_i^{(1)}(T_1). \quad (22)$$

Therefore the left-hand side of equation (21) can be written as

$$\sum_{k=1}^{n} \sum_{i=1}^{s^{(k)}} [\epsilon y_i^{(k)}(T_k)\, z_i^{(k)}(T_k) - \epsilon y_i^{(k)}(0)\, z_i^{(k)}(0)]$$

$$= \sum_{k=2}^{n} \sum_{i=1}^{s^{(k)}} \epsilon y_i^{(k)}(T_k)\, z_i^{(k)}(T_k) + \sum_{i=1}^{s^{(1)}} \epsilon y_i^{(1)}(T_1)\, z_i^{(1)}(T_1)$$

$$- \sum_{i=1}^{s^{(1)}} \epsilon y_i^{(1)}(0)\, z_i^{(1)}(0) - \sum_{k=2}^{n} \sum_{i=1}^{s^{(k)}} \epsilon y_i^{(k)}(0)\, z_i^{(k)}(0)$$

$$= \sum_{k=2}^{n} \sum_{i=1}^{s^{(k)}} \epsilon y_i^{(k)}(T_k)\, z_i^{(k)}(T_k) + \sum_{i=1}^{s^{(1)}} \epsilon y_i^{(1)}(T_1)\, z_i^{(1)}(T_1) - 0$$

$$- \sum_{i=1}^{s^{(1)}} \epsilon y_i^{(1)}(T_1)\, z_i^{(1)}(T_1)$$

$$= \sum_{k=2}^{n} \sum_{i=1}^{s^{(k)}} \epsilon y_i^{(k)}(T_k)\, z_i^{(k)}(T_k). \quad (23)$$

For those branches connected to a combining point, as shown in Fig. 6.2$b$, we have, by using equations (9) and (18),

$$\sum_{i=1}^{s^{(n)}} \epsilon y_i^{(n)}(0) z_i^{(n)}(0) = \sum_{i=1}^{s^{(n)}} \sum_{k=1}^{n-1} \sum_{j=1}^{s^{(k)}} \epsilon y_j^{(k)}(T_k) \frac{\partial g_i^{(n)}}{\partial x_j^{(k)}} z_i^{(n)}(0)$$

$$= \sum_{k=1}^{n-1} \sum_{j=1}^{s^{(k)}} \epsilon y_j^{(k)}(T_k) \sum_{i=1}^{s^{(n)}} \frac{\partial g_i^{(n)}}{\partial x_j^{(k)}} z_i^{(n)}(0)$$

$$= \sum_{k=1}^{n-1} \sum_{j=1}^{s^{(k)}} \epsilon y_j^{(k)}(T_k) z_j^{(k)}(T_k)$$

$$= \sum_{k=1}^{n-1} \sum_{i=1}^{s^{(k)}} \epsilon y_i^{(k)}(T_k) z_i^{(k)}(T_k). \tag{24}$$

Therefore the left-hand side of equation (21) can be written as

$$\sum_{k=1}^{n} \sum_{i=1}^{s^{(k)}} [\epsilon y_i^{(k)}(T_k) z_i^{(k)}(T_k) - \epsilon y_i^{(k)}(0) z_i^{(k)}(0)]$$

$$= \sum_{i=1}^{s^{(n)}} \epsilon y_i^{(n)}(T_n) z_i^{(n)}(T_n) + \sum_{k=1}^{n-1} \sum_{i=1}^{s^{(k)}} \epsilon y_i^{(k)}(T_k) z_i^{(k)}(T_k)$$

$$- \sum_{k=1}^{n-1} \sum_{i=1}^{s^{(k)}} \epsilon y_i^{(k)}(0) z_i^{(k)}(0) - \sum_{i=1}^{s^{(n)}} \epsilon y_i^{(n)}(0) z_i^{(n)}(0)$$

$$= \sum_{i=1}^{s^{(n)}} \epsilon y_i^{(n)}(T_n) z_i^{(n)}(T_n) + \sum_{k=1}^{n-1} \sum_{i=1}^{s^{(k)}} \epsilon y_i^{(k)}(T_k) z_i^{(k)}(T_k)$$

$$- 0 - \sum_{k=1}^{n-1} \sum_{i=1}^{s^{(k)}} \epsilon y_i^{(k)}(T_k) z_i^{(k)}(T_k)$$

$$= \sum_{i=1}^{s^{(n)}} \epsilon y_i^{(n)}(T_n) z_i^{(n)}(T_n). \tag{25}$$

For those branches connected to a crossing point, as shown in Fig. 6.2$c$, we have, by using equations (10) and (19),

$$\sum_{p=m+1}^{n} \sum_{i=1}^{s^{(p)}} \epsilon y_i^{(p)}(0) z_i^{(p)}(0) = \sum_{p=m+1}^{n} \sum_{i=1}^{s^{(p)}} \sum_{k=1}^{m} \sum_{j=1}^{s^{(k)}} \epsilon y_j^{(k)}(T_k) \frac{\partial g_i^{(p)}}{\partial x_j^{(k)}} z_i^{(p)}(0)$$

$$= \sum_{k=1}^{m} \sum_{j=1}^{s^{(k)}} \epsilon y_j^{(k)}(T_k) \sum_{p=m+1}^{n} \sum_{i=1}^{s} \frac{\partial g_i^{(p)}}{\partial x_j^{(k)}} z_i^{(p)}(0)$$

$$= \sum_{k=1}^{m} \sum_{j=1}^{s^{(k)}} \epsilon y_j^{(k)}(T_k) z_j^{(k)}(T_k)$$

$$= \sum_{k=1}^{m} \sum_{i=1}^{s^{(k)}} \epsilon y_i^{(k)}(T_k) z_i^{(k)}(T_k). \tag{26}$$

Therefore the left-hand side of equation (21) can be written as

$$\sum_{k=1}^{n}\sum_{i=1}^{s^{(k)}}[\epsilon y_i^{(k)}(T_k)\, z_i^{(k)}(T_k) - \epsilon y_i^{(k)}(0)\, z_i^{(k)}(0)]$$

$$=\sum_{k=1}^{m}\sum_{i=1}^{s^{(k)}}\epsilon y_i^{(k)}(T_k)\, z_i^{(k)}(T_k) + \sum_{k=m+1}^{n}\sum_{i=1}^{s^{(k)}}\epsilon y_i^{(k)}(T_k)\, z_i^{(k)}(T_k)$$

$$-\sum_{k=1}^{m}\sum_{i=1}^{s^{(k)}}\epsilon y_i^{(k)}(0)\, z_i^{(k)}(0) - \sum_{k=m+1}^{n}\sum_{i=1}^{s^{(k)}}\epsilon y_i^{(k)}(0)\, z_i^{(k)}(0)$$

$$=\sum_{k=1}^{m}\sum_{i=1}^{s^{(k)}}\epsilon y_i^{(k)}(T_k)\, z_i^{(k)}(T_k) + \sum_{k=m+1}^{n}\sum_{i=1}^{s^{(k)}}\epsilon y_i^{(k)}(T_k)\, z_i^{(k)}(T_k)$$

$$- 0 - \sum_{k=1}^{m}\sum_{i=1}^{s^{(k)}}\epsilon y_i^{(k)}(T_k)\, z_i^{(k)}(T_k)$$

$$=\sum_{k=m+1}^{n}\sum_{i=1}^{s^{(k)}}\epsilon y_i^{(k)}(T_k)\, z_i^{(k)}(T_k). \tag{27}$$

The results represented by equations (23), (25), and (27) indicate that the left-hand side of equation (21) can be generally written as

$$\sum_{k=1}^{f}\sum_{i=1}^{s^{(k)}}\epsilon y_i^{(k)}(T_k)\, z_i^{(k)}(T_k),$$

where the summation is over only those branches containing the final state. Its number is designated as $f$.

By applying the definition of the Hamiltonian, equation (21) can now be written as

$$\sum_{k=1}^{f}\sum_{i=1}^{s^{(k)}}\epsilon y_i^{(k)}(T_k)\, z_i^{(k)}(T_k)$$

$$=\sum_{k=1}^{n}\int_0^{T_k}\left[\sum_{j=1}^{r^{(k)}}\frac{\partial H^{(k)}}{\partial \bar{\theta}_j^{(k)}}\,\epsilon \varphi_j^{(k)}\right]dt + 0(\epsilon^2). \tag{28}$$

Since $\bar{\theta}^{(k)}$, $k = 1, 2, \ldots, n$ is the sequence that maximizes

$$\sum_{k=1}^{f}\sum_{i=1}^{s^{(k)}} c_i^{(k)}\, x_i^{(k)}(T_k),$$

the effect of the perturbation represented by equation (14) can only be to make

$$\sum_{k=1}^{f}\sum_{i=1}^{s^{(k)}}\epsilon c_i^{(k)}\, y_i^{(k)}(T_k) \leq 0. \tag{29}$$

A combination of equations (11), (28), and (29) gives

$$\sum_{k=1}^{n} \int_0^{T_k} \left[ \sum_{j=1}^{r^{(k)}} \frac{\partial H^{(k)}}{\partial \bar{\theta}_j^{(k)}} \, \epsilon \varphi_j^{(k)} \right] dt + 0(\epsilon^2) \leq 0. \tag{30}$$

Now, since the perturbed functions $\theta^{(k)}$ are independent of each other, it may be concluded that the integrand of each integral in equation (30) must itself be nonpositive; thus considering only the linear terms, we obtain

$$\sum_{j=1}^{r^{(k)}} \frac{\partial H^{(k)}}{\partial \bar{\theta}_j^{(k)}} \, \epsilon \varphi_j^{(k)} \leq 0, \qquad k = 1, 2, \ldots, n,$$

which implies that

$$\frac{\partial H^{(k)}}{\partial \theta_j^{(k)}} = 0 \quad \text{at} \quad \theta_j^{(k)} = \bar{\theta}_j^{(k)}, \qquad j = 1, 2, \ldots, r,$$

when $\bar{\theta}_j^{(k)}$ lies in the interior of the region of $\theta^{(k)}$ or

$$H^{(k)} = \max \quad \text{at} \quad \theta_j^{(k)} = \bar{\theta}_j^{(k)}, \qquad i = 1, 2, \ldots, r$$

when $\bar{\theta}_j^{(k)}$ lies at a boundary of the constraints.

Although the derivations given here do not indicate that the first condition is equivalent to equation (12) [see ref. 3], it can be proved that they are equivalent [4, 5]. For further comments see Chapter 11.

The derivations given here are, strictly speaking, only for those processes in which each branch contains either an initial state or a final state. The derivation for processes other than these (the recycle process for example) is similar, but equations (23), (25), and (27) must be modified because some of the branches entering the junction points have no given initial states.

The result of this section has been obtained by a different approach for a more general class of constraints, inputs, and decisions in References 4 and 5. It is also shown there that the maximum of $H$ is constant in each branch of the process.

If the objective function is minimized instead of maximized, the optimal policy can be found by the same procedure except that equation (12) is replaced by

$$H^{(k)}(x, z, \theta) = \text{minimum}. \tag{31}$$

## 3.  AN EXAMPLE [2]

To illustrate the use of the optimization procedure presented, let us consider the simple feedback loop shown in Fig. 6.3.

The process consists of four branches with the following performance equations:

$$\frac{dx_1^{(1)}}{dt} = 0, \tag{32}$$

$$\frac{dx_1^{(2)}}{dt} = -ax_1^{(2)} + \theta_1^{(2)}, \tag{33}*$$

$$\frac{dx_1^{(3)}}{dt} = 0, \tag{34}$$

$$\frac{dx_1^{(4)}}{dt} = 0. \tag{35}$$

The junction equations are

$$x_1^{(2)}(0) = \alpha x_1^{(1)}(T_1) + \beta x_1^{(4)}(T_4), \tag{36}$$

$$x_1^{(3)}(0) = x_1^{(2)}(T_2), \tag{37}$$

$$x_1^{(4)}(0) = x_1^{(2)}(T_2). \tag{38}$$

We wish to find the decision function $\theta_1^{(2)}(t)$ to minimize the integral $\frac{1}{2}\int_0^{T_2} [(x_1^{(2)})^2 + (\theta_1^{(2)})^2]\, dt$ with the initial state given as

$$x_1^{(1)}(0) = \gamma. \tag{39}$$

To solve this problem we introduce a second state variable

$$x_2^{(2)}(t) = \frac{1}{2}\int_0^t [(x_1^{(2)})^2 + (\theta_1^{(2)})^2]\, dt.$$

It follows immediately that the performance equations for $x_2$ are

$$\frac{dx_2^{(1)}}{dt} = \frac{dx_2^{(3)}}{dt} = \frac{dx_2^{(4)}}{dt} = 0, \tag{40}$$

$$\frac{dx_2^{(2)}}{dt} = \frac{1}{2}(x_1^{(2)})^2 + \frac{1}{2}(\theta_1^{(2)})^2. \tag{41}$$

The junction equations are

$$x_2^{(2)}(0) = 0, \tag{42}$$

$$x_2^{(3)}(0) = x_2^{(2)}(T_2), \tag{43}$$

$$x_2^{(4)}(0) = 0. \tag{44}$$

---

* Note that this equation is identical to equation (2.9).

The initial state is

$$x_2^{(1)}(0) = 0. \tag{45}$$

The optimization problem is now transformed into one of minimizing $x_2^{(3)}(T_3)$ for a process described by equations (32) through (45). Since the objective function is $x_2^{(3)}(T_3)$, we have $c_1^{(3)} = 0$ and $c_2^{(3)} = 1$.

According to equations (6) and (7), we write

$$H^{(1)} = H^{(3)} = H^{(4)} = 0,$$

$$H^{(2)} = -az_1^{(2)} x_1^{(2)} + \tfrac{1}{2}z_2^{(2)}(x_1^{(2)})^2 + z_1^{(2)} \theta_1^{(2)} + \tfrac{1}{2}z_2^{(2)}(\theta_1^{(2)})^2, \tag{46}$$

$$\frac{dz_1^{(1)}}{dt} = \frac{dz_1^{(3)}}{dt} = \frac{dz_1^{(4)}}{dt} = \frac{dz_2^{(1)}}{dt} = \frac{dz_2^{(3)}}{dt} = \frac{dz_2^{(4)}}{dt} = 0, \tag{47}$$

$$\frac{dz_1^{(2)}}{dt} = +az_1^{(2)} - z_2^{(2)} x_1^{(2)}, \tag{48}$$

$$\frac{dz_2^{(2)}}{dt} = 0. \tag{49}$$

According to equations (8) and (9), we have at the combining point

$$z_1^{(1)}(T_1) = \alpha \, z_1^{(2)}(0), \tag{50}$$

$$z_1^{(4)}(T_4) = \beta \, z_1^{(2)}(0), \tag{51}$$

$$z_2^{(1)}(T_1) = 0, \tag{52}$$

$$z_2^{(4)}(T_4) = 0, \tag{53}$$

and at the separating point

$$z_1^{(2)}(T_2) = z_1^{(3)}(0) + z_1^{(4)}(0), \tag{54}$$

$$z_2^{(2)}(T_2) = z_2^{(3)}(0). \tag{55}$$

Applying equation (11), we have

$$z_1^{(3)}(T_3) = 0, \tag{56}$$

$$z_2^{(3)}(T_3) = 1. \tag{57}$$

It is seen from equations (47) and (49) that

$$z_i^{(k)}(t) = \text{constant}, \qquad \begin{array}{l} i = 1, 2, \, k = 1, 3, 4, \\ i = 2, \, k = 2. \end{array} \tag{58}$$

Using equations (56), (57), and (58) to simplify equations (54) and (55) gives

$$z_1^{(2)}(T_2) = z_1^{(4)}(0) = z_1^{(4)}(T_4), \tag{59}$$

$$z_2^{(2)}(t) = 1. \tag{60}$$

From equations (51) and (59) we have

$$\beta z_1^{(2)}(0) = z_1^{(2)}(T_2). \tag{61}$$

Substitution of $z_2^{(2)}(t) = 1$ into equation (46) gives

$$H^{(2)} = -az_1^{(2)}\,x_1^{(2)} + \tfrac{1}{2}(x_1^{(2)})^2 + z_1^{(2)}\,\theta_1^{(2)} + \tfrac{1}{2}(\theta_1^{(2)})^2. \tag{62}$$

According to equation (31), assuming that the minimum of $H^{(2)}$ occurs at the stationary point, we can obtain $\theta_1^{(2)}(t)$ by putting

$$\frac{\partial H^{(2)}}{\partial \theta_1^{(2)}} = 0.$$

The result is

$$\theta_1^{(2)}(t) = -z_1^{(2)}(t) \tag{63}$$

Inserting the expression for $\theta_1^{(2)}(t)$ into equation (33), we obtain

$$\frac{dx_1^{(2)}}{dt} = -ax_1^{(2)} - z_1^{(2)}. \tag{64}$$

From equation (48) we have

$$\frac{dz_1^{(2)}}{dt} = -x_1^{(2)} + az_1^{(2)} \tag{65}$$

Equations (64) and (65) can be integrated to give

$$x_1^{(2)}(t) = A_1 e^{\lambda t} + A_2 e^{-\lambda t} \tag{66}*$$

$$z_1^{(2)}(t) = -A_3 e^{\lambda t} + A_4 e^{-\lambda t}, \tag{67}$$

where

$$\lambda = \sqrt{a^2 + 1}, \quad A_3 = (\lambda + a)A_1, \quad \text{and} \quad A_4 = (\lambda - a)A_2.$$

The constants $A_1$ and $A_2$ are to be determined by equations (36) and (61).

It is seen from equation (35) that $x_1^{(4)}$ is constant. Substitution of equations (38) and (39) into (36) yields

$$x_1^{(2)}(0) = \alpha\gamma + \beta x_1^{(2)}(T_2). \tag{68}$$

By applying equations (61) and (68) to (66) and (67) we have

$$A_1 = \frac{\alpha\gamma/(1 - \beta e^{\lambda T_2})}{1 - \dfrac{(a + \lambda)(1 - \beta e^{-\lambda T_2})(\beta - e^{\lambda T_2})}{(a - \lambda)(1 - \beta e^{\lambda T_2})(\beta - e^{-\lambda T_2})}},$$

---

* It should be noted that this solution is identical to that obtained for the simple example in Section 2.2 [see equation (2.21)]. The difference comes in evaluating constants $A_1$ and $A_2$ from the boundary and mixing conditions. This point is clarified further in a later chapter.

and

$$A_2 = \frac{\alpha\gamma/(1 - \beta e^{\lambda T_2})}{\dfrac{1 - \beta e^{-\lambda T_2}}{1 - \beta e^{\lambda T_2}} - \dfrac{(a - \lambda)(\beta - e^{-\lambda T_2})}{(a + \lambda)(\beta - e^{\lambda T_2})}}.$$

Since $\theta_1^{(2)}(t) = -z_1^{(2)}(t)$, the optimal policy is

$$\theta_1^{(2)}(t) = (a + \lambda)A_1 e^{\lambda t} + (a - \lambda)A_2 e^{-\lambda t}.$$

## REFERENCES

1. Pontryagin, L. S., V. G. Boltyanskii, R. V. Gamkrelidze, and E. F. Mishchenko, *The Mathematical Theory of Optimal Processes* (English translation by K. N. Trirogoff), Interscience, New York, 1962.
2. Wang, C. S., and L. T. Fan, "The Optimization of Continuous Complex Processes by the Maximum Principle," *J. Electron. Control*, **17**, No. 2, 199 (August 1964).
3. Denn, M. M., "On the Optimization of Continuous Complex Systems by the Maximum Principle," *Int. J. Control*, **1**, 497 (1965).
4. Denn, M. M., "the Optimization of Complex Systems," Ph.D. Thesis, University of Minnesota, 1964.
5. Denn, M. M., and R. Aris, "Green's Functions and Optimal Systems III: Complex Interconnected Structures," *Ind. Eng. Chem., Fundamentals*, **4**, 248 (1965).

# 7

# *Applications of the Computational Algorithm for Complex Processes*

In this chapter we shall apply the computational algorithm for complex continuous processes discussed in Chapter 6 to chemical processing systems. Geometrically or topologically complex systems are common in the chemical process industry. To show the use of the algorithm and to give readers a concrete idea of what should be expected in dealing with these systems, we shall first present hypothetical processes which contain separating, combining, or crossing points and then solve them analytically. The performance equations of the hypothetical processes are kept relatively simple in order to give a clear presentation of basic procedures involved in employing the algorithm. We shall then proceed to apply the algorithm to determine the optimal temperature profiles for complex tubular reactor systems.

As we shall see later, the solution of almost every practical optimization problem arising from complex processes requires the use of a high-speed and high-capacity computer. Although a digital computer has been used to carry out the numerical solutions for most of the problems in this chapter, it is believed that an analog or a hybrid computer would be as powerful and as convenient in solving similar problems.

## 1.   OPTIMIZATION OF PROCESSES WITH SEPARATING POINTS

*a. A Hypothetical Process.*   Suppose that we have a process that contains a separating point, as shown in Fig. 7.1.  The process consists of three branches with the following performance equations:

$$\frac{dx_1^{(n)}}{dt} = -ax_1^{(n)} + \theta^{(n)}, \tag{1}$$

$$\frac{dx_2^{(n)}}{dt} = \tfrac{1}{2}(x_1^{(n)})^2 + \tfrac{1}{2}(\theta^{(n)})^2, \qquad n = 1, 2, 3. \tag{2}$$

We can see that the equations for all three branches have the same form.

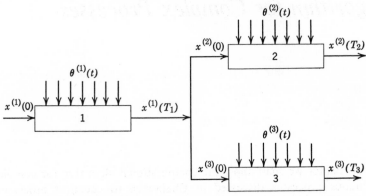

**Fig. 7.1**  Schematic diagram for a process involving a separating point.

Flow of the state variables is such that at the separating point we have

$$x_1^{(2)}(0) = x_1^{(1)}(T_1), \tag{3}$$
$$x_2^{(2)}(0) = x_2^{(1)}(T_1), \tag{4}$$
$$x_1^{(3)}(0) = x_1^{(1)}(T_1), \tag{5}$$
$$x_2^{(3)}(0) = x_2^{(1)}(T_1). \tag{6}$$

The initial conditions are

$$x_1^{(1)}(0) = \alpha_1,$$
$$x_2^{(1)}(0) = 0. \tag{7}$$

It can be seen from equation (2) that the second state variable $x_2$ is dependent on the first state variable $x_1$. In this case $x_2$ may be called the secondary state variable with respect to the primary state variable $x_1$ [1]. We wish to determine the optimal decisions $\bar{\theta}^{(n)}(t)$, $n = 1, 2, 3$ along every branch in order to minimize the objective function

$$S = x_2^{(2)}(T_2) + x_2^{(3)}(T_3), \tag{8}$$

where $x_2^{(2)}(T_2)$ and $x_2^{(3)}(T_3)$ are the final values of $x_2$ at branches 2 and 3.

The Hamiltonian function $H^{(n)}$ for each branch is, according to equation (6.6),

$$H^{(n)} = -az_1^{(n)} x_1^{(n)} + \tfrac{1}{2}z_2^{(n)}(x_1^{(n)})^2 + z_1^{(n)}\,\theta^{(n)} + \tfrac{1}{2}z_2^{(n)}(\theta^{(n)})^2,$$

$$n = 1, 2, 3. \quad (9)$$

According to equation (6.7), the adjoint variables for each branch are given by

$$\frac{dz_1^{(n)}}{dt} = -\frac{\partial H^{(n)}}{\partial x_1^{(n)}} = az_1^{(n)} - z_2^{(n)}\,x_1^{(n)}, \quad (10)$$

$$\frac{dz_2^{(n)}}{dt} = -\frac{\partial H^{(n)}}{\partial x_2^{(n)}} = 0, \qquad n = 1, 2, 3. \quad (11)$$

According to equation (6.8) and the junction equations (3) through (6), we have at the separating point

$$z_1^{(1)}(T_1) = \sum_{k=2}^{3} \sum_{j=1}^{2} \frac{\partial g_j^{(k)}}{\partial x_1^{(1)}(T_1)}\, z_j^{(k)}(0)$$

$$= \frac{\partial}{\partial x_1^{(1)}(T_1)} [x_1^{(1)}(T_1)\, z_1^{(2)}(0) + x_2^{(1)}(T_1)\, z_2^{(2)}(0)$$

$$+ x_1^{(1)}(T_1)\, z_1^{(3)}(0) + x_2^{(1)}(T_1)\, z_2^{(3)}(0)]$$

$$= z_1^{(2)}(0) + z_1^{(3)}(0). \quad (12)$$

Similarly, we have

$$z_2^{(1)}(T_1) = z_2^{(2)}(0) + z_2^{(3)}(0). \quad (13)$$

Since the objective function is generally given as

$$S = \sum_{k=2}^{3} \sum_{i=1}^{2} c_i^{(k)}\, x_i^{(k)}(T_k)$$

$$= c_1^{(2)}\, x_1^{(2)}(T_2) + c_2^{(2)}\, x_2^{(2)}(T_2) + c_1^{(3)}\, x_1^{(3)}(T_3) + c_2^{(3)}\, x_2^{(3)}(T_3),$$

we see that for this problem

$$c_1^{(2)} = c_1^{(3)} = 0,$$

$$c_2^{(2)} = c_2^{(3)} = 1.$$

Thus, according to equation (6.11), we have at the final point

$$z_1^{(2)}(T_2) = 0, \quad (14)$$

$$z_1^{(3)}(T_3) = 0, \quad (15)$$

$$z_2^{(2)}(T_2) = z_2^{(3)}(T_3) = 1. \quad (16)$$

Solving equation (11) subject to the boundary conditions given in equation (16) gives

$$z_2^{(2)}(t) = 1, \qquad 0 \le t \le T_2,$$
$$z_2^{(3)}(t) = 1, \qquad 0 \le t \le T_3. \tag{17}$$

Substituting equation (17) into equation (13), we obtain

$$z_2^{(1)}(T_1) = 2. \tag{18}$$

Combining equation (18) with equation (11), we have

$$z_2^{(1)}(t) = 2, \qquad 0 \le t \le T_1. \tag{19}$$

By comparing the performance equations given in equations (1) and (2) and the final conditions for the adjoint variables given in equations (14), (15) and (16) with those given in the example in Chapter 2 we can obtain the optimal solutions for branches 2 and 3:

$$\bar{\theta}^{(2)}(t) = -z_1^{(2)}(t), \qquad 0 \le t \le T_2, \tag{20}$$

$$x_1^{(2)}(t) = B_1 e^{\lambda t} + B_2 e^{-\lambda t}, \qquad\qquad 0 \le t \le T_2, \tag{21}$$

$$z_1^{(2)}(t) = -B_1(\lambda + a)e^{\lambda t} + B_2(\lambda - a)e^{-\lambda t}, \qquad 0 \le t \le T_2. \tag{22}$$

where $B_1$ and $B_2$ are integration constants and $\lambda = \sqrt{a^2 + 1}$.

$$\bar{\theta}^{(3)}(t) = -z_1^{(3)}(t), \qquad 0 \le t \le T_3, \tag{23}$$

$$x_1^{(3)}(t) = C_1 e^{\lambda t} + C_2 e^{-\lambda t}, \qquad 0 \le t \le T_3, \tag{24}$$

$$z_1^{(3)}(t) = -C_1(\lambda + a)e^{\lambda t} + C_2(\lambda - a)e^{-\lambda t}, \qquad 0 \le t \le T_3. \tag{25}$$

where $C_1$ and $C_2$ are integration constants. Before evaluating these integration constants we shall determine the optimal solution for branch 1.

Substitution of equation (19) into equation (9) for $n = 1$ gives

$$H^{(1)} = -az_1^{(1)} x_1^{(1)} + (x_1^{(1)})^2 + z_1^{(1)} \theta^{(1)} + (\theta^{(1)})^2. \tag{26}$$

Setting

$$\frac{\partial H^{(1)}}{\partial \theta^{(1)}} = 0,$$

we have

$$\frac{\partial H^{(1)}}{\partial \theta^{(1)}} = z_1^{(1)} + 2\theta^{(1)} = 0$$

or

$$z_1^{(1)}(t) = -2\bar{\theta}^{(1)}(t). \tag{27}$$

By substituting equation (27) and $z_2^{(1)} = 2$ into equations (1) and (10), respectively, we obtain

$$\frac{dx_1^{(1)}}{dt} = -ax_1^{(1)} - \tfrac{1}{2}z_1^{(1)}, \tag{28}$$

$$\frac{dz_1^{(1)}}{dt} = az_1^{(1)} - 2x_1^{(1)}. \tag{29}$$

This set of simultaneous differential equations can be solved by using the method of substitution as shown in Chapter 2. The final results are

$$x_1^{(1)}(t) = A_1 e^{\lambda t} + A_2 e^{-\lambda t}, \qquad 0 \le t \le T_1, \tag{30}$$

$$z_1^{(1)}(t) = -2A_1(\lambda + a)e^{\lambda t} + 2A_2(\lambda - a)e^{-\lambda t}, \qquad 0 \le t \le T_1, \tag{31}$$

where $A_1$ and $A_2$ are integration constants. Comparison of equation (31) with equations (22) and (25) shows that equation (31) differs in form from the other two by a factor of 2. This difference is attributed to the boundary condition given by equation (18). Since, however, the optimal decision for branch 1 is given by equation (27), namely

$$\bar{\theta}^{(1)}(t) = -\tfrac{1}{2}z_1^{(1)}(t)$$

instead of

$$\bar{\theta}^{(n)}(t) = -z_1^{(n)}(t), \qquad n = 2, 3,$$

which has been obtained for branches 2 and 3, the functional dependences of $\bar{\theta}^{(n)}(t)$ on $t$ are the same for all three branches if all the integration constants are equal for each branch. To evaluate the integration constants $A_1$, $A_2$, $B_1$, $B_2$, $C_1$, and $C_2$ appearing in equations (21), (22), (24), (25), (30), and (31) we first summarize the boundary conditions:

$$x_1^{(1)}(0) = \alpha_1, \tag{7}$$

$$x_1^{(2)}(0) = x_1^{(1)}(T_1), \tag{3}$$

$$x_1^{(3)}(0) = x_1^{(1)}(T_1), \tag{5}$$

$$z_1^{(1)}(T_1) = z_1^{(2)}(0) + z_1^{(3)}(0), \tag{12}$$

$$z_1^{(2)}(T_2) = 0, \tag{14}$$

$$z_1^{(3)}(T_3) = 0. \tag{15}$$

It is seen that we have six boundary conditions with which to solve for the six unknown constants.

By combining equations (14), (15), (22), and (25) we obtain

$$z_1^{(2)}(T_2) = -B_1(\lambda + a)e^{\lambda T_2} + B_2(\lambda - a)e^{-\lambda T_2} = 0,$$

$$z_1^{(3)}(T_3) = -C_1(\lambda + a)e^{\lambda T_3} + C_2(\lambda - a)e^{-\lambda T_3} = 0,$$

or

$$B_2 = B_1 \frac{\lambda + a}{\lambda - a} e^{2\lambda T_2} = B_1 \lambda_1 e^{2\lambda T_2} \tag{32}$$

and

$$C_2 = C_1 \frac{\lambda + a}{\lambda - a} e^{2\lambda T_3} = C_1 \lambda_1 e^{2\lambda T_3}, \tag{33}$$

where

$$\lambda_1 = \frac{\lambda + a}{\lambda - a}.$$

By combining equations (12), (22), (25), and (31) we obtain

$$2A_1(\lambda + a)e^{\lambda T_1} - 2A_2(\lambda - a)e^{-\lambda T_1}$$
$$= B_1(\lambda + a) - B_2(\lambda - a) + C_1(\lambda + a) - C_2(\lambda - a). \tag{34}$$

From equations (7) and (30) we have

$$\alpha_1 = A_1 + A_2$$

or

$$A_2 = \alpha_1 - A_1 \tag{35}$$

Substitution of equations (32), (33), and (35) into (34) gives

$$2A_1[(\lambda + a)e^{\lambda T_1} + (\lambda - a)e^{-\lambda T_1}] - 2\alpha_1(\lambda - a)e^{-\lambda T_1}$$
$$= B_1(\lambda + a)(1 - e^{2\lambda T_2}) + C_1(\lambda + a)(1 - e^{2\lambda T_3}) \tag{36}$$

Combining equations (3), (21), and (30), we obtain

$$x_1^{(2)}(0) = B_1 + B_2 = A_1 e^{\lambda T_1} + A_2 e^{-\lambda T_1}.$$

Substitution of equations (32) and (35) into the preceding equation yields

$$B_1\left( 1 + \lambda_1 e^{2\lambda T_2} \right) = A_1(e^{\lambda T_1} - e^{-\lambda T_1}) + \alpha_1 e^{-\lambda T_1}.$$

Solving for $B_1$, we have

$$B_1 = A_1 \frac{e^{\lambda T_1} - e^{-\lambda T_1}}{1 + \lambda_1 e^{2\lambda T_2}} + \frac{\alpha_1 e^{-\lambda T_1}}{1 + \lambda_1 e^{2\lambda T_2}}$$

or

$$B_1 = m_1 A_1 + n_1, \tag{37}$$

where

$$m_1 = \frac{e^{\lambda T_1} - e^{-\lambda T_1}}{1 + \lambda_1 e^{2\lambda T_2}} \quad \text{and} \quad n_1 = \frac{\alpha_1 e^{-\lambda T_1}}{1 + \lambda_1 e^{2\lambda T_2}}.$$

Similarly, we have

$$C_1 = m_2 A_1 + n_2, \tag{38}$$

where

$$m_2 = \frac{e^{\lambda T_1} - e^{-\lambda T_1}}{1 + \lambda_1 e^{2\lambda T_3}} \quad \text{and} \quad n_2 = \frac{\alpha_1 e^{-\lambda T_1}}{1 + \lambda_1 e^{2\lambda T_3}}.$$

Substitution of equations (37) and (38) into (36) yields

$$2A_1[(\lambda + a)e^{\lambda T_1} + (\lambda - a)e^{-\lambda T_1}] - 2\alpha_1(\lambda - a)e^{-\lambda T_1}$$
$$= (m_1 A_1 + n_1)(\lambda + a)(1 - e^{2\lambda T_2}) + (m_2 A_1 + n_2)(\lambda + a)(1 - e^{2\lambda T_3}).$$

By simplifying this equation we obtain

$$A_1 = \frac{n_1 \lambda_1(1 - e^{2\lambda T_2}) + n_2 \lambda_1(1 - e^{2\lambda T_3}) + 2\alpha_1 e^{-\lambda T_1}}{2\lambda_1 e^{\lambda T_1} + 2e^{-\lambda T_1} - m_1 \lambda_1(1 - e^{2\lambda T_2}) - m_2 \lambda_1(1 - e^{2\lambda T_3})}. \tag{39}$$

The integration constants $B_1$ and $C_1$ can then be recovered from equations (37) and (38) as

$$B_1 = \left[ \frac{n_1 \lambda_1(1 - e^{2\lambda T_2}) + n_2 \lambda_1(1 - e^{2\lambda T_3}) + 2\alpha_1 e^{-\lambda T_1}}{2\lambda_1 e^{\lambda T_1} + 2e^{-\lambda T_1} - m_1 \lambda_1(1 - e^{2\lambda T_2}) - m_2 \lambda_1(1 - e^{2\lambda T_3})} \right] m_1 + n_1, \tag{40}$$

$$C_1 = \left[ \frac{n_1 \lambda_1(1 - e^{2\lambda T_2}) + n_2 \lambda_1(1 - e^{2\lambda T_3}) + 2\alpha_1 e^{-\lambda T_1}}{2\lambda_1 e^{\lambda T_1} + 2e^{-\lambda T_1} - m_1 \lambda_1(1 - e^{2\lambda T_2}) - m_2 \lambda_1(1 - e^{2\lambda T_3})} \right] m_2 + n_2, \tag{41}$$

By substituting equations (39), (40), and (41) into equations (35), (32), and (33), respectively we can obtain the integration constants $A_2$, $B_2$, and $C_2$. The optimal decisions for all three branches are recovered from equations (20), (23), and (27). Once the optimal decisions and $x_1^{(n)}(t)$, $n = 1, 2, 3$ have been determined $x_2^{(n)}(t)$, $n = 1, 2, 3$ can be obtained by integrating equation (2).

**b. A First-Order Irreversible Consecutive Reaction, $A \xrightarrow{k_1} B \xrightarrow{k_2} C$, Taking Place in a Series of Tubular Reactors with Intermediate Product Withdrawal.** In this part we consider a complex continuous process consisting of two tubular chemical reactors connected in series with exit flow from the intermediate point, as shown in Fig. 7.2. The reactions taking place in the reactors are the first-order irreversible consecutive reactions discussed in Section 4.2, part b, in which the intermediate product $B$ is maximized. In Chapter 4, however, the reaction was carried out in a single tubular reactor. In this section we deal with a process that is more complex in geometry than a simple tubular reactor and involves two tubular reactors of length $L_1$ and $L_2$ connected in series by a separating point in which a portion of the product is removed as an intermediate product.

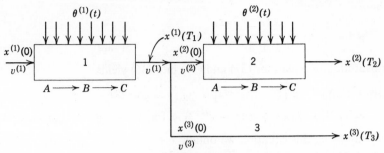

**Fig. 7.2** Schematic diagram of two tubular reactors connected in series with product withdrawn from the intermediate point for the reaction $A \to B \to C$.

The steady state differential material balance for reactant $i$ in the differential section $dl$ of the $k$th branch, $k = 1, 2$, can be written

{rate of input of component $i$ to the differential section $dl$
  of the $k$th branch}

— {rate of output of component $i$ from the differential section
    $dl$ of the $k$th branch}

+ {rate of production of component $i$ in the differential section
    $dl$ of the $k$th branch}

= 0,

$$\{v^{(k)} x_i^{(k)}\} - \left\{ v^{(k)} x_i^{(k)} + v^{(k)} \frac{dx_i^{(k)}}{dl} \, dl \right\} + A^{(k)} \, dl \{R_i^{(k)}\} = 0,$$

or

$$\frac{dx_i^{(k)}}{dl} = \frac{A^{(k)}}{v^{(k)}} \{R_i^{(k)}\}, \qquad i = 1, 2, \quad \text{and} \quad k = 1, 2, \tag{42a}$$

where $v^{(k)}$ and $A^{(k)}$ are total volumetric flow rate and cross-sectional area, respectively, for the $k$th branch. Here $R_i^{(k)}$ is the rate of production of component $i$ in a unit volume of the $k$th branch. If we let $x_1$ and $x_2$ be the molar concentration of $A$ and $B$, respectively, the performance equations for each branch can be written, according to equation (42a), as

$$\frac{dx_1^{(1)}}{dl} = \frac{A^{(1)}}{v^{(1)}} \{R_1^{(1)}\}, \qquad 0 \le l \le L_1, \tag{42b}$$

$$\frac{dx_2^{(1)}}{dl} = \frac{A^{(1)}}{v^{(1)}} \{R_2^{(1)}\}, \qquad 0 \le l \le L_1, \tag{42c}$$

$$\frac{dx_1^{(2)}}{dl} = \frac{A^{(2)}}{v^{(2)}} \{R_1^{(2)}\}, \qquad 0 \le l \le L_2, \tag{42d}$$

$$\frac{dx_2^{(2)}}{dl} = \frac{A^{(2)}}{v^{(2)}} \{R_2^{(2)}\}, \qquad 0 \le l \le L_2. \tag{42e}$$

Since the mechanism of reaction is the same for branches 1 and 2, we can write

$$R_1^{(k)} = -k_1^{(k)} x_1^{(k)} \tag{42f}$$

$$R_2^{(k)} = k_1^{(k)} x_1^{(k)} - k_2^{(k)} x_2^{(k)}, \qquad k = 1, 2. \tag{42g}$$

If we define the holding time as $t = l/(v/A)$, substitution of equations (42f) and (42g) into equations (42b) through (42e) yields

$$\frac{dx_1^{(1)}}{dt} = -k_1^{(1)} x_1^{(1)}, \qquad x_1^{(1)}(0) = \alpha_1, \tag{43}$$

$$\frac{dx_2^{(1)}}{dt} = k_1^{(1)} x_1^{(1)} - k_2^{(1)} x_2^{(1)}, \qquad x_2^{(1)}(0) = \alpha_2, \tag{44}$$

$$\frac{dx_1^{(2)}}{dt} = -k_1^{(2)} x_1^{(2)}, \tag{45}$$

$$\frac{dx_2^{(2)}}{dt} = k_1^{(2)} x_1^{(2)} - k_2^{(2)} x_2^{(2)}. \tag{46}$$

where $\alpha_1$ and $\alpha_2$ are the inlet concentrations of $A$ and $B$, respectively. Here $k_1$ and $k_2$ are temperature-dependent-specific-rate constants of the Arrhenius type as given in equation (4.25).

Since no transformation is taking place and no control action is imposed on branch 3, we have the following performance equations for that branch:

$$\frac{dx_1^{(3)}}{dt} = \frac{dx_2^{(3)}}{dt} = 0. \tag{47}$$

Since the outlet stream of component $i$ from reactor 1 splits into two streams at the separating point, the concentration of component $i$ in both streams at this junction must be equal; that is,

$$x_1^{(1)}(T_1) = x_1^{(2)}(0), \tag{48}$$

$$x_1^{(1)}(T_1) = x_1^{(3)}(0), \tag{49}$$

$$x_2^{(1)}(T_1) = x_2^{(2)}(0), \tag{50}$$

$$x_2^{(1)}(T_1) = x_2^{(3)}(0), \tag{51}$$

where

$$T_k = \frac{L_k}{v^{(k)}/A^{(k)}}$$

is the total holding time of the $k$th reactor, $k = 1, 2$.

According to equations (6.6) and (6.7), we write

$$H^{(1)} = -k_1^{(1)} x_1^{(1)} z_1^{(1)} + (k_1^{(1)} x_1^{(1)} - k_2^{(1)} x_2^{(1)}) z_2^{(1)}, \tag{52}$$

$$H^{(2)} = -k_1^{(2)} x_1^{(2)} z_1^{(2)} + (k_1^{(2)} x_1^{(2)} - k_2^{(2)} x_2^{(2)}) z_2^{(2)}, \tag{53}$$

$$H^{(3)} = 0, \tag{54}$$

$$\frac{dz_1^{(1)}}{dt} = k_1^{(1)} z_1^{(1)} - k_1^{(1)} z_2^{(1)}, \tag{55}$$

$$\frac{dz_2^{(1)}}{dt} = k_2^{(1)} z_2^{(1)}, \tag{56}$$

$$\frac{dz_1^{(2)}}{dt} = k_1^{(2)} z_1^{(2)} - k_1^{(2)} z_2^{(2)}, \tag{57}$$

$$\frac{dz_2^{(2)}}{dt} = k_2^{(2)} z_2^{(2)}, \tag{58}$$

$$\frac{dz_1^{(3)}}{dt} = \frac{dz_2^{(3)}}{dt} = 0. \tag{59}$$

According to equation (6.8), we have at the separating point

$$\begin{aligned} z_1^{(1)}(T_1) &= z_1^{(2)}(0) + z_1^{(3)}(0), \\ z_2^{(1)}(T_1) &= z_2^{(2)}(0) + z_2^{(3)}(0). \end{aligned} \tag{60}$$

Since we wish to maximize the concentration of the intermediate product $B$ at the ends of branches 2 and 3, we have the objective function

$$S = x_2^{(2)}(T_2) + x_2^{(3)}(T_3).$$

Consequently,

$$c_2^{(2)} = c_2^{(3)} = 1, \tag{61}$$

$$c_1^{(2)} = c_1^{(3)} = 0. \tag{62}$$

Substituting equations (61) and (62) into (6.11), we have at the final points

$$z_1^{(2)}(T_2) = z_1^{(3)}(T_3) = 0, \tag{63}$$

$$z_2^{(2)}(T_2) = z_2^{(3)}(T_3) = 1. \tag{64}$$

The optimal temperature, $\bar{\theta}(t)$, is determined from the condition that $H$ is maximum at every point of each branch. Assuming that the maximum of $H$ occurs at the stationary point, the optimal decision for branch 1 can be obtained from

$$\frac{\partial H^{(1)}}{\partial \theta^{(1)}} = -x_1^{(1)} z_1^{(1)} \frac{dk_1^{(1)}}{d\theta^{(1)}} + \left( \frac{dk_1^{(1)}}{d\theta^{(1)}} x_1^{(1)} - \frac{dk_2^{(1)}}{d\theta^{(1)}} x_2^{(1)} \right) z_2^{(1)} = 0$$

or

$$(z_2^{(1)} x_1^{(1)} - z_1^{(1)} x_1^{(1)}) k_{10} E_1 \exp\left(\frac{-E_1}{R\theta^{(1)}}\right) - z_2^{(1)} x_2^{(1)} k_{20} E_2 \exp\left(\frac{-E_2}{R\theta^{(1)}}\right) = 0. \tag{65}$$

Solving this equation for $\theta^{(1)}$, we have

$$\bar{\theta}^{(1)}(t) = \left(\frac{E_1 - E_2}{R}\right)\left\{\ln\left[\xi \frac{x_1^{(1)}(z_2^{(1)} - z_1^{(1)})}{x_2^{(1)} z_2^{(1)}}\right]\right\}^{-1}, \qquad 0 \le t \le T_1 \tag{66}$$

where

$$\xi = \frac{k_{10} E_1}{k_{20} E_2}.$$

Similarly, for branch 2, we have

$$\bar{\theta}^{(2)}(t) = \left(\frac{E_1 - E_2}{R}\right)\left\{\ln\left[\xi \frac{x_1^{(2)}(z_2^{(2)} - z_1^{(2)})}{x_2^{(2)} z_2^{(2)}}\right]\right\}^{-1}, \qquad 0 \le t \le T_2. \tag{67}$$

Substituting equation (66) into (43), (44), (55), and (56) and equation (67) into (45), (46), (57), and (58), we obtain

$$\frac{dx_1^{(1)}}{dt} = -k_{10}\left[\xi \frac{x_1^{(1)}}{x_2^{(1)}}\left(\frac{z_2^{(1)} - z_1^{(1)}}{z_2^{(1)}}\right)\right]^{\lambda_1} x_1^{(1)}, \tag{68}$$

$$\frac{dx_2^{(1)}}{dt} = k_{10}\left[\xi \frac{x_1^{(1)}}{x_2^{(1)}}\left(\frac{z_2^{(1)} - z_1^{(1)}}{z_2^{(1)}}\right)\right]^{\lambda_1} x_1^{(1)}$$
$$- k_{20}\left[\xi \frac{x_1^{(1)}}{x_2^{(1)}}\left(\frac{z_2^{(1)} - z_1^{(1)}}{z_2^{(1)}}\right)\right]^{\lambda_2} x_2^{(1)}, \tag{69}$$

$$\frac{dz_1^{(1)}}{dt} = k_{10}\left[\xi \frac{x_1^{(1)}}{x_2^{(1)}}\left(\frac{z_2^{(1)} - z_1^{(1)}}{z_2^{(1)}}\right)\right]^{\lambda_1} (z_1^{(1)} - z_2^{(1)}), \tag{70}$$

$$\frac{dz_2^{(1)}}{dt} = k_{20}\left[\xi \frac{x_1^{(1)}}{x_2^{(1)}}\left(\frac{z_2^{(1)} - z_1^{(1)}}{z_2^{(1)}}\right)\right]^{\lambda_2} z_2^{(1)}, \tag{71}$$

$$\frac{dx_1^{(2)}}{dt} = -k_{10}\left[\xi \frac{x_1^{(2)}}{x_2^{(2)}}\left(\frac{z_2^{(2)} - z_1^{(2)}}{z_2^{(2)}}\right)\right]^{\lambda_1} x_1^{(2)}, \tag{72}$$

$$\frac{dx_2^{(2)}}{dt} = k_{10}\left[\xi \frac{x_1^{(2)}}{x_2^{(2)}}\left(\frac{z_2^{(2)} - z_1^{(2)}}{z_2^{(2)}}\right)\right]^{\lambda_1} x_1^{(2)}$$
$$- k_{20}\left[\xi \frac{x_1^{(2)}}{x_2^{(2)}}\left(\frac{z_2^{(2)} - z_1^{(2)}}{z_2^{(2)}}\right)\right]^{\lambda_2} x_2^{(2)}, \tag{73}$$

$$\frac{dz_1^{(2)}}{dt} = k_{10}\left[\xi \frac{x_1^{(2)}}{x_2^{(2)}}\left(\frac{z_2^{(2)} - z_1^{(2)}}{z_2^{(2)}}\right)\right]^{\lambda_1} (z_1^{(2)} - z_2^{(2)}), \tag{74}$$

$$\frac{dz_2^{(2)}}{dt} = k_{20}\left[\xi \frac{x_1^{(2)}}{x_2^{(2)}}\left(\frac{z_2^{(2)} - z_1^{(2)}}{z_2^{(2)}}\right)\right]^{\lambda_2} z_2^{(2)}, \tag{75}$$

where

$$\lambda_1 = \frac{E_1}{E_2 - E_1} \quad \text{and} \quad \lambda_2 = \frac{E_2}{E_2 - E_1}.$$

For this system of eight differential equations we need eight boundary conditions, which can be summarized as follows:

$$x_1^{(1)}(0) = \alpha_1, \tag{43}$$

$$x_2^{(1)}(0) = \alpha_2, \tag{44}$$

$$x_1^{(1)}(T_1) = x_1^{(2)}(0), \tag{48}$$

$$x_2^{(1)}(T_1) = x_2^{(2)}(0), \tag{50}$$

$$z_1^{(2)}(T_2) = 0, \tag{63}$$

$$z_2^{(2)}(T_2) = 1, \tag{64}$$

$$z_1^{(1)}(T_1) = z_1^{(2)}(0), \tag{76}$$

$$z_2^{(1)}(T_1) = z_2^{(2)}(0) + 1. \tag{77}$$

Equations (76) and (77) are obtained by combining equations (59), (63), and (64) with (60).

The numerical calculations for the system described by equations (68) through (75) are illustrated by the use of the following data (see the numerical data given in Section 4.2, part b):

$$k_{10} = 0.535 \times 10^{11} \, (\text{min})^{-1},$$

$$k_{20} = 0.461 \times 10^{18} \, (\text{min})^{-1},$$

$$E_1 = 18,000 \, \text{cal/mole},$$

$$E_2 = 30,000 \, \text{cal/mole},$$

$$R = 2 \, \text{cal/mole} \, °K,$$

$$T_1 = 10 \, \text{min},$$

$$T_2 = 8 \, \text{min},$$

$$\alpha_1 = 0.72 \, \text{moles/liter},$$

$$\alpha_2 = 0.24 \, \text{moles/liter}.$$

An approximate iterative Runge-Kutta method (see Appendix I) was used with a backward integration procedure to obtain the numerical results tabulated in Table 7.1 and plotted in Figs. 7.3a and b. The numerical procedure is as follows:

1. Differentiate equation (68) with respect to $x_1^{(1)}(T_1)$, equation (69) with respect to $x_2^{(1)}(T_1)$, equation (72) with respect to $x_1^{(2)}(T_2)$, and equation (73) with respect to $x_2^{(2)}(T_2)$ to obtain four additional first-order differential

**Table 7.1.** Computational Results for the Reaction $A \rightarrow B \rightarrow C$
Taking Place in Two Tubular Reactors in Series with
Intermediate Product Withdrawal

| $\eta_2$ | $x_1^{(2)}$ | $x_2^{(2)}$ | $z_1^{(2)}$ | $z_2^{(2)}$ | $\theta^{(2)}$ |
|------|---------|---------|---------|---------|--------|
| 1.0 | 0.11315 | 0.70630 | 0.00000 | 1.00000 | 327.66 |
| 0.9 | 0.11901 | 0.70387 | 0.04917 | 0.99515 | 327.72 |
| 0.8 | 0.12522 | 0.70111 | 0.09591 | 0.99027 | 327.79 |
| 0.7 | 0.13178 | 0.69801 | 0.14033 | 0.98538 | 327.85 |
| 0.6 | 0.13873 | 0.69455 | 0.18253 | 0.98046 | 327.93 |
| 0.5 | 0.14609 | 0.69069 | 0.22261 | 0.97552 | 328.00 |
| 0.4 | 0.15389 | 0.68640 | 0.26067 | 0.97055 | 328.08 |
| 0.3 | 0.16217 | 0.68166 | 0.29679 | 0.96555 | 328.17 |
| 0.2 | 0.17097 | 0.67642 | 0.33105 | 0.96051 | 328.26 |
| 0.1 | 0.18031 | 0.67064 | 0.36355 | 0.95542 | 328.36 |
| 0.0 | 0.19026 | 0.66429 | 0.39436 | 0.95030 | 328.47 |

| $\eta_1$ | $x_1^{(1)}$ | $x_2^{(1)}$ | $z_1^{(1)}$ | $z_2^{(1)}$ | $\theta^{(1)}$ |
|------|---------|---------|---------|---------|--------|
| 1.0 | 0.19026 | 0.66429 | 0.39436 | 1.95030 | 334.15 |
| 0.9 | 0.21205 | 0.65235 | 0.55271 | 1.92134 | 334.39 |
| 0.8 | 0.23688 | 0.63752 | 0.69462 | 1.89178 | 334.68 |
| 0.7 | 0.26538 | 0.61919 | 0.82149 | 1.86144 | 335.02 |
| 0.6 | 0.29831 | 0.59658 | 0.93455 | 1.83009 | 335.42 |
| 0.5 | 0.33678 | 0.56863 | 1.03493 | 1.79738 | 335.92 |
| 0.4 | 0.38229 | 0.53383 | 1.12361 | 1.76282 | 336.54 |
| 0.3 | 0.43717 | 0.48988 | 1.20146 | 1.72561 | 337.35 |
| 0.2 | 0.50520 | 0.43303 | 1.26921 | 1.68435 | 338.48 |
| 0.1 | 0.59363 | 0.35607 | 1.32739 | 1.63616 | 340.20 |
| 0.0 | 0.72084 | 0.24071 | 1.37616 | 1.57259 | 343.58 |

equations. Assume that only $x_1^{(1)}$ is a function of $x_1^{(1)}(T_1)$, only $x_2^{(1)}$ is a function of $x_2^{(1)}(T_1)$, only $x_1^{(2)}$ is a function of $x_1^{(2)}(T_2)$, and only $x_2^{(2)}$ is a function of $x_2^{(2)}(T_2)$.

2. Assume values for $x_1^{(2)}(T_2)$ and $x_2^{(2)}(T_2)$.* Note that

$$z_1^{(2)}(T_2) = 0,$$

$$z_2^{(2)}(T_2) = 1,$$

$$\frac{dx_1^{(2)}}{dx_1^{(2)}(T_2)}\bigg|_{t=T_2} = 1,$$

---

* For this problem the assumed values of $x_1^{(2)}(T_2)$ and $x_2^{(2)}(T_2)$ were carefully chosen. Backward integration was used to obtain a table of optimal solutions (see Section 4.2, part b). From this table the approximate values of $x_1^{(2)}(T_2)$ and $x_2^{(2)}(T_2)$ were selected. This was necessary because meaningless results would be obtained if $x_1$, $x_2$, or $[(z_2 - z_1)/z_2]$ became negative in any branch.

and

$$\frac{dx_2^{(2)}}{dx_2^{(2)}(T_2)}\bigg|_{t=T_2} = 1.$$

3. Use the fourth-order Runge-Kutta method with backward integration to obtain

$$x_1^{(2)}(0),\ x_2^{(2)}(0),\ z_1^{(2)}(0),\ z_2^{(2)}(0),\ \frac{dx_1^{(2)}}{dx_1^{(2)}(T_2)}\bigg|_{t=0},\quad \text{and}\quad \frac{dx_2^{(2)}}{dx_2^{(2)}(T_2)}\bigg|_{t=0}.$$

4. Obtain $x_1^{(1)}(T_1)$, $x_2^{(1)}(T_1)$, $z_1^{(1)}(T_1)$, and $z_2^{(1)}(T_1)$ from equations (48), (50), (76), and (77), respectively. Note that

$$\frac{dx_1^{(1)}}{dx_1^{(1)}(T_1)}\bigg|_{t=T_1} = 1 \quad \text{and}\quad \frac{dx_2^{(1)}}{dx_2^{(1)}(T_1)}\bigg|_{t=T_1} = 1.$$

5. Integrate backward by employing the fourth-order Runge-Kutta method to obtain

$$x_1^{(1)}(0),\ x_2^{(1)}(0),\ z_1^{(1)}(0),\ z_2^{(1)}(0),\ \frac{dx_1^{(1)}}{dx_1^{(1)}(T_1)}\bigg|_{t=0},\quad \text{and}\quad \frac{dx_2^{(1)}}{dx_2^{(1)}(T_1)}\bigg|_{t=0}.$$

6. Use the derivative approximations

$$\frac{dx_1^{(1)}}{dx_1^{(1)}(T_1)}\bigg|_{t=0} \approx \frac{x_1^{(1)}(0) - \alpha_1}{x_1^{(1)}(T_1) - \xi_1^{(1)}},$$

$$\frac{dx_2^{(1)}}{dx_2^{(1)}(T_1)}\bigg|_{t=0} \approx \frac{x_2^{(1)}(0) - \alpha_2}{x_2^{(1)}(T_1) - \xi_2^{(1)}}.$$

to compute $\xi_1^{(1)}$ and $\xi_2^{(1)}$ which are better approximations to the values of $x_1^{(1)}(T_1)$ and $x_2^{(1)}(T_1)$ than those obtained in step 4.

7. Obtain from equations (48) and (50) closer approximations to the correct values of $x_1^{(2)}(0)$ and $x_2^{(2)}(0)$. Let these values be $\xi_1^{(1)}$ and $\xi_2^{(1)}$.

8. Use the modified derivative approximations

$$\frac{dx_1^{(2)}}{dx_1^{(2)}(T_2)}\bigg|_{t=0} \approx \frac{\frac{1}{2}(x_1^{(2)}(0) - \xi_1^{(1)})}{x_1^{(2)}(T_2) - \xi_1^{(2)}},$$

$$\frac{dx_2^{(2)}}{dx_2^{(2)}(T_2)}\bigg|_{t=0} \approx \frac{\frac{1}{2}(x_2^{(2)}(0) - \xi_2^{(1)})}{x_2^{(2)}(T_2) - \xi_2^{(2)}}$$

to obtain $\xi_1^{(2)}$ and $\xi_2^{(2)}$, which are the new trial values for $x_1^{(2)}(T_2)$ and $x_2^{(2)}(T_2)$.

9. Repeat steps 3 through 8, using the new trial values, until the computed values of $x_1^{(1)}(0)$ and $x_2^{(1)}(0)$ are approximately equal to $\alpha_1$ and $\alpha_2$, respectively.

10. Calculate the optimal decisions $\bar{\theta}^{(1)}(t)$, $\bar{\theta}^{(2)}(t)$ according to equations (66) and (67).

The computational procedure was programmed on an IBM 1620 computer. About six minutes were consumed for each trial calculation. For the first assumed values $x_1^{(2)}(T_2) = 0.115$, $x_2^{(2)}(T_2) = 0.72$, the computer took about two hours to obtain the solution shown in Table 7.1.

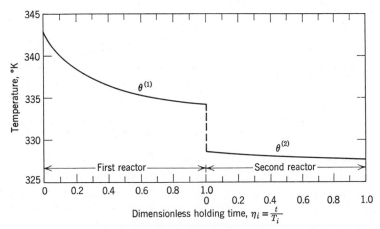

**Fig. 7.3a** Optimal temperature profiles in two tubular reactors connected in series with product withdrawn from the intermediate point for the reaction $A \rightarrow B \rightarrow C$.

For additional solutions and further detail on the numerical solution the reader is referred to Reference 2.

The results are presented in terms of dimensonless time; that is

$$\eta_i = \frac{t}{T_i}$$

as shown in Figs. 7.3a and b. Figure 3a shows that the optimal temperature profile for reactor 2 is almost constant; that is, it is almost an isothermal reactor. However, it depends on the specific numerical data assigned to solve the problem and may not always be true.

It should be noted that the geometry of the reactor arrangement in this problem is equivalent to one reactor of total holding time $T = T_1 + T_2$ with a side exit stream at $t = T_1$. The problem in Section 4.2, part b, is equivalent to the problem where the concentration of $B$ from the main exit stream is to be maximized.

In this problem a linear combination of the concentration of $B$ from the side exit stream and the main exit stream is maximized, so that when the

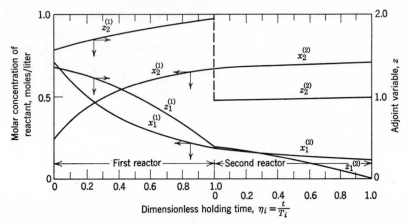

**Fig. 7.3b** Optimal concentration profiles in two tubular reactors connected in series with product withdrawn from the intermediate point for the reaction $A \to B \to C$.

flow rates in each stream are fixed the total quantity produced is maximized. From the boundary conditions in equations (64) and (77) we can see that the optimization problem treated in this example is different from the optimization problem treated in Section 4.2, part b, where the amount of $B$ produced in a simple tubular reactor is maximized.

## 2. OPTIMIZATION OF PROCESSES WITH COMBINING POINTS

**a. A Hypothetical Process.** Suppose that we have a process that contains a combining point, as shown in Fig. 7.4. The process consists of three branches with the following performance equations:

$$\frac{dx_1^{(1)}}{dt} = -ax_1^{(1)} + \theta^{(1)}, \qquad x_1^{(1)}(0) = \alpha_1, \qquad (78)$$

$$\frac{dx_2^{(1)}}{dt} = \tfrac{1}{2}(x_1^{(1)})^2 + \tfrac{1}{2}(\theta^{(1)})^2, \qquad x_2^{(1)}(0) = 0, \qquad (79)$$

$$\frac{dx_1^{(2)}}{dt} = -x_1^{(2)}\,\theta^{(2)} + \tfrac{1}{2}(\theta^{(2)})^2, \qquad x_1^{(2)}(0) = \alpha_2, \qquad (80)$$

$$x_2^{(2)}(t) = 0, \qquad\qquad\qquad 0 \le t \le T_2, \qquad (81)$$

$$\frac{dx_1^{(3)}}{dt} = -ax_1^{(3)} + \theta^{(3)}, \qquad (82)$$

$$\frac{dx_2^{(3)}}{dt} = \tfrac{1}{2}(x_1^{(3)})^2 + \tfrac{1}{2}(\theta^{(3)})^2, \qquad (83)$$

where $x_i^{(k)}$, $k = 1, 2, 3$ is the $i$th state variable for the $k$th branch and $\theta^{(k)}$ is the decision variable for the $k$th branch. The junction equations are defined as

$$x_1^{(3)}(0) = \beta_1 x_1^{(1)}(T_1) + \beta_2 x_1^{(2)}(T_2), \tag{84}$$

$$x_2^{(3)}(0) = \beta_1 x_2^{(1)}(T_1), \tag{85}$$

where $\beta_1$ and $\beta_2$ are constants.

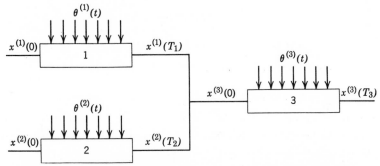

**Fig. 7.4** Schematic diagram for a process involving a combining point.

We now wish to minimize $x_2^{(3)}(T_3)$ for a process described by equations (78) through (85). Since the objective function is $x_3^{(2)}(T_3)$, we have $c_1^{(3)} = 0$ and $c_2^{(3)} = 1$.

According to equations (6.6) and (6.7), we write for each branch

$$H^{(1)} = z_1^{(1)}(-ax_1^{(1)} + \theta^{(1)}) + z_2^{(1)}[\tfrac{1}{2}(x_1^{(1)})^2 + \tfrac{1}{2}(\theta^{(1)})^2], \tag{86}$$

$$H^{(2)} = z_1^{(2)}[-x_1^{(2)}\theta^{(2)} + \tfrac{1}{2}(\theta^{(2)})^2], \tag{87}$$

$$H^{(3)} = z_1^{(3)}(-ax_1^{(3)} + \theta^{(3)}) + z_2^{(3)}[\tfrac{1}{2}(x_1^{(3)})^2 + \tfrac{1}{2}(\theta^{(3)})^2], \tag{88}$$

$$\frac{dz_1^{(1)}}{dt} = az_1^{(1)} - z_2^{(1)} x^{(1)}, \tag{89}$$

$$\frac{dz_2^{(1)}}{dt} = 0, \tag{90}$$

$$\frac{dz_1^{(2)}}{dt} = z_1^{(2)} \theta^{(2)}, \tag{91}$$

$$\frac{dz_1^{(3)}}{dt} = az_1^{(3)} - z_2^{(3)} x_1^{(3)}, \tag{92}$$

$$\frac{dz_2^{(3)}}{dt} = 0. \tag{93}$$

According to equations (6.9), (84), and (85), we have at the combining point

$$z_1^{(1)}(T_1) = \beta_1 z_1^{(3)}(0), \tag{94}$$

$$z_2^{(1)}(T_1) = \beta_1 z_2^{(3)}(0), \tag{95}$$

$$z_1^{(2)}(T_2) = \beta_2 z_1^{(3)}(0). \tag{96}$$

By applying equation (6.11) we have at the final points

$$z_1^{(3)}(T_3) = 0, \tag{97}$$

$$z_2^{(3)}(T_3) = 1. \tag{98}$$

From equations (93) and (98) it is seen that

$$z_2^{(3)}(t) = 1, \qquad 0 \le t \le T_3. \tag{99}$$

Since the decision variable is not constrained, the minimum of the Hamiltonian for each branch occurs at the stationary point. We obtain $\theta^{(n)}(t)$ from equations (86), (87), and (88) as

$$\frac{\partial H^{(1)}}{\partial \theta^{(1)}} = z_1^{(1)} + z_2^{(1)} \theta^{(1)} = 0,$$

or

$$\bar{\theta}^{(1)} = -\frac{z_1^{(1)}}{z_2^{(1)}}, \tag{100}$$

$$\frac{\partial H^{(2)}}{\partial \theta^{(2)}} = -z_1^{(2)} x_1^{(2)} + \theta^{(2)} z_1^{(2)} = 0,$$

or

$$\bar{\theta}^{(2)} = x_1^{(2)}, \tag{101}$$

$$\frac{\partial H^{(3)}}{\partial \theta^{(3)}} = z_1^{(3)} + z_2^{(3)} \theta^{(3)} = 0,$$

or

$$\bar{\theta}^{(3)} = -\frac{z_1^{(3)}}{z_2^{(3)}}. \tag{102}$$

Substituting equation (99) into equation (95), we obtain

$$z_2^{(1)}(T_1) = \beta_1. \tag{103}$$

Combining equations (90) and (103) and inserting the resulting equation into (100), we have

$$\bar{\theta}^{(1)} = -\frac{z_1^{(1)}}{\beta_1}. \tag{104}$$

Insertion of equation (99) into equation (102) yields

$$\bar{\theta}^{(3)} = -z_1^{(3)}. \tag{105}$$

Substituting equations (101), (104), and (105) into equations (78), (80), (82), (89), (91), and (92), we have

$$\frac{dx_1^{(1)}}{dt} = -ax_1^{(1)} - \frac{z_1^{(1)}}{\beta_1}, \tag{106}$$

$$\frac{dx_1^{(2)}}{dt} = -(x_1^{(2)})^2 + \tfrac{1}{2}(x_1^{(2)})^2 = -\tfrac{1}{2}(x_1^{(2)})^2, \tag{107}$$

$$\frac{dx_1^{(3)}}{dt} = -ax_1^{(3)} - z_1^{(3)}, \tag{108}$$

$$\frac{dz_1^{(1)}}{dt} = az_1^{(1)} - \beta_1 x_1^{(1)}, \tag{109}$$

$$\frac{dz_1^{(2)}}{dt} = z_1^{(2)} x_1^{(2)}, \tag{110}$$

$$\frac{dz_1^{(3)}}{dt} = az_1^{(3)} - x_1^{(3)}. \tag{111}$$

Equations (106) and (109) can be integrated simultaneously to give

$$x_1^{(1)}(t) = B_1 e^{\lambda t} + B_2 e^{-\lambda t}, \qquad\qquad 0 \le t \le T_1 \tag{112}$$
$$z_1^{(1)}(t) = -\beta_1 B_1 (\lambda + a) e^{\lambda t} + \beta_1 B_2 (\lambda - a) e^{-\lambda t}, \qquad 0 \le t \le T_1 \tag{113}$$

where $\lambda = \sqrt{a^2 + 1}$ and $B_1$ and $B_2$ are integration constants. Similarly, for branch 3, equations (108) and (111) can be integrated to give

$$x_1^{(3)}(t) = A_1 e^{\lambda t} + A_2 e^{-\lambda t}, \qquad\qquad 0 \le t \le T_3, \tag{114}$$
$$z_1^{(3)}(t) = -A_1(\lambda + a) e^{\lambda t} + A_2(\lambda - a) e^{-\lambda t}, \qquad 0 \le t \le T_3. \tag{115}$$

To obtain the optimal solution for branch 2, equation (107) is integrated first. The result is then substituted into equation (110) which is then integrated. The results are

$$x_1^{(2)}(t) = \frac{2}{t - C_1}, \qquad\qquad 0 \le t \le T_2, \tag{116}$$

$$z_1^{(2)}(t) = C_2(t - C_1)^2, \qquad 0 \le t \le T_2. \tag{117}$$

Thus we have a system of six simultaneous equations to solve for six integration constants, $A_1$, $A_2$, $B_1$, $B_2$, $C_1$, and $C_2$, subject to the following set of boundary conditions:

$$x_1^{(1)}(0) = \alpha_1, \tag{78}$$

$$x_1^{(2)}(0) = \alpha_2, \tag{80}$$

$$x_1^{(3)}(0) = \beta_1 x_1^{(1)}(T_1) + \beta_2 x_1^{(2)}(T_2), \tag{84}$$

$$z_1^{(1)}(T_1) = \beta_1 z_1^{(3)}(0), \tag{94}$$

$$z_1^{(2)}(T_2) = \beta_2 z_1^{(3)}(0), \tag{96}$$

$$z_1^{(3)}(T_3) = 0. \tag{97}$$

Substituting the boundary conditions into equations (112) through (117), we have

$$\alpha_1 = B_1 + B_2, \tag{118}$$

$$\alpha_2 = -\frac{2}{C_1}, \tag{119}$$

$$\beta_1 x_1^{(1)}(T_1) + \beta_2 x_1^{(2)}(T_2) = A_1 + A_2, \tag{120}$$

$$\beta_1 z_1^{(3)}(0) = -\beta_1 B_1 (\lambda + a) e^{\lambda T_1} + \beta_1 B_2 (\lambda - a) e^{-\lambda T_1}, \tag{121}$$

$$\beta_2 z_1^{(3)}(0) = C_2 (T_2 - C_1)^2, \tag{122}$$

$$A_1 (\lambda + a) e^{\lambda T_3} - A_2 (\lambda - a) e^{-\lambda T_3} = 0. \tag{123}$$

Rewriting equations (118), (119), and (123), we have

$$B_2 = \alpha_1 - B_1, \tag{124}$$

$$C_1 = -\frac{2}{\alpha_2}, \tag{125}$$

$$A_2 = \frac{k}{\lambda - a} A_1, \tag{126}$$

where

$$k = (\lambda + a) e^{2\lambda T_3}.$$

Substituting equations (124), (125), and (126) into (120), (121), and (122), we obtain

$$\beta_1 x_1^{(1)}(T_1) + \beta_2 x_1^{(2)}(T_2) = A_1 \left( 1 + \frac{k}{\lambda - a} \right), \tag{127}$$

$$z_1^{(3)}(0) = -B_1 (\lambda + a) e^{\lambda T_1} + (\alpha_1 - B_1)(\lambda - a) e^{-\lambda T_1}, \tag{128}$$

$$\beta_2 z_1^{(3)}(0) = C_2 \left( T_2 + \frac{2}{\alpha_2} \right)^2. \tag{129}$$

But, from equations (112), (116), and (115), we have

$$x_1^{(1)}(T_1) = B_1 e^{\lambda T_1} + (\alpha_1 - B_1)e^{-\lambda T_1}, \tag{130}$$

$$x_1^{(2)}(T_2) = \frac{2}{T_2 + 2/\alpha_2} = \frac{2\alpha_2}{T_2\alpha_2 + 2}, \tag{131}$$

$$z_1^{(3)}(0) = A_1(k - \lambda - a). \tag{132}$$

By substituting equations (130) and (131) into (127) and inserting equation (132) into (128) and (129) we have

$$\left(1 + \frac{k}{\lambda - a}\right)A_1 - \beta_1(e^{\lambda T_1} - e^{-\lambda T_1})B_1 = \beta_1\alpha_1 e^{-\lambda T_1} + \frac{2\beta_2\alpha_2}{T_2\alpha_2 + 2}, \tag{133}$$

$$(\lambda + a - k)A_1 - [(\lambda + a)e^{\lambda T_1} + (\lambda - a)e^{-\lambda T_1}]B_1 = -\alpha_1(\lambda - a)e^{-\lambda T_1}, \tag{134}$$

$$\beta_2(\lambda + a - k)A_1 + \left(T_2 + \frac{2}{\alpha_2}\right)^2 C_2 = 0. \tag{135}$$

Let

$$m = \frac{[(\lambda + a)e^{\lambda T_1} + (\lambda - a)e^{-\lambda T_1}]}{(\lambda + a) - k},$$

$$h = \frac{\alpha_1(\lambda - a)e^{-\lambda T_1}}{(\lambda + a) - k},$$

$$n = \frac{\beta_1(e^{\lambda T_1} - e^{-\lambda T_1})}{1 + k/(\lambda - a)},$$

$$f = \frac{\beta_1\alpha_1 e^{-\lambda T_1} + 2\beta_2\alpha_2/(T_2\alpha_2 + 2)}{1 + k/(\lambda - a)},$$

$$g = \frac{(T_2 + 2/\alpha_2)^2}{[(\lambda + a) - k]\beta_2}.$$

Then equations (133) through (135) can be written as

$$A_1 - nB_1 + 0 = f, \tag{136}$$

$$A_1 - mB_1 + 0 = -h, \tag{137}$$

$$A_1 + 0 + gC_2 = 0. \tag{138}$$

Solving the last three equations for $A_1$, $B_1$, and $C_2$, we have

$$A_1 = \frac{\begin{vmatrix} f & -n & 0 \\ -h & -m & 0 \\ 0 & 0 & g \end{vmatrix}}{\begin{vmatrix} 1 & -n & 0 \\ 1 & -m & 0 \\ 1 & 0 & g \end{vmatrix}} = \frac{mf + nh}{m - n}, \tag{139}$$

$$B_1 = \frac{\begin{vmatrix} 1 & f & 0 \\ 1 & -h & 0 \\ 1 & 0 & g \end{vmatrix}}{\begin{vmatrix} 1 & -n & 0 \\ 1 & -m & 0 \\ 1 & 0 & g \end{vmatrix}} = \frac{h + f}{m - n}, \tag{140}$$

$$C_2 = \frac{\begin{vmatrix} 1 & -n & f \\ 1 & -m & -h \\ 1 & 0 & 0 \end{vmatrix}}{\begin{vmatrix} 1 & -n & 0 \\ 1 & -m & 0 \\ 1 & 0 & g \end{vmatrix}} = -\frac{nh + mf}{(m - n)g}. \tag{141}$$

Equations (124), (125), and (126) may now be written as

$$B_2 = \alpha_1 - \frac{h + f}{m - n}, \tag{142}$$

$$C_1 = -\frac{2}{\alpha_2}, \tag{125}$$

$$A_2 = \left(\frac{k}{\lambda - a}\right)\left(\frac{mf + nh}{m - n}\right). \tag{143}$$

Substituting equations (140) and (142) into (112) and (113), we obtain

$$x_1^{(1)}(t) = \left(\frac{h + f}{m - n}\right)e^{\lambda t} + \left(\alpha_1 - \frac{h + f}{m - n}\right)e^{-\lambda t}, \quad 0 \le t \le T_1 \tag{144}$$

$$z_1^{(1)}(t) = -\beta_1\left[\left(\frac{h + f}{m - n}\right)(\lambda + a)e^{\lambda t} - \left(\alpha_1 - \frac{h + f}{m - n}\right)(\lambda - a)e^{-\lambda t}\right],$$
$$0 \le t \le T_1. \tag{145}$$

Similarly, by substituting equations (125) and (141) into (116) and (117) we obtain

$$x_1^{(2)}(t) = \frac{2\alpha_2}{t\alpha_2 + 2}, \qquad\qquad 0 \le t \le T_2, \qquad (146)$$

$$z_1^{(2)}(t) = -\left[\frac{nh + mf}{(m - n)g}\right]\left(\frac{2 + t\alpha_2}{\alpha_2}\right)^2, \qquad 0 \le t \le T_2. \qquad (147)$$

Finally, substituting equations (139) and (143) into (114) and (115), we obtain

$$x_1^{(3)}(t) = \left(\frac{mf + nh}{m - n}\right)\left[e^{\lambda t} + \left(\frac{k}{\lambda - a}\right)e^{-\lambda t}\right], \qquad 0 \le t \le T_3, \quad (148)$$

$$z_1^{(3)}(t) = -\left(\frac{mf + nh}{m - n}\right)[(\lambda + a)e^{\lambda t} - ke^{-\lambda t}], \qquad 0 \le t \le T_3. \quad (149)$$

Substitution of equations (145), (146), and (149) into (104), (101), and (105), respectively, yields the optimal solution of this system. Once the optimal decision has been obtained, the functional dependence of $x_2^{(n)}(t)$, $n = 1, 3$ on $t$ can be obtained by integrating equations (79) and (83).

*b.   A First-Order Irreversible Consecutive Reaction $A \xrightarrow{k_1} B \xrightarrow{k_2} C$ Taking Place in a Series of Tubular Reactors with Intermediate Feed.* In Section 1, part b, we dealt with a continuous complex process which involved a separating point and a first-order irreversible consecutive

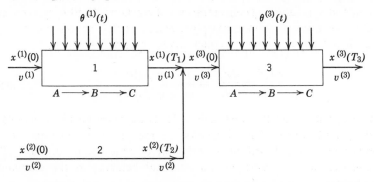

**Fig. 7.5**   Schematic diagram of two tubular reactors connected in series with additional fresh feed fed at an intermediate point for the reaction $A \to B \to C$.

reaction. In this part we shall consider a similar problem which involves a combining point rather than a separating point. In the schematic diagram of this process (Fig. 7.5) $v^{(k)}$ represents the volumetric flow rate through the $k$th branch. Note that the geometrical arrangement of the two tubular reactors is similar to that of Section 1, part b, except that additional fresh feed is introduced at an intermediate point. The length of reactors, $L_1$, $L_3$ and the cross-sectional areas, $A^{(1)}$, $A^{(3)}$ are all specified, i.e. the volumes of the reactors are fixed, or alternatively the holding time of the reactors are given with fixed volumetric flow rates. We wish to maximize the intermediate product $B$ at the end of branch 3 by proper choice of temperature along the two tubular reactors for given inlet concentrations of both feeds.

From the material balance for each component, as carried out in Section 1, part b, the performance equations for branches 1 and 3 in which the reactions take place can be written as

$$\frac{dx_1^{(1)}}{dt} = -k_1^{(1)} x_1^{(1)}, \qquad x_1^{(1)}(0) = \alpha_1, \tag{150}$$

$$\frac{dx_2^{(1)}}{dt} = k_1^{(1)} x_1^{(1)} - k_2^{(1)} x_2^{(1)}, \qquad x_2^{(1)}(0) = \alpha_{2,} \tag{151}$$

$$\frac{dx_1^{(3)}}{dt} = -k_1^{(3)} x_1^{(3)}, \tag{152}$$

$$\frac{dx_2^{(3)}}{dt} = k_1^{(3)} x_1^{(3)} - k_2^{(3)} x_2^{(3)}. \tag{153}$$

where $x_1$, $x_2$, $t$, $k_1$, and $k_2$ are the same as defined in Section 1, part b, and $\alpha_1$ and $\alpha_2$ are the feed concentrations of reactants $A$ and $B$, respectively. Because no transformations take place and no control actions are imposed in branch 2, the performance equations for branch 2 are

$$\frac{dx_1^{(2)}}{dt} = \frac{dx_2^{(2)}}{dt} = 0, \qquad \begin{matrix} x_1^{(2)}(0) = \beta_1, \\ x_2^{(2)}(0) = \beta_2, \end{matrix} \tag{154}$$

where $\beta_1$ and $\beta_2$ are the intermediate feed concentrations of reactants $A$ and $B$, respectively. The derivation of the junction equations at the combining point is based on the principle of conservation of mass. The application of this principle (the material balance) at the combining point yields

$$v^{(3)} x_1^{(3)}(0) = v^{(1)} x_1^{(1)}(T_1) + v^{(2)} x_1^{(2)}(T_2), \tag{155a}$$

where $v^{(k)}$, $k = 1, 2, 3$, is the total volumetric flow rate through the $k$th branch. If we let $\gamma_1 = v^{(1)}/v^{(3)}$ and $\gamma_2 = v^{(2)}/v^{(3)}$, equation (155a) can be rewritten as

$$x_1^{(3)}(0) = \gamma_1 x_1^{(1)}(T_1) + \gamma_2 x_1^{(2)}(T_2). \tag{155b}$$

According to equation (154) the concentrations of reactants 1 and 2 remain constant along branch 2. Thus for reactant 1 we have

$$x_1^{(2)}(0) = x_1^{(2)}(t) = x_1^{(2)}(T_2) = \beta_1. \tag{156}$$

By substituting equation (156) into equation (155b) we obtain a junction equation at the combining point for reactant 1:

$$x_1^{(3)}(0) = \gamma_1 x_1^{(1)}(T_1) + \gamma_2 \beta_1. \tag{157a}$$

Similarly, we have for reactant 2

$$x_2^{(3)}(0) = \gamma_1 x_2^{(1)}(T_1) + \gamma_2 \beta_2. \tag{157b}$$

The initial states are

$$
\begin{aligned}
x_1^{(1)}(0) &= \alpha_1, \\
x_2^{(1)}(0) &= \alpha_2,
\end{aligned}
\tag{158}
$$

According to equations (6.6) and (6.7), we obtain

$$H^{(1)} = z_1^{(1)}(-k_1^{(1)} x_1^{(1)}) + z_2^{(1)} (k_1^{(1)} x_1^{(1)} - k_2^{(1)} x_2^{(1)}), \tag{159}$$

$$H^{(2)} = 0, \tag{160}$$

$$H^{(3)} = z_1^{(3)}(-k_1^{(3)} x_1^{(3)}) + z_2^{(3)}(k_1^{(3)} x_1^{(3)} - k_2^{(3)} x_2^{(3)}), \tag{161}$$

$$\frac{dz_1^{(1)}}{dt} = k_1^{(1)} z_1^{(1)} - k_1^{(1)} z_2^{(1)}, \tag{162}$$

$$\frac{dz_2^{(1)}}{dt} = k_2^{(1)} z_2^{(1)}, \tag{163}$$

$$\frac{dz_1^{(2)}}{dt} = \frac{dz_2^{(2)}}{dt} = 0, \tag{164}$$

$$\frac{dz_1^{(3)}}{dt} = k_1^{(3)} z_1^{(3)} - k_1^{(3)} z_2^{(3)}, \tag{165}$$

$$\frac{dz_2^{(3)}}{dt} = k_2^{(3)} z_2^{(3)}. \tag{166}$$

According to equations (6.9), (157a), and (157b), we have at the combining point

$$z_1^{(1)}(T_1) = \gamma_1 z_1^{(3)}(0), \tag{167}$$

$$z_2^{(1)}(T_1) = \gamma_1 z_2^{(3)}(0). \tag{168}$$

Since the problem is to maximize the product $B$ at the outlet of branch 3, the objective function is $x_2^{(3)}(T_3)$. Consequently, we have $c_1^{(3)} = 0$ and $c_2^{(3)} = 1$. Thus, according to equation (6.11), we have at the final point

$$z_1^{(3)}(T_3) = 0, \tag{169}$$

$$z_2^{(3)}(T_3) = 1. \tag{170}$$

The optimal temperature, $\bar{\theta}(t)$, is determined in the manner given in Section 1, part b, and the results are substituted into equations (150) through (153) and equations (162) through (166). These results are

$$\bar{\theta}^{(n)}(t) = \left(\frac{E_1 - E_2}{R}\right) \left\{ \ln\left[ \xi \frac{x_1^{(n)}(z_2^{(n)} - z_1^{(n)})}{x_2^{(n)} z_2^{(n)}} \right] \right\}^{-1}, \tag{171}$$

where

$$n = 1, 3 \quad \text{and} \quad \xi = \frac{k_{10}E_1}{k_{20}E_2},$$

and

$$\frac{dx_1^{(1)}}{dt} = -k_{10}\left[ \xi \frac{x_1^{(1)}}{x_2^{(1)}} \left( \frac{z_2^{(1)} - z_1^{(1)}}{z_2^{(1)}} \right) \right]^{\lambda_1} x_1^{(1)}, \tag{172}$$

$$\frac{dx_2^{(1)}}{dt} = k_{10}\left[ \xi \frac{x_1^{(1)}}{x_2^{(1)}} \left( \frac{z_2^{(1)} - z_1^{(1)}}{z_2^{(1)}} \right) \right]^{\lambda_1} x_1^{(1)} \\ - k_{20}\left[ \xi \frac{x_1^{(1)}}{x_2^{(1)}} \left( \frac{z_2^{(1)} - z_1^{(1)}}{z_2^{(1)}} \right) \right]^{\lambda_2} x_2^{(1)}, \tag{173}$$

$$\frac{dx_1^{(3)}}{dt} = -k_{10}\left[ \xi \frac{x_1^{(3)}}{x_2^{(3)}} \left( \frac{z_2^{(3)} - z_1^{(3)}}{z_2^{(3)}} \right) \right]^{\lambda_1} x_1^{(3)}, \tag{174}$$

$$\frac{dx_2^{(3)}}{dt} = k_{10}\left[ \xi \frac{x_1^{(3)}}{x_2^{(3)}} \left( \frac{z_2^{(3)} - z_1^{(3)}}{z_2^{(3)}} \right) \right]^{\lambda_1} x_1^{(3)} \\ - k_{20}\left[ \xi \frac{x_1^{(3)}}{x_2^{(3)}} \left( \frac{z_2^{(3)} - z_1^{(3)}}{z_2^{(3)}} \right) \right]^{\lambda_2} x_2^{(3)}, \tag{175}$$

$$\frac{dz_1^{(1)}}{dt} = k_{10}\left[ \xi \frac{x_1^{(1)}}{x_2^{(1)}} \left( \frac{z_2^{(1)} - z_1^{(1)}}{z_2^{(1)}} \right) \right]^{\lambda_1} (z_1^{(1)} - z_2^{(1)}), \tag{176}$$

$$\frac{dz_2^{(1)}}{dt} = k_{20}\left[ \xi \frac{x_1^{(1)}}{x_2^{(1)}} \left( \frac{z_2^{(1)} - z_1^{(1)}}{z_2^{(1)}} \right) \right]^{\lambda_2} z_2^{(1)}, \tag{177}$$

$$\frac{dz_1^{(3)}}{dt} = k_{10}\left[ \xi \frac{x_1^{(3)}}{x_2^{(3)}} \left( \frac{z_2^{(3)} - z_1^{(3)}}{z_2^{(3)}} \right) \right]^{\lambda_1} (z_1^{(3)} - z_2^{(3)}), \tag{178}$$

$$\frac{dz_2^{(3)}}{dt} = k_{20}\left[ \xi \frac{x_1^{(3)}}{x_2^{(3)}} \left( \frac{z_2^{(3)} - z_1^{(3)}}{z_2^{(3)}} \right) \right]^{\lambda_2} z_2^{(3)}. \tag{179}$$

To solve this system of eight differential equations we need the eight boundary conditions given by equations (157a), (157b), and (158) and (167) through (170).

The numerical calculations for the system described by equations (172) through (179) are illustrated by use of the following data:

$$k_{10} = 0.535 \times 10^{11}/\text{min},$$
$$k_{20} = 0.461 \times 10^{18}/\text{min},$$
$$E_1 = 18,000 \text{ cal/mole},$$
$$E_2 = 30,000 \text{ cal/mole},$$
$$R = 2 \text{ cal/mole } °K,$$
$$T_1 = 8 \text{ min},$$
$$T_3 = 10 \text{ min},$$
$$\alpha_1 = 0.72 \text{ moles/liter},$$
$$\alpha_2 = 0.24 \text{ moles/liter},$$
$$\gamma_1 = 0.5 \text{ dimensionless},$$
$$\gamma_2 = 0.5 \text{ dimensionless},$$
$$\beta_1 = 0.7 \text{ moles/liter},$$
$$\beta_2 = 0.25 \text{ moles/liter}$$

Backward integration by an approximate iterative Runge-Kutta method (see Appendix I) was used to obtain the numerical results tabulated in Table 7.2 and plotted in Figs. 7.6a and b. The numerical procedure is similar to that in Section 1, part b, in which a separating branch has been considered, but the convergence is much slower because of the boundary conditions given in equations (157a), (157b), (167), and (168). For additional solutions for various values of $\gamma_1$ and for further detail on the numerical solution see Reference 2.

The results were verified independently by two different methods which are the material balance of reactant $C$ and the perturbation check. The latter is carried out by evaluating the change of the yield of reactant $B$ with the change of the temperature around the optimal value.

## 3. OPTIMIZATION OF RECYCLE PROCESSES

Recycle processes are employed widely in the chemical and process industries. The basic principle of recycle processes, as it is applied to a chemical reaction system, is to feed back a portion of the product into the reactor inlet and to mix it continuously with fresh feed. This process is a complex one in that both separating and combining points appear simultaneously in the process.

***Table 2.7.***  Computational Results for the Reaction $A \rightarrow B \rightarrow C$
Taking Place in Two Tubular Reactors Connected in Series
with Intermediate Feed

| $\eta_3$ | $x_1^{(3)}$ | $x_2^{(3)}$ | $z_1^{(3)}$ | $z_2^{(3)}$ | $\theta^{(3)}$ |
|---|---|---|---|---|---|
| 1.0 | 0.15552 | 0.67714 | 0.00000 | 1.00000 | 334.24 |
| 0.9 | 0.17344 | 0.66939 | 0.10252 | 0.98501 | 334.44 |
| 0.8 | 0.19378 | 0.65937 | 0.19437 | 0.96982 | 334.67 |
| 0.7 | 0.21700 | 0.64665 | 0.27648 | 0.95436 | 334.93 |
| 0.6 | 0.24364 | 0.63068 | 0.34972 | 0.93856 | 335.25 |
| 0.5 | 0.27442 | 0.61074 | 0.41484 | 0.92231 | 335.62 |
| 0.4 | 0.31033 | 0.58588 | 0.47256 | 0.90544 | 336.07 |
| 0.3 | 0.35270 | 0.55477 | 0.52348 | 0.88776 | 336.63 |
| 0.2 | 0.40351 | 0.51545 | 0.56814 | 0.86891 | 337.35 |
| 0.1 | 0.46590 | 0.46482 | 0.60701 | 0.84834 | 338.32 |
| 0.0 | 0.54543 | 0.39735 | 0.64046 | 0.82499 | 340.00 |

| $\eta_1$ | $x_1^{(1)}$ | $x_2^{(1)}$ | $z_1^{(1)}$ | $z_2^{(1)}$ | $\theta^{(1)}$ |
|---|---|---|---|---|---|
| 1.0 | 0.39084 | 0.54469 | 0.32023 | 0.41249 | 327.70 |
| 0.9 | 0.41136 | 0.52684 | 0.32478 | 0.41045 | 327.97 |
| 0.8 | 0.43349 | 0.50738 | 0.32910 | 0.40834 | 328.28 |
| 0.7 | 0.45747 | 0.48609 | 0.33319 | 0.40613 | 328.63 |
| 0.6 | 0.48360 | 0.46266 | 0.33707 | 0.40383 | 329.02 |
| 0.5 | 0.51225 | 0.43673 | 0.34074 | 0.40140 | 329.48 |
| 0.4 | 0.54392 | 0.40780 | 0.34419 | 0.39880 | 330.03 |
| 0.3 | 0.57930 | 0.37517 | 0.34744 | 0.39601 | 330.69 |
| 0.2 | 0.61942 | 0.33782 | 0.35049 | 0.39294 | 331.51 |
| 0.1 | 0.66589 | 0.29415 | 0.35333 | 0.38948 | 332.59 |
| 0.0 | 0.72160 | 0.24126 | 0.35600 | 0.38540 | 334.00 |

In this section we consider several types of chemical reactions that take place in a tubular reactor with recycle. Various mathematical models are used to represent tubular reactors according to the extent of fluid (reacting stream) mixing in the reactors. We first consider the behavior of an autocatalytic reaction in a plug flow reactor with recycle. We then proceed to a first-order reversible reaction in a recycled tubular reactor by taking into account the effects of axial diffusion. In the final problem a plug flow reactor with part of the product recycled through a second plug flow reactor is considered.

***a.  Autocatalytic Reaction.***    An autocatalytic reaction in which one of the products acts catalytically presents a rather unusual problem because its

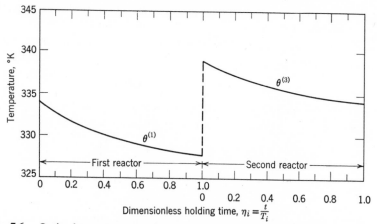

**Fig. 7.6a** Optimal temperature profiles in two tubular reactors connected in series with additional fresh feed fed at an intermediate point for the reaction $A \rightarrow B \rightarrow C$.

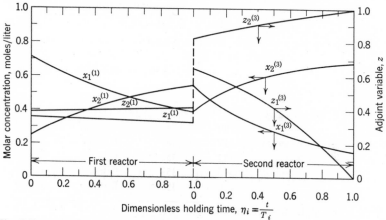

**Fig. 7.6b** Optimal concentration profiles in two tubular reactors connected in series with fresh feed fed at an intermediate point for the reaction $A \rightarrow B \rightarrow C$.

rate of reaction is influenced by both reactants and products. In this section we consider an autocatalytic reaction of the type

$$A + R \underset{k_2}{\overset{k_1}{\rightleftharpoons}} R + R$$

in a tubular reactor in which a portion of the product stream is recycled into the inlet stream and mixed continuously with the fresh feed stream, as shown in Fig. 7.7. The system consists of four branches: the feed line (branch 1) of length $L_1$, the reactor (branch 2) of length $L_2$, the discharge line (branch 3) of length $L_3$, and the recycle line (branch 4) of length $L_4$, with the total volumetric flow rates of $v^{(1)}$, $v^{(2)}$, $v^{(3)}$, and $v^{(4)}$, respectively.

We shall assume that the kinetic equation can be written, with respect to production of reactant $A$, as

$$R_A = -k_1(C_A)^a(C_R)^r + k_2(C_R)^s, \tag{180}$$

where $C_i$ is the molar concentration of component $i$, and $a$, $r$, and $s$ are the order of the reaction. We have at every point along the reactor

$$C_0 = C_{A_0} + C_{R_0} = C_A + C_R,$$

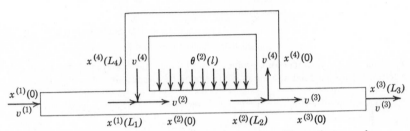

**Fig. 7.7**  Schematic diagram of a tubular reactor with product recycle.

where $C_{i_0}$ is the initial molar concentration of reactant $i$. Therefore (180) can be rewritten as

$$R_A = -k_1(C_A)^a(C_0 - C_A)^r + k_2(C_0 - C_A)^s.$$

By rearranging this equation we obtain

$$R_A = -k_1\left(\frac{C_A}{C_0}\right)^a\left(1 - \frac{C_A}{C_0}\right)^r(C_0)^{a+r} + k_2(C_0)^s\left(1 - \frac{C_A}{C_0}\right)^s. \tag{181}$$

The steady-state differential material balance for reactant $A$ in a differential section $dl$ of the reactor yields

{rate of input of component $A$ at the inlet of the differential
section $dl$ of the reactor}

— {rate of output of component $A$ at the outlet of the differential
section $dl$ of the reactor}

+ {rate of production of component $A$ in the differential section
$dl$ of the reactor}

= 0

or

$$\{v^{(2)}\,C_A^{(2)}\} - \left\{v^{(2)}\,C_A^{(2)} + v^{(2)}\frac{dC_A^{(2)}}{dl}\,dl\right\} + A^{(2)}\,dl\{R_A\} = 0,$$

where $A^{(2)}$ is the cross-sectional area of branch 2. For a reactor with a unit cross-sectional area this equation reduces to

$$v^{(2)} \frac{dC_A^{(2)}}{dl} = \{R_A\}$$

or

$$\frac{dC_A^{(2)}}{dl} = \frac{1}{v^{(2)}} \{R_A\}.$$

By substituting equation (181) into this equation we obtain

$$\frac{dC_A^{(2)}}{dl} = -\frac{1}{v^{(2)}} \left[ k_1 \left( \frac{C_A^{(2)}}{C_0} \right)^a \left( 1 - \frac{C_A^{(2)}}{C_0} \right)^r (C_0)^{a+r} - k_2 \left( 1 - \frac{C_A^{(2)}}{C_0} \right)^s (C_0)^s \right]. \quad (182)$$

In terms of the fractional molar concentration, $x_1 = C_A/C_0$, we can rewrite equation (182) as

$$\frac{dx_1^{(2)}}{dl} = -\frac{1}{v^{(2)}} [k_1(x_1^{(2)})^a (1 - x_1^{(2)})^r (C_0)^{a+r-1} - k_2(1 - x_1^{(2)})^s (C_0)^{s-1}], \quad (183)$$

where subscript 1 refers to reactant $A$ (component 1). If we let $C_0 = C_A + C_R = 1$ at any point along the reactor, equation (183) can be replaced by

$$\frac{dx_1^{(2)}}{dl} = -\frac{1}{v^{(2)}} [k_1(x_1^{(2)})^a (1 - x_1^{(2)})^r - k_2(1 - x_1^{(2)})^s]. \quad (184)$$

Since no transformations are taking place and no control actions are imposed on branch 1 (the feed line), branch 3 (the discharge line), and branch 4 (the recycle line), the performance equations for these branches are

$$\frac{dx_1^{(1)}}{dl} = \frac{dx_1^{(3)}}{dl} = \frac{dx_1^{(4)}}{dl} = 0. \quad (185)$$

The material balance at the combining point gives

$$v^{(2)} x_1^{(2)}(0) = v^{(1)} x_1^{(1)}(L_1) + v^{(4)} x_1^{(4)}(L_4)$$

or

$$x_1^{(2)}(0) = \alpha x_1^{(1)}(L_1) + \beta x_1^{(4)}(L_4), \quad (186)$$

where

$$\alpha = \frac{v^{(1)}}{v^{(2)}} \quad \text{and} \quad \beta = \frac{v^{(4)}}{v^{(2)}}.$$

Since the outlet stream from branch 2 splits into two streams, recycle and discharge, mechanically, the concentration of component 1 at the separating point is the same with respect to all streams:

$$x_1^{(2)}(L_2) = x_1^{(3)}(0), \tag{187}$$

$$x_1^{(2)}(L_2) = x_1^{(4)}(0). \tag{188}$$

Equation (186) represents the combination of state variables from the feed and recycle streams at the combining point and equations (187) and (188) represent the condition of the state variables at the separating point. This example of a recycle process is therefore an application of a process that involves both combining and separating points simultaneously. The initial state is given by

$$x_1^{(1)}(0) = \gamma. \tag{189}$$

We now wish to find the temperature profile, denoted by $\theta_1^{(2)}(l)$, which maximizes the yield of product $R$, or, equivalently, to minimize $x_1^{(3)}(L_3)$. Since the objective function is $x_1^{(3)}(L_3)$, we have $c_1^{(3)} = 1$.

The Hamiltonian and the adjoint variables, according to equations (6.6) and (6.7), then become

$$H^{(1)} = H^{(3)} = H^{(4)} = 0, \tag{190}$$

$$H^{(2)} = \left\{ -\frac{k_1(\theta_1^{(2)})}{v^{(2)}} [(x_1^{(2)})^a (1 - x_1^{(2)})^r] + \frac{k_2(\theta_1^{(2)})}{v^{(2)}} (1 - x_1^{(2)})^s \right\} z_1^{(2)}, \tag{191}$$

$$\frac{dz_1^{(1)}}{dl} = \frac{dz_1^{(3)}}{dl} = \frac{dz_1^{(4)}}{dl} = 0, \tag{192}$$

$$\frac{dz_1^{(2)}}{dl} = \frac{k_1(\theta_1^{(2)})}{v^{(2)}} [a(x_1^{(2)})^{a-1}(1 - x_1^{(2)})^r - r(x_1^{(2)})^a (1 - x_1^{(2)})^{r-1}] z_1^{(2)}$$

$$+ \frac{k_2(\theta_1^{(2)})}{v^{(2)}} [s(1 - x_1^{(2)})^{s-1}] z_1^{(2)}. \tag{193}$$

When the minimum of $H^{(2)}$ occurs at the stationary point, we obtain the optimal decision function, $\theta_1^{(2)}(l)$, by putting

$$\frac{\partial H^{(2)}}{\partial \theta_1^{(2)}} = 0. \tag{194}$$

Partial differentiation of equation (191) with respect to $\theta^{(2)}$ yields

$$\frac{\partial H^{(2)}}{\partial \theta_1^{(2)}} = -\frac{z_1^{(2)}}{v^{(2)}} \left\{ [(x_1^{(2)})^a (1 - x_1^{(2)})^r] \frac{dk_1(\theta_1^{(2)})}{d\theta_1^{(2)}} - (1 - x^{(2)})^s \frac{dk_2(\theta_1^{(2)})}{d\theta_1^{(2)}} \right\}. \tag{195}$$

If we let the reaction constants $k_1$ and $k_2$ be of the Arrhenius type and of the form

$$k_1(\theta_1^{(2)}) = k_{10} e^{-E_1/R\theta_1^{(2)}}, \tag{196}$$

$$k_2(\theta_1^{(2)}) = k_{20} e^{-E_2/R\theta_1^{(2)}}, \tag{197}$$

the differentiation of equations (196) and (197) with respect to $\theta_1^{(2)}$ yields

$$\frac{dk_1(\theta_1^{(2)})}{d\theta_1^{(2)}} = \frac{k_{10}E_1}{R(\theta_1^{(2)})^2} e^{-E_1/R\theta_1^{(2)}}, \tag{198}$$

$$\frac{dk_2(\theta_1^{(2)})}{d\theta_1^{(2)}} = \frac{k_{20}E_2}{R(\theta_1^{(2)})^2} e^{-E_2/R\theta_1^{(2)}}, \tag{199}$$

respectively.

Substituting equations (198) and (199) into (195) and solving for $\bar{\theta}_1^{(2)}(l)$, according to equation (194), we obtain

$$\bar{\theta}_1^{(2)}(l) = \left(\frac{E_1 - E_2}{R}\right)\frac{1}{\ln\left[\xi(x_1^{(2)})^a(1 - x_1^{(2)})^{r-s}\right]}, \tag{200}$$

where

$$\xi = \frac{k_{10}E_1}{k_{20}E_2}.$$

Substituting equation (200) into (196) and (197), we have

$$k_1(\theta_1^{(2)}) = k_{10}[\xi(x_1^{(2)})^a(1 - x_1^{(2)})^{r-s}]^{\lambda_1}, \tag{201}$$

$$k_2(\theta_1^{(2)}) = k_{20}[\xi(x_1^{(2)})^a(1 - x_1^{(2)})^{r-s}]^{\lambda_2}, \tag{202}$$

where

$$\lambda_1 = \frac{E_1}{E_2 - E_1} \quad \text{and} \quad \lambda_2 = \frac{E_2}{E_2 - E_1}.$$

Substituting equations (201) and (202) into (184), we have

$$\frac{dx_1^{(2)}}{dl} = -\frac{1}{v^{(2)}}[k_{10}(\xi)^{\lambda_1}(x_1^{(2)})^{a(\lambda_1+1)}(1 - x_1^{(2)})^{r(\lambda_1+1)-\lambda_1 s}$$
$$- k_{20}(\xi)^{\lambda_2}(x_1^{(2)})^{a\lambda_2}(1 - x_1^{(2)})^{r\lambda_2-s(\lambda_2-1)}]. \tag{203}$$

If for simplicity we assume that the activation energies of the forward and backward reactions are such that

$$\frac{E_2}{E_1} = 2 \quad \text{or} \quad \lambda_1 = 1 \quad \text{and} \quad \lambda_2 = 2,$$

integration of equation (203) leads to

$$l = \frac{v^{(2)}}{k_{20}(\xi)^2 - k_{10}\xi}\int\frac{dx_1^{(2)}}{(x_1^{(2)})^{2a}(1 - x_1^{(2)})^{2r-s}}. \tag{204}$$

For the actual numerical calculations three different examples are considered:

1. All the reactions are first-order with respect to each component; that is, $a = r = s = 1$.

2. The forward reaction is first-order with respect to each component and the backward reaction is zeroth-order; that is, $a = r = 1$ and $s = 0$.

3. The forward reaction is first-order with respect to each component and the backward reaction is second-order, that is, $a = r = 1$ and $s = 2$.

The integration of equation (204) for these three examples yields, respectively,

$$l = \frac{v^{(2)}}{k_{20}(\xi)^2 - k_{10}\xi}\left\{-\left[\frac{1}{x_1^{(2)}(l)}\right] - \ln\left[\frac{1}{x_1^{(2)}(l)} - 1\right]\right\} + C_1, \tag{205}$$

$$l = \frac{v^{(2)}}{k_{20}(\xi)^2 - k_{10}\xi}\left\{-\frac{1 - 2x_1^{(2)}(l)}{x_1^{(2)}(l)[1 - x_1^{(2)}(l)]} - 2\ln\left[\frac{1}{x_1^{(2)}(l)} - 1\right]\right\} + C_2, \tag{206}$$

$$l = \frac{v^{(2)}}{k_{20}(\xi)^2 - k_{10}\xi}\left[-\frac{1}{x_1^{(2)}(l)}\right] + C_3. \tag{207}$$

The integration constants $C_1$, $C_2$, and $C_3$ are obtained by using the junction equations given in equations (186) and (188) and the initial state given in equation (189). The results are

$$C_1 = \frac{v^{(2)}}{k_{20}(\xi)^2 - k_{10}\xi}\left\{\frac{1}{\alpha\gamma + \beta x_1^{(2)}(L_2)} + \ln\left[\frac{1}{\alpha\gamma + \beta x_1^{(2)}(L_2)} - 1\right]\right\}, \tag{208}$$

$$C_2 = \frac{v^{(2)}}{k_{20}(\xi)^2 - k_{10}\xi}\left\{\frac{1 - 2[\alpha\gamma + \beta x_1^{(2)}(L_2)]}{[\alpha\gamma + \beta x_1^{(2)}(L_2)][1 - \alpha\gamma - \beta x_1^{(2)}(L_2)]}\right.$$
$$\left. + 2\ln\left[\frac{1}{\alpha\gamma + \beta x_1^{(2)}(L_2)} - 1\right]\right\}, \tag{209}$$

$$C_3 = \frac{v^{(2)}}{k_{20}(\xi)^2 - k_{10}\xi}\left[\frac{1}{\alpha\gamma + \beta x_1^{(2)}(L_2)}\right]. \tag{210}$$

By substituting equations (208), (209), and (210) into (205), (206), and (207) we obtain

$$l = \frac{v^{(2)}}{k_{10}\xi - k_{20}(\xi)^2}\left\{\frac{1}{x_1^{(2)}(l)} + \ln\left[\frac{1}{x_1^{(2)}(l)} - 1\right]\right.$$
$$\left. - \left[\frac{1}{\alpha\gamma + \beta x_1^{(2)}(L_2)}\right] - \ln\left[\frac{1}{\alpha\gamma + \beta x_1^{(2)}(L_2)} - 1\right]\right\}, \tag{211}$$

$$l = \frac{v^{(2)}}{k_{10}\xi - k_{20}(\xi)^2}\left(\frac{1 - 2x_1^{(2)}(l)}{x_1^{(2)}(l)[1 - x_1^{(2)}(l)]} + 2\ln\left[\frac{1}{x_1^{(2)}(l)} - 1\right]\right.$$
$$- 2\ln\left[\frac{1}{\alpha\gamma + \beta x_1^{(2)}(L_2)} - 1\right] - \left\{\frac{1 - 2[\alpha\gamma + \beta x_1^{(2)}(L_2)]}{[\alpha\gamma + \beta x_1^{(2)}(L_2)][1 - \alpha\gamma - \beta x_1^{(2)}(L_2)]}\right\}\right), \tag{212}$$

$$l = \frac{v^{(2)}}{k_{10}\xi - k_{20}(\xi)^2}\left[\frac{1}{x_1^{(2)}(l)} - \frac{1}{\alpha\gamma + \beta x_1^{(2)}(L_2)}\right]. \tag{213}$$

*Table 7.3.* The Values of $k_{20}$ Used for Numerical Calculations

| | $k_{20}(\text{hr}^{-1})$ | $\xi = \dfrac{k_{10}E_1}{k_{20}E_2}$ | $\gamma = x_1^{(1)}(0)$ |
|---|---|---|---|
| $s = 0$ | $1.150 \times 10^7$ | $1.09 \times 10^{-2}$ | 0.85; 0.91; 0.95; 0.97; 0.99 |
| $s = 1$ | $1.995 \times 10^7$ | $6.29 \times 10^{-3}$ | 0.99 |
| $s = 2$ | $3.460 \times 10^7$ | $3.63 \times 10^{-3}$ | 0.99 |

The optimal decision $\bar{\theta}^{(2)}(l)$ is recovered from equations (211), (212), and (213), together with equation (200). For the numerical calculations of equations (211), (212), and (213) a few trial-and-error steps are required.

The numerical data used for equations (211), (212), (213) and (200) are given in Table 7.3 and in the following:

$$v^{(1)} = 1000 \text{ ft}^3/\text{hr},$$
$$E_1 = 10,000 \text{ Btu/lb-mole},$$
$$E_2 = 20,000 \text{ Btu/lb-mole},$$
$$k_{10} = 2.51 \times 10^5/\text{hr}.$$

It is worth noting that the magnitude of $k_{20}$, the frequency factor of the reaction-rate constant for the backward reaction, is taken in such a way that it increases as the order of reaction increases.

The results of the optimal temperature and concentration profiles for all three examples considered here are plotted in Figs. 7.8 through 7.10, with $\beta$, the fraction of product recycled, as a parameter and with the initial concentration of $A$, $\gamma = 0.99$. A better picture of the relative behavior of the conditions leading to the optimal performance of the autocatalytic reactors is perhaps obtained in a plot of conversion against $\beta$, as shown in Figs. 7.11, 7.12, and 7.13. It should be noted in these figures that each conversion corresponds to a particular value of $\beta$ and that the optimal conversion is given in each case; that is, the optimal temperature and concentration profiles are given for each value of $\beta$. Figures 7.11 and 7.12 show a certain level of $\beta$ at which we should operate to obtain the maximum conversion. For instance, the maximum conversion is obtained if we operate at $\beta = 0.15$ and $\gamma = 0.99$ for $s = 1$. Figure 7.11 also shows that for $s = 0$, depending on the initial concentration of $A$, the reaction does not proceed until a sufficient amount of product $R$ is recycled and mixed with the fresh feed. For instance, at $\gamma = 0.99$, no product $R$ is formed until the fraction of product recycled reaches 0.25.

**b. Optimal Temperature Profile for a First-Order Reversible Reaction Taking Place in a Recycling Tubular Reactor Accompanied by Axial Diffusion.** In Section 4.2, part d, we discussed the same reaction carried out in a tubular reactor with axial diffusion but without product recycle.

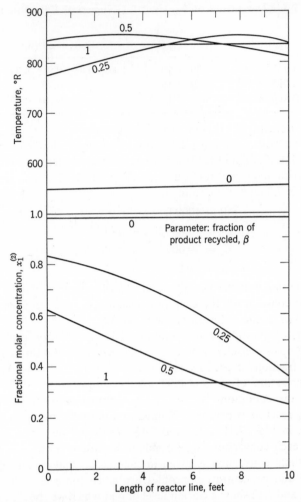

***Fig. 7.8*** Optimal concentration and temperature profiles for the autocatalytic reaction $A + R \rightleftharpoons R + R$ with the initial concentration of $\gamma = 0.99$ and with zero-order backward reaction.

In this section we consider a similar problem, except that the additional effect of product recycle on the optimal performance of the reactor is included (Fig. 7.7). As shown in this figure, the process consists of four branches, the feed line (branch 1) of length $L_1$, the reactor (branch 2) of length $L_2$, the discharge line (branch 3) of length $L_3$, and the recycle line (branch 4) of length $L_4$, with total volumetric flow rates of $v^{(1)}$, $v^{(2)}$, $v^{(3)}$, and $v^{(4)}$, respectively.

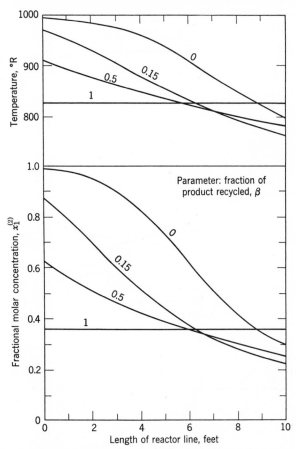

**Fig. 7.9** Optimal concentration and temperature profiles for the autocatalytic reaction $A + R \rightleftharpoons R + R$ with the initial concentration of $\gamma = 0.99$ and with the first-order backward reaction.

For a first-order reversible reaction

$$A \underset{k_2}{\overset{k_1}{\rightleftharpoons}} B$$

the rate of production of component $A$ is given by

$$R_A = -k_1 C_A + k_2 C_B, \tag{214}$$

where $C_i$ is molar concentration of component $i$ and $k_i$ is the specific rate constant given in equations (196) and (197).

The steady-state differential material balance of reactant $A$ in a

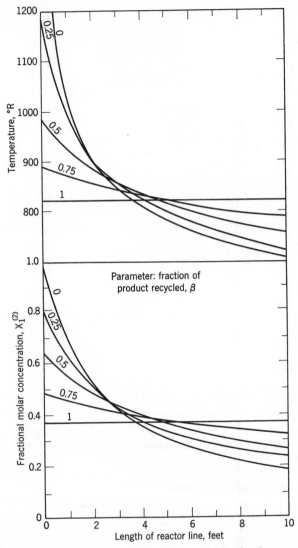

*Fig. 7.10*   Optimal concentration and temperature profiles for the autocatalytic reaction $A + R \rightleftharpoons R + R$, with the initial concentration of $\gamma = 0.99$ and with the second-order backward reaction.

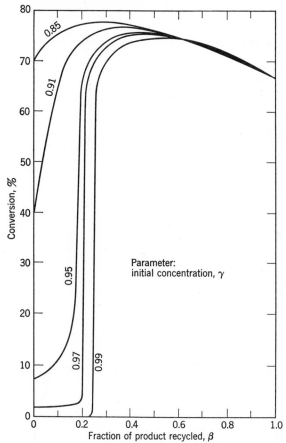

**Fig. 7.11** Maximum conversion versus fraction of product recycled for autocatalytic reaction $A + R \rightleftharpoons R + R$, zero-order with respect to the backward reaction.

differential length $dl$ of the reactor is given by

{rate of input of reactant $A$ due to bulk flow at the inlet of the differential section $dl$}

+ {rate of input of reactant $A$ due to diffusion at the inlet of the differential section $dl$}

− {rate of output of reactant $A$ due to bulk flow at the outlet of the differential section $dl$}

− {rate of output of reactant $A$ due to diffusion at the outlet of the differential section $dl$}

+ {rate of production of reactant $A$ due to the chemical reaction in the differential section $dl$}

= 0

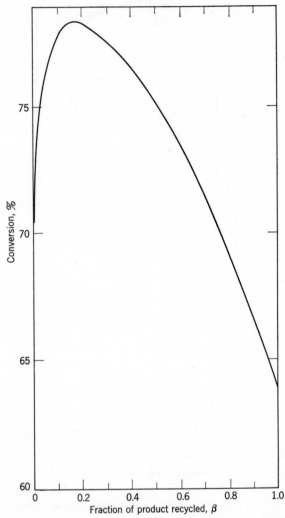

**Fig. 7.12** Maximum conversion versus fraction of product recycled for the auto-catalytic reaction $A + R \rightleftharpoons R + R$. Initial concentration $\gamma = 0.99$. First-order with respect to the reversible reaction.

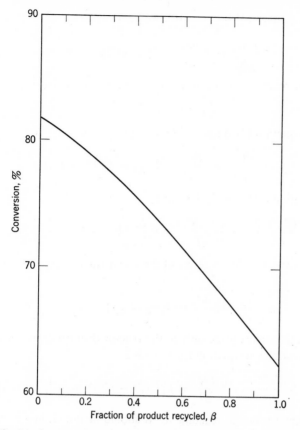

**Fig. 7.13** Maximum conversion versus fraction of product recycled for the auto-catalytic reaction $A + R \rightleftharpoons R + R$. Initial concentration $\gamma = 0.99$. Second-order with respect to the reversible reaction.

or

$$\{vC_A\} + \left\{-DS\,\frac{dC_A}{dl}\right\} - \left\{vC_A + v\,\frac{dC_A}{dl}\,dl\right\}$$

$$- \left\{-DS\,\frac{dC_A}{dl} - DS\,\frac{d^2C_A}{dl^2}\,dl\right\} + S\,dl\,\{R_A\} = 0, \quad (215)$$

where $D$ is the diffusivity and $S$ is the cross-sectional area of the reactor. Simplifying equation (215) by assuming a unit cross-sectional area, we obtain

$$D\,\frac{d^2C_A}{dl^2} - v\,\frac{dC_A}{dl} = -R_A. \quad (216)$$

Substituting equation (214) into (216), we have

$$D \frac{d^2C_A}{dl^2} - v \frac{dC_A}{dl} = k_1C_A - k_2C_B. \tag{217}$$

Since only the reactants $A$ and $B$ are involved, we know that

$$C_0 = C_A + C_B. \tag{218}$$

Substituting equation (218) into (217), we obtain

$$D \frac{d^2C_A}{dl^2} - v \frac{dC_A}{dl} = k_1C_A - k_2(C_0 - C_A). \tag{219}$$

Dividing equation (219) by $C_0$, we have

$$D \frac{d^2(C_A/C_0)}{dl^2} - v \frac{d(C_A/C_0)}{dl} = k_1\left(\frac{C_A}{C_0}\right) - k_2\left(1 - \frac{C_A}{C_0}\right). \tag{220}$$

If we write equation (220) in terms of the molar fraction $x_A = C_A/C_0$, we obtain

$$D \frac{d^2x_A}{dl^2} - v \frac{dx_A}{dl} = k_1x_A - k_2(1 - x_A). \tag{221}$$

Since the reaction takes place only in the reactor (branch 2), we have the following performance equation for branch 2:

$$D \frac{d^2x_1^{(2)}}{dl^2} - v^{(2)} \frac{dx_1^{(2)}}{dl} = k_1^{(2)} x_1^{(2)} - k_2^{(2)}(1 - x_1^{(2)}), \tag{222}$$

where subscript 1 refers to reactant $A$. It should be noted, however, that the cross-sectional area for branch 2 is assumed to be unity in the derivation. Since no transformations take place in branches 1, 3, and 4, we have

$$\frac{dx_1^{(1)}}{dl} = \frac{dx_1^{(3)}}{dl} = \frac{dx_1^{(4)}}{dl} = 0. \tag{223}$$

The boundary conditions for use with equation (222) have been reported in Reference 3 and are given in equations (4.80) and (4.81). At the combining point, however, we have the following conservation of mass equation:

$$v^{(1)} x_1^{(1)}(L_1) + v^{(4)} x_1^{(4)}(L_4) = v^{(2)} x_1^{(2)}(0^-)$$

or

$$x_1^{(2)}(0^-) = \alpha x_1^{(1)}(L_1) + \beta x_1^{(4)}(L_4), \tag{224}$$

where

$$\alpha = \frac{v^{(1)}}{v^{(2)}} \quad \text{and} \quad \beta = \frac{v^{(4)}}{v^{(2)}}.$$

Since the boundary condition at the reactor inlet is

$$v^{(2)}\, x_1^{(2)}(0^-) = v^{(2)}\, x_1^{(2)}(0^+) - D\,\frac{dx_1^{(2)}(0^+)}{dl} \tag{225}$$

or

$$x_1^{(2)}(0^-) = x_1^{(2)}(0^+) - \frac{D}{v^{(2)}}\,\frac{dx_1^{(2)}(0^+)}{dl}, \tag{226}$$

substitution of equation (224) into (226) gives

$$-\frac{dx_1^{(2)}(0^+)}{dl} = [\alpha x_1^{(1)}(L_1) + \beta x_1^{(4)}(L_4) - x_1^{(2)}(0^+)]\,\frac{v^{(2)}}{D}. \tag{227}$$

Since the outlet stream from branch 2 is mechanically divided into two streams, recycle and discharge, the concentration of reactant $A$ (component 1) after the separation remains unchanged. Thus we have

$$x_1^{(2)}(L_2) = x_1^{(3)}(0), \tag{228}$$

$$x_1^{(2)}(L_2) = x_1^{(4)}(0). \tag{229}$$

The initial state is assumed to be pure $A$; that is

$$x_1^{(1)}(0) = 1.0. \tag{230}$$

From equation (223) it is seen that

$$x_1^{(1)}(0) = x_1^{(1)}(l) = x_1^{(1)}(L_1) = 1.0, \tag{231}$$

$$x_1^{(4)}(0) = x_1^{(4)}(l) = x_1^{(4)}(L_4). \tag{232}$$

By substituting equations (229), (231), and (232) into (227), we obtain

$$\frac{dx_1^{(2)}(0^+)}{dl} = \frac{v^{(2)}}{D}\,[x_1^{(2)}(0^+) - \alpha - \beta x_1^{(2)}(L_2)]. \tag{233}$$

The following transformation of variables,

$$\eta = \frac{l}{L_2},$$

$$M^{(2)} = \frac{v^{(2)} L_2}{2D},$$

$$F_1^{(2)} = \frac{2k_{10} L_2}{v^{(2)}},$$

$$F_2^{(2)} = \frac{2k_{20} L_2}{v^{(2)}},$$

$$\tag{234}$$

leads to the dimensionless form of equations (222) and (233) as

$$\frac{d^2 x_1^{(2)}}{d\eta^2} - 2M^{(2)} \frac{dx_1^{(2)}}{d\eta}$$

$$- M^{(2)}[(F_1^{(2)} e^{-E_1/R\theta^{(2)}} + F_2^{(2)} e^{-E_2/R\theta^{(2)}}) x_1^{(2)} - F_2^{(2)} e^{-E_2/R\theta^{(2)}}] = 0, \quad (235)$$

$$\frac{dx_1^{(2)}(0^+)}{d\eta} = 2M^{(2)}[x_1^{(2)}(0^+) - \alpha - \beta x_1^{(2)}(1)]. \quad (236)$$

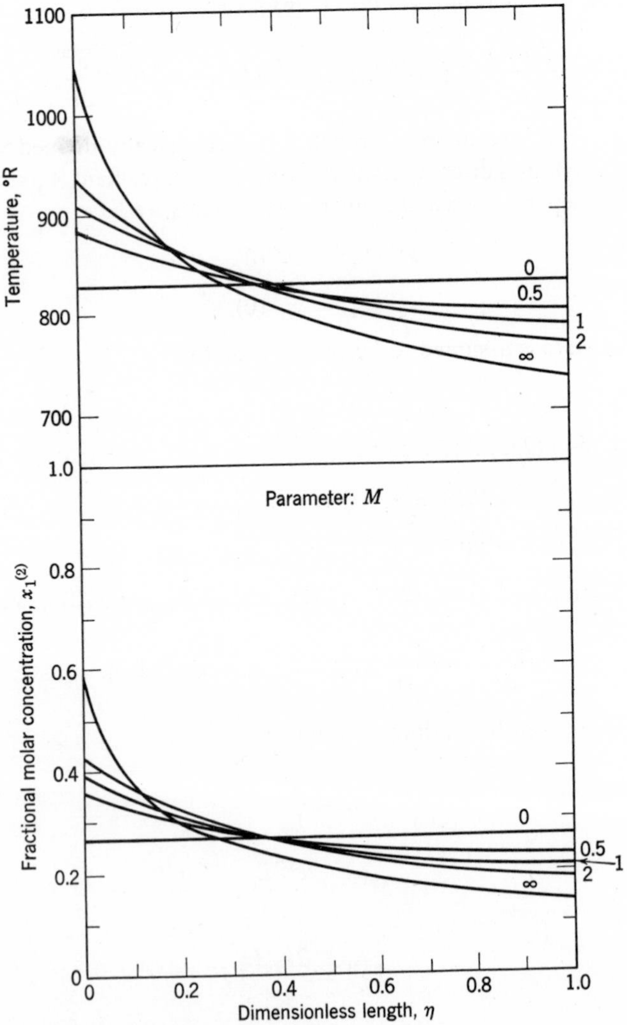

Fig. 7.14  Optimal concentration and temperature profiles for the first-order reversible reaction accompanied by diffusion (dispersion) with half of the product recycled, $\beta = 0.5$.

Another boundary condition [see Section 4.2, part d] is

$$\frac{dx_1^{(2)}(1)}{d\eta} = 0. \tag{237}$$

The optimal solution of this problem is obtained by using the procedure given in Section 4.2, part d. It is

$$\bar{\theta}^{(2)}(\eta) = - \frac{E_2 - E_1}{R \ln \{\xi[x_1^{(2)}/(1 - x_1^{(2)})]\}}, \tag{238}$$

where

$$\xi = \frac{F_1^{(2)} E_1}{F_2^{(2)} E_2} = \frac{k_{10} E_1}{k_{20} E_2}$$

and

$$\frac{d^2 x_1^{(2)}}{d\eta^2} = 2M^{(2)} \frac{dx_1^{(2)}}{d\eta} + M^{(2)} \xi (F_1^{(2)} - F_2^{(2)} \xi) \left[ \frac{(x_1^{(2)})^2}{1 - x_1^{(2)}} \right]. \tag{239}$$

Equation (239), together with the boundary conditions (236) and (237), form a boundary value problem. It is worth noting that equation (239) is identical to (4.98). The numerical integration of equation (239), which must satisfy equations (236) and (237), is slightly different from that given in Section 4.2, part d, because equation (236) involves the molar fractional concentration at the inlet and the outlet of the reactor.

The numerical procedure and data which were used to obtain the numerical solutions of equation (4.98) were also used to solve this problem.

The results are plotted in Figs. 7.14 and 7.15 with $M^{(2)}$ as a parameter for $\beta = 0.5$ and $0.75$, respectively.

### c. The Optimal Performance of a First-Order Reversible Reaction, $A \underset{k_2}{\overset{k_1}{\rightleftharpoons}} B$, Taking Place in a Tubular Reactor with a Recycling Tubular Reactor.

In this part we consider a continuous complex process consisting of two tubular reactors connected such that part of the exit flow from the one reactor is recycled through another reactor before it is mixed with incoming fresh feed, as shown in Fig. 7.16. The process consists of four branches; the feed line with length $L_1$ (branch 1), the first reactor of length $L_2$ (branch 2), the discharge line of length $L_3$ (branch 3), and the second reactor of length $L_4$ (branch 4), where the recycle stream reacts further before mixing with fresh feed.

Since the reaction takes place in branches 2 and 4 only and no transformation is taking place in branch 1, the feed line, and branch 3, the discharge line, we have the following performance equations for the

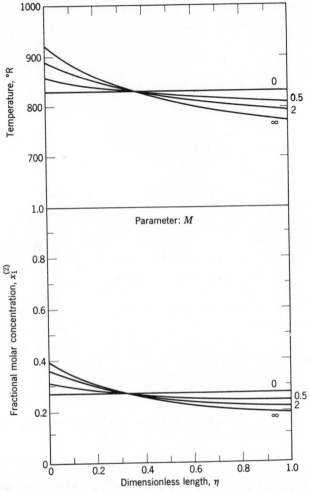

**Fig. 7.15** Optimal concentration and temperature profiles for the first-order reversible reaction accompanied by diffusion (dispersion) with fraction of product recycled, $\beta = 0.75$.

process [let $D = 0$ in equations (222) and (223) in the preceding part]:

$$\frac{dx_1^{(1)}}{dl} = 0, \tag{240}$$

$$\frac{dx_1^{(2)}}{dl} = -\frac{1}{v^{(2)}} [(k_1^{(2)} + k_2^{(2)}) x_1^{(2)} - k_2^{(2)}], \tag{241}$$

$$\frac{dx_1^{(3)}}{dl} = 0, \tag{242}$$

$$\frac{dx_1^{(4)}}{dl} = -\frac{1}{v^{(4)}} [(k_1^{(4)} + k_2^{(4)}) x_1^{(4)} - k_2^{(4)}], \tag{243}$$

where $v^{(k)}$ is the total volumetric flow rate through the $k$th branch. Here $k_1$ and $k_2$ are again assumed to follow the Arrhenius type equation given in equations (196) and (197), respectively. It should be noted that the cross-sectional areas for all of the branches are assumed to be unity in the foregoing derivation.

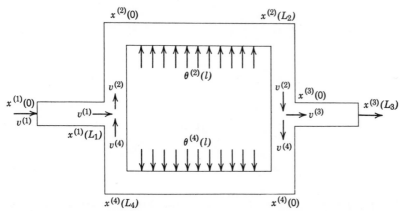

**Fig. 7.16** A schematic diagram of a tubular reactor with part of the product recycled through a second tubular reactor.

The mass balance at the combining point gives

$$v^{(2)}\, x_1^{(2)}(0) = v^{(1)}\, x_1^{(1)}(L_1) + v^{(4)}\, x_1^{(4)}(L_4) \tag{244}$$

or

$$x_1^{(2)}(0) = \alpha x_1^{(1)}(L_1) + \beta x_1^{(4)}(L_4), \tag{245}$$

where

$$\alpha = \frac{v^{(1)}}{v^{(2)}} \quad \text{and} \quad \beta = \frac{v^{(4)}}{v^{(2)}}.$$

The initial state is

$$x_1^{(1)}(0) = \gamma_1. \tag{246}$$

At the separating point we have the following junction equations:

$$x_1^{(2)}(L_2) = x_1^{(3)}(0), \tag{247}$$

$$x_1^{(2)}(L_2) = x_1^{(4)}(0). \tag{248}$$

From equations (240) and (246) we obtain

$$x_1^{(1)}(0) = x_1^{(1)}(l) = x_1^{(1)}(L_1) = \gamma_1. \tag{249}$$

By substituting equation (249) into (245), we obtain the junction equation at the combining point as

$$x_1^{(2)}(0) = \alpha\gamma_1 + \beta x_1^{(4)}(L_4). \tag{250}$$

According to equations (6.6) and (6.7), we have

$$H^{(1)} = H^{(3)} = 0, \tag{251}$$

$$H^{(2)} = -\frac{z_1^{(2)}}{v^{(2)}} [(k_1^{(2)} + k_2^{(2)}) \, x_1^{(2)} - k_2^{(2)}], \tag{252}$$

$$H^{(4)} = -\frac{z_1^{(4)}}{v^{(4)}} [(k_1^{(4)} + k_2^{(4)}) \, x_1^{(4)} - k_2^{(4)}], \tag{253}$$

$$\frac{dz_1^{(1)}}{dl} = \frac{dz_1^{(3)}}{dl} = 0, \tag{254}$$

$$\frac{dz_1^{(2)}}{dl} = \frac{z_1^{(2)}}{v^{(2)}} [k_1^{(2)} + k_2^{(2)}], \tag{255}$$

$$\frac{dz_1^{(4)}}{dl} = \frac{z_1^{(4)}}{v^{(4)}} [k_1^{(4)} + k_2^{(4)}]. \tag{256}$$

According to equations (6.9) and (245), we have at the combining point

$$z_1^{(1)}(L_1) = \alpha z_1^{(2)}(0), \tag{257}$$

$$z_1^{(4)}(L_4) = \beta z_1^{(2)}(0). \tag{258}$$

At the separating point we have, from equations (6.8), (247), and (248),

$$z_1^{(2}(L_2) = z_1^{(3)}(0) + z_1^{(4)}(0). \tag{259}$$

Since the problem is to maximize the product $B$ in the discharge line (branch 3) or, equivalently, to minimize $x_1^{(3)}(L_3)$, we have at the final point

$$z_1^{(3)}(L_3) = 1. \tag{260}$$

From equations (252) and (253), the optimal temperature profiles, $\bar{\theta}^{(2)}(l)$ and $\bar{\theta}^{(4)}(l)$, are determined by using the condition

$$\frac{\partial H}{\partial \theta} = 0,$$

which gives

$$\bar{\theta}^{(2)}(l) = \left(\frac{E_2 - E_1}{R}\right) \left\{ \ln \left[ \xi \left( \frac{1 - x_1^{(2)}(l)}{x_1^{(2)}(l)} \right) \right] \right\}^{-1}, \tag{261}$$

$$\bar{\theta}^{(4)}(l) = \left(\frac{E_2 - E_1}{R}\right) \left\{ \ln \left[ \xi \left( \frac{1 - x_1^{(4)}(l)}{x_1^{(4)}(l)} \right) \right] \right\}^{-1}. \tag{262}$$

Substitution of the two preceding equations into equations (241) and (243) and integration of the result yield

$$l_2 + C_1 = \frac{v^{(2)}}{k_{20}(\xi)^{-2} - k_{10}(\xi)^{-1}}\left[-\frac{1}{x_1^{(2)}(l)} - \ln x_1^{(2)}(l)\right], \quad (263)$$

$$l_4 + C_2 = \frac{v^{(4)}}{k_{20}(\xi)^{-2} - k_{10}(\xi)^{-1}}\left[-\frac{1}{x_1^{(4)}(l)} - \ln x_1^{(4)}(l)\right], \quad (264)$$

where $\xi = k_{20}E_2/k_{10}E_1$, $E_1/(E_2 - E_1) = 1$, $E_2/(E_2 - E_1) = 2$, and $C_1$ and $C_2$ are integration constants. These constants are evaluated by use of the junction equations given in (250) and (248), respectively. Substituting equation (250) into (263), we have

$$C_1 = \frac{v^{(2)}}{k_{20}(\xi)^{-2} - k_{10}(\xi)^{-1}}\left\{\frac{-1}{\alpha\gamma_1 + \beta x_1^{(4)}(L_4)} - \ln\left[\alpha\gamma_1 + \beta x_1^{(4)}(L_4)\right]\right\}. \quad (265)$$

Substituting equation (265) into equation (263), we have

$$l_2 = \frac{v^{(2)}}{k_{20}(\xi)^{-2} - k_{10}(\xi)^{-1}}\left\{\frac{1}{\alpha\gamma_1 + \beta x_1^{(4)}(L_4)}\right.$$
$$\left. + \ln\left[\alpha\gamma_1 + \beta x_1^{(4)}(L_4)\right] - \frac{1}{x_1^{(2)}(l)} - \ln x_1^{(2)}(l)\right\}. \quad (266)$$

Similarly, we substitute equation (248) into (264) to obtain

$$C_2 = \frac{v^{(2)}}{k_{20}(\xi)^{-2} - k_{10}(\xi)^{-1}}\left[-\frac{1}{x_1^{(2)}(L_2)} - \ln x_1^{(2)}(L_2)\right]. \quad (267)$$

Substitution of equation (267) into equation (264) yields

$$l_4 = \frac{v^{(4)}}{k_{20}(\xi)^{-2} - k_{10}(\xi)^{-1}}\left[\frac{1}{x_1^{(2)}(L_2)} + \ln x_1^{(2)}(L_2) - \frac{1}{x_1^{(4)}(l)} - \ln x_1^{(4)}(l)\right]. \quad (268)$$

Equations (266) and (268), together with (261) and (262), form the optimal solution for this problem. It should be noted, however, that equations (266) and (268) are not coupled, and consequently the numerical computation does not require much labor.

The numerical computation of the optimal solutions of equations (261), (262), (266), and (268) is illustrated by the use of the same numerical data as those given in Section 4.2, part a. In addition, however, we need the following:

$$L_4 = 10 \text{ ft},$$
$$v^{(1)} = 1000 \text{ ft}^3/\text{hr}.$$

Here $v^{(1)}$ is the equivalent of $G/\rho$ in Section 4.2, part a. The optimal temperature and concentration profiles thus obtained are plotted in Figs. 7.17 and 7.18 with $\beta$ as a parameter. In Fig. 7.17 the curves for $\beta = 0$ are, as expected, identical to those in Figs. 4.3 and 4.4 for the simple tubular reactor.

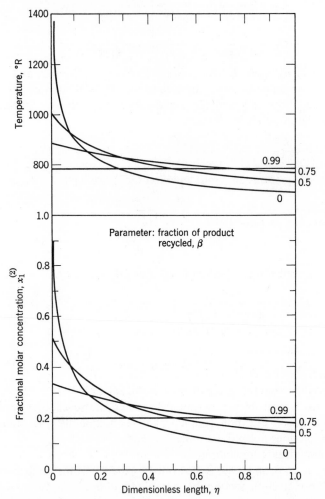

**Fig. 7.17** Optimal concentration and temperature profiles in the first reactor (branch 2) for the reaction $A \rightleftharpoons B$.

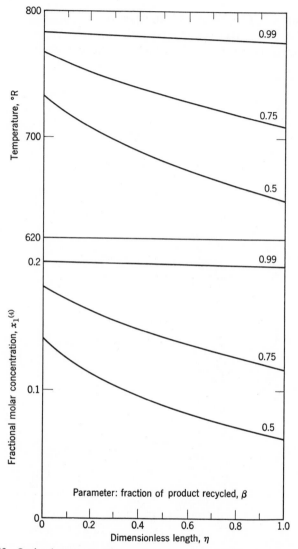

**Fig. 7.18** Optimal concentration and temperature profiles in the second reactor (branch 4) for the reaction $A \rightleftharpoons B$.

## 4. OPTIMIZATION OF PROCESSES WITH CROSSING BRANCHES

We shall consider a hypothetical complex process containing a crossing point at which two branches combine and then split as shown in Fig. 7.19. The process consists of four branches with the following performance equations:

$$\frac{dx_1^{(1)}}{dt} = -x_1^{(1)}\,\theta^{(1)}, \tag{269}$$

$$\frac{dx_2^{(1)}}{dt} = \tfrac{1}{2}x_1^{(1)}(\theta^{(1)})^2, \tag{270}$$

$$\frac{dx_1^{(2)}}{dt} = 0, \tag{271}$$

$$\frac{dx_2^{(2)}}{dt} = 0, \tag{272}$$

$$\frac{dx_1^{(3)}}{dt} = -x_1^{(3)} + \theta^{(3)}, \tag{273}$$

$$\frac{dx_2^{(3)}}{dt} = x_1^{(3)} + \tfrac{1}{2}(\theta^{(3)})^2, \tag{274}$$

$$\frac{dx_1^{(4)}}{dt} = -x_1^{(4)} + \theta^{(4)}, \tag{275}$$

$$\frac{dx_2^{(4)}}{dt} = x_1^{(4)} + \tfrac{1}{2}(\theta^{(4)})^2. \tag{276}$$

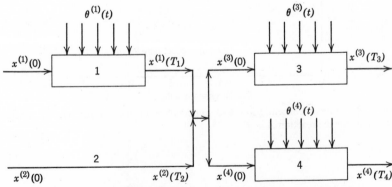

**Fig. 7.19**  Schematic diagram for a process involving a crossing point.

The junction equations are

$$x_1^{(3)}(0) = x_1^{(4)}(0), \tag{277}$$

$$x_2^{(3)}(0) = x_2^{(4)}(0), \tag{278}$$

$$x_1^{(3)}(0) = \gamma_1 x_1^{(1)}(T_1) + \gamma_2 x_1^{(2)}(T_2), \tag{279}$$

$$x_2^{(3)}(0) = \gamma_1 x_2^{(1)}(T_1) + \gamma_2 x_2^{(2)}(T_2), \tag{280}$$

where $\gamma_1$ and $\gamma_2$ are constants. The initial states are

$$x_1^{(1)}(0) = \alpha_1, \tag{281}$$

$$x_2^{(1)}(0) = \alpha_2, \tag{282}$$

$$x_1^{(2)}(0) = \beta_1, \tag{283}$$

$$x_2^{(2)}(0) = \beta_2. \tag{284}$$

We wish to find the decision functions $\theta^{(k)}$, $k = 1, 3, 4$, to minimize the objective function

$$S = x_2^{(3)}(T_3) + x_2^{(4)}(T_4), \tag{285}$$

where $x_2^{(3)}(T_3)$ and $x_2^{(4)}(T_4)$ are the final values of $x_2$ at branches 3 and 4.

The Hamiltonian function for each branch, according to equation (6.6), is

$$H^{(1)} = -x_1^{(1)}\theta^{(1)} z_1^{(1)} + \tfrac{1}{2}x_1^{(1)}(\theta^{(1)})^2 z_2^{(1)}, \tag{286}$$

$$H^{(2)} = 0, \tag{287}$$

$$H^{(3)} = [-x_1^{(3)} + \theta^{(3)}] z_1^{(3)} + [x_1^{(3)} + \tfrac{1}{2}(\theta^{(3)})^2] z_2^{(3)}, \tag{288}$$

$$H^{(4)} = [-x_1^{(4)} + \theta^{(4)}] z_1^{(4)} + [x_1^{(4)} + \tfrac{1}{2}(\theta^{(4)})^2] z_2^{(4)}. \tag{289}$$

The adjoint variables for each branch are, according to equation (6.7),

$$\frac{dz_1^{(1)}}{dt} = \theta^{(1)} z_1^{(1)} - \tfrac{1}{2}(\theta^{(1)})^2 z_2^{(1)}, \tag{290}$$

$$\frac{dz_1^{(3)}}{dt} = z_1^{(3)} - z_2^{(3)}, \tag{291}$$

$$\frac{dz_1^{(4)}}{dt} = z_1^{(4)} - z_2^{(4)}, \tag{292}$$

$$\frac{dz_2^{(1)}}{dt} = \frac{dz_1^{(2)}}{dt} = \frac{dz_2^{(2)}}{dt} = \frac{dz_2^{(3)}}{dt} = \frac{dz_2^{(4)}}{dt} = 0. \tag{293}$$

According to equation (6.10) and (277) through (280), we have at the crossing point

$$z_1^{(1)}(T_1) = \gamma_1[z_1^{(3)}(0) + z_1^{(4)}(0)], \tag{294}$$

$$z_2^{(1)}(T_1) = \gamma_1[z_2^{(3)}(0) + z_2^{(4)}(0)], \tag{295}$$

$$z_1^{(2)}(T_2) = \gamma_2[z_1^{(3)}(0) + z_1^{(4)}(0)], \tag{296}$$

$$z_2^{(2)}(T_2) = \gamma_2[z_2^{(3)}(0) + z_2^{(4)}(0)]. \tag{297}$$

Since the objective function is $x_2^{(3)}(T_3) + x_2^{(4)}(T_4)$, we see that

$$c_1^{(3)} = c_1^{(4)} = 0,$$
$$c_2^{(3)} = c_2^{(4)} = 1.$$

Thus, according to equation (6.11), we have at the final point

$$z_1^{(3)}(T_3) = z_1^{(4)}(T_4) = 0, \tag{298}$$
$$z_2^{(3)}(T_3) = z_2^{(4)}(T_4) = 1. \tag{299}$$

It is seen from equation (293) that

$$z_2^{(k)}(t) = \text{constant}, \qquad k = 1, 2, 3, 4.$$

We have therefore

$$z_2^{(3)}(0) = z_2^{(3)}(t) = z_2^{(3)}(T_3) = 1, \tag{300}$$
$$z_2^{(4)}(0) = z_2^{(4)}(t) = z_2^{(4)}(T_4) = 1, \tag{301}$$

and by substituting equations (300) and (301) into (295) and (297) we obtain

$$z_2^{(1)}(t) = 2\gamma_1, \tag{302}$$
$$z_2^{(2)}(t) = 2\gamma_2, \tag{303}$$

Substitution of equations (300), (301), and (302) into (286), (288), and (289) yields

$$H^{(1)} = -x_1^{(1)}\,\theta^{(1)}\,z_1^{(1)} + \gamma_1 x_1^{(1)}(\theta^{(1)})^2, \tag{304}$$
$$H^{(3)} = [-x_1^{(3)} + \theta^{(3)}]\,z_1^{(3)} + [x_1^{(3)} + \tfrac{1}{2}(\theta^{(3)})^2], \tag{305}$$
$$H^{(4)} = [-x_1^{(4)} + \theta^{(4)}]\,z_1^{(4)} + [x_1^{(4)} + \tfrac{1}{2}(\theta^{(4)})^2]. \tag{306}$$

Since the decision variable is not constrained, the minimum of the Hamiltonian for each branch occurs at a stationary point and consequently we obtain the optimal decisions $\bar{\theta}_1^{(k)}(t)$, $k = 1, 3, 4$, as follows:

$$\frac{\partial H^{(1)}}{\partial \theta^{(1)}} = -x_1^{(1)}\,z_1^{(1)} + 2\gamma_1 x_1^{(1)}\theta^{(1)} = 0,$$

$$\bar{\theta}^{(1)}(t) = \frac{z_1^{(1)}}{2\gamma_1}, \tag{307}$$

$$\frac{\partial H^{(3)}}{\partial \theta^{(3)}} = z_1^{(3)} + \theta^{(3)},$$

$$\bar{\theta}^{(3)}(t) = -z_1^{(3)}, \tag{308}$$

$$\frac{\partial H^{(4)}}{\partial \theta^{(4)}} = z_1^{(4)} + \theta^{(4)},$$

or

$$\bar{\theta}^{(4)}(t) = -z_1^{(4)}. \tag{309}$$

By substituting equations (307), (308), and (309), together with (300) and (301), into equations (269) through (276) and (290) through (292) we obtain

$$\frac{dx_1^{(1)}}{dt} = -\frac{x_1^{(1)}z_1^{(1)}}{2\gamma_1}, \tag{310}$$

$$\frac{dx_2^{(1)}}{dt} = \frac{x_1^{(1)}(z_1^{(1)})^2}{8(\gamma_1)^2}, \tag{311}$$

$$\frac{dx_1^{(3)}}{dt} = -x_1^{(3)} - z_1^{(3)}, \tag{312}$$

$$\frac{dx_2^{(3)}}{dt} = x_1^{(3)} + \tfrac{1}{2}(z_1^{(3)})^2, \tag{313}$$

$$\frac{dx_1^{(4)}}{dt} = -x_1^{(4)} - z_1^{(4)}, \tag{314}$$

$$\frac{dx_2^{(4)}}{dt} = x_1^{(4)} + \tfrac{1}{2}(z_1^{(4)})^2 \tag{315}$$

$$\frac{dz_1^{(1)}}{dt} = \frac{(z_1^{(1)})^2}{4\gamma_1}, \tag{316}$$

$$\frac{dz_1^{(3)}}{dt} = z_1^{(3)} - 1, \tag{317}$$

$$\frac{dz_1^{(4)}}{dt} = z_1^{(4)} - 1. \tag{318}$$

Integrating equations (316), (317), and (318), we obtain

$$z_1^{(1)}(t) = \frac{-4\gamma_1}{t - 4\gamma_1 A_1}, \tag{319}$$

$$z_1^{(3)}(t) = A_2 e^t + 1, \tag{320}$$

$$z_1^{(4)}(t) = A_3 e^t + 1. \tag{321}$$

Substitution of equation (298) into (320) and (321) yields

$$A_2 = -e^{-T_3}, \tag{322}$$

$$A_3 = -e^{-T_4}. \tag{323}$$

By substituting the expressions $A_2$ and $A_3$ into equations (320) and (321) we obtain

$$z_1^{(3)}(t) = 1 - e^{-(T_3 - t)}, \tag{324}$$

$$z_1^{(4)}(t) = 1 - e^{-(T_4 - t)}. \tag{325}$$

and by substituting equations (324) and (325) at $t = 0$ into equation (294) we have

$$z_1^{(1)}(T_1) = -\gamma_1(e^{-T_3} + e^{-T_4} - 2). \tag{326}$$

Solving equation (319) for the constant $A_1$ by use of equation (326), we obtain

$$A_1 = \frac{T_1}{4\gamma_1} - \frac{1}{\gamma_1 \xi}, \tag{327}$$

where

$$\xi = e^{-T_3} + e^{-T_4} - 2.$$

Substituting equation (327) into (319), we obtain

$$z_1^{(1)}(t) = \frac{-4\gamma_1 \xi}{4 - (T_1 - t)\xi}. \tag{328}$$

By substituting equation (328) into (310) and rearranging the result we obtain

$$\frac{dx_1^{(1)}}{x_1^{(1)}} = \frac{2\xi \, dt}{(4 - T_1\xi) + \xi t}. \tag{329}$$

Integration of equation (329) yields

$$x_1^{(1)} = A_4(4 - T_1\xi + \xi t)^2. \tag{330}$$

Substituting equation (324) into (312), we have

$$\frac{dx_1^{(3)}}{dt} + x_1^{(3)} = e^{-(T_3 - t)} - 1. \tag{331}$$

Solving this first-order linear differential equation, we obtain

$$x_1^{(3)}(t) = e^{-t} + \tfrac{1}{2}e^{-(T_3 - t)} - 1 + A_5. \tag{332}$$

Similarly, for branch 4, since we have the same performance equation as in branch 3,

$$x_1^{(4)}(t) = e^{-t} + \tfrac{1}{2}e^{-(T_4 - t)} - 1 + A_6. \tag{333}$$

The integration constants $A_4$, $A_5$, and $A_6$ are solved by use of equations (281), (279), and (277). Substituting equation (281) into (330), we obtain

$$\alpha_1 = A_4(4 - T_1\xi)^2$$

or

$$A_4 = \frac{\alpha_1}{(4 - T_1\xi)^2}. \tag{334}$$

Substituting equation (334) into (330), we obtain

$$x_1^{(1)}(t) = \alpha_1 \left( 1 + \frac{\xi t}{4 - \xi T_1} \right)^2. \tag{335}$$

Substituting equations (335) and (283) into (279), we have

$$x_1^{(3)}(0) = \gamma_1 \alpha_1 \left( 1 + \frac{\xi T_1}{4 - T_1 \xi} \right)^2 + \gamma_2 \beta_1 \tag{336}$$

$[x_1^{(2)}(0) = x_1^{(2)}(t) = x_1^{(2)}(T_2) = \beta_1$ because of equation (271)]. Substituting equation (336) into (332), we have

$$A_5 = \gamma_1 \alpha_1 \left( 1 + \frac{\xi T_1}{4 - T_1 \xi} \right)^2 + \gamma_2 \beta_1 - \tfrac{1}{2} e^{-T_3}. \tag{337}$$

Thus equation (332) can be written

$$x_1^{(3)}(t) = e^{-t} + \tfrac{1}{2} e^{-T_3}(e^t - 1) + \lambda_1, \tag{338}$$

where

$$\lambda_1 = \gamma_1 \alpha_1 \left( 1 + \frac{\xi T_1}{4 - \xi T_1} \right)^2 + \gamma_2 \beta_1 - 1.$$

Similarly, for branch 4 we have

$$x_1^{(4)}(t) = e^{-t} + \tfrac{1}{2} e^{-T_4}(e^t - 1) + \lambda_1. \tag{339}$$

The functional dependence of $x_2^{(k)}(t)$, $k = 1, 3, 4$, can be obtained by integrating equations (311), (313), and (315), after the proper values of $x_1^{(k)}$ and $z_2^{(k)}$, $k = 1, 3, 4$, are substituted into them as follows:

For branch 1 substitution of equations (335) and (328) into (311) yields

$$\frac{dx_2^{(1)}}{dt} = \frac{2\alpha_1(\xi)^2}{(4 - T_1 \xi)^2}. \tag{340}$$

Integration of equation (340) leads to

$$x_2^{(1)}(t) = \frac{2\alpha_1(\xi)^2 t}{(4 - T_1 \xi)^2} + A_7. \tag{341}$$

The initial state given in equation (282) enables us to solve for the integration constant $A_7$ in equation (341) as

$$\alpha_2 = A_7. \tag{342}$$

Thus we have

$$x_2^{(1)}(t) = \frac{2\alpha_1(\xi)^2 t}{(4 - T_1 \xi)^2} + \alpha_2. \tag{343}$$

For branch 3, substitution of equations (338) and (324) into (313) yields

$$\frac{dx_2^{(3)}}{dt} = e^{-t} + \tfrac{1}{2}e^{-T_3}(e^t - 1) + \lambda_1 + \tfrac{1}{2}[1 - e^{-(T_3-t)}]^2. \qquad (344)$$

Integrating equation (344), we have

$$x_2^{(3)}(t) = -e^{-t} + \tfrac{1}{4}e^{-2(T_3-t)} - \tfrac{1}{2}e^{-(T_3-t)} + \lambda_2 t + A_8, \qquad (345)$$

where

$$\lambda_2 = \lambda_1 - \tfrac{1}{2}e^{-T_3} + \tfrac{1}{2}.$$

Substitution of equations (284) and (343) into (280) yields

$$x_2^{(3)}(0) = \frac{2\gamma_1\alpha_1(\xi)^2 T_1}{(4 - T_1\xi)^2} + \alpha_2\gamma_1 + \gamma_2\beta_2 \qquad (346)$$

$[x_2^{(2)}(0) = x_2^{(2)}(t) = x_2^{(2)}(T_2) = \beta_2$ because of (272)]. Substituting equation (346) into (345), we obtain

$$-1 + \tfrac{1}{4}e^{-2T_3} - \tfrac{1}{2}e^{-T_3} + A_8 = \frac{2\gamma_1\alpha_1(\xi)^2 T_1}{(4 - T_1\xi)^2} + \alpha_2\gamma_1 + \gamma_2\beta_2$$

or

$$A_8 = \frac{2\gamma_1\alpha_1(\xi)^2 T_1}{(4 - T_1\xi)^2} + \alpha_2\gamma_1 + \gamma_2\beta_2 + 1 - \tfrac{1}{4}e^{-2T_3} + \tfrac{1}{2}e^{-T_3}. \qquad (347)$$

Substituting equation (347) into equation (345), we have

$$x_2^{(3)}(t) = -e^{-t} + \tfrac{1}{4}e^{-2T_3}(e^{2t} - 1) + \tfrac{1}{2}e^{-T_3}(1 - e^t) + \lambda_2 t + \lambda_3, \qquad (348)$$

where

$$\lambda_3 = 1 + \gamma_2\beta_2 + \alpha_2\gamma_1 + \frac{2\gamma_1\alpha_1(\xi)^2 T_1}{(4 - T_1\xi)^2}.$$

Similarly, for branch 4 we finally obtain

$$x_2^{(4)}(t) = -e^{-t} + \tfrac{1}{4}e^{-2T_4}(e^{2t} - 1) + \tfrac{1}{2}e^{-T_4}(1 - e^t) + \lambda_4 t + \lambda_3, \qquad (349)$$

where

$$\lambda_4 = \lambda_1 + \tfrac{1}{2} - \tfrac{1}{2}e^{-T_4}.$$

## REFERENCES

1. Fan, L. T., and C. S. Wang, *The Discrete Maximum Principle: A Study of Multistage Systems Optimization*, Wiley, New York (1964).
2. Ko, Y. C., "Optimal Design of Flow Chemical Reactors With Complex Geometry," M. S. Thesis, Kansas State University, 1965.
3. Fan, L. T., and Ahn, Y. K., "Critical Evaluations of Boundary Conditions for Tubular Flow Reactors," *Ind. Eng. Chem., Process Design Develop.*, **1,** 90 (1962).

# 8

# Optimization of Composite Processes

The optimization of complex discrete processes has already been extensively treated [1], and a complex continuous system is discussed in the preceding chapters. Many of the processes in practice, however, are often encountered in combined form. For convenience, such a complex process is called a composite process. In this chapter a general method of obtaining directly the optimal policy for a composite process, without decomposing it into subprocesses, is presented [2].

## 1. STATEMENT OF THE ALGORITHM

The algorithm stated in this section is applicable to a composite process consisting of the three basic types shown in Figs. 8.1, 8.2, and 8.3. Although the branch number notation employed and the derivation given are for processes with only one junction point, the algorithm is applicable to processes with more than one junction point.

In a simple continuous process contained in a composite process the change of the state can be described by repeating the following performance equations given in preceding chapters

$$\frac{dx_i}{dt} = f_i(x_1(t), x_2(t), \ldots, x_s(t); \ \theta_1(t), \ldots, \theta_r(t)), t_0 \leq t \leq T,$$

$$i = 1, 2, \ldots, s,$$

or, in vector form,

$$\frac{dx}{dt} = f(x(t); \theta(t)). \tag{1}$$

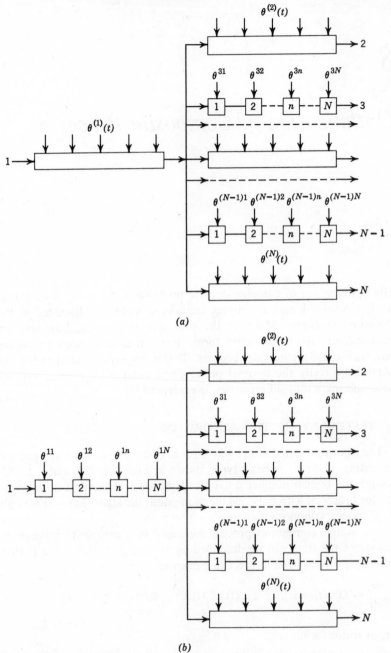

*Fig. 8.1* Separating points in a composite process: (*a*) with continuous first branch; (*b*) with discrete first branch.

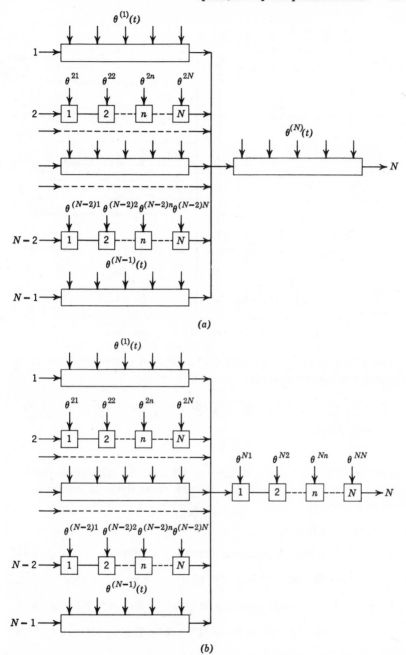

*Fig. 8.2* Combining points in a composite process: (*a*) with continuous last branch; (*b*) with discrete last branch.

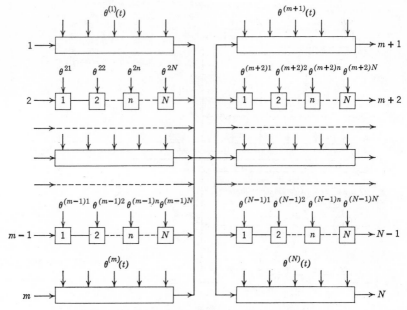

*Fig. 8.3*  A crossing point in a composite process.

For a simple discrete process contained in a composite process the performance equations are [1]

$$x_i^n = T_i^n(x_1^{n-1}, x_2^{n-1}, \ldots, x_s^{n-1}; \theta_1^n, \theta_2^n, \ldots, \theta_r^n), \qquad i = 1, 2, \ldots, s,$$

or, in vector form,

$$x^n = T^n(x^{n-1}; \theta^n). \tag{2}$$

The junction points are defined in Chapter 6. The corresponding junction equations, however, are different from those of complex continuous processes.

1. Separating points:

a. If the first branch (entering stream) is continuous (see Fig. 8.1a),

$$x^{(k)}(0) \quad \text{or} \quad x^{k0} = g^{(k)}(x^{(1)}(T_1)), \qquad k = 2, \ldots, N. \tag{3}$$

b. If the first branch (entering stream) is discrete (see Fig. 8.1b),

$$x^{(k)}(0) \quad \text{or} \quad x^{k0} = g^{(k)}(x^{1N}), \qquad k = 2, \ldots, N. \tag{4}*$$

---

* We denote the $n$th stage in the $k$th discrete branch by $kn$. Other subscripts and superscripts are defined in Chapter 6.

2. Combining points (see Fig. 8.2):

$$x^{(N)}(0) \quad \text{or} \quad x^{N0} = g^{(N)}(x^{1N}, x^{2N}, \ldots, x^{d'N}, x^{(d'+1)}(T_{d'+1}), \ldots,$$

$$x^{(N-1)}(T_{N-1})). \quad (5)$$

$c'$ and $d'$ denote the number of continuous branches and the number of discrete branches, respectively, entering a junction point. Similarly, we use $c''$ and $d''$ to denote the number of continuous and discrete branches leaving the junction point. The total number of continuous branches is represented by $c$ and that of the discrete branches, by $d$.

3. Crossing points (see Fig. 8.3):

$$x^{(k)}(0) \quad \text{or} \quad x^{k0} = g^{(k)}(x^{1N}, x^{2N}, \ldots, x^{d'N}, x^{(d'+1)}(T_{d'+1}), \ldots, x^{(m)}(T_m)),$$

$$(6)$$

$$k = m + 1, m + 2, \ldots, N.$$

The optimization problem under consideration may be stated as follows: given all the performance equations, junction equations, lengths, number of stages, and initial states of a composite process consisting of a path with $N$ branches, $b$ initial points, and $c'' + d''$ final points, find the optimal decision vector function of each continuous branch and the optimal decision vector at each stage in the discrete branch to maximize a certain linear function of the final states of the process—the objective function,

$$S = \sum_{c''} \sum_{i=1}^{s^{(c'')}} c_i^{(c'')} x_i^{(c'')}(T_{c''}) + \sum_{d''} \sum_{i=1}^{s^{(d'')}} c_i^{d''N} x_i^{d''N},$$

where $c_i$ are constants, the superscripts $c''$ and $d''$ denote the labels of continuous and discrete branches, respectively, and $\sum_{c''}$ and $\sum_{d''}$ indicate the summation over all continuous and discrete branches with end points. Similarly, we use $\sum_{c'}$ and $\sum_{d'}$ to denote the summation over all continuous and discrete branches with initial points and $\sum_c$ and $\sum_d$ to denote the summation over all the continuous and discrete branches.

To find the optimal decision vectors, we introduce adjoint vectors and Hamiltonian functions to satisfy the following relationships:

1. For the continuous branches:

$$H^{(k)}(x^{(k)}, z^{(k)}, \theta^{(k)}) = \sum_{i=1}^{s^{(k)}} z_i^{(k)} f_i^{(k)}(x_1^{(k)}, \ldots, x_{s^{(k)}}^{(k)}; \theta_1^{(k)}, \ldots, \theta_r^{(k)}), \quad (7)$$

$$\frac{dz_i^{(k)}}{dt} = -\frac{\partial H^{(k)}}{\partial x_i^{(k)}} = -\sum_{j=1}^{s^{(k)}} z_j \frac{\partial f_j^{(k)}(x^{(k)}; \theta^{(k)})}{\partial x_i^{(k)}}, \quad i = 1, 2, \ldots, s^{(k)}. \quad (8)$$

2. For the discrete branches:

$$H^{kn} = \sum_{i=1}^{s^{(k)}} z_i^{kn} \, T_i^{kn}(x_1^{k(n-1)}, \ldots, x_{s^{(k)}}^{k(n-1)}; \theta_1^{kn}, \theta_2^{kn}, \ldots, \theta_r^{kn}), \qquad (9)$$

$$z_i^{k(n-1)} = \frac{\partial H^{kn}}{\partial x_i^{k(n-1)}}, \qquad i = 1, 2, \ldots, s^{(k)}. \qquad (10)$$

The values of the components of the adjoint vectors at the final points of the streams entering each junction point satisfy the following relationship.

a. Separating points:
i. If the first branch is continuous,

$$z_i^{(1)}(T_1) = \sum_{c''} \sum_{j=1}^{s^{(c'')}} \frac{\partial g_j^{(c'')}}{\partial x_i^{(1)}} z_j^{(c'')}(0) + \sum_{d''} \sum_{j=1}^{s^{(d'')}} \frac{\partial g_j^{(d'')}}{\partial x_i^{(1)}} z_j^{d''0}, \qquad i = 1, 2, \ldots, s^{(1)}.$$
$$(11)$$

ii. If the first branch is discrete,

$$z_i^{1N} = \sum_{c''} \sum_{j=1}^{s^{(c'')}} \frac{\partial g_j^{(c'')}}{\partial x_i^{1N}} z_j^{(c'')}(0) + \sum_{d''} \sum_{j=1}^{s^{(d'')}} \frac{\partial g_j^{(d'')}}{\partial x_i^{1N}} z_j^{d''0}, \qquad i = 1, 2, \ldots, s^{(1)}. \quad (12)$$

b. Combining points:
For the case in which branch $N$ is either continuous or discrete we have the following:
i. For the continuous entering branches

$$z_i^{(k)}(T_k) = \sum_{j=1}^{s^{(N)}} \frac{\partial g_j^{(N)}}{\partial x_i^{(k)}} z_j^{(N)}(0), \qquad \begin{matrix} i = 1, 2, \ldots, s^{(k)}, \\ k = 1, 2, \ldots, c'. \end{matrix} \qquad (13)^*$$

ii. For the discrete entering branches.

$$z_i^{kN} = \sum_{j=1}^{s^{(N)}} \frac{\partial g_j^{(N)}}{\partial x_i^{kN}} z_j^{(N)}(0), \qquad \begin{matrix} i = 1, 2, \ldots, s^{(k)}, \\ k = c' + 1, c' + 2, \ldots, N - 1. \end{matrix} \qquad (14)^*$$

c. Crossing points:
i. For the continuous entering branches:

$$z_i^{(k)}(T_k) = \sum_{c''} \sum_{j=1}^{s^{(c'')}} \frac{\partial g_j^{(c'')}}{\partial x_i^{(k)}} z_j^{(c'')}(0)$$
$$+ \sum_{d''} \sum_{j=1}^{s^{(d'')}} \frac{\partial g_j^{(d'')}}{\partial x_i^{(k)}} z_j^{d''0}, \qquad \begin{matrix} i = 1, 2, \ldots, s^{(k)}, \\ k = 1, \ldots, c'. \end{matrix} \qquad (15)$$

---

* Equations (13) and (14) are written for the case branch $N$ is continuous. If it is discrete, $z_j^{(N)}(0)$ in the equations is replaced by $z_j^{N0}$.

ii. For the discrete entering branches:

$$z_i^{kN} = \sum_{c''} \sum_{j=1}^{s^{(c'')}} \frac{\partial g_j^{(c'')}}{\partial x_i^{kN}} z_j^{(c'')}(0)$$

$$+ \sum_{d''} \sum_{j=1}^{s^{(d'')}} \frac{\partial g_j^{(d'')}}{\partial x_i^{kN}} z_j^{d''0}, \qquad \begin{aligned} & i = 1, 2, \ldots, s^{(k)}, \\ & k = c' + 1, \ldots, m. \end{aligned} \qquad (16)$$

d. Final points:

$$z_i^{(c'')}(T_{c''}) = c_i^{(c'')}, \qquad i = 1, 2, \ldots, s^{(c'')},$$

$$z_i^{d''N} = c_i^{d''N}, \qquad i = 1, 2, \ldots, s^{(d'')}. \qquad (17)$$

The optimal decisions are then determined by the following conditions:

$$\frac{\partial H^{(k)}}{\partial \theta^{(k)}} = 0 \quad \text{or} \quad H^{(k)} = \text{maximum at every point } t, \qquad t_0 \leq t \leq T_k \quad (18)*$$

for every continuous branch and

$H^{kn} = $ maximum if the optimal decision vector lies on the boundary
of the region $\theta^{kn}$, $\qquad\qquad\qquad\qquad\qquad\qquad\qquad (19)\dagger$

$\dfrac{\partial H^{kn}}{\partial \theta^{kn}} = 0 \quad$ if the optimal decision vector is an interior point of the
region $\theta^{kn}$,

for every discrete branch.

## 2. DERIVATION OF THE ALGORITHM

Let $\bar{\theta}^{(k)}(t)$ and $\bar{\theta}^{kn}$ be the optimal decision vector functions of the $k$th continuous and discrete branch, respectively, and $\bar{x}^{(k)}(t)$ and $\bar{x}^{kn}$ be the corresponding optimal state vector functions of the $k$th branch. Then we have

$$\theta^{(k)}(t, \epsilon) = \bar{\theta}^{(k)}(t) + \epsilon \varphi^{(k)}(t) + 0(\epsilon^2), \qquad (20)$$

$$\theta^{kn} = \bar{\theta}^{kn} + \epsilon \varphi^{kn} + 0(\epsilon^2), \qquad (21)$$

and

$$x^{(k)}(t, \epsilon) = \bar{x}^{(k)}(t) + \epsilon y^{(k)}(t) + 0(\epsilon^2), \qquad (22)$$

$$x^{kn} = \bar{x}^{kn} + \epsilon y^{kn} + 0(\epsilon^2). \qquad (23)$$

---

\* If $\theta$ is not constrained, it can be proved that these two conditions are equivalent for the continuous branches. See Chapter 11 and related references given in that chapter for further comments.

† Discussions of the sufficiency and necessity of the optimal conditions, as well as the first and second variations, are presented in References 1, 4, 6, 7 and also in Chapter 11.

The results given here have been obtained by a different method under more general constraints, inputs, and decisions in References 4, 5.

By means of Taylor's expansion the variational equations are obtained as

$$\epsilon \frac{dy_i^{(k)}}{dt} = \sum_{j=1}^{s^{(k)}} \epsilon y_j^{(k)} \frac{\partial f_i^{(k)}(\bar{x}^{(k)}; \bar{\theta}^{(k)})}{\partial \bar{x}_j^{(k)}} + \sum_{j=1}^{r^{(k)}} \epsilon \varphi_j^{(k)} \frac{\partial f_i^{(k)}(\bar{x}^{(k)}; \bar{\theta}^{(k)})}{\partial \bar{\theta}_j^{(k)}} + 0(\epsilon^2), \quad (24)$$

$$\epsilon y_i^{kn} = \sum_{j=1}^{s^{(k)}} \epsilon y_j^{k(n-1)} \frac{\partial T_i^{kn}(\bar{x}^{k(n-1)}; \bar{\theta}^{kn})}{\partial \bar{x}_j^{k(n-1)}} + \sum_{j=1}^{r^{(k)}} \epsilon \varphi_j^{kn} \frac{\partial T_i^{kn}(\bar{x}^{k(n-1)}; \bar{\theta}^{kn})}{\partial \bar{\theta}_j^{kn}} + 0(\epsilon^2).$$
$$(25)$$

The relationships between the variations of the state vectors of different branches at the junction points are obtained by expanding the junction equations in powers of $\epsilon y_i$ as follows:

1. Separating points:

a. If the first branch (entering stream) is continuous

$$\epsilon y_i^{(k)}(0) \quad \text{or} \quad \epsilon y_i^{k0} = \sum_{j=1}^{s^{(1)}} \epsilon y_j^{(1)}(T_1) \frac{\partial g_i^{(k)}}{\partial x_j^{(1)}} + 0(\epsilon^2), \qquad \begin{array}{l} i = 1, 2, \ldots, s^{(k)}, \\ k = 2, 3, \ldots, N. \end{array} \quad (26)^*$$

b. If the first branch (entering stream) is discrete

$$\epsilon y_i^{(k)}(0) \quad \text{or} \quad \epsilon y_i^{k0} = \sum_{j=1}^{s^{(1)}} \epsilon y_j^{1N} \frac{\partial g_i^{(k)}}{\partial x_j^{1N}} + 0(\epsilon^2), \qquad \begin{array}{l} i = 1, 2, \ldots, s^{(k)}, \\ k = 2, 3, \ldots, N. \end{array} \quad (27)$$

2. Combining points:

$$\epsilon y_i^{(N)}(0) \quad \text{or} \quad \epsilon y_i^{N0} = \sum_{c'} \sum_{j=1}^{s^{(c')}} \epsilon y_j^{(c')}(T_{c'}) \frac{\partial g_i^{(N)}}{\partial x_j^{(c')}}$$
$$+ \sum_{d'} \sum_{j=1}^{s^{(d')}} \epsilon y_j^{d'N} \frac{\partial g_i^{(N)}}{\partial x_j^{d'N}} + 0(\epsilon^2), \qquad i = 1, 2, \ldots, s^{(N)}. \quad (28)$$

3. Crossing points:

$$\epsilon y_i^{(k)}(0) \quad \text{or} \quad \epsilon y_i^{k0} = \sum_{c'} \sum_{j=1}^{s^{(c')}} \epsilon y_j^{(c')}(T_{c'}) \frac{\partial g_i^{(k)}}{\partial x_j^{(c')}}$$
$$+ \sum_{d'} \sum_{j=1}^{s^{(d')}} \epsilon y_j^{d'N} \frac{\partial g_i^{(k)}}{\partial x_j^{d'N}} + 0(\epsilon^2), \qquad \begin{array}{l} i = 1, 2, \ldots, s^{(k)}, \\ k = m+1, \ldots, N. \end{array} \quad (29)$$

Since all the initial states of the process are given and fixed, we have

$$y_i^{(k)}(0) = y_i^{k0} = 0, \qquad \begin{array}{l} i = 1, 2, \ldots, s^{(k)}, \\ k = 1, 2, \ldots, b, \end{array} \quad (30)$$

---

* For the $k$th continuous branch we consider the first term of the left-hand side and for the $k$th discrete branch we consider the second term.

where $b$ denotes the number of entering branches with fixed initial states. For continuous branches we consider

$$\frac{d}{dt} \sum_{i=1}^{s^{(k)}} \epsilon y_i^{(k)} z_i^{(k)} = \sum_{i=1}^{s^{(k)}} \epsilon z_i^{(k)} \frac{dy_i^{(k)}}{dt} + \sum_{i=1}^{s^{(k)}} \epsilon y_i^{(k)} \frac{dz_i^{(k)}}{dt}. \tag{31}$$

Substitution of equations (8) and (24) into equation (31) yields

$$\frac{d}{dt} \sum_{i=1}^{s^{(k)}} \epsilon y_i^{(k)} z_i^{(k)} = \sum_{i=1}^{s^{(k)}} z_i^{(k)} \sum_{j=1}^{r^{(k)}} \epsilon \varphi_j^{(k)} \frac{\partial f_i^{(k)}(\bar{x}^{(k)}; \bar{\theta}^{(k)})}{\partial \bar{\theta}_j^{(k)}} + 0(\epsilon^2). \tag{32}$$

By integrating equation (32) from $t = 0$ to $t = T_k$, we obtain

$$\epsilon \sum_{i=1}^{s^{(k)}} [y_i^{(k)}(T_k) z_i^{(k)}(T_k) - y_i^{(k)}(0) z_i^{(k)}(0)]$$

$$= \int_0^T \sum_{i=1}^{s^{(k)}} z_i^{(k)} \left[ \sum_{j=1}^{r^{(k)}} \epsilon \varphi_j^{(k)} \frac{\partial f_i^{(k)}(\bar{x}^{(k)}; \bar{\theta}^{(k)})}{\partial \bar{\theta}_j^{(k)}} \right] dt + 0(\epsilon^2). \tag{33}$$

For discrete branches we multiply equation (25) by $z_i^{kn}$, employ equation (10), and sum from $n = 1$ to $n = N$ and from $i = 1$ to $i = s^{(k)}$ to produce

$$\epsilon \sum_{i=1}^{s^{(k)}} (y_i^{kN} z_i^{kN} - y_i^{k0} z_i^{k0}) = \sum_{n=1}^{N} \sum_{i=1}^{s^{(k)}} z_i^{kn} \sum_{j=1}^{r^{(k)}} \epsilon \varphi_j^{kn} \frac{\partial T_i^{kn}(\bar{x}^{k(n-1)}; \bar{\theta}^{kn})}{\partial \bar{\theta}_j^{kn}} + 0(\epsilon^2). \tag{34}$$

Summing equations (33) and (34) over all the continuous and discrete branches and adding the resulting equations, we have in terms of the Hamiltonian function

$$\sum_{c} \sum_{i=1}^{s^{(c)}} \epsilon [y_i^{(c)}(T_c) z_i^{(c)}(T_c) - y_i^{(c)}(0) z_i^{(c)}(0)]$$

$$+ \sum_{d} \sum_{i=1}^{s^{(d)}} \epsilon [y_i^{dN} z_i^{dN} - y_i^{d0} z_i^{d0}]$$

$$= \sum_{c} \int_0^T \left[ \sum_{j=1}^{r^{(c)}} \frac{\partial H^{(c)}}{\partial \bar{\theta}_j^{(c)}} \epsilon \varphi_j^{(c)} \right] dt$$

$$+ \sum_{d} \sum_{n=1}^{N} \sum_{j=1}^{r^{(d)}} \frac{\partial H^{dn}}{\partial \bar{\theta}_j^{dn}} \epsilon \varphi_j^{dn} + 0(\epsilon^2). \tag{35}$$

For the branches containing the initial points or states we have in the left-hand side of equation (35)

$$\epsilon y_i^{(k)}{}'(0)\, z_i^{(k)}{}'(0) = 0,$$

and
$$\epsilon y_i^{k0}\, z_i^{k0} = 0, \qquad\qquad k = 1, 2, \ldots, b. \qquad (36)$$

In the following we consider the three basic types of junction points separately. It is shown that they lead to the same conclusion [equations (18) and (19)]. For those branches connected to a separating point, if the entering stream is continuous, we have from equations (11) and (26)

$$\sum_{c''} \sum_{i=1}^{s^{(c'')}} \epsilon y_i^{(c'')}{}'(0)\, z_i^{(c'')}{}'(0) + \sum_{d''} \sum_{i=1}^{s^{(d'')}} \epsilon y_i^{d''0}\, z_i^{d''0}$$

$$= \sum_{c''} \sum_{i=1}^{s^{(c'')}} \sum_{j=1}^{s^{(1)}} \epsilon y_j^{(1)}(T_1) \frac{\partial g_i^{(c'')}}{\partial x_j^{(1)}} z_i^{(c'')}{}'(0) + \sum_{d''} \sum_{i=1}^{s^{(d'')}} \sum_{j=1}^{s^{(1)}} \epsilon y_j^{(1)}(T_1) \frac{\partial g_i^{d('')}}{\partial x_j^{(1)}} z_i^{d''0} + 0(\epsilon^2)$$

$$= \sum_{j=1}^{s^{(1)}} \epsilon y_j^{(1)}(T_1) \left[ \sum_{c''} \sum_{i=1}^{s^{(c'')}} \frac{\partial g_i^{(c'')}}{\partial x_j^{(1)}} z_i^{(c'')}{}'(0) + \sum_{d''} \sum_{i=1}^{s^{(d'')}} \frac{\partial g_i^{(d'')}}{\partial x_j^{(1)}} z_i^{d''0} \right] + 0(\epsilon^2)$$

$$= \sum_{j=1}^{s^{(1)}} \epsilon y_j^{(1)}(T_1)\, z_j^{(1)}{}'(T_1) + 0(\epsilon^2)$$

$$= \sum_{i=1}^{s^{(1)}} \epsilon y_i^{(1)}(T_1)\, z_i^{(1)}{}'(T_1) + 0(\epsilon^2). \qquad (37)$$

By using equations (36) and (37) the left-hand side of equation (35) becomes for a separating point

$$\sum_{c''} \sum_{i=1}^{s^{(c'')}} \epsilon[y_i^{(c'')}(T_{c''})\, z_i^{(c'')}(T_{c''}) - y_i^{(c'')}(0)\, z_i^{(c'')}(0)]$$

$$+ \sum_{d''} \sum_{i=1}^{s^{(d'')}} \epsilon[y_i^{d''N} z_i^{d''N} - y_i^{d''0} z_i^{d''0}] + \sum_{i=1}^{s^{(1)}} \epsilon[y_i^{(1)}(T_1)\, z_i^{(1)}(T_1) - y_i^{(1)}(0)\, z_i^{(1)}(0)]$$

$$= \sum_{c''} \sum_{i=1}^{s^{(c'')}} \epsilon y_i^{(c'')}(T_{c''})\, z_i^{(c'')}(T_{c''}) + \sum_{d''} \sum_{i=1}^{s^{(d'')}} \epsilon y_i^{d''N} z_i^{d''N}, \qquad (38)$$

where the last bracketed quantity on the left-hand side is separated from the first bracketed quantity on the left-hand side of equation (35). Recall that $d'' = d$ for this case. Equation (35) thus becomes

$$\sum_{c''} \sum_{i=1}^{s^{(c'')}} \epsilon y_i^{(c'')}(T_{c''})\, z_i^{(c'')}(T_{c''}) + \sum_{d''} \sum_{i=1}^{s^{(d'')}} \epsilon y_i^{d''N} z_i^{d''N}$$

$$= \sum_c \int_0^T \sum_{j=1}^{r^{(c)}} \frac{\partial H^{(c)}}{\partial \bar\theta_j^{(c)}} \epsilon \varphi_j^{(c)}\, dt + \sum_d \sum_{n=1}^{N} \sum_{j=1}^{r^{(d)}} \frac{\partial H^{dn}}{\partial \bar\theta_j^{dn}} \epsilon \varphi_j^{dn} + 0(\epsilon^2). \qquad (39)$$

If the objective function is to be maximized, the perturbation of the decision variables can only be to make

$$\left[ \sum_{c''} \sum_{i=1}^{s^{(c'')}} \epsilon c_i^{(c'')} \, y_i^{(c'')}(T_{c''}) + \sum_{d''} \sum_{i=1}^{s^{(d'')}} \epsilon c_i^{d''N} \, y_i^{d''N} \right] \le 0. \tag{40}$$

A combination of equations (17), (39), and (40) gives

$$\sum_c \int_0^T \left[ \sum_{j=1}^{r^{(c)}} \frac{\partial H^{(c)}}{\partial \bar{\theta}_j^{(c)}} \, \epsilon \varphi_j^{(c)} \right] dt + \sum_d \sum_{n=1}^{N} \sum_{j=1}^{r^{(d)}} \frac{\partial H^{dn}}{\partial \bar{\theta}_j^{dn}} \, \epsilon \varphi_j^{dn} + 0(\epsilon^2) \le 0. \tag{41}$$

Since the perturbation of each decision variable is independent both in the continuous branches and the stages in the discrete branches, it may be concluded that the integrand of each integral and each term containing a set of independent variables must itself be nonpositive. Thus

$$\sum_{j=1}^{r^{(c)}} \frac{\partial H^{(c)}}{\partial \bar{\theta}_j^{(c)}} \, \epsilon \varphi_j^{(c)} + 0(\epsilon^2) \le 0 \tag{42}$$

and

$$\sum_{j=1}^{r^{(d)}} \frac{\partial H^{dn}}{\partial \bar{\theta}_j^{dn}} \, \epsilon \varphi_j^{dn} + 0(\epsilon^2) \le 0. \tag{43}$$

Since the perturbation of each decision variable may be in either direction, we must have

$$\frac{\partial H^{(c)}}{\partial \bar{\theta}_j^{(c)}} = 0 \quad \text{and} \quad \frac{\partial H^{dn}}{\partial \bar{\theta}_j^{dn}} = 0 \tag{44}$$

when the decision variables are unconstrained. If the optimal value of a decision variable is a boundary point, we see from equations (42) and (43) that the Hamiltonian must be maximized.

For those branches connected to a separating point, if the entering stream is discrete and if only the linear terms in $\epsilon$ are considered, we have by using equations (12) and (27)

$$\begin{aligned}
\sum_{c''} &\sum_{i=1}^{s^{(c'')}} \epsilon y_i^{(c'')}(0) \, z_i^{(c'')}(0) + \sum_{d''} \sum_{i=1}^{s^{(d'')}} \epsilon y_i^{d''0} \, z_i^{d''0} \\
&= \sum_{c''} \sum_{i=1}^{s^{(c'')}} \sum_{j=1}^{s^{(1)}} \epsilon y_j^{1N} \frac{\partial g_i^{(c'')}}{\partial x_j^{1N}} \, z_i^{(c'')}(0) + \sum_{d''} \sum_{i=1}^{s^{(d'')}} \sum_{j=1}^{s^{(1)}} \epsilon y_j^{1N} \frac{\partial g_i^{(d'')}}{\partial x_j^{1N}} \, z_i^{d''0} \\
&= \sum_{j=1}^{s^{(1)}} \epsilon y_j^{1N} \left[ \sum_{c''} \sum_{j=1}^{s^{(c'')}} \frac{\partial g_i^{(c'')}}{\partial x_j^{1N}} \, z_i^{(c'')}(0) + \sum_{d''} \sum_{i=1}^{s^{(d'')}} \frac{\partial g_i^{(d'')}}{\partial x_j^{1N}} \, z_i^{d''0} \right] \\
&= \sum_{j=1}^{s^{(1)}} \epsilon y_j^{1N} z_j^{1N} \\
&= \sum_{i=1}^{s^{(1)}} \epsilon y_i^{1N} z_i^{1N}. \tag{45}
\end{aligned}$$

By use of equations (36) and (45), equation (35) is reduced to

$$\sum_{d''}\sum_{i=1}^{s^{(d'')}} \epsilon y_i^{d''N} z_i^{d''N} + \sum_{c''}\sum_{i=1}^{s^{(c'')}} \epsilon y_i^{(c'')}(T_{c''}) z_i^{(c'')}(T_{c''})$$

$$= \sum_d \sum_{n=1}^{N} \sum_{j=1}^{r^{(d)}} \frac{\partial H^{dn}}{\partial \bar{\theta}_j^{dn}} \epsilon \varphi_j^{dn} + \sum_c \int_0^T \sum_{j=1}^{r^{(c)}} \frac{\partial H^{(c)}}{\partial \bar{\theta}_j^{(c)}} \epsilon \varphi_j^{(c)} \, dt + 0(\epsilon^2). \quad (46)$$

It is worth recalling that $c'' = c$ for this case.

If the objective function is to be maximized, the perturbation of the decision variables can only be to make

$$\left[ \sum_{d''}\sum_{i=1}^{s^{(d'')}} \epsilon c_i^{d''N} y_i^{d''N} + \sum_{c''}\sum_{i=1}^{s^{(c'')}} \epsilon c_i^{(c'')} y_i^{(c'')}(T_{c''}) \right] \leq 0 \quad (47)$$

or

$$\sum_d \sum_{n=1}^{N} \sum_{j=1}^{r^{(d)}} \frac{\partial H^{dn}}{\partial \bar{\theta}_j^{dn}} \epsilon \varphi_j^{dn} + 0(\epsilon^2) \leq 0 \quad (48)$$

and

$$\sum_c \int_0^T \left[ \sum_{j=1}^{r^{(c)}} \frac{\partial H^{(c)}}{\partial \bar{\theta}_j^{(c)}} \epsilon \varphi_j^{(c)} \right] dt + 0(\epsilon^2) \leq 0. \quad (49)$$

Following similar reasoning, we obtain equations (42) and (43)

$$\sum_{j=1}^{r^{(c)}} \frac{\partial H^{(c)}}{\partial \bar{\theta}_j^{(c)}} \epsilon \varphi_j^{(c)} + 0(\epsilon^2) \leq 0, \quad (50)$$

$$\sum_{j=1}^{r^{(d)}} \frac{\partial H^{dn}}{\partial \bar{\theta}_j^{dn}} \epsilon \varphi_j^{dn} + 0(\epsilon^2) \leq 0. \quad (51)$$

For those branches connected to a combining point, if the leaving branch is continuous and if only the linear terms are considered, we have from equations (13), (14), and (28)

$$\sum_{i=1}^{s^{(N)}} \epsilon y_i^{(N)}(0) \, z_i^{(N)}(0)$$

$$= \sum_{i=1}^{s^{(N)}} \left[ \sum_{c'}\sum_{j=1}^{s^{(c')}} \epsilon y_j^{(c')}(T_{c'}) \frac{\partial g_i^{(N)}}{\partial x_j^{(c')}} + \sum_{d'}\sum_{j=1}^{s^{(d')}} \epsilon y_j^{d'N} \frac{\partial g_i^{(N)}}{\partial x_j^{d'N}} \right] z_i^{(N)}(0)$$

$$= \sum_{c'}\sum_{i=1}^{s^{(N)}}\sum_{j=1}^{s^{(c')}} \epsilon y_j^{(c')}(T_{c'}) \frac{\partial g_i^{(N)}}{\partial x_j^{(c')}} z_i^{(N)}(0) + \sum_{d'}\sum_{i=1}^{s^{(N)}}\sum_{j=1}^{s^{(d')}} \epsilon y_j^{d'N} \frac{\partial g_i^{(N)}}{\partial x_j^{d'N}} z_i^{(N)}(0)$$

$$= \sum_{c'}\sum_{j=1}^{s^{(c')}} \epsilon y_j^{(c')}(T_{c'}) \sum_{i=1}^{s^{(N)}} \frac{\partial g_i^{(N)}}{\partial x_j^{(c')}} z_i^{(N)}(0) + \sum_{d'}\sum_{j=1}^{s^{(d')}} \epsilon y_j^{d'N} \sum_{i=1}^{s^{(N)}} \frac{\partial g_i^{(N)}}{\partial x_j^{d'N}} z_i^{(N)}(0)$$

$$= \sum_{c'}\sum_{j=1}^{s^{(c')}} \epsilon y_j^{(c')}(T_{c'}) \, z_i^{(c')}(T_{c'}) + \sum_{d'}\sum_{j=1}^{s^{(d')}} \epsilon y_j^{d'N} z_j^{d'N}. \quad (52)$$

Recall that for this case $d' = d$. The left-hand side of equation (35) becomes, by use of equations (36) and (52),

$$\sum_c \sum_{i=1}^{s^{(c)}} \epsilon[y_i^{(c)}(T_c) z_i^{(c)}(T_c) - y_i^{(c)}(0) z_i^{(c)}(0)]$$

$$+ \sum_d \sum_{i=1}^{s^{(d)}} \epsilon[y_i^{dN} z_i^{dN} - y_i^{d0} z_i^{d0}]$$

$$= \sum_{i=1}^{s(N)} \epsilon y_i^{(N)}(T_N) z_i^{(N)}(T_N) + \sum_{c'} \sum_{i=1}^{s^{(c')}} \epsilon y_i^{(c')}(T_{c'}) z_i^{(c')}(T_{c'})$$

$$- \sum_{i=1}^{s(N)} \epsilon y_i^{(N)}(0) z_i^{(N)}(0) - \sum_{c'} \sum_{i=1}^{s^{(c')}} \epsilon y_i^{(c')}(0) z_i^{(c')}(0)$$

$$+ \sum_{d'} \sum_{i=1}^{s^{(d')}} \epsilon[y_i^{d'N} z_i^{d'N} - y_i^{d'0} z_i^{d'0}]$$

$$= \sum_{i=1}^{s(N)} \epsilon y_i^{(N)}(T_N) z_i^{(N)}(T_N). \tag{53}$$

Equating this to the right-hand side of equation (35) gives

$$\sum_{i=1}^{s(N)} \epsilon y_i^{(N)}(T_N) z_i^{(N)}(T_N)$$

$$= \sum_c \int_0^T \left[ \sum_{j=1}^{r^{(c)}} \frac{\partial H^{(c)}}{\partial \bar{\theta}_j^{(c)}} \epsilon \varphi_j^{(c)} \right] dt + \sum_d \sum_{n=1}^N \sum_{j=1}^{r^{(d)}} \frac{\partial H^{dn}}{\partial \bar{\theta}_j^{dn}} \epsilon \varphi_j^{dn} + 0(\epsilon^2). \tag{54}$$

If the objective function is to be maximized, the perturbation of the decision variables can only be to make

$$\sum_{i=1}^{s(N)} \epsilon c_i^{(N)} y_i^{(N)} \leq 0 \tag{55}$$

or

$$\sum_{j=1}^{r^{(c)}} \frac{\partial H^{(c)}}{\partial \bar{\theta}_j^{(c)}} \epsilon \varphi_j^{(c)} + 0(\epsilon^2) \leq 0 \tag{56}$$

$$\sum_{j=1}^{r^{(d)}} \frac{\partial H^{dn}}{\partial \bar{\theta}_j^{dn}} \epsilon \varphi_j^{dn} + 0(\epsilon^2) \leq 0. \tag{57}$$

If the leaving stream is discrete and if only the linear terms are considered, by using equations (13), (14), and (28) we have

$$\sum_{i=1}^{s(N)} \epsilon y_i^{N0} z_i^{N0} = \sum_{i=1}^{s(N)} \left[ \sum_{c'} \sum_{j=1}^{s^{(c')}} \epsilon y_j^{(c')}(T_{c'}) \frac{\partial g_i^{(N)}}{\partial x_j^{(c')}} + \sum_{d'} \sum_{j=1}^{s^{(d')}} \epsilon y_j^{d'N} \frac{\partial g_i^{(N)}}{\partial x_j^{d'N}} \right] z_i^{N0}$$

$$= \sum_{c'} \sum_{i=1}^{s(N)} \sum_{j=1}^{s^{(c')}} \epsilon y_j^{(c')}(T_{c'}) \frac{\partial g_i^{(N)}}{\partial x_j^{(c')}} z_i^{N0} + \sum_{d'} \sum_{i=1}^{s(N)} \sum_{j=1}^{s^{(d')}} \epsilon y_j^{d'N} \frac{\partial g_i^{(N)}}{\partial x_j^{d'N}} z_i^{N0}$$

$$= \sum_{c'} \sum_{j=1}^{s^{(c')}} \epsilon y_j^{(c')}(T_{c'}) \sum_{i=1}^{s(N)} \frac{\partial g_i^{(N)}}{\partial x_j^{(c')}} z_i^{N0} + \sum_{d'} \sum_{j=1}^{s^{(d')}} \epsilon y_j^{d'N} \sum_{i=1}^{s(N)} \frac{\partial g_i^{(N)}}{\partial x_j^{d'N}} z_i^{N0}$$

$$= \sum_{c'} \sum_{j=1}^{s^{(c')}} \epsilon y_j^{(c')}(T_{c'}) z_j^{(c')}(T_{c'}) + \sum_{d'} \sum_{j=1}^{s^{(d')}} \epsilon y_j^{d'N} z_j^{d'N}. \tag{58}$$

Note that for this case $c' = c$. By using equations (36) and (58) the left-hand side of equation (35) becomes

$$\sum_c \sum_{i=1}^{s^{(c)}} \epsilon[y_i^{(c)}(T_c)\, z_i^{(c)}(T_c) - y_i^{(c)}(0)\, z_i^{(c)}(0)]$$

$$+ \sum_d \sum_{i=1}^{s^{(d)}} \epsilon[y_i^{dN} z_i^{dN} - y_i^{d0}\, z_i^{d0}]$$

$$= \sum_{c'} \sum_{i=1}^{s^{(c')}} \epsilon y_i^{(c')}(T_{c'})\, z_i^{(c')}(T_{c'}) + \sum_{i=1}^{s^{(N)}} \epsilon y_i^{NN} z_i^{NN}$$

$$+ \sum_{d'} \sum_{i=1}^{s^{(d')}} \epsilon y_i^{d'N} z_i^{d'N} - \sum_{i=1}^{s^{(N)}} \epsilon y_i^{N0} z_i^{N0}$$

$$= \sum_{c'} \sum_{i=1}^{s^{(c')}} \epsilon y_i^{(c')}(T_{c'})\, z_i^{(c')}(T_{c'}) + \sum_{i=1}^{s^{(N)}} \epsilon y_i^{NN} z_i^{NN}$$

$$+ \sum_{d'} \sum_{i=1}^{s^{(d')}} \epsilon y_i^{d'N} z_i^{d'N}$$

$$- \sum_{c'} \sum_{j=1}^{s^{(c')}} \epsilon y_j^{(c')}(T_{c'})\, z_j^{(c')}(T_{c'}) - \sum_{d'} \sum_{j=1}^{s^{(d')}} \epsilon y_j^{d'N} z_j^{d'N}$$

$$= \sum_{i=1}^{s^{(N)}} \epsilon y_i^{NN} z_i^{NN}. \tag{59}$$

Equating equation (59) to the right-hand side of equation (35) gives

$$\sum_{i=1}^{s^{(N)}} \epsilon y_i^{NN} z_i^{NN} = \sum_c \int_0^T \left[ \sum_{j=1}^{r^{(c)}} \frac{\partial H^{(c)}}{\partial \bar{\theta}_j^{(c)}} \epsilon \varphi_j^{(c)} \right] dt + \sum_d \sum_{n=1}^N \sum_{j=1}^{r^{(d)}} \frac{\partial H^{dn}}{\partial \bar{\theta}_j^{dn}} \epsilon \varphi_j^{dn} + 0(\epsilon^2) \tag{60}$$

Therefore we have

$$\sum_{j=1}^{r^{(c)}} \frac{\partial H^{(c)}}{\partial \bar{\theta}_j^{(c)}} \epsilon \varphi_j^{(c)} + 0(\epsilon^2) \leq 0 \tag{61}$$

and

$$\sum_{j=1}^{r^{(d)}} \frac{\partial H^{dn}}{\partial \bar{\theta}_j^{dn}} \epsilon \varphi_j^{dn} + 0(\epsilon^2) \leq 0. \tag{62}$$

For those branches connected to a crossing point, by using equations (15), (16), and (29), considering only the linear terms and recalling that $\sum_{c'}$ denotes summation over all the entering streams that are continuous, $\sum_{d'}$ denotes summation over all the entering streams that are discrete, and $\sum_{c''}$ and $\sum_{d''}$ denote summation over all the continuous and discrete leaving streams, respectively, we have

$$
\sum_{c''} \sum_{i=1}^{s^{(c'')}} \epsilon y_i^{(c'')}(0)\, z_i^{(c'')}(0) + \sum_{d''} \sum_{i=1}^{s^{(d'')}} \epsilon y_i^{d''0} z_i^{d''0}
$$

$$
= \sum_{c''} \sum_{i=1}^{s^{(c'')}} \left[ \sum_{c'} \sum_{j=1}^{s^{(c')}} \epsilon y_j^{(c')}(T_{c'}) \frac{\partial g_i^{(c'')}}{\partial x_j^{(c')}} + \sum_{d'} \sum_{j=1}^{s^{(d')}} \epsilon y_j^{d'N} \frac{\partial g_i^{(c'')}}{\partial x_j^{d'N}} \right] z_i^{(c'')}(0)
$$

$$
+ \sum_{d''} \sum_{i=1}^{s^{(d'')}} \left[ \sum_{c'} \sum_{j=1}^{s^{(c')}} \epsilon y_j^{(c')}(T_{c'}) \frac{\partial g_i^{(d'')}}{\partial x_j^{(c')}} + \sum_{d'} \sum_{j=1}^{s^{(d')}} \epsilon y_j^{d'N} \frac{\partial g_i^{(d'')}}{\partial x_j^{d'N}} \right] z_i^{d''0}
$$

$$
= \sum_{c'} \sum_{j=1}^{s^{(c')}} \epsilon y_j^{(c')}(T_{c'})\, z_j^{(c')}(T_{c'}) + \sum_{d'} \sum_{j=1}^{s^{(d')}} \epsilon y_j^{d'N} z_j^{d'N}. \tag{63}
$$

By use of equations (36) and (63) the left-hand side of equation (35) can be written as

$$
\sum_{c} \sum_{i=1}^{s^{(c)}} \epsilon[y_i^{(c)}(T_c)\, z_i^{(c)}(T_c) - y_i^{(c)}(0)\, z_i^{(c)}(0)] + \sum_{d} \sum_{i=1}^{s^{(d)}} \epsilon[y_i^{dN} z_i^{dN} - y_i^{d0} z_i^{d0}]
$$

$$
= \sum_{c'} \sum_{i=1}^{s^{(c')}} \epsilon y_i^{(c')}(T_{c'})\, z_i^{(c')}(T_{c'}) + \sum_{c''} \sum_{i=1}^{s^{(c'')}} \epsilon y_i^{(c'')}(T_{c''})\, z_i^{(c'')}(T_{c''})
$$

$$
+ \sum_{d'} \sum_{i=1}^{s^{(d')}} \epsilon y_i^{d'N} z_i^{d'N} + \sum_{d''} \sum_{i=1}^{s^{(d'')}} \epsilon y_i^{d''N} z_i^{d''N}
$$

$$
- \left[ \sum_{c''} \sum_{i=1}^{s^{(c'')}} \epsilon y_i^{(c'')}(0)\, z_i^{(c'')}(0) + \sum_{d''} \sum_{i=1}^{s^{(d'')}} \epsilon y_i^{d''0} z_i^{d''0} \right]
$$

$$
= \sum_{c''} \sum_{i=1}^{s^{(c'')}} \epsilon y_i^{(c'')}(T_{c''})\, z_i^{(c'')}(T_{c''}) + \sum_{d''} \sum_{i=1}^{s^{(d'')}} \epsilon y_i^{d''N} z_i^{d''N}. \tag{64}
$$

It is worth recalling that

$$
c = c' + c'',
$$
$$
d = d' + d'',
$$
$$
N = c + d.
$$

Equating the right-hand side of equation (64) to equation (35) gives

$$
\sum_{c''} \sum_{i=1}^{s^{(c'')}} \epsilon y_i^{(c'')}(T_{c''})\, z_i^{(c'')}(T_{c''}) + \sum_{d''} \sum_{i=1}^{s^{(d'')}} \epsilon y_i^{d''N} z_i^{d''N}
$$

$$
= \sum_{c} \int_0^T \left[ \sum_{j=1}^{r^{(c)}} \frac{\partial H^{(c)}}{\partial \bar{\theta}_j^{(c)}} \epsilon \varphi_j^{(c)} \right] dt + \sum_{d} \sum_{n=1}^{N} \sum_{j=1}^{r^{(d)}} \frac{\partial H^{dn}}{\partial \bar{\theta}_j^{dn}} \epsilon \varphi_j^{dn} + 0(\epsilon^2). \tag{65}
$$

If the objective function is to be maximized, the perturbation of the decision variables can only be to make

$$\sum_{i=1}^{s^{(d'')}} \epsilon c_i^{d''N} y_i^{d''N} \leq 0 \tag{66}$$

and

$$\sum_{i=1}^{s^{(c'')}} \epsilon c_i^{(c'')} y_i^{(c'')}(T_{c''}) \leq 0 \tag{67}$$

or

$$\sum_{j=1}^{r^{(c)}} \frac{\partial H^{(c)}}{\partial \bar{\theta}_j^{(c)}} \epsilon \varphi_j^{(c)} + 0(\epsilon^2) \leq 0 \tag{68}$$

and

$$\sum_{j=1}^{r^{(d)}} \frac{\partial H^{dn}}{\partial \bar{\theta}_j^{dn}} \epsilon \varphi_j^{dn} + 0(\epsilon^2) \leq 0. \tag{69}$$

## 3.  AN EXAMPLE

To illustrate the use of the algorithm for composite processes let us consider the problem that has been solved by applying the sequential union of the maximum principle and dynamic programming [3].  The composite process consists of the discrete unit and continuous unit shown in Fig. 8.4.  For the discrete unit we have

$$x_1^{11} = x_1^{10} + \theta^{11},$$
$$x_1^{10} = \gamma. \tag{70}$$

For the continuous unit we have

$$\frac{dx_1^{(2)}}{dt} = -ax_1^{(2)} + \theta^{(2)},$$
$$x_1^{(2)}(0) = x_1^{11}. \tag{71}$$

We wish to minimize the total cost, $p^{(1)} + p^{(2)}$, where

$$p^{(1)} = x_1^{11} - \mu\theta^{11}, \tag{72}$$

$$p^{(2)} = \frac{1}{2} \int_0^{T_2} [(x_1^{(2)})^2 + (\theta_2^{(2)})^2] \, dt. \tag{73}$$

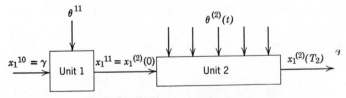

*Fig. 8.4*  A simple composite process.

To solve the problem, we introduce an additional state variable such that

$$x_2^{(2)}(t) = \frac{1}{2} \int_0^t [(x_1^{(2)})^2 + (\theta^{(2)})^2] \, dt + x_2^{11}, \tag{74}$$

$$\frac{dx_2^{(2)}}{dt} = \tfrac{1}{2}[(x_1^{(2)})^2 + (\theta^{(2)})^2], \tag{75}$$

$$x_2^{(2)}(0) = x_1^{11} - \mu\theta^{(1)} = x_2^{11}. \tag{76}$$

Hence, for the continuous branch, we have

$$H^{(2)} = z_1^{(2)}[-ax_1^{(2)} + \theta^{(2)}] + z_2^{(2)}[\tfrac{1}{2}(x_1^{(2)})^2 + \tfrac{1}{2}(\theta^{(2)})^2], \tag{77}$$

$$\frac{dz_1^{(2)}}{dt} = -\frac{\partial H}{\partial x_1^{(2)}} = az_1^{(2)} - z_2^{(2)} x_1^{(2)}, \qquad z_1^{(2)}(T_2) = 0, \tag{78}$$

$$\frac{dz_2^{(2)}}{dt} = -\frac{\partial H}{\partial x_2^{(2)}} = 0, \qquad z_2^{(2)}(T) = 1. \tag{79}$$

It follows from equation (79) that

$$z_2^{(2)}(t) = 1.$$

Assuming that the Hamiltonian attains its minimum in the interior point of the region of $\theta(t)$, we obtain the optimal decision [see Section 2.2]

$$\theta^{(2)}(t) = -z_1^{(2)}(t) = \bar{\theta}(t). \tag{80}$$

The corresponding $x(t)$ and $z(t)$ are found from equations (71) and (78) as

$$x_1^{(2)}(t) = x_1^{11}(\alpha e^{\lambda t} + \beta e^{-\lambda t}), \tag{81}$$

$$z_1^{(2)}(t) = x_1^{11}[\alpha(\lambda + a)e^{\lambda t} - \beta(\lambda - a)e^{-\lambda t}], \tag{82}$$

where

$$\lambda = \sqrt{a^2 + 1};$$

$\alpha$, $\beta$ are constants that can be determined from the boundary conditions

$$x_1^{(2)}(0) = x_1^{11}$$

and

$$z_1^{(2)}(T_2) = 0.$$

The junction equation is

$$x_1^{(2)}(0) = x_1^{11}.$$

Hence, by using equation (14), we obtain

$$z_1^{11} = z_1^{(2)}(0). \tag{83}$$

The Hamiltonian for the discrete unit is

$$\begin{aligned} H^{11} &= z_1^{11}(x_1^{10} + \theta^{11}) + z_2^{11}(x_1^{11} - \mu\theta^{11}) \\ &= z_1^{(2)}(0)(x_1^{10} + \theta^{11}) + (x_1^{10} + \theta^{11} - \mu\theta^{11}). \end{aligned} \tag{84}$$

Assuming that $H^{11}$ is stationary in the interior of the admissible range of $\theta^{11}$, we obtain the optimal decision from the condition

$$\frac{\partial H}{\partial \theta^{11}} = 0,$$

which gives

$$z_1^{(2)}(0) = -(1 - \mu). \tag{85}$$

From equation (82) we have

$$
\begin{aligned}
z_1^{(2)}(0) &= x_1^{11}[\alpha(\lambda + a) - \beta(\lambda - a)] \\
&= (x_1^{10} + \theta^{11})[\alpha(\lambda + a) - \beta(\lambda - a)].
\end{aligned} \tag{86}
$$

Solving for $\theta^{11}$ from equations (85) and (86) gives

$$
\begin{aligned}
\bar{\theta}^{11} &= \frac{-(1 - \mu)}{\alpha(\lambda + a) - \beta(\lambda - a)} - x_1^{10} \\
&= \frac{-(1 - \mu)}{\alpha(\lambda + a) - \beta(\lambda - a)} - \gamma.
\end{aligned} \tag{87}
$$

The minimum cost is obtained by substituting equations (80), (81), and (87) into equations (72) and (73) and adding the resulting values as

$$p^{(1)} + p^{(2)} = \mu\gamma - \frac{1}{C}\left(\frac{\mu - 1}{2}\right)^2,$$

where

$$C = \frac{1}{2}\left[\frac{e^{\lambda T_2} - e^{-\lambda T_2}}{(\lambda + a)e^{\lambda T_2} + (\lambda - a)e^{\lambda T_2}}\right] = \text{constant}.$$

## REFERENCES

1. Fan, L. T., and C. S. Wang, *The Discrete Maximum Principle: A Study of Multistage Systems Optimization*, Wiley, New York, 1964.
2. Fan, L. T., and S. J. Chen, "Optimization of Composite Processes," unpublished report, Kansas State University, September 1964.
3. Fan, L. T., W. S. Hwang, S. J. Chen, and L. S. Fan, "A Sequential Union of the Maximum Principle and Dynamic Programming," *J. Electron. Control*, **17**, No. 5, 593 (1964).
4. Denn, M. M., "The Optimization of Complex Systems," Ph.D. Thesis, University of Minnesota, 1964.
5. Denn, M. M., and R. Aris, "Green's Functions and Optimal Systems III: Complex Interconnected Systems," *Ind. Eng. Chem., Fundamentals*, **4**, 248 (1965).
6. Denn, M. M., and R. Aris, "Second-Order Variational Equations and the Strong Maximum Principle," *Chem. Eng. Sci.*, **20**, 373 (1965).
7. Denn, M. M., "On 'The Optimization of Continuous Complex Systems by the Maximum Principle'," *Int. J. Control*, **1**, 497 (1965).

# 9

# Combined Use of the Maximum Principle and Dynamic Programming

The computational algorithm for topologically complex processes in Chapter 6 is valid only for continuous processes. Even though the algorithm presented in Chapter 8 is applicable to processes composed of both discrete and continuous processes (composite processes), it is not necessarily the most convenient technique in dealing with their optimization. The best design job requires the "optimal" use of every tool available. Remembering that we are dealing with the optimization of a process, and "optimizing a process" is itself a process, we shall be too absent-minded if we forget to optimize what we are doing.

In some cases the best method may be to employ several techniques jointly, as illustrated by Lee [1]. Among many of the recently developed dynamic optimization techniques, dynamic programming and the maximum principle appear to be two of the most powerful for optimizing complex processes consisting of more than one process unit. Each of these methods, however, has comparative advantages over the other, depending on the problem to be solved. By combining these techniques it is often possible to handle the optimization of a complicated process with less effort.

## 1. A COMPARISON OF THE MAXIMUM PRINCIPLE AND DYNAMIC PROGRAMMING

The dynamic programming method reduces a complicated problem into a simple algorithm ideally suited for modern computers. It is based on the principle of optimality and employs the technique of invariant imbedding [2]. Dynamic programming, however, has its limitations. Since we are imbedding a whole family of processes to obtain the solution of one particular process, dynamic programming is often an expensive proposition both in time and in space; and, since both the computer time and the required memory increase rapidly with an increase in the number of state variables, this technique in general can be used successfully only for problems with a small number of state variables. Even if we have a considerable amount of computer time, the available memory in most modern computers still limits the use of the dynamic programming technique to problems of not more than three or four state variables. It is not suited for solving continuous problems in which the application of dynamic programming leads to a set of partial differential equations. It is possible, of course, to convert this set of partial differential equations into a system of finite difference equations and to apply the method of dynamic programming to solve continuous problems. The computational difficulty will be even more pronounced in this case, however, because a very small increment of finite difference equations must be taken to obtain a solution with reasonable accuracy.

Another disadvantage of dynamic programming is that it cannot be easily applied to processes in which the optimum conditions at any stage can be disturbed by conditions in the following stages. This is a fairly serious limitation if we consider the various countercurrent operations employed in the chemical and petroleum industries. Even a simple feedback process is difficult to treat because of the increased amount of computer memory and time which is required.

However, the definite and significant advantage of dynamic programming in the optimization of processes with constraints on state variables cannot be neglected. Processes with bounded state variables give no trouble with this method because the optimal decisions determined for the entire allowable policy domain automatically satisfy the constraints.

On the other hand, the maximum principle can be used to control most constraints of ordinary optimum design problems, with the exception of those in the state variables which cannot be handled routinely (see Section 2.4, part j). By the use of the maximum principle the optimization problem is essentially reduced to a maximum- or minimum-seeking problem subject to a set of ordinary differential equations and certain inequality constraints. This set of ordinary differential equations usually forms a two-point boundary value problem. Thus we are still limited by the difficulties encountered in the solution of a set of simultaneous nonlinear differential equations with two-point boundary conditions. Nevertheless, the number of state variables that can be treated by generally available computing equipment when the maximum principle is used may be larger than that when the dynamic programming technique is used. As mentioned in Chapter 4, the maximum principle is probably better suited than dynamic programming to the solution of continuous problems.

Another salient feature of dynamic programming is that it can be used to handle processes for which the transformation at each stage is expressed in a form other than that of a mathematical equation (for example, a table or a graph). The maximum principle, on the other hand, is applicable only to processes with well-defined performance equations, and the transformation function must be continuously differentiable with respect to the state variables.

We shall show that the combined use of the maximum principle and dynamic programming can be employed for the optimization of some complex processes.

A process can be separated into different units and each unit can be optimized by either of the two methods (or by any other appropriate optimization method). The over-all process is optimized by connecting the different units by using the principle of optimality. We refer to this combination as the sequential union of the maximum principle and dynamic programming.

On the other hand, it is worth noting that the discrete version of the maximum principle contains only the necessary conditions for a local extremum and that there will be no assurance that the optimal policy found by the maximum principle will be the global optimal policy. Since the method of dynamic programming employs the so-called imbedding technique, which is in spirit similar to the exhaustive search, the optimal policy obtained by dynamic programming will always be the global optimal policy provided that the interpolation error inherent to the method is small. It is thus proposed that when an accurate solution is desired or required the method of dynamic programming be employed first to locate the approximate position of the global maximum and that the maximum principle then be applied to pinpoint it. This combination may be called the parallel union of the maximum principle and dynamic programming.

In the following section we present in detail the method of the sequential union.

## 2. SEQUENTIAL UNION OF THE MAXIMUM PRINCIPLE AND DYNAMIC PROGRAMMING

The essential steps in the application of the sequential union of the maximum principle and dynamic programming are summarized as follows [1]:

1. An entire process is divided into different units (subprocesses).
2. An appropriate optimization method is applied to each unit.

3. The optimum of the entire process is obtained by the principle of optimality.

The separation of a process into different units is arbitrary and is often dictated by knowledge of the process and its requirements. For example, a chemical manufacturing process which requires a reactor, an extractor, and a heat exchanger may be divided into three or more

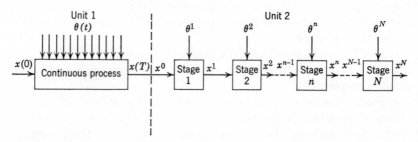

*Fig. 9.1* A schematic representation of a two-unit process.

units. In the purification of a chemical compound from a mixture by several distillation columns we can consider each column as a unit or we can consider all of them as a single unit, depending on the requirements of optimization and on the complexity and physical characteristics of the process.

Each unit may be composed of a number of stages, or it may represent a continuous process. In a series of stirred tank reactors each stirred tank may be considered as a stage. A tubular flow reactor may be considered as a continuous process consisting of an infinite number of stirred tanks.

A two-unit process will illustrate the method of sequential union. The arrangements of the units and the number of stages in each unit are shown in Fig. 9.1, in which unit 1 is a continuous process and unit 2 is a discrete process. We shall assume that the maximum principle is to be applied to unit 1 and dynamic programming to unit 2. The over-all optimum is then obtained by applying the principle of optimality.

For the continuous simple process of unit 1 we know from Section 2.1 that the performance equations are generally given by

$$\frac{dx_i}{dt} = f_i(x_1, \ldots, x_s; \theta_1, \ldots, \theta_r), \qquad i = 1, 2, \ldots, s,$$

or, in vector form,

$$\frac{dx}{dt} = f(x; \theta). \tag{1}$$

Our aim is usually to optimize a linear combination of the final values of the state variables of this unit, that is, to maximize (or minimize) the quantity

$$S = \sum_{i=1}^{s} c_i x_i(T), \tag{2}$$

with the initial condition $x(t_0) = \alpha$ given. To do this we generally introduce an $s$-dimensional adjoint vector $z(t)$ and a Hamiltonian function $H$, which satisfy the following relations:

$$H(z, x, t) = \sum_{i=1}^{s} z_i f_i(x; \theta), \tag{3}$$

$$\frac{dz_i}{dt} = -\frac{\partial H}{\partial x_i}, \qquad i = 1, 2, \ldots, s, \tag{4}$$

and the boundary conditions

$$x(t_0) = \alpha, \qquad z_i(T) = c_i, \qquad i = 1, \ldots, s. \tag{5}$$

The optimal solution is obtained only if the function $H$ is maximized (or minimized) at every moment from $t = t_0$ to $t = T$, subject to equations (1), (4), and (5).

For the discrete process of unit 2 the transformation of the process stream at the $n$th stage may be described by a set of difference equations [2]:

$$x_i{}^n = T_i{}^n(x_1^{n-1}, x_2^{n-1}, \ldots, x_s^{n-1}; \theta_1{}^n, \theta_2{}^n, \ldots, \theta_r{}^n)^*, \qquad i = 1, 2, \ldots, s$$

or, in vector form,

$$x^n = T^n(x^{n-1}; \theta^n), \tag{6}$$

which is the performance equation of this unit. Suppose that the return function (interval profit function) from stage $n$ of unit 2 is $h(x^{n-1}; \theta^n)$ and we wish to maximize the total profit represented by

$$h(x^0; \theta^1) + h(x^1; \theta^2) + \cdots + h(x^{n-1}; \theta^n) + \cdots + h(x^{N-1}; \theta^N). \tag{7}$$

It should be noted that after the optimal values of the decision variables have been determined the value of this maximum depends only on the initial state of the state variable and the number of stages. Thus we let

$$g_N(x^0) = \max_{\{\theta^n\}} [h(x^0; \theta^1) + \cdots + h(x^{N-1}; \theta^N)]. \tag{8}\dagger$$

* The superscript $n$ indicates the stage number.
† Subscript $N$ indicates the total number of stages but not the $N$th stage.

Using the principle of optimality and equation (6), we obtain a recurrence relation as

$$g_N(x^0) = \max_{\theta^1} \{h(x^0; \theta^1) + g_{N-1}[T(x^0; \theta^1)]\} \qquad (9)$$

for $N = 2, 3, \ldots, N$. For $N = 1$ we have

$$g_1(x^0) = \max_{\theta^1} h(x^0; \theta^1). \qquad (10)$$

Thus the optimization problem of unit 2 can be solved recursively by using equations (9) and (10).

To obtain the over-all optimum for the process the optimum of unit 2 must be achieved first by the method of dynamic programming [3]. Since unit 1 is to be optimized by the maximum principle, special attention must be given to the objective function for this unit. Because we have already obtained the optimum of unit 2 by dynamic programming, equation (2) can be modified to include the effects of unit 2. It should be noted that the optimum return for unit 2 is in general given in tabular form. For every possible combination of the initial condition $x^0$ the value of the optimum return $g_N(x^0)$ [see equation (9)] is listed. To use the function $g_N(x^0)$ in establishing the return function for unit 1 it must first be expressed in analytical form. This can be done sometimes by appropriate correlation methods. For example, a polynomial approximation appears to be promising in these correlations. In a one-state variable process the $g_N(x^0)$ may be represented in analytical form (e.g., see Example 1).

When the function $g_N(x^0)$ is expressed analytically, the objective function for the entire process can be obtained. If we let $\int_0^T h(x; \theta)\, dt$ be the return (profit or cost) from unit 1, the objective function for the over-all system is

$$S = g_N[x(T)] + \int_0^T h(x; \theta)\, dt, \qquad (11)$$

where $x(T) = x^0$; that is, $x(T)$ represents the final value of the state vector of unit 1 and is equal to the initial value of the state vector of unit 2. Equation (11), which corresponds to the recurrence relation equation (9), is established by the principle of optimality. The method outlined by equations (1) through (5) may now be modified to take into account the objective function, equation (11). To accomplish this we introduce a new state variable as

$$x_{s+1}(T) = g_N[x(T)] + \int_0^T h(x; \theta)\, dt \qquad (12)$$

or

$$x_{s+1}(t) = g_N[x(t)] + \int_0^t h(x; \theta)\, dt \qquad (13)$$

and

$$\frac{dx_{s+1}}{dt} = \sum_{i=1}^{s} \frac{\partial g_N(x)}{\partial x_i} \frac{dx_i}{dt} + h(x; \theta). \tag{14}$$

Our object is now transformed into that of maximizing the final value of $x_{s+1}$. The Hamiltonian function $H$ in equation (3) is modified as

$$H(x, z, \theta) = \sum_{i=1}^{s+1} z_i f_i(x; \theta) \tag{15}$$

and the new adjoint variable $z_{s+1}$ is introduced as

$$\frac{dz_{s+1}}{dt} = -\frac{\partial H}{\partial x_{s+1}} = 0. \tag{16}$$

The boundary conditions for the adjoint variables, equation (5), should be changed to

$$z_i(T) = 0, \qquad i = 1, 2, \ldots, s,$$
$$z_{s+1}(T) = 1. \tag{17}$$

From equations (16) and (17) we obtain $z_{s+1}(t) = 1$; hence we have

$$H(x, z, \theta) = \sum_{i=1}^{s} z_i f_i(x; \theta) + \frac{dx_{s+1}}{dt}. \tag{18}$$

All other relationships of equations (1) and (4) remain the same. This optimization problem can now be solved by using methods introduced in the preceding chapters. Once the optimization calculation for unit 1 is completed the final values $x(T)$ are obtained. These values provide the optimal initial values for unit 2, whose optimal policy can be recovered by using equations (9) and (10).

So far we have dealt with a system whose first unit is optimized by employing the maximum principle. When the first unit in the sequence is not to be optimized by the maximum principle, the same procedure is still applicable. However, we must, in general, calculate a grid of values associated with the unit optimized by the maximum principle, since in this case the initial conditions of the units using the maximum principle are not given. Generally there are no given initial conditions for any unit except the first one. When the grid of values is obtained, the optimal policy of the units preceding this unit can also be obtained by applying the principle of optimality. Note that if the unit which is to be optimized by using the maximum principle is a one-state variable process and the functional dependence of the optimal value with respect to the feed condition to this unit can be obtained analytically, the calculation of a grid of values is not necessary.

In what follows we present several examples to illustrate the use of the method of sequential union. The examples are chosen so that the over-all optimum can be obtained from the analytical solution without the calculation of a grid of values.

**Example 1.** In this example we consider a two-unit process consisting of a tubular reactor of length $L_1$ (continuous process), followed by a two-stage cross-current extractor (discrete process) shown in Fig. 9.2.

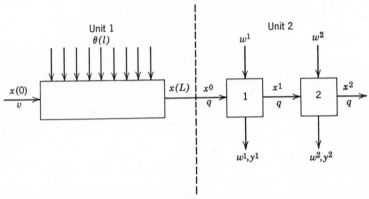

**Fig. 9.2** A schematic diagram for a process with a tubular reactor followed by a two-stage cross-current liquid-liquid extraction system.

It is considered that an autocatalytic reaction of the type

$$B + R \underset{k_2}{\overset{k_1}{\rightleftharpoons}} R + R$$

takes place in the tubular reactor. The product stream is then fed to the liquid-liquid extractor for purification. It is assumed that reactant $B$ is immiscible in the solvent and only the product $R$ is extracted. It is desired to maximize the over-all net profit by finding the optimal temperature profile along the tubular reactor and by allocating the optimal amount of washing water at each of the two extractors.

We first optimize unit 2 by using dynamic programming and proceed to optimize unit 1 by the maximum principle. The over-all optimum is then obtained by use of the principle of optimality.

The performance equation of a tubular reactor in which an autocatalytic reaction is taking place is given on a mass fraction basis [see equation (7.184)] as

$$\frac{dx_1}{dl} = \frac{A}{v} [k_1(1 - x_1)^b(x_1)^r - k_2(x_1)^s], \tag{19}$$

where    $v =$ the total volumetric flow rate, ft³/hr,

        $A =$ the cross-sectional area of the tubular reactor, ft²,

$k_1$ and $k_2 =$ the Arrhenius-type reaction rate constants given in equation (4.25), hr⁻¹,

      $x_1 =$ the fractional mass concentration of $R$, dimensionless,

$b$, $r$, and $s =$ the order of reactions.

We derive the transformation equation of unit 2 by considering it as an $n$-stage process as shown in Fig. 9.3. The material balance with respect to product $R$ around the $n$th stage gives [4]

$$w^n y^n = q(x_1^{n-1} - x_1^{\,n}), \tag{20}$$

where $w =$ the washing water rate, lb/hr,

      $y =$ the composition of the product $R$ at the outlet of the extractor,

      $q = v\rho_m$, mass flow rate, lb/hr, assumed to be constant,

     $\rho_m =$ the density of the mixture (assumed to be constant), lb/ft³

or

$$u^n y^n = x_1^{n-1} - x_1^{\,n}, \tag{21}$$

where

$$u^n = \frac{w^n}{q}. \tag{22}$$

Let $Q_N = \sum_{n=1}^{N} w^n y^n = q(x_1^{\,0} - x_1^{\,N})$ be the total amount of $R$ extracted and $G_N = \sum_{n=1}^{N} w^n$ be the total amount of washing water supplied. The net profit function for unit 2 may be written as

$$P_N = Q_N - \lambda G_N, \tag{23}$$

where $\lambda$ is the relative cost of the washing water and can be regarded as a Lagrange multiplier. Equation (23) is equivalent to

$$P_N = q \sum_{n=1}^{N} (x_1^{n-1} - x_1^{\,n}) - \lambda \sum_{n=1}^{N} w^n. \tag{24}$$

Substitution of equation (22) into (24) gives

$$P_N = q \left[ \sum_{n=1}^{N} (x_1^{n-1} - x_1^{\,n}) - \lambda \sum_{n=1}^{N} u^n \right] = q \sum_{n=1}^{N} u^n (y^n - \lambda), \tag{25}$$

which together with equation (20) are the performance equations of unit 2.

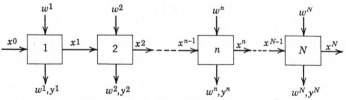

*Fig. 9.3* A schematic diagram of a multistage cross-current liquid-liquid extraction system.

We now consider the return function of unit 2. From equation (25) the maximum return function of unit 2 is

$$f_N(x_1^0) = \max_{\{u^n\}} \sum_{n=1}^{N} u^n(y^n - \lambda), \qquad x_1^0 = a. \tag{26}$$

If a linear equilibrium relationship is assumed in each stage, the relation between the concentrations $x_1^n$ and $y^n$ is

$$x_1^n = \alpha y^n. \tag{27}$$

Substituting equation (27) into (26), we have

$$f_N(a) = \max_{\{u^n\}} \sum_{n=1}^{N} u^n\left(\frac{x_1^n}{\alpha} - \lambda\right). \tag{28}$$

According to equation (9), we have the following recursive relation:

$$f_N(a) = \max_{u^1}\left[u^1\left(\frac{x_1^1}{\alpha} - \lambda\right) + f_{N-1}(x_1^1)\right], \tag{29}$$

with $x_1^0 = a$ and $f_0(a) = 0$.

For a two-stage extraction process $(N = 2)$, combining equations (21) and (27), gives for the second stage

$$x_1^2 = x_1^1 - u^2y^2 = \alpha y^2$$

or

$$x_1^2 = \frac{\alpha x_1^1}{u^2 + \alpha}. \tag{30}$$

Equation (29) for $N = 2$ is

$$f_2(a) = \max_{u^1}\left[u^1\left(\frac{x_1^1}{\alpha} - \lambda\right) + f_1(x_1^1)\right], \tag{31}$$

where

$$f_1(x_1^1) = \max_{u^2}\left[u^2\left(\frac{x_1^2}{\alpha} - \lambda\right)\right]. \tag{32}$$

By substituting equation (30) into (32) we obtain

$$f_1(x_1^1) = \max_{u^2}\left[u^2\left(\frac{x_1^1}{\alpha + u^2} - \lambda\right)\right]. \tag{33}$$

By partially differentiating the quantity in the bracket of equation (33) with respect to $u^2$ and setting it equal to zero to solve for $\overline{u^2}$ we obtain

$$\overline{u^2} = \sqrt{\frac{x_1^1\alpha}{\lambda}} - \alpha, \tag{34}$$

provided that $x_1{}^1 > \lambda\alpha$. By substituting equation (34) into (30) we obtain

$$x_1{}^2 = \sqrt{\alpha x_1{}^1 \lambda}. \tag{35}$$

Substituting equation (34) into (33), we have

$$f_1(x_1{}^1) = x_1{}^1 - 2\sqrt{\alpha x_1{}^1 \lambda} + \alpha\lambda. \tag{36}$$

This is the optimal interval return function for the second stage of the extraction process with respect to the outlet condition of the first stage. Similarly, for the first stage, by applying equation (31), we have

$$f_2(a) = \max_{u^1} \left[ u^1\left(\frac{x_1{}^1}{\alpha} - \lambda\right) + f_1(x_1{}^1) \right]. \tag{37}$$

By substituting equation (36) into (37) we obtain

$$f_2(a) = \max_{u^1} \left[ u^1\left(\frac{x_1{}^1}{\alpha} - \lambda\right) + x_1{}^1 - 2\sqrt{\alpha x_1{}^1 \lambda} + \alpha\lambda \right]. \tag{38}$$

Combining equations (21) and (27) for $n = 1$, we have for the first stage

$$x_1{}^1 = x_1{}^0 - u^1 y^1 = \alpha y^1$$

or

$$x_1{}^1 = \frac{x_1{}^0 \alpha}{u^1 + \alpha} = \frac{a\alpha}{u^1 + \alpha}. \tag{39}$$

By substituting equation (39) into (38) and simplifying the resulting equation we obtain

$$f_2(a) = \max_{u^1} \left[ a - u^1\lambda - 2\sqrt{\frac{(\alpha)^2 \lambda a}{u^1 + \alpha}} + \alpha\lambda \right]. \tag{40}$$

By partially differentiating the quantity in the bracket of equation (40) with respect to $u^1$ and setting it equal to zero to solve for $\overline{u^1}$ we obtain

$$\overline{u^1} = \left(\frac{(\alpha)^2 a}{\lambda}\right)^{\!1/3} - \alpha. \tag{41}$$

Substitution of equation (41) into (39) yields

$$x_1{}^1 = [\alpha\lambda(a)^2]^{1/3}. \tag{42}$$

Substituting equation (41) into (40), we have

$$f_2(a) = a - 3[(\alpha)^2(\lambda)^2 a]^{1/3} + 2\alpha\lambda. \tag{43}$$

By substituting equation (42) into (34) and noting (41) we obtain the optimal policy for the two-stage extraction unit:

$$\overline{u^1} = \overline{u^2} = \left(\frac{(\alpha)^2 a}{\lambda}\right)^{\!1/3} - \alpha. \tag{44}$$

This means that the washing water is divided equally between the two stages.

To obtain the optimum for the over-all process or the maximum combined profit from the reactor and purification sections the objective function must be established for the entire process. Since no product $R$ can be sold until it is purified, there is no direct return available from unit 1. The operating cost for unit 1 is assumed to be proportional to the amount of reactant $B$ converted into the product $R$:

$$\beta[x_1(L) - x_1(0)], \tag{45}$$

where $\beta$ is a proportionality constant and $x_1(L)$ and $x_1(0)$ are the fractional mass concentrations of $R$ at the outlet and inlet of the reactor, respectively.

Since we have already established the maximum profit from the purification section, the over-all net profit function can be written from equations (43) and (45), according to the principle of optimality [see equation (11)]:

$$S = x_1^0 - 3[(\alpha)^2(\lambda)^2 x_1^0]^{\frac{1}{3}} + 2\alpha\lambda - \beta[x_1(L) - x_1(0)]. \tag{46}$$

Remembering that $x_1(L) = x_1^0$, we can rewrite equation (46) as

$$S = x_1(L) - 3[(\alpha)^2(\lambda)^2 x_1(L)]^{\frac{1}{3}} + 2\alpha\lambda - \beta[x_1(L) - x_1(0)]. \tag{47}$$

We now wish to find the decision function $\theta(l)$ which maximizes this objective function.

To solve this problem we introduce a second state variable $x_2$, defined as

$$x_2(l) = x_1(l) - 3[(\alpha)^2(\lambda)^2 x_1(l)]^{\frac{1}{3}} + 2\alpha\lambda - \beta[x_1(l) - x_1(0)]. \tag{48}$$

Differentiation of equation (48) with respect to $l$ gives

$$\frac{dx_2}{dl} = (1 - \beta)\frac{dx_1}{dl} - (\alpha\lambda)^{\frac{2}{3}}x_1^{-\frac{2}{3}}\frac{dx_1}{dl}. \tag{49}$$

This equation and equation (19) form the complete performance equations for unit 1. The initial conditions are

$$x_1(0) = \gamma, \tag{50}$$

$$x_2(0) = \gamma - 3[(\alpha)^2(\lambda)^2\gamma]^{\frac{1}{3}} + 2\alpha\lambda. \tag{51}$$

By substituting equation (19) into (49), we obtain

$$\frac{dx_2}{dl} = [1 - \beta - (\alpha\lambda)^{\frac{2}{3}}x_1^{-\frac{2}{3}}][k_1(1 - x_1)^b(x_1)^r - k_2(x_1)^s]\frac{A}{v}. \tag{52}$$

According to equations (3) and (4), we can write the Hamiltonian $H$ and the adjoint variables for this unit as

$$H = \frac{Az_1}{v}[k_1(1 - x_1)^b(x_1)^r - k_2(x_1)^s]$$

$$+ \frac{Az_2}{v}[k_1(1 - x_1)^b(x_1)^r - k_2(x_1)^s][1 - \beta - (\alpha\lambda)^{\frac{2}{3}}(x_1)^{-\frac{2}{3}}], \quad (53)$$

$$\frac{dz_1}{dl} = -\frac{Az_1}{v}[-bk_1(1 - x_1)^{b-1}(x_1)^r + k_1(1 - x_1)^b r(x_1)^{r-1} - k_2 s(x_1)^{s-1}]$$

$$- \frac{Az_2}{v}[-bk_1(1 - x_1)^{b-1}(x_1)^r + k_1(1 - x_1)^b r(x_1)^{r-1} - k_2 s(x_1)^{s-1}]$$

$$\times [1 - \beta - (\alpha\lambda)^{\frac{2}{3}}(x_1)^{-\frac{2}{3}}]$$

$$- \frac{Az_2}{v}[k_1(1 - x_1)^b(x_1)^r - k_2(x_1)^s][\tfrac{2}{3}(x_1)^{-\frac{5}{3}}(\alpha\lambda)^{\frac{2}{3}}], \quad (54)$$

$$\frac{dz_2}{dl} = 0. \quad (55)$$

Since the objective function is $x_2(L)$, we have $c_1 = 0$ and $c_2 = 1$. According to equation (5), we have

$$z_1(L) = 0, \quad (56)$$

$$z_2(L) = 1. \quad (57)$$

By combining equation (57) with (55) we obtain

$$z_2(l) = 1. \quad (58)$$

Substituting equation (58) into (53), we have

$$H = \frac{A}{v}[k_1(1 - x_1)^b(x_1)^r - k_2(x_1)^s]\{z_1 + [1 - \beta - (\alpha\lambda)^{\frac{2}{3}}(x_1)^{-\frac{2}{3}}]\}. \quad (59)$$

When the maximum of $H$ occurs at the stationary point, we can obtain the optimal decision function $\theta(l)$ by partially differentiating equation (59) with respect to $\theta$ and setting it equal to zero; that is

$$\frac{\partial H}{\partial \theta} = \frac{A\{z_1 + [1 - \beta - (\alpha\lambda)^{\frac{2}{3}}(x_1)^{-\frac{2}{3}}]\}}{v}$$

$$\times \left[(1 - x_1)^b(x_1)^r \frac{dk_1}{d\theta} - (x_1)^s \frac{dk_2}{d\theta}\right] = 0.$$

Substituting equation (4.9) into this equation for $dk_1/d\theta$ and $dk_2/d\theta$ and solving for $\theta$, we have

$$\bar{\theta}(l) = \left(\frac{E_1 - E_2}{R}\right) \frac{1}{\ln[\xi(x_1)^{r-s}(1 - x_1)^b]}, \quad (60)$$

where

$$\xi = \frac{k_{10}E_1}{k_{20}E_2}.$$

Substituting equation (60) into (19), we have

$$\frac{dx_1}{dl} = \frac{A}{v} \{ k_{10}(1 - x_1)^b (x_1)^r [\xi(x_1)^{r-s}(1 - x_1)^b]^{\lambda_1}$$
$$- (x_1)^s k_{20} [\xi(x_1)^{r-s}(1 - x_1)^b]^{\lambda_2} \}, \quad (61)$$

where

$$\lambda_1 = \frac{E_1}{E_2 - E_1} \quad \text{and} \quad \lambda_2 = \frac{E_2}{E_2 - E_1}.$$

In integrating equation (61) the activation energies are chosen, as they frequently are, in order that

$$\frac{E_2}{E_1} = 2 \quad \text{or} \quad \lambda_1 = 1 \quad \text{and} \quad \lambda_2 = 2. \quad (62)$$

We are reminded again that equation (61) is valid for any values of $E_1$ and $E_2$. Equation (62) is chosen for the simplification of the problem.

By substituting equation (62) into (61) and simplifying the resulting equation we obtain

$$\frac{dx_1}{dl} = \frac{A}{v} [k_{10}\xi - k_{20}(\xi)^2][(1 - x_1)^{2b}(x_1)^{2r-s}]. \quad (63)$$

If we assume that the reaction is first-order with respect to each component for the forward reaction and second-order with respect to the backward reaction, that is, $b = r = 1$ and $s = 2$, equation (63) can be integrated as

$$\frac{1}{1 - x_1} = \frac{Al}{v} [k_{10}\xi - k_{20}(\xi)^2] + C. \quad (64)$$

The integration constant $C$ is evaluated by using equation (50) as

$$\frac{1}{1 - \gamma} = C. \quad (65)$$

Substituting equation (65) into (64), we have

$$l = \frac{v}{A\xi(k_{10} - k_{20}\xi)} \left( \frac{1}{1 - x_1} - \frac{1}{1 - \gamma} \right). \quad (66)$$

By combining equations (60) and (66) we can obtain the optimal policy for unit 1.

Solving equation (66) for $x_1(L)$, we have

$$L = \frac{v}{A\xi(k_{10} - k_{20}\xi)}\left(\frac{1}{1 - x_1(L)} - \frac{1}{1 - \gamma}\right)$$

or

$$x_1(L) = \frac{(v/A)\gamma + L\xi(k_{10} - k_{20}\xi)(1 - \gamma)}{v/A + L\xi(k_{10} - k_{20}\xi)(1 - \gamma)}. \tag{67}$$

$$[x_1(L) = x_1{}^0 = a]$$

Substitution of equation (67) into (45) and (43) gives the optimal profit for the reactor and the purification section, respectively. The over-all optimal net profit is obtained by substituting equation (67) into (47).

Equations (60) and (66) are identical to (7.200) and (7.213) because we have assumed that the operating cost for the tubular reactors is a function of the state variable only [see equation (45)]. However, the optimal solution will be different if the cost is also a function of the decision variable.

**Example 2** [5]. Let a system be composed of the two units shown schematically in Fig. 9.4. Unit 1 is a discrete process characterized by the following performance equation:

$$x_1{}^1 = x_1{}^0 + \theta^1, \qquad x_1{}^0 = \gamma_1. \tag{68}*$$

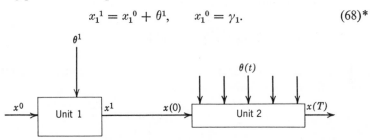

**Fig. 9.4** A schematic representation of a two-unit process consisting of a discrete unit followed by a continuous unit.

The interval cost for this unit is

$$S_1(x_1{}^0; \theta^1) = x_1{}^1 - \mu\theta^1, \tag{69}$$

where $\mu$ is a constant.

Unit 2 is a continuous process characterized by the following performance equation:

$$\frac{dx_1}{dt} = -ax_1 + \theta, \qquad x_1(0) = x_1{}^1. \tag{70}$$

---

* Superscripts indicate the stage number in unit 1. The exponents are written with parentheses or brackets such as $(x^n)^2$ or $(\theta^n)^2$.

The interval cost (generally interval return) for this unit is

$$S_2(x_1{}^1; \theta) = \tfrac{1}{2} \int_0^T [(x_1)^2 + (\theta)^2] \, dt, \qquad 0 \le t \le T. \tag{71}$$

The problem is to minimize the total cost $(S_1 + S_2)$ by an optimal choice of $\theta^1$ and $\theta(t)$. A process involving characteristics such as those represented by equations (68) and (70) cannot be optimized easily by solely using the method of dynamic programming.

It may be noted that the performance equation and objective function for unit 2 (a continuous process) are the same as those given in the example in Chapter 2. Unit 2 is optimized by using the maximum principle, and the over-all optimum is then obtained by the principle of optimality.

From equation (9) we can write the objective function for the entire process as

$$f_2(x_1{}^0) = \min_{\theta^1} \, [S_1(x_1{}^0; \theta^1) + f_1(x_1{}^1)], \tag{72}$$

where $f(x_1{}^1)$ is the minimum of the objective function for a single unit process consisting of unit 2 only (the interval return function of unit 2).

To obtain the optimum for unit 2 by using the maximum principle we introduce a new state variable $x_2(t)$ as

$$x_2(t) = \tfrac{1}{2} \int_0^t [(x_1)^2 + (\theta)^2] \, dt. \tag{73}$$

Since the interval cost function to be minimized in unit 2 is the interval cost itself, we have

$$f_1(x_1{}^1) = \min_{\theta(t)} \, \{S_2\} = \min_{\theta(t)} \, \{x_2(T)\}. \tag{74}$$

The optimal policy and the corresponding value of the state variable for unit 2 (see the example in Section 2.2) is obtained as

$$x_1(t) = A_1 e^{\lambda t} + A_2 e^{-\lambda t}, \tag{75}$$

$$\theta(t) = A_1(\lambda + a)e^{\lambda t} - A_2(\lambda - a)e^{-\lambda t}, \tag{76}$$

where

$$\lambda = \sqrt{a^2 + 1},$$

$$A_1 = \frac{(\lambda - a)e^{-\lambda T} x_1{}^1}{(\lambda + a)e^{\lambda T} + (\lambda - a)e^{-\lambda T}},$$

$$A_2 = \frac{(\lambda + a)e^{\lambda T} x_1{}^1}{(\lambda + a)e^{\lambda T} + (\lambda - a)e^{-\lambda T}},$$

or [see (2.27)]

$$\bar{\theta}(t) = \frac{x_1{}^1[e^{-\lambda(T-t)} - e^{\lambda(T-t)}]}{(\lambda + a)e^{\lambda T} + (\lambda - a)e^{-\lambda T}} \cdot \tag{77}$$

By substituting equations (75) and (76) into (71) and integrating the result, we obtain the minimum value of $x_2(T)$ [see equation (2.29)]:

$$f_1(x_1{}^1) = \frac{(x_1{}^1)^2}{2} \left[ \frac{e^{\lambda T} - e^{-\lambda T}}{(\lambda + a)e^{\lambda T} + (\lambda - a)e^{-\lambda T}} \right]. \tag{78}$$

If we let

$$\frac{1}{2} \left[ \frac{e^{\lambda T} - e^{-\lambda T}}{(\lambda + a)e^{\lambda T} + (\lambda - a)e^{-\lambda T}} \right] = C = \text{constant},$$

we obtain

$$f_1(x_1{}^1) = C(x_1{}^1)^2. \tag{79}$$

Replacing $f_1(x_1{}^1)$ in equation (72) with (79), we obtain the recursive function

$$f_2(x_1{}^0) = \min_{\theta^1} \{S_1(x_1{}^0; \theta^1) + C[x_1{}^1(\theta^1)]^2\}. \tag{80}$$

Substitution of equations (68) and (69) into (80) yields

$$f_2(x_1{}^0) = \min_{\theta^1} [(x_1{}^1 - \mu\theta^1) + C(x_1{}^0 + \theta^1)^2]$$

or

$$f_2(x_1{}^0) = \min_{\theta^1} [(x_1{}^0 + \theta^1 - \mu\theta^1) + C(x_1{}^0 + \theta^1)^2]. \tag{81}$$

When the minimum of the quantity in the bracket occurs at a stationary point within the admissible domain, the optimal $\theta^1$ can be obtained from

$$\frac{\partial[(x_1{}^0 + \theta^1 - \mu\theta^1) + C(x_1{}^0 + \theta^1)^2]}{\partial \theta^1} = 1 - \mu + 2C(x_1{}^0 + \theta^1) = 0.$$

Thus we have the optimal decision for unit 1:

$$\bar{\theta}^1 = \frac{\mu - 1}{2C} - \gamma_1, \tag{82}$$

where

$$x_1{}^0 = \gamma_1.$$

It can be shown that the optimal decision $\bar{\theta}^1$ obtained here is the same as that given by (8.87). By substituting this value of $\theta^1$ back into equation (81) we obtain

$$f_2(x_1{}^0) = \mu\gamma_1 - \frac{1}{C}\left(\frac{\mu - 1}{2}\right)^2. \tag{83}$$

By substituting equation (82) into (68) we obtain

$$x_1^{1} = \frac{\mu - 1}{2C}. \tag{84}$$

This is the optimal feed condition of unit 2. By substituting this value of $x_1^{1}$ into equation (77) we obtain the optimal decision for unit 2 as

$$\bar{\theta}(t) = \frac{(\mu - 1)[e^{-\lambda(T-t)} - e^{\lambda(T-t)}]}{2C[(\lambda + a)e^{\lambda T} + (\lambda - a)e^{-\lambda T}]}. \tag{85}$$

The minimum cost for each unit is then obtained by substituting the optimal decision of each unit, equations (82) and (85), into the interval cost function of the respective units, (69) and (71). The minimum value of the total cost (the objective function) for the process can thus be obtained analytically by summing up the cost of each unit. The computational algorithm for composite complex processes given in Chapter 8 was also used to solve this problem.

**Example 3** [5].    The process to be considered is shown schematically in Fig. 9.5. Unit 1 is the same as that in Example 2. Unit 2, however, is a continuous process consisting of four branches whose positions are indicated as 1, 2, 3, and 4 in Fig. 9.5, with the following performance equations:

$$\frac{dx_1^{(1)}}{dt} = 0, \tag{86}*$$

$$\frac{dx_1^{(2)}}{dt} = -ax_1^{(2)} + \theta^{(2)}, \tag{87}$$

$$\frac{dx_1^{(3)}}{dt} = 0, \tag{88}$$

$$\frac{dx_1^{(4)}}{dt} = 0. \tag{89}$$

The junction equations are

$$x_1^{(2)}(0) = \alpha x_1^{(1)}(T_1) + \beta x_1^{(4)}(T_4), \tag{90}$$

$$x_1^{(3)}(0) = x_1^{(2)}(T_2), \tag{91}$$

$$x_1^{(4)}(0) = x_1^{(2)}(T_2), \tag{92}$$

where $\alpha$ and $\beta$ are constants.

---

* Superscripts in parentheses indicate branches in unit 2.

The interval cost from unit 2 is given as

$$S_2(x_1^{\,1}; \theta^{(2)}(t)) = \tfrac{1}{2}\int_0^{T_2} [(x_1^{(2)})^2 + (\theta^{(2)})^2]\, dt.$$

The problem, as in the preceding example, is to minimize the total cost (the objective function) that is, $(S_1 + S_2)$. The functional relationships given in equations (72), (73), and (74) still hold.

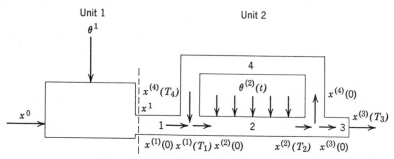

**Fig. 9.5** A process with feedback to an internal point.

It can be seen that the performance equations and the objective function for unit 2 are the same as those given in the example in Chapter 6. The optimal value of the state variable and the optimal policy for a single unit process consisting of unit 2 [see equations (6.66) and (6.67)] are found to be

$$x_1^{(2)}(t) = A_1 e^{\lambda t} + A_2 e^{-\lambda t}, \tag{93}$$

$$\theta^{(2)}(t) = A_3 e^{\lambda t} + A_4 e^{-\lambda t}, \tag{94}$$

where

$$A_1 = \frac{\alpha x_1^{\,1}/(1 - \beta e^{\lambda T_2})}{1 - (a + \lambda)(1 - \beta e^{-\lambda T_2})(\beta - e^{\lambda T_2})/[(a - \lambda)(1 - \beta e^{\lambda T_2})(\beta - e^{-\lambda T_2})]} \tag{95}$$

$$A_2 = \frac{\alpha x_1^{\,1}/(1 - \beta e^{\lambda T_2})}{(1 - \beta e^{-\lambda T_2})/(1 - \beta e^{\lambda T_2}) - (a - \lambda)(\beta - e^{-\lambda T_2})/[(a + \lambda)(\beta - e^{\lambda T_2})]} \tag{96}$$

$$A_3 = (a + \lambda)A_1, \tag{97}$$

$$A_4 = (a - \lambda)A_2, \tag{98}$$

$$\lambda = \sqrt{a^2 + 1}.$$

From equations (97) and (98) and the value of $\lambda$ we can see that

$$A_1 A_2 + A_3 A_4 = 0.$$

Therefore

$$f_1(x_1^{-1}) = \tfrac{1}{2}\int_0^{T_2} [(x_1^{(2)})^2 + (\theta^{(2)})^2]\,dt$$

$$= \tfrac{1}{2}\int_0^{T_2} [(A_1)^2 + (A_3)^2]e^{2\lambda t}\,dt + \tfrac{1}{2}\int_0^{T_2} [(A_2)^2 + (A_4)^2]e^{-2\lambda t}\,dt$$

$$= \frac{(A_1)^2 + (A_3)^2}{4\lambda}(e^{2\lambda T_2} - 1) - \frac{(A_2)^2 + (A_4)^2}{4\lambda}(e^{-2\lambda T_2} - 1). \tag{99}$$

By letting

$$B_1 = \frac{A_1}{x_1^{-1}}, \qquad B_2 = \frac{A_2}{x_1^{-1}}, \qquad B_3 = \frac{A_3}{x_1^{-1}}, \qquad B_4 = \frac{A_4}{x_1^{-1}} \tag{100}$$

and comparing equation (100) with equations (95) through (98), we see that $B_1$, $B_2$, $B_3$, and $B_4$ are all constant; that is, they are not functions of $x_1^{-1}$. Equation (99) therefore becomes

$$f_1(x_1^{-1}) = (x_1^{-1})^2\left[\frac{(B_1)^2 + (B_3)^2}{4\lambda}(e^{2\lambda T_2} - 1) - \frac{(B_2)^2 + (B_4)^2}{4\lambda}(e^{-2\lambda T_2} - 1)\right]$$

$$= (x_1^{-1})^2\left[\frac{(a + \lambda)(B_1)^2}{2}(e^{2\lambda T_2} - 1)\right.$$

$$\left. + \frac{(a - \lambda)(B_2)^2}{2}(e^{-2\lambda T_2} - 1)\right].$$

If we let

$$\frac{(a + \lambda)(B_1)^2(e^{2\lambda T_2} - 1) + (a - \lambda)(B_2)^2(e^{-2\lambda T_2} - 1)}{2} = C',$$

we have

$$f_1(x_1^{-1}) = C'(x_1^{-1})^2. \tag{101}$$

The recursive function, equation (72), then becomes

$$f_2(x_1^{0}) = \min_{\theta^1}\{S_1(x_1^0 ; \theta^1) + C'[x_1^{-1}(\theta^1)]^2\}. \tag{102}$$

By substituting equations (68) and (69) into equation (102) we obtain

$$f_2(x_1^{0}) = \min_{\theta^1}[(x_1^{-1} - \mu\theta^1) + C'(x_1^{0} + \theta^1)^2],$$

or

$$f_2(x_1^{0}) = \min_{\theta^1}[(x_1^{0} + \theta^1 - \mu\theta^1) + C'(x_1^{0} + \theta^1)^2]. \tag{103}$$

The optimal decision $\theta^1$ is obtained [see equation (82)] as

$$\overline{\theta^1} = \frac{\mu - 1}{2C'} - \gamma_1, \tag{104}$$

where

$$x_1{}^0 = \gamma_1.$$

By substituting this value of $\theta^1$ back into equation (103) we obtain the minimum value of the objective function:

$$f_2(x_1{}^0) = \mu\gamma_1 - \frac{1}{C'}\left(\frac{\mu - 1}{2}\right)^2. \tag{105}$$

Substitution of equation (104) into equation (68) gives

$$x_1{}^1 = \frac{\mu - 1}{2C'}.$$

This is the optimal feed condition of unit 2. By combining this value of $x_1{}^1$ with equations (94) through (98) we can obtain the optimal decisions for unit 2.

It is seen from this example that for a discrete process followed by a continuous process with a simple feedback to the interval point the combined method appears to be very useful. It is often difficult to solve this type of problem either by dynamic programming or by the maximum principle alone.

**Example 4.** In this example we consider a chemical process consisting of a continuous stirred tank reactor followed by a tubular reactor with product recycle to an interval point, as shown in Fig. 9.6. Unit 2 (the tubular reactor) consists of four branches: the feed line of length $L_1$ (branch 1), the reactor of length $L_2$ (branch 2), the discharge line of length $L_3$ (branch 3), and the recycle line of length $L_4$ (branch 4), with total volumetric flow rate of $v^{(1)}$, $v^{(2)}$, $v^{(3)}$, and $v^{(4)}$, respectively. In unit 1 (CSTR) the volumetric flow rate and the volume of reactor are given as $v$ and $V$, respectively.

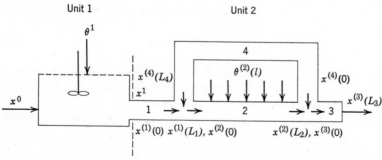

*Fig. 9.6* A schematic diagram for a process with a CSTR followed by a tubular reactor with product recycled to an internal point.

A first-order reversible chemical reaction

$$A \underset{k_2}{\overset{k_1}{\rightleftharpoons}} B$$

is taking place in this series of reactors. We wish to maximize the conversion of product $B$ at the end of the tubular reactor by the proper manipulation of the temperature in the stirred tank reactor and the temperature profile along the tubular reactor.

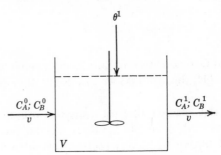

*Fig. 9.7*   A simple sketch for a CSTR.

The topology of this process is the same as that of Example 3. We shall follow the procedures of Examples 2 and 3 to solve this problem. First, the maximum principle is applied to optimize the tubular reactor unit and the over-all optimum is then obtained by the principle of optimality.

Let us establish the performance equations for both units as follows:

A simple sketch of the CSTR of unit 1 is shown in Fig. 9.7. A steady-state material balance for the $i$th component over the reactor is given by

{rate of input of the $i$th component}

+ {rate of production of the $i$th component}

= {rate of output of the $i$th component};

that is,

$$vC_i^0 + R_iV = vC_i^1, \tag{106)*}$$

where $C_i^0$ = inlet mass concentration of the $i$th component, lb-moles/ft³,
$C_i^1$ = outlet mass concentration of the $i$th component, lb-moles/ft³,
$v$ = total volumetric flow rate, ft³/hr,
$R_i$ = mass reaction rate of production for $i$th component, lb-moles/(ft³)(hr),
$V$ = volume of reactor, ft³.

---

* Superscripts indicate the stage in unit 1.

For the reaction

$$A \underset{k_2}{\overset{k_1}{\rightleftharpoons}} B,$$

in which both the forward and backward reactions are assumed to be first-order, the reaction rate $R_B$ in terms of the production of component $B$ is given by

$$R_B = k_1 C_A{}^1 - k_2 C_B{}^1, \tag{107}$$

where the specific reaction rate $k_i$ follows Arrhenius' law as

$$\begin{aligned} k_1 &= k_{10} e^{-E_1/R\theta^1}, \\ k_2 &= k_{20} e^{-E_2/R\theta^1}, \end{aligned} \tag{108}$$

where the reaction temperature $\theta^1$ is the decision variable. All other notation is defined in Chapter 4. Substitution of equation (107) into (106) for component $B$ gives

$$vC_B{}^0 + (k_1 C_A{}^1 - k_2 C_B{}^1)V = vC_B{}^1.$$

Dividing this equation by $v(C_A{}^1 + C_B{}^1)$, we obtain

$$\frac{C_B{}^0}{C_A{}^1 + C_B{}^1} + \left( k_1 \frac{C_A{}^1}{C_A{}^1 + C_B{}^1} - k_2 \frac{C_B{}^1}{C_A{}^1 + C_B{}^1} \right) \frac{V}{v} = \frac{C_B{}^1}{C_A{}^1 + C_B{}^1}.$$

If we assume that $C_A{}^0 + C_B{}^0 = C_A{}^1 + C_B{}^1 = \text{constant}$ and let $V/v = t$, the preceding equation becomes

$$x_1{}^0 + t(k_1 x_2{}^1 - k_2 x_1{}^1) = x_1{}^1, \tag{109}$$

where

$$x_1{}^0 = \frac{C_B{}^0}{C_A{}^0 + C_B{}^0}, \qquad x_1{}^1 = \frac{C_B{}^1}{C_A{}^1 + C_B{}^1}, \qquad x_2{}^1 = \frac{C_A{}^1}{C_A{}^1 + C_B{}^1}.$$

In equation (109) $x_1{}^1$ and $x_2{}^1$ represent the fractional mass concentration of $B$ and $A$, respectively, at the outlet of CSTR and $t$ is the holding time in the reactor.

Since $x_1{}^1 + x_2{}^1 = 1$, equation (109) can be replaced by

$$x_1{}^1 = \frac{x_1{}^0 + tk_1(\theta^1)}{1 + t[k_1(\theta^1) + k_2(\theta^1)]}. \tag{110}$$

Equation (110) is the performance equation for unit 1.

A steady-state material balance with respect to component $B$ over a differential section $dl$ in branch 2 of unit 2 [see equation (4.5)] leads to

$$\frac{dx_1^{(2)}}{dl} = -\frac{A^{(2)}}{v^{(1)} + v^{(4)}} [(k_1 + k_2) x_1^{(2)} - k_1], \tag{111}$$

where $A^{(2)} = $ the cross-sectional area of the tubular reactor (branch 2),

$v^{(1)} = $ the volumetric flow rate in the feed line,

$v^{(4)} = $ the volumetric flow rate in the recycle line.

Since no transformation is taking place and no control action is imposed on branches 1, 3, and 4, we have the following performance equations:

$$\frac{dx_1^{(1)}}{dl} = \frac{dx_1^{(3)}}{dl} = \frac{dx_1^{(4)}}{dl} = 0 \tag{112}$$

for the feed, discharge, and recycle lines, respectively. The initial state of unit 2, according to equation (112), is

$$x_1^{(1)}(0) = x_1^{(1)}(L_1) = x_1^{\ 1}. \tag{113}$$

Conservation of mass at the combining point requires that the junction equation be

$$v^{(2)}x_1^{(2)}(0) = v^{(1)}x_1^{(1)}(L_1) + v^{(4)}x_1^{(4)}(L_4)$$

or

$$x_1^{(2)}(0) = \alpha x_1^{(1)}(L_1) + \beta x_1^{(4)}(L_4), \tag{114}$$

where

$$\alpha = \frac{v^{(1)}}{v^{(1)} + v^{(4)}}, \qquad \beta = \frac{v^{(4)}}{v^{(1)} + v^{(4)}}, \qquad v^{(2)} = v^{(1)} + v^{(4)}.$$

The junction equations at the separating point are

$$x_1^{(3)}(0) = x_1^{(2)}(L_2),$$
$$x_1^{(4)}(0) = x_1^{(2)}(L_2). \tag{115}$$

By substituting equations (112), (113), and (115) into equation (114), we obtain

$$x_1^{(2)}(0) = \alpha x_1^{\ 1} + \beta x_1^{(2)}(L_2). \tag{116}$$

We wish to maximize the yield of product $B$, that is, to maximize the objective function

$$\begin{aligned} S &= x_1^{(3)}(L_3) - x_1^{\ 0} \\ &= x_1^{(2)}(L_2) - x_1^{\ 0}. \end{aligned} \tag{117}$$

This objective function can also be written as

$$\begin{aligned} S &= (x_1^{\ 1} - x_1^{\ 0}) + (x_1^{(2)}(L_2) - x_1^{\ 1}) \\ &= S_1 + S_2, \end{aligned}$$

where

$$S_1 = x_1^{\ 1} - x_1^{\ 0}, \tag{118}$$

$$S_2 = x_1^{(2)}(L_2) - x_1^{\ 1}. \tag{119}$$

We can consider that $S_1$ and $S_2$ are the interval profits from unit 1 and unit 2, respectively. Thus the problem becomes one of maximizing the total profit $(S_1 + S_2)$ by a proper choice of temperature in the CSTR and the tubular reactor. According to equation (9), we write the recursive relation as

$$g_2(x_1^{\,0}) = \max_{\theta^1} [S_1(x_1^{\,0}; \theta^1) + g_1(x_1^{\,1})], \tag{120}$$

where

$$g_1(x_1^{\,1}) = \max_{\theta^{(2)}(l)} [S_2(x_1^{\,1}; \theta^{(2)}(l))] = \max_{\theta^{(2)}(l)} [x_1^{(2)}(L_2) - x_1^{\,1}]. \tag{121}$$

First we shall optimize unit 2 by using the maximum principle and then obtain the over-all optimum with equation (120). In optimizing unit 2, we consider the feed concentration to the tubular reactor to be given for the time being; that is, $x_1^{\,1} = a = $ constant. Thus maximizing the interval profit represented in equation (119) is equivalent to maximizing $x_1^{(2)}(L_2)$. By this consideration the optimization of unit 2 reduces to the class of problems similar to the example in Chapter 6 and the simple recycle process for the autocatalytic reaction in Section 7.3, part a.

According to equations (6.6) and (6.7), we write

$$H^{(1)} = H^{(3)} = H^{(4)} = 0, \tag{122}$$

$$H^{(2)} = -\frac{A^{(2)}}{v^{(1)} + v^{(4)}} [(k_1 + k_2) x_1^{(2)} - k_1] z_1^{(2)}, \tag{123}$$

$$\frac{dz_1^{(1)}}{dl} = \frac{dz_1^{(3)}}{dl} = \frac{dz_1^{(4)}}{dl} = 0, \tag{124}$$

$$\frac{dz_1^{(2)}}{dl} = \frac{A^{(2)}}{v^{(1)} + v^{(4)}} (k_1 + k_2) z_1^{(2)}. \tag{125}$$

Since the objective function is $x_1^{(2)}(L_2)$, we have $c_1^{(2)} = 1$. Thus at the final point we have

$$z_1^{(2)}(L_2) = 1. \tag{126}$$

Comparing equations (111), (125), and (126) with the corresponding equations in Section 4.1, part a, we see that the optimal decision is expressed as follows [see equation (4.12)]:

$$\overline{\theta^{(2)}}(l) = \frac{E_2 - E_1}{R \ln \{\xi[x_1^{(2)}/(1 - x_1^{(2)})]\}}, \tag{127}$$

where

$$\xi = \frac{k_{20}E_2}{k_{10}E_1}.$$

Substitution of equation (127) into (111) [see equation (4.16)] yields

$$\frac{dx_1^{(2)}}{dl} = \frac{A^{(2)}}{v^{(1)} + v^{(4)}}$$

$$\times \frac{k_{10}\xi^{-\lambda_1}(1 - x_1^{(2)})^{\lambda_1+1}(x_1^{(2)})^{\lambda_2-1} - k_{20}\xi^{-\lambda_2}(1 - x_1^{(2)})^{\lambda_2}(x_1^{(2)})^{\lambda_1}}{(x_1^{(2)})^{\lambda_1+\lambda_2-1}}, \tag{128}$$

where

$$\lambda_1 = \frac{E_1}{E_2 - E_1}, \qquad \lambda_2 = \frac{E_2}{E_2 - E_1}.$$

In the integration of equation (128) the activation energies of the forward and backward reactions have been chosen such that

$$\frac{E_2}{E_1} = 2$$

or

$$\lambda_1 = 1, \qquad \lambda_2 = 2. \tag{129}$$

By substituting these values of $\lambda_i$ into equation (128) and performing the integration, we obtain

$$\frac{v^{(1)} + v^{(4)}}{A^{(2)}(k_{10}\xi^{-1} - k_{20}\xi^{-2})}\left[\frac{1}{1 - x_1^{(2)}} + \ln(1 - x_1^{(2)})\right] = l + C. \tag{130}$$

We evaluate the integration constant $C$ by the use of the initial condition given in equation (116). Thus

$$C = \frac{v^{(1)} + v^{(4)}}{A^{(2)}(k_{10}\xi^{-1} - k_{20}\xi^{-2})}$$

$$\times \left(\frac{1}{1 - [\alpha x_1^1 + \beta x_1^{(2)}(L_2)]} + \ln\{1 - [\alpha x_1^1 + \beta x_1^{(2)}(L_2)]\}\right). \tag{131}$$

Substitution of this equation into equation (130) yields

$$\frac{v^{(1)} + v^{(4)}}{A^{(2)}(k_{10}\xi^{-1} - k_{20}\xi^{-2})}\left(\frac{1}{1 - x_1^{(2)}} + \ln(1 - x_1^{(2)})\right.$$

$$\left. - \frac{1}{1 - [\alpha x_1^1 + \beta x_1^{(2)}(L_2)]} - \ln\{1 - [\alpha x_1^1 + \beta x_1^{(2)}(L_2)]\}\right) = l. \tag{132}$$

Equation (132) represents the optimal concentration along the tubular reactor. At the end of the reactor, that is, at $l = L_2$, equation (132) involves only one unknown, $x_1^{(2)}(L_2)$. It is seen that equation (132) cannot be solved explicitly for $x_1^{(2)}(L_2)$. In other words, we cannot express $g_1(x_1^1)$ [see equation (121)] explicitly as a function of $x_1^{(2)}(L_2)$ or $x_1^1$. The optimum value of $x_1^{(2)}(L_2)$ with regard to $x_1^1$, the inlet condition of unit 2, can thus be implicitly given by the following equation:

$$C'\left\{\frac{1}{1 - \bar{y}} + \ln(1 - \bar{y}) - \frac{1}{1 - (\alpha x_1^1 + \beta\bar{y})}\right.$$

$$\left. - \ln[1 - (\alpha x_1^1 + \beta\bar{y})]\right\} - L_2 = 0 \tag{133}$$

or

$$F(x_1{}^1, \bar{y}) = 0, \tag{134}$$

where $\bar{y}$ represents the optimum value of $x_1^{(2)}(L_2)$ and

$$C' = \frac{v^{(1)} + v^{(4)}}{(k_{10}\xi^{-1} - k_{20}\xi^{-2})A^{(2)}} \,.$$

Hence we finally have

$$g_1(x_1{}^1) = \max_{\theta^2(l)} [x_1^{(2)}(L_2) - x_1{}^1] = \bar{y} - x_1{}^1. \tag{135}$$

For the optimization of unit 2 we consider $x_1{}^1$ as a given initial condition. The functional interdependence $g_1(x_1{}^1)$ is implicitly given by equation (133) or (134). By substituting equations (118) and (135) into equation (120) we obtain

$$g_2(x_1{}^0) = \max_{\theta^1} (x_1{}^1 - x_1{}^0 + \bar{y} - x_1{}^1) = \max_{\theta^1} (\bar{y} - x_1{}^0). \tag{136}$$

The quantity in parentheses is a function of $\theta^1$ and $x_1{}^0$ because $\bar{y}$ is a function of $x_1{}^1$ which, in turn, is a function of $\theta^1$, represented in equation (110). These functional relationships are denoted as

$$G(x_1{}^0; \theta^1) = \bar{y} - x_1{}^0.$$

When the maximum value of $G(x_1{}^0; \theta^1)$ occurs at the stationary point with respect to $\theta^1$, the optimal value of $\theta^1$ can be obtained by setting

$$\frac{\partial G}{\partial \theta^1} = \frac{d\bar{y}}{dx_1{}^1} \frac{dx_1{}^1}{d\theta^1} = 0. \tag{137}$$

We evaluate $d\bar{y}/dx_1{}^1$ by

$$\frac{d\bar{y}}{dx_1{}^1} = -\frac{\partial F/\partial x_1{}^1}{\partial F/\partial \bar{y}}\,. \tag{138}$$

According to equation (138), we obtain from equation (133)

$$\frac{\partial F}{\partial x_1{}^1} = -C' \frac{\alpha(\alpha x_1{}^1 + \beta \bar{y})}{[1 - (\alpha x_1{}^1 + \beta \bar{y})]^2},$$

$$\frac{\partial F}{\partial \bar{y}} = C' \frac{\bar{y}[1 - (\alpha x_1{}^1 + \beta \bar{y})]^2 - \beta(1 - \bar{y})^2(\alpha x_1{}^1 + \beta \bar{y})}{(1 - \bar{y})^2[1 - (\alpha x_1{}^1 + \beta \bar{y})]^2}.$$

By substituting the last two equations into equation (138) we obtain

$$\frac{d\bar{y}}{dx_1{}^1} = \frac{\alpha(1 - \bar{y})^2(\alpha x_1{}^1 + \beta \bar{y})}{\bar{y}[1 - (\alpha x_1{}^1 + \beta \bar{y})]^2 - \beta(1 - \bar{y})^2(\alpha x_1{}^1 + \beta \bar{y})}\,. \tag{139}$$

Differentiating equation (110) with respect to $\theta^1$ yields for $x_1{}^0 = 0$

$$\frac{dx_1{}^1}{d\theta^1} = \frac{(dk_1/d\theta^1)t + (t)^2[k_2(dk_1/d\theta^1) - k_1(dk_2/d\theta^1)]}{[1 + (k_1 + k_2)t]^2}\,.$$

Recalling that the functions $k_1(\theta^1)$ and $k_2(\theta^1)$ are given in equation (108), we find that the differentiation of the preceding equation becomes

$$\frac{dx_1^{\,1}}{d\theta^1} = \frac{[tk_{10}/R(\theta^1)^2][E_1 e^{-E_1/R\theta^1} + tk_{20}(E_1 - E_2)e^{-(E_1+E_2)/R\theta^1}]}{[1 + k_1(\theta^1) + k_2(\theta^1)t]^2}. \quad (140)$$

By substituting equations (139) and (140) into equation (137) we obtain

$$\frac{\partial G}{\partial \theta^1} = \frac{tk_{10}\,[E_1 e^{-E_1/R\theta^1} + tk_{20}(E_1 - E_2)e^{-(E_1+E_2)/R\theta^1}]}{R(\theta^1)^2[1 + (k_2 + k_1)t]^2}$$

$$\cdot \frac{\alpha(1 - \bar{y})^2(\alpha x_1^{\,1} + \beta \bar{y})}{\bar{y}[1 - (\alpha x_1^{\,1} + \beta \bar{y})]^2 - \beta(1 - \bar{y})^2(\alpha x_1^{\,1} + \beta \bar{y})} = 0. \quad (141)$$

Since $\alpha x_1^{\,1} + \beta \bar{y} \neq 0$ and $1 - \bar{y} \neq 0$ for any conversion less than 100 per cent, the only possibility that equation (141) is equal to zero is

$$\theta^1 \to \infty$$

or

$$E_1 e^{-E_1/R\theta^1} - tk_{20}(E_2 - E_1)e^{-(E_1+E_2)/R\theta^1} = 0.$$

When the value of temperature must be finite, the latter case would give the optimal temperature as

$$\overline{\theta^1} = -\frac{E_2}{R \ln (\lambda_1/tk_{20})}, \quad (142)$$

where $\lambda_1$ has the same value as in equation (128) and $t$ is the holding time in unit 1 defined as $V/v$. (The physical significance of the case in which $\theta \to \infty$ is given in [6].)

Equation (142) is the same as equation (4.100b), which is the optimal temperature for a single CSTR. Thus the optimal decision to be made at the CSTR remains the same, or, in other words, it is independent of the downstream condition. This is actually observed from equation (141). Equating (141) to zero is equivalent to equating (140) to zero, which yields the optimal decision for a single CSTR.

We come to the conclusion that the optimal policy for this two-unit system is to choose the temperature that will maximize the outlet concentration of unit 1, to let this outlet concentration be the given inlet condition of unit 2, and then to maximize the outlet concentration of unit 2 by the proper choice of temperature along the tubular reactor. These facts may also be verified by the following reasoning: equation (139) indicates how $x_1^{\,1}$ affects the optimal final concentration $\bar{y}$. Equation (130) indicates that 100 per cent conversion $(x_1^{(2)}(L_2) = 1)$ gives rise to a reactor with infinite length; that is, the conversion must be less than 100 per cent. Therefore the following inequality must hold for the numerator of equation (139):

$$\alpha(1 - \bar{y})^2(\alpha x_1^{\,1} + \beta \bar{y}) > 0. \quad (143)$$

Furthermore, we have $\bar{y} > (\alpha x_1{}^1 + \beta \bar{y})$ and $\beta \leq 1$; hence the following inequality must hold for the denominator of equation (139):

$$\bar{y}[1 - (\alpha x_1{}^1 + \beta \bar{y})]^2 > \beta(1 - \bar{y})^2(\alpha x_1{}^1 + \beta \bar{y}). \qquad (144)$$

Since both the numerator and denominator of equation (139) are positive, we have the following inequality:

$$\frac{d\bar{y}}{dx_1{}^1} > 0.$$

In other words, $\bar{y}$ is an increasing function with respect to $x_1{}^1$. To obtain a higher value of $\bar{y}$ we must have a higher value of $x_1{}^1$, regardless of the operating policy in unit 2. This simple but surprising result appears to be a consequence of the characteristics of the single reversible reaction $A \rightleftharpoons B$ and the objective function of the process under consideration. This discussion, as well as equations (127) and (142), can also be considered as a direct consequence of the general result obtained in References 6 and 7 that the optimal policy with a single state variable is always disjoint.

The numerical data chosen for the calculation of equations (110), (127), (132), and (142) are

$$A^{(2)} = 1 \text{ ft}^2,$$
$$k_{10} = 2.51 \times 10^5/\text{hr},$$
$$k_{20} = 1.995 \times 10^7/\text{hr},$$
$$E_1 = 10,000 \text{ Btu/lb-mole},$$
$$E_2 = 20,000 \text{ Btu/lb-mole},$$
$$v^{(1)} = 1000 \text{ ft}^3/\text{hr},$$
$$t = 2.5 \times 10^{-3} \text{ hr},$$
$$x_1{}^0 = 0,$$
$$L_2 = 10 \text{ ft},$$
$$R = 2 \text{ Btu/lb-mole } °R.$$

From equation (142) the optimal temperature in the CSTR is calculated as

$$\overline{\theta^1} = 930.4°R.$$

With this temperature the optimum outlet concentration from the CSTR is calculated according to equation (110) as

$$x_1{}^1 = 0.583.$$

By substituting this optimal feed condition of the tubular reactor into equation (132) and solving for $x_1^{(2)}$ by trial and error we obtain the optimal

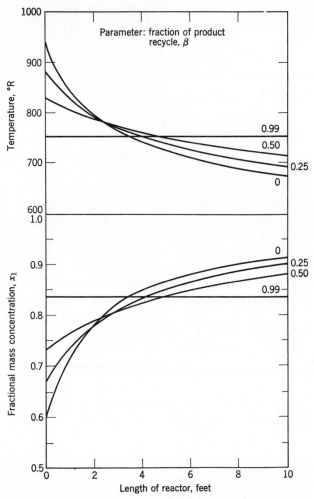

**Fig. 9.8** Optimal temperature and concentration profiles in a tubular reactor with product recycle for the reaction $A \underset{k_2}{\overset{k_1}{\rightleftharpoons}} B$.

concentration profiles along the reactor. The optimum final product thus achieved without recycle is

$$\bar{y} = 0.916.$$

The optimal temperature profiles along the reactor can be recovered from equation (127). The results of calculations with a fractional recycle rate $\beta$ as the parameter are shown in Fig. 9.8.

It is worthwhile to mention that the optimal solution obtained can be verified by the perturbation technique. This is accomplished by investigating the vicinity of the optimal decision to determine whether it increases the value of the objective function. For this problem we have made the following perturbation check shown in Table 9.1. In this table the values

*Table 9.1.* Perturbation Check for the Results of Example 4

|  |  | $\theta^1(°R)$ | $x_1^1$ | $x_1^{(2)}(L_2)$ |
|---|---|---|---|---|
| | a1 | 930.4 | 0.583 | 0.9161 |
| $\beta = 0$ | a2 | 910 | 0.5815 | 0.9158 |
| | a3 | 960 | 0.5814 | 0.9156 |
| | b1 | 930.4 | 0.583 | 0.883 |
| $\beta = 0.5$ | b2 | 880 | 0.568 | 0.881 |
| | b3 | 980 | 0.575 | 0.882 |

of $x_1^{(2)}(L_2)$ in rows a1 and b1 are the optimal values for $\beta = 0$ and $\beta = 0.5$, respectively.

It is also worth mentioning that the optimal temperature obtained from equation (142) for the CSTR is essentially the same as the optimal temperature at the inlet of the tubular reactor without product recycle, given by equation (127). This again shows the disjoint character of the optimal temperature for the reaction $A \underset{k_2}{\overset{k_1}{\rightleftharpoons}} B$; that is, the temperature should always be chosen so that the rate of reaction will be as large as possible.

## REFERENCES

1. Lee, E. S., "Optimum Design and Operation of Chemical Processes," Ind. Eng. Chem. **55**, No. 37 (1963).
2. Fan, L. T., and C. S. Wang, *The Discrete Maximum Principle, A Study of Multistage Systems Optimization*, Wiley, New York, 1964.
3. Bellman, R., Dreyfus, S. E., *Applied Dynamic Programming*, Princeton University Press, Princeton, New Jersey, 1962.
4. Aris, R., D. F. Rudd, and N. R. Amundson, "On Optimum Cross-Current Extraction," *Chem. Eng. Sci.*, **12**, 88 (1963).
5. Fan, L. T., W. S. Hwang, S. J. Chen, and L. S. Fan, "A Sequential Union of the Maximum Principle and Dynamic Programming," *J. Electron. Control* **17**, 593 (1964).
6. Denn, M. M., "The Optimization of Complex Systems," Ph.D. Thesis, University of Minnesota, 1964.
7. Denn, M. M., and R. Aris, "Second-Order Variational Equations and the Strong Maximum Principle," *Chem. Eng. Sci.*, **20**, 373 (1965).

# 10

## Vector-Matrix Formulation of the Maximum Principle Algorithms for Highly Nonsequential Processes

The basic algorithm for the optimization of simple continuous processes was discussed in Chapter 2. We can see that it is a special case of the more general maximum principle algorithm formulated in Chapter 6, which, in turn, can be recognized as a special case of the algorithm for the optimization of composite processes presented in Chapter 8. Since a composite process consists of continuous and discrete processes, the algorithm of Chapter 6 can be obtained by dropping all terms that stem from branches with discrete characteristics in the algorithm in Chapter 8. The algorithm constructed in Chapter 8 is therefore the most general; it also covers the algorithm in Reference 1. Its notation and formulation however, are somewhat bulky largely because the presentation was done in scalar quantities. Consequently, as the system becomes highly nonsequential and the numbers of state and decision variables increase, use of the algorithms presented so far becomes less convenient. We therefore adopt a different approach to reconstruct the computational algorithm in a form particularly suitable for dealing with highly nonsequential complex systems and processes with many variables. We shall employ a vector-matrix formulation to simplify both the mathematical manipulation and the notation.

### 1. DESCRIPTION OF A COMPLEX DISCRETE SYSTEM

In this section we consider a highly nonsequential discrete system schematically sketched in Fig. 10.1. The system consists of $N$ interconnected

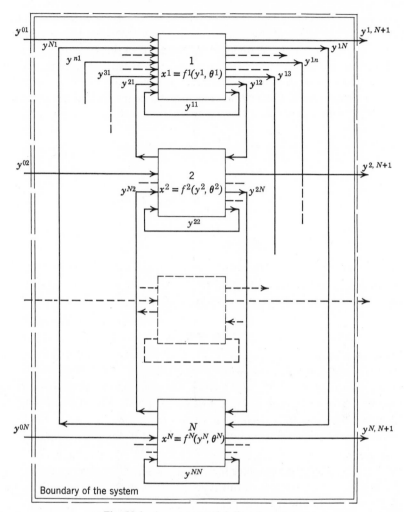

*Fig. 10.1* A nonsequential discrete system.

discrete units, each of which is identified by a number $n$, $n = 1, 2, \ldots, N$. It must be emphasized that this numbering is completely arbitrary, since we no longer associate any sequential nature or concept of branches to these units. Even the units of a branch may be assigned numbers that are not necessarily in sequence. An immediate advantage of this notion is that the topology of the system may be altered without renumbering each unit.

A stream leaving the $n$th unit and entering the $\nu$th unit, $\nu = 1, 2,$

$\ldots, n, \ldots, N$, is identified as the $n\nu$th stream.* These streams do not flow across the boundary of the system; hence they are called the recirculated streams. There may be as many as $(N)^2$ streams of this type in the system. Moreover, the $n\nu$th stream is an output stream with respect to the $n$th unit and an input stream with respect to the $\nu$th unit.

The properties of the $n\nu$th stream may be characterized by a vector† $y^{n\nu}$ of $l^{n\nu}$ component quantities; that is

$$y^{n\nu} = \begin{bmatrix} y_1^{n\nu} \\ y_2^{n\nu} \\ \cdot \\ \cdot \\ \cdot \\ y_{l^{n\nu}}^{n\nu} \end{bmatrix}, \qquad n, \nu = 1, 2, \ldots, N.$$

The dependency of the dimension of the vector $y^{n\nu}$ on the real positive integer $l^{n\nu}$ implies that the number of components of the recirculated streams may be different for different values of $n$ and $\nu$. This dependency may be expressed as

$$y^{n\nu} \in R^{l^{n\nu}}.$$

This notation is used throughout the rest of this chapter. ($R$ simply implies that the components of the vector $y^{n\nu}$ are all real.)

As shown in Fig. 10.1, streams also flow across the boundary of the system. The properties of such streams that flow into the $n$th unit are denoted by $y^{0n} \in R^{l^{0n}}$; that is, a vector of $l^{0n}$ components. Similarly, properties of a stream leaving the $n$th unit and flowing across and out of the boundary are denoted by $y^{n,N+1} \in R^{l^{n,N+1}}$. Accordingly, $y^{0n}$ and $y^{n,N+1}$ are called the boundary input and output, respectively. There may be as many as $2N$ streams of this type—$N$ streams of boundary inputs and $N$ streams of boundary outputs.

The outputs from the $n$th unit, including the boundary output $y^{n,N+1}$ and all the recirculated outputs $y^{n\nu}$, $\nu = 1, 2, \ldots, N$, are dependent on the state of the unit $x^n \in R^{s^n}$. This functional relationship may be

---

* Physically there may be more than one $n\nu$th stream, but they are considered collectively as one vector stream.

† In this chapter a vector is always written as a column vector. When a row vector is needed, it will be obtained as the transpose of a column vector. For example,

$$(y^{n\nu})^T = [y_1^{n\nu} y_2^{n\nu} \cdots y_{l^{n\nu}}^{n\nu}].$$

The superscript $T$ denotes the transpose.

expressed by

$$y^{nm} = v^{nm}(x^n), \qquad n = 1, 2, \ldots, N \quad \text{and} \quad m = 1, 2, \ldots, N, N + 1,$$

$$\text{(1)}$$

provided that all other parameters are specified. A special but very common case of this functional relationship is that in which all outputs are directly equal to the state itself; for this we have

$$y^{nm} = x^n, \qquad n = 1, 2, \ldots, N \quad \text{and} \quad m = 1, 2, \ldots, N, N + 1. \quad \text{(2)}$$

On the other hand, all inputs to the $n$th unit, including the boundary input $y^{0n}$ and all recirculated outputs, $y^{vn}$, $v = 1, 2, \ldots, N$, form the total input to this unit, which is denoted by $y^n \in R^{l^n}$. This functional relationship may be expressed by

$$y^n = w^n(y^{0n}, y^{1n}, \ldots, y^{nn}, \ldots, y^{Nn}), \qquad n = 1, 2, \ldots, N, \quad \text{(3)}$$

or

$$y^n = w^n(y^{\mu n}), \qquad n = 1, 2, \ldots, N, \quad \text{and} \quad \mu = 0, 1, \ldots, N, \quad \text{(4)}$$

provided that all other parameters are specified. A special case of equation (4) corresponding to that given in equation (2) is that in which the total input is a linear combination of all the inputs, for which we have

$$y^n = \sum_{\mu=0}^{N} \alpha^{\mu n} y^{\mu n}; \qquad \sum_{\mu=0}^{N} \alpha^{\mu n} = 1, \qquad n = 1, 2, \ldots, N, \quad \text{(5)}$$

where $\alpha^{\mu n}$ are non-negative scalar constants. The dimensions of the vectors $y^n$, $x^n$, $y^{nm}$, and $y^{0n}$ are, in this case, identical and may be expressed by $l^n = s^n = l^{nm} = l^{0n} = s$.

The relation between the state $x^n$, the total input $y^n$, and the decision $\theta^n \in R^{r^n}$ for a given unit usually takes the form

$$x^n = f^n(y^n, \theta^n), \qquad n = 1, 2, \ldots, N, \quad \text{(6)}$$

which we call the unit equation of the $n$th unit rather than the performance equation.

The form of a unit equation implies that the state $x^n$ is uniquely determined by the value of the total input $y^n$ and the decision $\theta^n$ of the unit but not by the values of individual recirculated and/or boundary inputs. This means that the unit equation is independent of the topology of the system, which is described by equations (1) and (4).

In many optimization problems the boundary inputs $y^{0n}$, $n = 1, 2, \ldots, N$, are specified. If they are, the system described by equations (1), (4), and (6) is deterministic in that, if a set of $\theta^n$, $n = 1, 2, \ldots, N$, is chosen, all other vector quantities are uniquely defined. In this chapter we confine ourselves to this class of problems as we have done in all preceding chapters.

## 2. THE STATEMENT OF THE PROBLEM AND THE DERIVATION OF THE ALGORITHM FOR DISCRETE SYSTEMS

The optimization problem we shall consider may be stated as follows: Suppose that the description of a system is given by

$$x^n = f^n(y^n, \theta^n),$$

$$y^n = w^n(y^{\mu n}),$$

$$y^{nm} = v^{nm}(x^n), \tag{7}$$

$$y^{0n} = a^{0n},$$

$$n = 1, 2, \ldots, N, \quad m = 1, 2, \ldots, N+1, \quad \mu = 0, 1, \ldots, N,$$

where $a^{0n} \in R^{l^{0n}}$, $n = 1, 2, \ldots, N$, are given constant vectors (that is, the values of the boundary inputs are preassigned). We are to choose a set of $\theta^n$, $n = 1, 2, \ldots, N$, such that the scalar function $S$ (the objective function) of the boundary outputs

$$
\begin{aligned}
S &= \sum_{n=1}^{N} (c^{n,N+1})^T y^{n,N+1} \\
&= \sum_{n=1}^{N} [c_1^{n,N+1}, c_2^{n,N+1}, \ldots, c_{l^n,N+1}^{n,N+1}]
\begin{bmatrix}
y_1^{n,N+1} \\
y_2^{n,N+1} \\
\cdot \\
\cdot \\
\cdot \\
y_{l^n,N+1}^{n,N+1}
\end{bmatrix} \\
&= \sum_{n=1}^{N} \sum_{i=1}^{l^{n,N+1}} c_i^{n,N+1} y_i^{n,N+1}
\end{aligned}
\tag{8}
$$

attains its maximum value. Here $c^{n,N+1} \in R^{l^{n,N+1}}$, $n = 1, 2, \ldots, N$, are given constant vectors and the superscript $T$ denotes the transpose.*

To derive the optimization algorithm for this problem we first assume that the functions $f^n(y^n, \theta^n)$, $w^n(y^{\mu n})$, and $v^{nm}(x^n)$ are continuous in their

---

* Check the second footnote on page 276.

arguments and that the first partial derivatives exist and are continuous in their arguments. Furthermore, we assume that a set of optimal decisions denoted by $\bar{\theta}^n$ can be found such that the objective function $S$ attains its maximum at $\bar{y}^{n,N+1}$ and that the corresponding state of the system is described by

$$\bar{x}^n = f^n(\bar{y}^n, \bar{\theta}^n),$$
$$\bar{y}^n = w^n(\bar{y}^{\mu n}),$$
$$\bar{y}^{nm} = v^{nm}(\bar{x}^n),$$
$$\bar{y}^{0n} = a^{0n},$$
(9)

$$n = 1, 2, \ldots, N, \qquad m = 1, 2, \ldots, N+1, \qquad \mu = 0, 1, \ldots, N;$$

thus

$$\max S = \sum_{n=1}^{N} (c^{n,N+1})^T \bar{y}^{n,N+1}.$$
(10)

Here all the upperbarred quantities denote those corresponding to the optimal decision $\bar{\theta}^n$.

Suppose that equation (7) represents a system slightly perturbed away from its optimal state given by equation (9) because of a small perturbation in the decisions given by

$$|\delta\theta^n| = |\theta^n - \bar{\theta}^n| < \epsilon\varphi^n, \qquad n = 1, 2, \ldots, N,$$

where $\epsilon$ is a small positive number and $\varphi^n \in R^{r^n}$. The variational equations of the perturbed system about the optimal system are then given by

$$\delta x^n = \frac{\partial f^n}{\partial y^n} \delta y^n + \frac{\partial f^n}{\partial \theta^n} \delta\theta^n,$$
(11)

$$\delta y^n = \sum_{\mu=0}^{N} \frac{\partial w^n}{\partial y^{\mu n}} \delta y^{\mu n},$$
(12)

$$\delta y^{nm} = \frac{\partial v^{nm}}{\partial x^n} \delta x^n,$$
(13)

$$\delta y^{0n} = 0, \qquad n = 1, 2, \ldots, N,$$
(14)

$$m = 1, 2, \ldots, N+1,$$

where $\delta p = p - \bar{p}$, $p = x^n, y^n, y^{\mu n}, y^{nm}$, and $y^{0n}$. Because of the continuity assumption all neglected terms are of the order $\epsilon^2$ and of orders higher than $\epsilon^2$, and the signs of both sides of equations (11), (12), and (13) are the same if $\epsilon$ is sufficiently small. The partial derivatives are evaluated at the upperbarred quantities. These partial derivatives are matrices; for example, the matrix

$$\frac{\partial f^n}{\partial y^n} = \begin{bmatrix} \dfrac{\partial f_1^n}{\partial y_1^n} & \dfrac{\partial f_1^n}{\partial y_2^n} & \cdots & \dfrac{\partial f_1^n}{\partial y_l^n} \\[2ex] \dfrac{\partial f_2^n}{\partial y_1^n} & \dfrac{\partial f_2^n}{\partial y_2^n} & & \dfrac{\partial f_2^n}{\partial y_l^n} \\ \cdot & & & \\ \cdot & & & \\ \cdot & & & \\ \dfrac{\partial f_s^n}{\partial y_1^n} & \dfrac{\partial f_s^n}{\partial y_2^n} & \cdots & \dfrac{\partial f_s^n}{\partial y_l^n} \end{bmatrix}$$

is an $s^n \times l^n$ matrix; that is, a matrix with $s^n$ rows and $l^n$ columns.

We now define a set of adjoint vectors, $z^n \in R^{s^n}$, $u^n \in R^{l^n}$, $z^{nm} \in R^{l^{nm}}$, and $z^{\mu n} \in R^{l^{\mu n}}$ by

$$u^n = \left(\frac{\partial f^n}{\partial y^n}\right)^T z^n, \tag{15}$$

$$z^{\mu n} = \left(\frac{\partial w^n}{\partial y^{\mu n}}\right)^T u^n, \tag{16}$$

$$z^n = \sum_{m=1}^{N+1} \left(\frac{\partial v^{nm}}{\partial x^n}\right)^T z^{nm}, \tag{17}$$

$$z^{n,N+1} = c^{n,N+1}, \qquad\qquad n = 1, 2, \ldots, N, \tag{18}$$

$$\mu = 0, 1, 2, \ldots, N.$$

Comparison of equations (11), (12), and (13) with (15), (16), and (17) shows that $z^n$, $u^n$, $z^{nm}$, and $z^{\mu n}$ correspond to $x^n$, $y^n$, $y^{nm}$, and $y^{\mu n}$, respectively. Multiplication of equation (11) by $(z^n)^T$ followed by a summation on $n$ from $n = 1$ to $N$ yields, by virtue of equation (15), the following results:

$$\sum_{n=1}^N (z^n)^T \, \delta x^n = \sum_{n=1}^N (z^n)^T \frac{\partial f^n}{\partial y^n} \, \delta y^n + \sum_{n=1}^N (z^n)^T \frac{\partial f^n}{\partial \theta^n} \, \delta \theta^n$$

$$= \sum_{n=1}^N (u^n)^T \, \delta y^n + \sum_{n=1}^N (z^n)^T \frac{\partial f^n}{\partial \theta^n} \, \delta \theta^n. \tag{19}$$

Similarly, by multiplying equation (12) by $(u^n)^T$ and summing from $n = 1$ to $N$ we obtain by use of equation (16)

$$\sum_{n=1}^N (u^n)^T \, \delta y^n = \sum_{n=1}^N \sum_{\mu=0}^N (z^{\mu n})^T \, \delta y^{\mu n}; \tag{20}$$

by multiplying equation (13) by $(z^{nm})^T$ and taking a double summation from $n = 1$ to $N$ and from $m = 1$ to $N + 1$ we obtain by use of equation (17)

$$\sum_{n=1}^{N} \sum_{m=1}^{N+1} (z^{nm})^T \, \delta y^{nm} = \sum_{n=1}^{N} (z^n)^T \, \delta x^n. \tag{21}$$

Adding equations (19), (20), and (21) side by side and cancelling similar terms on the left- and right-hand sides, we have

$$\sum_{n=1}^{N} (z^{n,N+1})^T \, \delta y^{n,N+1} = \sum_{n=1}^{N} (z^{0n})^T \, \delta y^{0n} + \sum_{n=1}^{N} (z^n)^T \frac{\partial f^n}{\partial \theta^n} \, \delta \theta^n. \tag{22}$$

Because of equations (14) and (18), we have

$$\sum_{n=1}^{N} (c^{n,N+1})^T \, \delta y^{n,N+1} = \sum_{n=1}^{N} (z^n)^T \frac{\partial f^n}{\partial \theta^n} \, \delta \theta^n. \tag{23}$$

On the other hand, the variation of the objective function $S$ from equation (8) is

$$\delta S = \sum_{n=1}^{N} (c^{n,N+1})^T \, \delta y^{n,N+1}. \tag{24}$$

Since equation (10) has been assumed, it is necessary that $\delta S$ be zero for all free variations $\delta \theta^n$, $n = 1, 2, \ldots, N$, and that $\delta S$ be negative for all one-sided variations when the optimal decisions are at the boundaries of a constraint in the form of

$$G^n(\theta^n) \geq 0, \qquad n = 1, 2, \ldots, N. \tag{25}$$

Hence it is necessary that from equations (23) and (24)

$$\sum_{n=1}^{N} (z^n)^T \frac{\partial f^n}{\partial \theta^n} \, \delta \theta^n \leq 0.$$

Furthermore, the variations are independent and thus it is necessary that

$$(z^n)^T \frac{\partial f^n}{\partial \theta^n} \, \delta \theta^n \leq 0. \tag{26}$$

By defining the Hamiltonian as

$$H^n = (z^n)^T f^n(y^n, \theta^n) = (f^n)^T z^n, \qquad n = 1, 2, \ldots, N \tag{27}$$

the necessary condition given by equation (26) can be written as

$$\left( \frac{\partial H^n}{\partial \theta^n} \right) \delta \theta^n \leq 0. \tag{28}^*$$

---

* $\partial H^n / \partial \theta^n$ is a row vector given by $[\partial H^n / \partial \theta_1{}^n, \partial H^n / \partial \theta_2{}^n, \ldots, \partial H^n / \partial \theta_{rn}^n]$ according to the matrix convention adopted here. Therefore $(\partial H^n / \partial \theta^n)^T$ is a column vector.

However, for free variations of $\theta^n$ a necessary and sufficient condition [2] for $\delta S$ to be zero is given by

$$\left(\frac{\partial H^n}{\partial \theta^n}\right) = 0. \tag{29}$$

The necessary part of this statement follows from consideration of the special variation:

$$\widetilde{\delta\theta^n} = \epsilon\widetilde{\varphi^n} = \epsilon\left(\frac{\partial H^n}{\partial \theta^n}\right)^T, \tag{30}$$

for the inner product

$$\left(\frac{\partial H^n}{\partial \theta^n}\right)\widetilde{\delta\theta^n} = \epsilon\left(\frac{\partial H^n}{\partial \theta^n}\right)\left(\frac{\partial H^n}{\partial \theta^n}\right)^T$$

is a non-negative scalar quantity that vanishes only when the vector $(\partial H^n/\partial \theta^n)$ is a null vector. However, since $\delta S = 0$ is only a necessary condition for maximizing $S$, equation (29) is a necessary but not a sufficient condition for maximizing $S$ for free variations of $\theta^n$. When any of the $\theta^n, n = 1, 2, \ldots, N$ lie at a boundary, it is necessary and sufficient that we have the following condition for all allowable variations in order to make $\delta S < 0$.

$$\left(\frac{\partial H^n}{\partial \theta^n}\right)\delta\theta^n < 0. \tag{31}$$

This is equivalent to the condition that $H^n$ be maximum at the boundary. Thus we are led to the conclusion that in order for the objective function $S$ to attain its local maximum (minimum) value it is necessary (but not sufficient) to choose a set of decisions $\theta^n, n = 1, 2, \ldots, N$ such that [2] (a) the Hamiltonian is made stationary* with respect to the optimal decision when it is not constrained (or it lies in the interior of the admissible domain of $\theta^n$), that is,

$$\bar{\theta}^n : \frac{\partial H^n}{\partial \theta^n} \equiv (z^n)^T \frac{\partial f^n}{\partial \theta^n} = 0, \qquad n = 1, 2, \ldots, N, \tag{32}†$$

or (b) the Hamiltonian is made a maximum (minimum) with respect to $\bar{\theta}^n$ when it lies on a constraint, that is

$$\theta^n : H^n = \max(\min), \qquad n = 1, 2, \ldots, N. \tag{33}$$

This is the so-called weakened form of the local maximum principle or simply the local weak maximum principle. Unlike the continuous case, which we discuss in a later section, this is in general the strongest statement that can be made when units of a system have discrete characteristics.

---

* At a stationary point all the first partial derivatives vanish. It may be a local maximum or minimum or a saddle point [1].

† $\bar{\theta}^n$: is to be read as "choose $\bar{\theta}^n$ such that"

For a more detailed discussion readers are referred to the works of Denn and Aris [2, 3], Jordan and Polak [4], and Horn and Jackson [5, 6].

Adjoint equations, defined by (16), (17), and (18), can be combined to eliminate the $z^{\mu n}$. From equations (17) and (18) we have

$$z^n = \left(\frac{\partial y^{n,N+1}}{\partial x^n}\right)^T c^{n,N+1} + \sum_{\nu=1}^{N} \left(\frac{\partial v^{n\nu}}{\partial x^n}\right)^T z^{n\nu} \tag{34}$$

and from equation (16) we have

$$z^{n\nu} = \left(\frac{\partial w^\nu}{\partial y^{n\nu}}\right)^T u^\nu. \tag{35}$$

By substituting equation (35) into (34) we obtain

$$z^n = \left(\frac{\partial v^{n,N+1}}{\partial x^n}\right)^T c^{n,N+1} + \sum_{\nu=1}^{N} \left(\frac{\partial v^{n\nu}}{\partial x^n}\right)^T \left(\frac{\partial w^\nu}{\partial y^{n\nu}}\right)^T u^\nu, \tag{36}$$

which, in fact, is the boundary condition for equation (15); that is

$$u^n = \left(\frac{\partial f^n}{\partial y^n}\right)^T z^n. \tag{15}$$

We shall call equations (15) and (36) collectively the adjoint system of a discrete system.

## 3.  FURTHER DISCUSSIONS AND SOME EXAMPLES OF DISCRETE SYSTEMS

As already mentioned the configuration of a discrete system can be completely described by the use of equations (1) and (4).  Let us consider in this section a special case in which these equations are given as

$$y^{nm} = v^{nm}(x^n) = x^n, \tag{37}$$

$$y^n = w^n(y^{\mu n}) = \sum_{\mu=0}^{N} \Gamma^{\mu n} y^{\mu n}, \qquad n = 1, 2, \ldots, N, \tag{38}$$

$$\mu = 0, 1, \ldots, N, \qquad\qquad m = 1, 2, \ldots, N+1.$$

Here the vectors $x^n$, $y^n$, $y^{nm}$, and $y^{\mu n}$ all have $s$ components, and the $\Gamma^{\mu n}$ are diagonal matrices defined as

$$\Gamma^{\mu n} = \begin{bmatrix} \alpha_1^{\mu n} & 0 & \cdots & 0 \\ 0 & \alpha_2^{\mu n} & & \cdot \\ 0 & & & \cdot \\ \cdot & & & \cdot \\ \cdot & & & \\ \cdot & & & \\ 0 & & \cdots & \alpha_s^{\mu n} \end{bmatrix}, \qquad \begin{array}{l} n = 1, 2, \ldots, N, \\ \mu = 0, 1, \ldots, N, \end{array} \tag{39}$$

where the diagonal elements $\alpha_k^{\mu n}$, $k = 1, 2, \ldots, s$ are non-negative constants. This special yet very common case covers many problems treated in Reference 1.

Equation (37) means that the state of a unit itself is the output variable and equation (38) shows that the $k$th component of $y^n$, $1 \leq k \leq s$, is a linear sum of the $k$th component of all the $y^{\mu n}$. These two equations can be combined to give

$$y^n = \Gamma^{0n} a^{0n} + \sum_{v=1}^{N} \Gamma^{vn} x^v, \qquad n = 1, 2, \ldots, N, \tag{40}$$

in which we have substituted $a^{0n}$ for $y^{0n}$. Equation (40) is the boundary condition for the unit equations of the system in which the state is given by

$$x^n = f^n(y^n, \theta^n), \qquad n = 1, 2, \ldots, N. \tag{41}$$

The corresponding adjoint system for this case can be obtained from equations (15) and (36) as

$$z^n = c^{n,N+1} + \sum_{v=1}^{N} \Gamma^{nv} u^v, \qquad n = 1, 2, \ldots, N, \tag{42}$$

$$u^n = \left(\frac{\partial f^n}{\partial y^n}\right)^T z^n, \qquad n = 1, 2, \ldots, N. \tag{43}$$

Equations (42) and (43) may be combined further to eliminate $u^n$. A combination of these two equations gives

$$z^n = c^{n,N+1} + \sum_{v=1}^{N} \Gamma^{nv} \left(\frac{\partial f^v}{\partial y^v}\right)^T z^v, \qquad n = 1, 2, \ldots, N, \tag{44}$$

from which the required $z^n$ can be computed. The objective function $S$ defined by equation (8) now also takes the form

$$S = \sum_{n=1}^{N} (c^{n,N+1})^T x^n = \sum_{n=1}^{N} \sum_{i=1}^{s} c_i^{n,N+1} x_i^n \tag{45}$$

because of equation (37).

There are many cases for which the unit equations of a discrete system are obtainable in the form

$$h^n(x^n, y^n, \theta^n) = 0 \tag{46}$$

rather than in the form of equation (6),

$$x^n = f^n(y^n, \theta^n). \tag{6}$$

A unit equation of the form given by equation (46) is usually the consequence of the application of the laws of conservation to the system (or, more rigorously speaking, to each unit in the system). If we assume that the unit equation is given originally in the form of equation (46) and that equation (6) is the solution for $x^n$ from it, it can be shown by the chain rules that

$$\frac{\partial h^n}{\partial y^n} = - \frac{\partial h^n}{\partial x^n} \frac{\partial f^n}{\partial y^n}, \tag{47}$$

$$\frac{\partial h^n}{\partial \theta^n} = - \frac{\partial h^n}{\partial x^n} \frac{\partial f^n}{\partial \theta^n}, \qquad n = 1, 2, \ldots, N, \tag{48}$$

and that the inverse of the matrix $\partial h^n / \partial x^n$ exists. Hence we can solve equations (47) and (48) for $\partial f^n / \partial y^n$ and $\partial f^n / \partial \theta^n$, which can be substituted into the adjoint system, equation (44) and into the optimal condition equation (32) whenever it is applicable. However, if we define a new set of adjoint variables $\widetilde{z^n}$ by the transformation

$$z^n = - \left(\frac{\partial h^n}{\partial x^n}\right)^T \widetilde{z^n}, \qquad n = 1, 2, \ldots, N, \tag{49}$$

substitution of equations (47) and (49) into (44) gives

$$-\left(\frac{\partial h^n}{\partial x^n}\right)^T \widetilde{z^n} = c^{n,N+1} - \sum_{v=1}^{N} \Gamma^{nv} \left(\frac{\partial f^v}{\partial y^v}\right)^T \left(\frac{\partial h^v}{\partial x^v}\right)^T \widetilde{z^v}$$

$$= c^{n,N+1} + \sum_{v=1}^{N} \Gamma^{nv} \left(- \frac{\partial h^v}{\partial x^v} \frac{\partial f^v}{\partial y^v}\right)^T \widetilde{z^v};$$

that is

$$-\left(\frac{\partial h^n}{\partial x^n}\right)^T \widetilde{z^n} = c^{n,N+1} + \sum_{v=1}^{N} \Gamma^{nv} \left(\frac{\partial h^v}{\partial y^v}\right)^T \widetilde{z^v}. \tag{50}$$

Similarly, substitution of equations (48) and (49) into equation (32) gives

$$\frac{\partial H^n}{\partial \theta^n} = (z^n)^T \frac{\partial f^n}{\partial \theta^n} = - (\widetilde{z^n})^T \frac{\partial h^n}{\partial x^n} \frac{\partial f^n}{\partial \theta^n} = (\widetilde{z^n})^T \frac{\partial h^n}{\partial \theta^n};$$

that is, the optimal condition can be obtained from

$$\frac{\partial H^n}{\partial \theta^n} = (\widetilde{z^n})^T \frac{\partial h^n}{\partial \theta^n} = 0, \qquad n = 1, 2, \ldots, N. \tag{51}$$

Equations (50) and (51) contain only partial derivatives of $h^n$ with respect to its arguments. The use of equations (50) and (51) may sometimes be more convenient than the use of the original equations (32) and (44).

**Example 1.** A complex discrete system (see Fig. 10.1) is described by

$$h_1^n(x^n, y^n, \theta^n) = y_1^n - \theta^n \varphi(x_1^n) - x_1^n = 0, \tag{52}$$

$$y_1^n = \alpha^{0n} a_1^{0n} + \sum_{\mu=1}^{N} \alpha^{\mu n} x_1^\mu, \qquad n = 1, 2, \ldots, N, \tag{53}$$

[see equation (40)], where $\alpha^{\mu n}$ are non-negative numbers defined as

$$\alpha^{\mu n} = \frac{\rho^{\mu n}}{\rho^n} = \frac{\rho^{\mu n}}{\sum\limits_{\mu=0}^{N} \rho^{\mu n}}, \qquad \begin{array}{l} n = 1, 2, \ldots, N, \\ \mu = 0, 1, \ldots, N, \end{array} \qquad (54)$$

which satisfy

$$\sum_{\mu=0}^{N} \alpha^{\mu n} = 1, \qquad n = 1, 2, \ldots, N. \qquad (55)$$

Here $\rho^{\mu n}$ is the mass flow rate of the $\mu n$th stream and $\rho^n$ is the total mass flow rate of the $n$th unit, defined by equation (54); $\alpha^{\mu n}$ is then seen to be the mass fraction of the $\mu n$th stream with respect to $\rho^n$. (Note that the $\mu n$th stream is an input stream with respect to the $n$th unit.) Each unit of the system may be visualized as an extraction unit so that equation (52) represents the mass balance of the concentration of the solute $x_1$; however, it is not necessary to attach any particular physical significance here.

Suppose that we are to maximize an objective function $P$ given by

$$P = \sum_{n=1}^{N} \rho^{0n} a_1^{0n} - \sum_{n=1}^{N} \rho^{n,N+1} x_1^n - \lambda \sum_{n=1}^{N} \rho^n \theta^n, \qquad (56)$$

which represents a profit function. This is equivalent to minimizing the cost function $S$ defined as

$$S = \sum_{n=1}^{N} \rho^{n,N+1} x_1^n + \lambda \sum_{n=1}^{N} \rho^n \theta^n. \qquad (57)$$

Here $\lambda$ is a given scalar constant. We also assume that all of the $\alpha^{\mu n}$ and $\rho^{n,N+1}$ are given. Then, from the law of the conservation of mass, we have

$$\rho^n = \sum_{\mu=0}^{N} \rho^{\mu n} = \sum_{m=1}^{N+1} \rho^{nm} = \rho^{n,N+1} + \sum_{v=1}^{N} \rho^{nv}, \qquad n = 1, 2, \ldots, N. \quad (58)$$

From equation (54) we have

$$\rho^{nv} = \alpha^{nv} \rho^v. \qquad (59)$$

Substitution of equation (59) into equation (58) yields

$$\rho^n = \rho^{n,N+1} + \sum_{v=1}^{N} \alpha^{nv} \rho^v, \qquad n = 1, 2, \ldots, N, \qquad (60)$$

which is a set of $N$ equations with $N$ unknown $\rho^n$, $n = 1, 2, \ldots, N$. Therefore $\rho^n$ can be computed and, accordingly, all $\rho^{\mu n}$ by equation (54). If we define a set of new variables $x_2^n$ and $y_2^n$ by

$$h_2^n(x^n, y^n, \theta^n) = y_2^n - x_2^n + \theta^n = 0, \qquad (61)$$

$$y_2^n = \alpha^{0n} a_2^{0n} + \sum_{v=1}^{N} \alpha^{vn} x_2^v, \qquad (62)$$

and

$$a_2^{0n} = 0, \qquad n = 1, 2, \ldots, N, \qquad (63)$$

we can show that

$$\sum_{n=1}^{N} \rho^n \theta^n = \sum_{n=1}^{N} \rho^n x_2{}^n - \sum_{n=1}^{N} \rho^n y_2{}^n$$

$$= \sum_{n=1}^{N} \rho^n x_2{}^n - \sum_{n=1}^{N} \rho^n \sum_{v=1}^{N} \alpha^{vn} x_2{}^v$$

$$= \sum_{n=1}^{N} \rho^n x_2{}^n - \sum_{n=1}^{N} \sum_{v=1}^{N} \rho^{vn} x_2{}^v$$

$$= \sum_{n=1}^{N} \rho^n x_2{}^n - \sum_{v=1}^{N} x_2{}^v \left( \sum_{n=1}^{N} \rho^{vn} \right)$$

$$= \sum_{n=1}^{N} \rho^n x_2{}^n - \sum_{v=1}^{N} x_2{}^v (\rho^v - \rho^{v,N+1})$$

$$= \sum_{n=1}^{N} \rho^n x_2{}^n - \sum_{n=1}^{N} \rho^n x_2{}^n + \sum_{n=1}^{N} \rho^{n,N+1} x_2{}^n$$

$$= \sum_{n=1}^{N} \rho^{n,N+1} x_2{}^n. \tag{64}$$

Hence the objective function $S$, equation (57), can be written as

$$S = \sum_{n=1}^{N} (\rho^{n,N+1} x_1{}^n + \lambda \rho^{n,N+1} x_2{}^n)$$

$$= \sum_{n=1}^{N} [\rho^{n,N+1} \quad \lambda \rho^{n,N+1}] \begin{bmatrix} x_1{}^n \\ x_2{}^n \end{bmatrix}. \tag{65}$$

Comparing this with equation (45), we see that

$$c^{n,N+1} = \begin{bmatrix} c_1^{n,N+1} \\ c_2^{n,N+1} \end{bmatrix} = \begin{bmatrix} \rho^{n,N+1} \\ \lambda \rho^{n,N+1} \end{bmatrix}, \qquad n = 1, 2, \ldots, N. \tag{66}$$

Furthermore, comparing equations (53) and (62) with (38), we see that in this example

$$\Gamma^{\mu n} = \begin{bmatrix} \alpha^{\mu n} & 0 \\ 0 & \alpha^{\mu n} \end{bmatrix}, \qquad n = 1, 2, \ldots, N,$$

$$= \alpha^{\mu n} I.$$

Similarly, we have

$$\frac{\partial h^n}{\partial y^n} = \begin{bmatrix} 1 & 0 \\ 0 & 1 \end{bmatrix} = I,$$

$$\frac{\partial h^n}{\partial x^n} = - \begin{bmatrix} 1 + \theta^n \dot{\varphi}(x_1{}^n) & 0 \\ 0 & 1 \end{bmatrix}, \qquad n = 1, 2, \ldots, N,$$

where

$$\dot{\varphi}(x_1{}^n) = \frac{d\varphi(x_1{}^n)}{dx_1{}^n}.$$

The adjoint system then, from equation (50), is

$$\begin{bmatrix} 1 + \theta^n \dot{\varphi}(x_1{}^n) & 0 \\ 0 & 1 \end{bmatrix} \begin{bmatrix} \widetilde{z_1^n} \\ \widetilde{z_2^n} \end{bmatrix} = \begin{bmatrix} \rho^{n,N+1} \\ \lambda\rho^{n,N+1} \end{bmatrix} + \sum_{\nu=1}^{N} \alpha^{n\nu} \begin{bmatrix} \widetilde{z_1^\nu} \\ \widetilde{z_2^\nu} \end{bmatrix} \qquad (67)$$

or

$$[1 + \theta^n \dot{\varphi}(x_1{}^n)]\widetilde{z_1^n} = \rho^{n,N+1} + \sum_{\nu=1}^{N} \alpha^{n\nu} \widetilde{z_1^\nu}, \qquad (68)$$

$$\widetilde{z_2^n} = \lambda\rho^{n,N+1} + \sum_{\nu=1}^{N} \alpha^{n\nu}\widetilde{z_2^\nu}. \qquad (69)$$

Comparing equation (69) with equation (60), we see that

$$\widetilde{z_2^n} = \lambda\rho^n, \qquad n = 1, 2, \ldots, N, \qquad (70)$$

is a solution of equation (69). On the other hand, if the optimal decision can be determined by equation (51), that is,

$$[\widetilde{z_1^n} \ \widetilde{z_2^n}] \begin{bmatrix} \dfrac{\partial h_1{}^n}{\partial\theta^n} \\[2mm] \dfrac{\partial h_2{}^n}{\partial\theta^n} \end{bmatrix} = 0,$$

we have the optimal condition

$$\widetilde{z_1^n}\frac{\partial h_1{}^n}{\partial\theta^n} + \widetilde{z_2^n}\frac{\partial h_2{}^n}{\partial\theta^n} = \widetilde{z_1^n}[-\varphi(x_1{}^n)] + \lambda\rho^n = 0. \qquad (71)$$

Solution of equation (71) for $\widetilde{z_1^n}$ gives

$$\widetilde{z_1^n} = \frac{\lambda\rho^n}{\varphi(x_1{}^n)}, \qquad n = 1, 2, \ldots, N, \qquad (72)$$

which, in turn, gives

$$\frac{\widetilde{z_1^\nu}}{\widetilde{z_1^n}} = \frac{\rho^\nu}{\rho^n}\frac{\varphi(x_1{}^n)}{\varphi(x_1{}^\nu)}, \qquad n, \nu = 1, 2, \ldots, N. \qquad (73)$$

By rewriting equation (68) in the form

$$1 + \theta^n \dot{\varphi}(x_1{}^n) = \sum_{\nu=1}^{N} \alpha^{n\nu}\frac{\widetilde{z_1^\nu}}{\widetilde{z_1^n}} + \frac{1}{\widetilde{z_1^n}}\rho^{n,N+1} \qquad (74)$$

and substituting equations (72) and (73) into equation (74) we obtain

$$
\begin{aligned}
1 + \theta^n \dot{\varphi}(x_1^{\,n}) &= \sum_{v=1}^{N} \alpha^{nv} \frac{\rho^v}{\rho^n} \frac{\varphi(x_1^{\,n})}{\varphi(x_1^{\,v})} + \frac{\rho^{n,N+1}}{\rho^n} \frac{\varphi(x_1^{\,n})}{\lambda} \\
&= \sum_{v=1}^{N} \frac{\rho^{nv}}{\rho^n} \frac{\varphi(x_1^{\,n})}{\varphi(x_1^{\,v})} + \frac{\rho^{n,N+1}}{\rho^n} \frac{\varphi(x_1^{\,n})}{\lambda} \\
&= \sum_{m=1}^{N+1} \beta^{nm} \frac{\varphi(x_1^{\,n})}{\varphi(x_1^{\,m})},
\end{aligned}
\tag{75}
$$

in which

$$
\beta^{nm} \equiv \frac{\rho^{nm}}{\rho^n}, \qquad n = 1, 2, \ldots, N, \qquad m = 1, 2, \ldots, N+1
\tag{76}
$$

and

$$
\varphi(x_1^{N+1}) \equiv \lambda.
\tag{77}
$$

It can be seen that $\beta^{nm}$ is the mass fraction of the $nm$th output stream with respect to the total flow rate through the $n$th unit. Hence summation of $\beta^{nm}$ from $m = 1$ to $N + 1$ must yield

$$
\sum_{m=1}^{N+1} \beta^{nm} = \sum_{m=1}^{N+1} \frac{\rho^{nm}}{\rho^n} = \frac{\rho^n}{\rho^n} = 1.
\tag{78}
$$

Solving equation (75) for $\theta^n$ and making use of equation (78), we have

$$
\begin{aligned}
\theta^n &= \frac{1}{\dot{\varphi}(x_1^{\,n})} \left[ \sum_{m=1}^{N+1} \beta^{nm} \frac{\varphi(x_1^{\,n})}{\varphi(x_1^{\,m})} - 1 \right] \\
&= \frac{1}{\dot{\varphi}(x_1^{\,n})} \left[ \sum_{m=1}^{N+1} \beta^{nm} \frac{\varphi(x_1^{\,n})}{\varphi(x_1^{\,m})} - \sum_{m=1}^{N+1} \beta^{nm} \right] \\
&= \frac{1}{\dot{\varphi}(x_1^{\,n})} \left[ \sum_{m=1}^{N+1} \beta^{nm} \left( \frac{\varphi(x_1^{\,n})}{\varphi(x_1^{\,m})} - 1 \right) \right] \\
&= \frac{\varphi(x_1^{\,n})}{\dot{\varphi}(x_1^{\,n})} \sum_{m=1}^{N+1} \beta^{nm} \left[ \frac{1}{\varphi(x_1^{\,m})} - \frac{1}{\varphi(x_1^{\,n})} \right], \qquad n = 1, 2, \ldots, N.
\end{aligned}
\tag{79}
$$

By combining equations (52), (53), and (79) we finally obtain

$$
x_1^{\,n} = \alpha^{0n} a_1^{\,0n} + \sum_{v=1}^{N} \alpha^{vn} x_1^{\,v} - \frac{[\varphi(x_1^{\,n})]^2}{\dot{\varphi}(x_1^{\,n})} \sum_{m=1}^{N+1} \beta^{nm} \left[ \frac{1}{\varphi(x_1^{\,m})} - \frac{1}{\varphi(x_1^{\,n})} \right],
$$
$$
n = 1, 2, \ldots, N,
\tag{80}
$$

which is a set of $N$ equations with $N$ unknowns $x_1^{\,n}$, $n = 1, 2, \ldots, N$, and can be solved either analytically or numerically. It should be remembered that $\varphi(x_1^{N+1})$ is a constant and is equal to $\lambda$. Once $x_1^{\,n}$, $n = 1, 2, \ldots, N$, are computed from equation (80), substitution of these values into equation (79) gives the optimal decision $\theta^n$.

Reduction of the working equation (80) for a system of simpler configuration can be carried out as follows: since

$$\rho^{vn} = \alpha^{vn}\rho^n = \beta^{vn}\rho^v, \qquad n, v = 1, 2, \ldots, N,$$

$\alpha^{vn}$ and $\beta^{vn}$ are zero if there is no $v$th stream; that is, $\rho^{vn} = 0$. If there is no boundary input to the $n$th unit, $\alpha^{0n}$ vanishes. Similarly, if there is no boundary output from the $n$th unit, $\beta^{n,N+1}$ is zero. The nonvanishing $\alpha$ and $\beta$ must still satisfy equations (55) and (78).

We have defined $y_2^n$ and $x_2^n$ according to equation (62) so that the flow pattern of $x_2^n$ is identical to that of $x_1^n$ [see equations (53) and (62)]. Although this type of definition has some advantages, its use is not always necessary. Suppose that we define $y_2^n$ by

$$y_2^n = a_2^{0n}$$

in place of equation (62) and that equations (61) and (63) remain valid. It follows that

$$\sum_{n=1}^{N} \rho^n \theta^n = \sum_{n=1}^{N} \rho^n x_2^n - \sum_{n=1}^{N} \rho^n y_2^n = \sum_{n=1}^{N} \rho^n x_2^n$$

and

$$S = \sum_{n=1}^{N} (\rho^{n,N+1} x_1^n + \lambda \rho^n x_2^n).$$

A comparison of these equations with equation (45) gives

$$c^{n,N+1} = \begin{bmatrix} c_1^{n,N+1} \\ c_2^{n,N+1} \end{bmatrix} = \begin{bmatrix} \rho^{n,N+1} \\ \lambda \rho^n \end{bmatrix}.$$

The matrices $\Gamma^{nv}$, $n, v = 1, 2, \ldots, N$, now take the form

$$\Gamma^{nv} = \begin{bmatrix} \alpha^{nv} & 0 \\ 0 & 0 \end{bmatrix}.$$

Hence the adjoint system is

$$\begin{bmatrix} 1 + \theta^n \dot{\varphi}(x_1^n) & 0 \\ 0 & 1 \end{bmatrix} \begin{bmatrix} \widetilde{z}_1^n \\ \widetilde{z}_2^n \end{bmatrix} = \begin{bmatrix} c_1^{n,N+1} \\ c_2^{n,N+1} \end{bmatrix} + \sum_{v=1}^{N} \begin{bmatrix} \alpha^{nv} & 0 \\ 0 & 0 \end{bmatrix} \begin{bmatrix} \widetilde{z}_1^v \\ \widetilde{z}_2^v \end{bmatrix}$$

from which $\widetilde{z}_2^n$ can be obtained directly as $\lambda \rho^n$. The result is, as expected, the same as that in the alternate formulation.

**Example 2.** Let us now consider the system treated in Example 1 as a cross-current extraction process in which a solute is extracted from the solvent by the addition of washing water at each unit.

Let $x_1{}^n$ = the concentration of solute in the solvent leaving the $n$th unit,

$\rho^n$ = the total mass flow rate of solvent at the $n$th unit,

$\rho^{vn}$ = the mass flow rate of solvent in the $v$th stream,

$Q^n$ = the amount of washing water added to the $n$th unit,

$\varphi(x_1{}^n)$ = the concentration of solute in the washing water leaving the $n$th unit in equilibrium with $x_1{}^n$,

$y_1{}^n$ = the concentration of solute in the solvent entering the $n$th unit.

Then, on the assumption that the solvent and washing water are immiscible, the material balance for the solute about the $n$th unit is

$$\rho^n y_1{}^n - \rho^n x_1{}^n - Q^n \varphi(x_1{}^n) = 0. \tag{81}$$

Dividing equation (81) through by $\rho^n$ and putting $\theta^n = Q^n/\rho^n$, we have

$$y_1{}^n - x_1{}^n - \theta^n \varphi(x_1{}^n) = 0,$$

which is equation (52). Similarly, the material balance for the solute at the entrance point of the $n$th unit gives

$$\rho^n y_1{}^n = \rho^{0n} a_1{}^{0n} + \sum_{v=1}^{N} \rho^{vn} x_1{}^v, \tag{82}$$

where $a_1{}^{0n}$ is the concentration of solute in the $0n$th stream, that is, the boundary input stream of the $n$th unit. Dividing each term in equation (82) by $\rho^n$ and making use of the definition of $\alpha^{vn}$ given by equation (54), we have

$$y_1{}^n = \alpha^{0n} a_1{}^{0n} + \sum_{v=1}^{N} \alpha^{vn} x_1{}^v,$$

which is equation (53). The objective function given by equation (56) can easily be interpreted as the net profit if we consider $\lambda$ as the relative cost of washing water. The problem is then the optimal allocation of washing water so that the net profit can be maximized.

It follows from the results of Example 1 that the optimal amount of $\theta^n$ is given by equation (79) and that the concentration of solute in each unit can be determined by solving equation (80). To be definite let us assume that the configuration of the system is as sketched in Fig. 10.2.

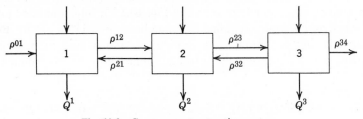

*Fig. 10.2*  Cross-current extraction system.

The mass flow rate of each stream is given as follows:

$$\rho^{01} = 1, \qquad \rho^{12} = \rho^{23} = 1.5, \qquad \rho^{21} = \rho^{32} = 0.5, \qquad \rho^{34} = 1.$$

From the definitions we have

$$\rho^1 = 1.5, \qquad \rho^2 = 2.0, \qquad \rho^3 = 1.5,$$

$$\alpha^{01} = \tfrac{2}{3}, \qquad \alpha^{02} = 0, \qquad \alpha^{03} = 0,$$

$$\alpha^{11} = 0, \qquad \alpha^{12} = \tfrac{3}{4}, \qquad \alpha^{13} = 0,$$

$$\alpha^{21} = \tfrac{1}{3}, \qquad \alpha^{22} = 0, \qquad \alpha^{23} = 1,$$

$$\alpha^{31} = 0, \qquad \alpha^{32} = \tfrac{1}{4}, \qquad \alpha^{33} = 0.$$

$$\beta^{11} = 0, \qquad \beta^{12} = 1, \qquad \beta^{13} = 0, \qquad \beta^{14} = 0,$$

$$\beta^{21} = \tfrac{1}{4}, \qquad \beta^{22} = 0, \qquad \beta^{23} = \tfrac{3}{4}, \qquad \beta^{24} = 0,$$

$$\beta^{31} = 0, \qquad \beta^{32} = \tfrac{1}{3}, \qquad \beta^{33} = 0, \qquad \beta^{34} = \tfrac{2}{3}.$$

Furthermore, we shall assume that the phase equilibrium is given by

$$\varphi(x_1{}^n) = -4(x_1{}^n)^2 + 2.2x_1{}^n, \qquad 0 \le x_1{}^n \le 0.25, \qquad n = 1, 2, \ldots, N \tag{83}$$

and that

$$a_1{}^{01} = 0.25. \tag{84}$$

By substituting all of the above data into equation (80) and solving the three simultaneous equations by the Newton-Raphson method we obtain the following results:

|         | Concentration of Solute, $x_1{}^n$ | Washing Water Allocation, $Q^n = \rho^n \theta^n$ |
|---------|:-----------------:|:-----------------:|
| Unit 1  | 0.11996           | 0.3486            |
| Unit 2  | 0.07595           | 0.1818            |
| Unit 3  | 0.04831           | 0.2849            |

## 4. DESCRIPTION OF A COMPLEX CONTINUOUS SYSTEM

In the next three sections we consider the optimization of the non-sequential continuous system shown in Fig. 10.3; $N$ interconnected units in the system are again identified by a number $n$, $n = 1, 2, \ldots, N$. By a continuous unit we mean, as a continuous branch used in preceding chapters, a one-dimensionally distributed unit whose unit equation can be written as

$$\frac{dx^n(\xi)}{d\xi} = f^n(x^n(\xi), \theta^n(\xi)), \qquad n = 1, 2, \ldots, N, \qquad 0 \le \xi \le L^n, \tag{85}$$

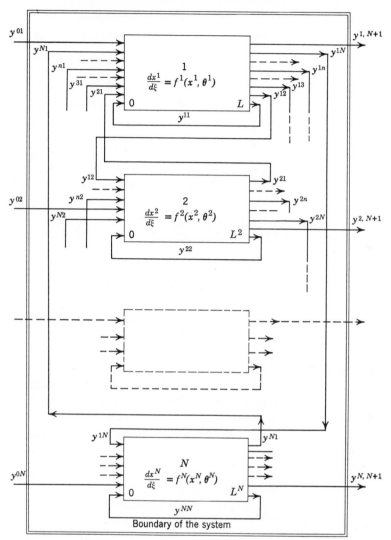

**Fig. 10.3** A nonsequential continuous system.

where $x^n(\xi) \in R^{s^n}$ is the state, $\theta^n(\xi) \in R^{r^n}$ is the decision, and $L^n$ is the "length" of the $n$th unit. The space coordinate is designated by $\xi$ to emphasize that it cannot be the time coordinate because the evolution of time is an irreversible process which does not permit the formation of a topologically or geometrically complex system.

As in a complex discrete system, properties of recirculated streams are denoted by $y^{vn} \in R^{l^{vn}}$, $n, v = 1, 2, \ldots, N$, and those of the boundary input and the boundary output are denoted by $y^{0n} \in R^{l^{0n}}$ and $y^{n,N+1} \in R^{l^{n,N+1}}$, respectively. The configuration of the system is then described by

$$x^n(0) = w^n(y^{\mu n}), \tag{86}$$

$$y^{nm} = v^{nm}(x^n(L^n)), \qquad n = 1, 2, \ldots, N, \tag{87}$$
$$\mu = 0, 1, \ldots, N,$$
$$m = 1, 2, \ldots, N + 1.$$

Obviously $x^n(0)$, the initial value of the state, is equivalent to $y^n$, the total input of a discrete system. Equations (86) and (87) show that the initial value of a state is related to the final value of all the states of the system.

## 5. THE STATEMENT OF THE PROBLEM AND THE DERIVATION OF THE ALGORITHM FOR CONTINUOUS SYSTEMS

The problem we shall consider is essentially the same as that considered for discrete systems, namely, to find a set of $\theta^n(\xi)$, $0 \le \xi \le L^n$, $n = 1$, $2, \ldots, N$, such that the objective function $S$

$$S = \sum_{n=1}^{N} (c^{n, N+1})^T y^{n, N+1} = \sum_{n=1}^{N} \sum_{i=1}^{l^{n, N+1}} c_i^{n, N+1} y_i^{n, N+1} \tag{88}$$

attains its maximum for some given $y^{0n} = a^{0n} \in R^{l^{0n}}$ and $c^{n, N+1} \in R^{l^{n, N+1}}$, $n = 1, 2, \ldots, N$. The system is described by equations (85), (86), and (87).

To obtain the solution to the problem we assume, as before, that the functions $f^n(x^n, \theta^n)$, $w^n(y^{\mu n})$, and $v^{nm}(x^n(L^n))$ are sufficiently regular. Assume that a set of optimal decisions $\bar{\theta}^n$ is found and that the corresponding state of the system and objective function are described by

$$\frac{d\bar{x}^n(\xi)}{d\xi} = f^n(\bar{x}^n(\xi), \bar{\theta}^n(\xi)), \tag{89}$$

$$\bar{x}^n(0) = w^n(\bar{y}^{\mu n}), \tag{90}$$

$$\bar{y}^{nm} = v^{nm}(\bar{x}^n(L^n)), \tag{91}$$

$$\bar{y}^{0n} = a^{0n}, \qquad \begin{array}{l} n = 1, 2, \ldots, N, \qquad \mu = 0, 1, 2, \ldots, N, \\ m = 1, 2, \ldots, N + 1, \end{array} \tag{92}$$

and

$$\max S = \sum_{n=1}^{N} (c^{n, N+1})^T \bar{y}^{n, N+1} \tag{93}$$

The variational equations of the perturbed system due to a small independent variation in the decisions $|\delta\theta^n(\xi)| = |\theta^n(\xi) - \bar{\theta}^n(\xi)| < \epsilon\varphi^n(\xi)$,

$n = 1, 2, \ldots, N$, are (the derivative of a variation is the variation of a derivative [8])

$$\delta \frac{dx^n(\xi)}{d\xi} = \frac{d\,\delta x^n(\xi)}{d\xi} = \frac{\partial f^n}{\partial x^n} \delta x^n(\xi) + \frac{\partial f^n}{\partial \theta^n} \delta \theta^n(\xi), \tag{94}$$

$$\delta x^n(0) = \sum_{\mu=0}^{N} \frac{\partial w^n}{\partial y^{\mu n}} \delta y^{\mu n}, \tag{95}$$

$$\delta y^{nm} = \frac{\partial v^{nm}}{\partial x^n} \delta x^n(L^n), \tag{96}$$

$$\delta y^{0n} = 0, \qquad \begin{array}{l} n = 1, 2, \ldots, N, \qquad \mu = 0, 1, 2, \ldots, N, \\ m = 1, 2, \ldots, N+1. \end{array} \tag{97}$$

Equations (94), (95), and (96) have the same sign on both sides and all the neglected terms are of order $\epsilon^2$, that is, $0(\epsilon^2)$, and of order higher than $\epsilon^2$ if $\epsilon$ is kept sufficiently small. The matrix elements are appropriately evaluated at the upperbarred quantities. For example, the matrix $\partial v^{nm}/\partial x^n$ is evaluated at $\bar{x}^n(L^n)$.

We now define a set of adjoint vectors $z^n(\xi) \in R^{s^n}$, $z^{nm} \in R^{l^{nm}}$, and $z^{\mu n} \in R^{l^{\mu n}}$ by

$$\frac{dz^n(\xi)}{d\xi} = -\left(\frac{\partial f^n}{\partial x^n}\right)^T z^n(\xi), \tag{98}$$

$$z^{\mu n} = \left(\frac{\partial w^n}{\partial y^{\mu n}}\right)^T z^n(0), \tag{99}$$

$$z^n(L^n) = \sum_{m=1}^{N+1} \left(\frac{\partial v^{nm}}{\partial x^n}\right)^T z^{nm}, \tag{100}$$

$$z^{n,N+1} = c^{n,N+1}, \qquad \begin{array}{l} n = 1, 2, \ldots, N, \\ \mu = 0, 1, 2, \ldots, N, \\ m = 1, 2, \ldots, N+1. \end{array} \tag{101}$$

It follows that

$$\frac{d}{d\xi}[(z^n)^T \delta x^n] = (z^n)^T \frac{d\,\delta x^n}{d\xi} + \frac{d(z^n)^T}{d\xi} \delta x^n$$

$$= (z^n)^T \left(\frac{\partial f^n}{\partial x^n}\right) \delta x^n + (z^n)^T \frac{\partial f^n}{\partial \theta^n} \delta \theta^n - \left[\left(\frac{\partial f^n}{\partial x^n}\right)^T z^n\right]^T \delta x^n$$

$$= (z^n)^T \left(\frac{\partial f^n}{\partial x^n}\right) \delta x^n + (z^n)^T \frac{\partial f^n}{\partial \theta^n} \delta \theta^n - (z^n)^T \left(\frac{\partial f^n}{\partial x^n}\right) \delta x^n$$

$$= (z^n)^T \frac{\partial f^n}{\partial \theta^n} \delta \theta^n, \tag{102}$$

which, on integrating from $\xi = 0$ to $\xi = L^n$ and summing from $n = 1$ to $n = N$, yields

$$\sum_{n=1}^{N} [(z^n(L^n))^T \, \delta x^n(L^n) - (z^n(0))^T \, \delta x^n(0)] = \sum_{n=1}^{N} \int_0^{L^n} (z^n)^T \frac{\partial f^n}{\partial \theta^n} \, \delta \theta^n \, d\xi. \quad (103)$$

From equations (95) and (99) we can show that

$$(z^n(0))^T \, \delta x^n(0) = \sum_{\mu=0}^{N} (z^n(0))^T \frac{\partial w^n}{\partial y^{\mu n}} \, \delta y^{\mu n} = \sum_{\mu=0}^{N} (z^{\mu n})^T \, \delta y^{\mu n}. \quad (104)$$

Similarly, from equations (96) and (100), we have

$$(z^n(L^n))^T \, \delta x^n(L^n) = \sum_{m=1}^{N+1} (z^{nm})^T \frac{\partial v^{nm}}{\partial x^n} \, \delta x^n(L^n) = \sum_{m=1}^{N+1} (z^{nm})^T \, \delta y^{nm}. \quad (105)$$

By substituting equations (104) and (105) into equation (103) we obtain

$$\sum_{n=1}^{N} \sum_{m=1}^{N+1} (z^{nm})^T \, \delta y^{nm} - \sum_{n=1}^{N} \sum_{\mu=0}^{N} (z^{\mu n})^T \, \delta y^{\mu n} = \sum_{n=1}^{N} \int_0^{L^n} (z^n)^T \frac{\partial f^n}{\partial \theta^n} \, \delta \theta^n \, d\xi. \quad (106)$$

Combining like terms and making use of equations (97) and (101), we obtain

$$\sum_{n=1}^{N} (c^{n,\,N+1})^T \, \delta y^{n,N+1} = \sum_{n=1}^{N} \int_0^{L^n} (z^n)^T \frac{\partial f^n}{\partial \theta^n} \, \delta \theta^n \, d\xi.$$

The term on the left is again seen to be the variation of the objective function $S$, defined by equation (88), which must be zero for free variations $\delta \theta^n$ and negative for all one-sided variations $\delta \theta^n$. Furthermore, the $\delta \theta^n(\xi)$ are all independent at any $\xi$ and $n$, $0 \leq \xi \leq L^n$, $n = 1, 2, \ldots, N$. Hence we must have

$$(z^n)^T \frac{\partial f^n}{\partial \theta^n} \, \delta \theta^n \leq 0, \quad (107)$$

or in terms of the Hamiltonian

$$H^n = (z^n(\xi))^T f^n(x^n(\xi), \theta^n(\xi)),$$

$$\frac{\partial H^n}{\partial \theta^n} \, \delta \theta^n \leq 0. \quad (108)$$

With this necessary condition further analysis (see Section 2) again leads us to the conclusion that the local weak maximum principle is valid; that is, in order to maximize (minimize) $S$,

$$\bar{\theta}^n(\xi): \quad \frac{\partial H^n}{\partial \theta^n} = 0, \qquad \begin{array}{l} n = 1, 2, \ldots, N, \\ 0 \leq \xi \leq L^n \end{array} \quad (109)$$

when there is no constraint imposed on $\theta^n$ (or $\bar{\theta}^n$ lies in the interior of the admissible domain of $\theta^n$).

$$\bar{\theta}^n(\xi): \ H^n = \max \ (\min), \quad \begin{matrix} n = 1, 2, \ldots, N, \\ 0 \leq \xi \leq L^n, \end{matrix} \qquad (110)$$

when $\theta^n$ lies on a constraint of the form

$$Q^n(\theta^n) \geq 0. \qquad (111)$$

However, the first part of the algorithm could have been strengthened if we had retained in the variational equations all the second-order terms* from the beginning of the derivation. Had we done this, along with the choice of special variation of the form

$$\delta\theta^n = \begin{cases} \epsilon\varphi^n(\xi), & 0 \leq \xi_1 \leq \xi \leq \xi_2 \leq L^n, \\ 0, & \text{otherwise,} \end{cases} \qquad (112)$$

it could have been shown that by making $\Delta\xi = \xi_2 - \xi_1$ sufficiently small the Hessian matrix whose $ij$th element is $\partial^2 H^n/(\partial\theta_i{}^n \ \partial\theta_j{}^n)$, $i, j = 1, 2, \ldots, r^n$, would have been negative definite when no constraint was imposed on the decision $\theta^n$ [3]. This argument and the weak principle give rise to the so-called local strong maximum principle which states that in order to maximize (minimize) the objective function $S$ the optimal choice of $\theta^n$ must be such that the Hamiltonian $H^n$ is made a maximum (minimum) with respect to $\theta^n$ at all $n$ and $\xi$, $n = 1, 2, \ldots, N, 0 \leq \xi \leq L^n$.

The adjoint system, equations (99), (100), and (101), can be combined to eliminate $z^{nm}$. From equation (99), we can write

$$z^{nv} = \left(\frac{\partial w^v}{\partial y^{nv}}\right)^T z^v(0),$$

and from equation (100), we have

$$\begin{aligned} z^n(L^n) &= \left(\frac{\partial v^{n,N+1}}{\partial x^n}\right)^T z^{n,N+1} + \sum_{v=1}^{N} \left(\frac{\partial v^{nv}}{\partial x^n}\right)^T z^{nv} \\ &= \left(\frac{\partial v^{n,N+1}}{\partial x^n}\right)^T c^{n,N+1} + \sum_{v=1}^{N} \left(\frac{\partial v^{nv}}{\partial x^n}\right)^T \left(\frac{\partial w^v}{\partial y^{nv}}\right)^T z^v(0), \end{aligned} \qquad (113)$$

which is, in fact, the boundary condition for the differential equation (98):

$$\frac{dz^n(\xi)}{d\xi} = -\left(\frac{\partial f^n}{\partial x^n}\right)^T z^n(\xi), \qquad n = 1, 2, \ldots, N, \qquad 0 \leq \xi \leq L^n. \quad (98)$$

We shall therefore call equations (98) and (113), collectively, the adjoint system of a continuous system.

---

* The second-order terms involve tensors of third order.

## 6. FURTHER DISCUSSION AND EXAMPLES

In this section we consider a special case in which the configuration of a continuous system is such that it is described by

$$y^{nm} = v^{nm}(x^n(L^n)) = x^n(L^n), \tag{114}$$

$$x^n(0) = w^n(y^{\mu n}) = \sum_{\mu=0}^{N} \Gamma^{\mu n} y^{\mu n}, \tag{115}$$

$$n = 1, 2, \ldots, N, \qquad \mu = 0, 1, \ldots, N, \qquad m = 1, 2, \ldots, N+1.$$

Here the vectors $x^n(\xi)$, $y^{nm}$, and $y^{\mu n}$ all have $s$ number of components and $\Gamma^{\mu n}$ are the same as that given by equation (39), namely

$$\Gamma^{\mu n} = \begin{bmatrix} \alpha_1^{\mu n} & & & 0 \\ & \alpha_2^{\mu n} & & \\ & & \cdot & \\ & & & \cdot \\ 0 & & & \alpha_s^{\mu n} \end{bmatrix}, \qquad \begin{matrix} \mu = 0, 1, \ldots, N, \\ n = 1, 2, \ldots, N, \end{matrix}$$

where the diagonal elements are non-negative constants. Equations (114) and (115) can then be combined to give

$$x^n(0) = \Gamma^{0n} a^{0n} + \sum_{\nu=1}^{N} \Gamma^{\nu n} x^\nu(L^\nu), \qquad n = 1, 2, \ldots, N, \tag{116}$$

in which we have made use of the condition $y^{0n} = a^{0n}$. Equation (116) is the boundary condition of the unit equation (85), namely

$$\frac{dx^n(\xi)}{d\xi} = f^n(x^n(\xi); \theta^n(\xi)).$$

The corresponding adjoint system for this system, from equations (98) and (113), is

$$\frac{dz^n(\xi)}{d\xi} = -\left(\frac{\partial f^n}{\partial x^n}\right)^T z^n(\xi), \tag{98}$$

$$z^n(L^n) = c^{n, N+1} + \sum_{\nu=1}^{N} \Gamma^{n\nu} z^\nu(0), \qquad n = 1, 2, \ldots, N. \tag{117}$$

The objective function $S$ defined by equation (88) now can be written

$$S = \sum_{n=1}^{N} (c^{n, N+1})^T x^n(L^n) = \sum_{n=1}^{N} \sum_{i=1}^{s} c_i^{n, N+1} x_i^n(L^n). \tag{118}$$

As mentioned in Section 3, the flow pattern of the components of the state vector are identical when the diagonal elements of its $\Gamma$ matrix are identical. This is usually true when the components of the state vector represent some real physical quantities. For a hypothetical component, however, we may find that it is advantageous to assign a different flow pattern to it.

**Example 1.**   Consider a complex continuous system (see Fig. 10.3) which is mathematically described by

$$\frac{dx_1{}^n}{d\xi} = f_1{}^n(x^n; \theta^n) = -a^n x_1{}^n + b^n \theta^n, \qquad 0 \le \xi \le L^n, \qquad (119)$$

$$x_1{}^n(0) = \alpha^{0n} a_1{}^{0n} + \sum_{\nu=1}^{N} \alpha^{\nu n} x_1{}^\nu(L^\nu), \qquad n = 1, 2, \ldots, N, \qquad (120)$$

where $a^n$, $b^n$, and $a_1{}^{0n}$ are given constants, and $\alpha^{\mu n}$, $\mu = 0, 1, \ldots, N$, are non-negative constants which satisfy the relationship

$$\sum_{\mu=0}^{N} \alpha^{\mu n} = 1, \qquad n = 1, 2, \ldots, N. \qquad (121)$$

Suppose that we are to minimize an objective function

$$S = \sum_{n=1}^{N} S^n = \sum_{n=1}^{N} \int_0^{L^n} \frac{\rho^n}{2} [(x_1{}^n)^2 + (\theta^n)^2] \, d\xi \qquad (122)$$

which represents a cost function and in which $\rho^n > 0$, $n = 1, 2, \ldots, N$ are some predetermined weighting factors. If we define

$$x_2{}^n(\xi) = \int_0^\xi \frac{\rho^n}{2} [(x_1{}^n)^2 + (\theta^n)^2] \, d\xi, \qquad (123)$$

we can see that

$$x_2{}^n(L^n) = S^n \quad \text{and} \quad x_2{}^n(0) = 0.$$

Hence we define a set of new variables by

$$\frac{dx_2{}^n}{d\xi} = f_2{}^n(x^n; \theta^n) = \frac{\rho^n}{2} [(x_1{}^n)^2 + (\theta^n)^2], \qquad 0 \le \xi \le L^n, \qquad (124)$$

$$x_2{}^n(0) = a_2{}^{0n}, \qquad (125)$$

$$a_2{}^{0n} = 0, \qquad n = 1, 2, \ldots, N. \qquad (126)$$

It follows that the objective function $S$ of equation (122) can be written as

$$S = \sum_{n=1}^{N} x_2{}^n(L^n), \qquad (127)$$

which, on comparison with equation (118), gives the constant $c^{n,N+1}$ as

$$c^{n,N+1} = \begin{bmatrix} c_1^{n,N+1} \\ c_2^{n,N+1} \end{bmatrix} = \begin{bmatrix} 0 \\ 1 \end{bmatrix}. \tag{128}$$

Since

$$\frac{\partial f^n}{\partial x^n} = \begin{bmatrix} -a^n & 0 \\ \rho^n x_1^n & 0 \end{bmatrix}, \qquad \Gamma^{vn} = \begin{bmatrix} \alpha^{vn} & 0 \\ 0 & 0 \end{bmatrix} \quad \text{and}$$

$$\Gamma^{0n} = \begin{bmatrix} \alpha^{0n} & 0 \\ 0 & 1 \end{bmatrix}, \qquad \begin{array}{l} n = 1, 2, \ldots, N, \\ v = 1, 2, \ldots, N; \end{array}$$

the adjoint system for the problem under consideration can be written as

$$\frac{d}{d\xi}\begin{bmatrix} z_1^n \\ z_2^n \end{bmatrix} = -\begin{bmatrix} -a^n & \rho^n x_1^n \\ 0 & 0 \end{bmatrix}\begin{bmatrix} z_1^n \\ z_2^n \end{bmatrix},$$

$$\begin{bmatrix} z_1^n(L^n) \\ z_2^n(L^n) \end{bmatrix} = \begin{bmatrix} c_1^{n,N+1} \\ c_2^{n,N+1} \end{bmatrix} + \sum_{v=1}^{N}\begin{bmatrix} \alpha^{nv} & 0 \\ 0 & 0 \end{bmatrix}\begin{bmatrix} z_1^v(0) \\ z_2^v(0) \end{bmatrix},$$

or, in component form,

$$\frac{dz_1^n}{d\xi} = a^n z_1^n - \rho^n x_1^n z_2^n, \tag{129}$$

$$\frac{dz_2^n}{d\xi} = 0, \tag{130}$$

$$z_1^n(L^n) = \sum_{v=1}^{N} \alpha^{nv} z_1^v(0), \tag{131}$$

$$z_2^n(L^n) = 1. \tag{132}$$

By combining equation (130) with equation (132) we obtain

$$z_2^n(\xi) = 1, \qquad 0 \le \xi \le L^n, \qquad n = 1, 2, \ldots, N, \tag{133}$$

as a solution. If we insert $z_2^n = 1$, the Hamiltonian becomes

$$H^n = -a^n z_1^n x_1^n + \frac{\rho^n}{2}(x_1^n)^2 + b^n z_1^n \theta^n + \frac{\rho^n}{2}(\theta^n)^2, \qquad n = 1, 2, \ldots, N. \tag{134}$$

This function obviously has only one minimum and no maximum with respect to $\theta^n$. Hence from

$$\frac{\partial H^n}{\partial \theta^n} = b^n z_1^n + \rho^n \theta^n = 0 \tag{135}$$

we obtain the optimal decisions as

$$\theta^n = -\frac{b^n}{\rho^n} z_1{}^n, \qquad n = 1, 2, \ldots, N. \tag{136}$$

Substituting equation (136) into (119) and equation (133) into (129), we have a set of simultaneous equations;

$$\frac{dx_1{}^n}{d\xi} = -a^n x_1{}^n - \frac{(b^n)^2}{\rho^n} z_1{}^n, \tag{137}$$

$$\frac{dz_1{}^n}{d\xi} = -\rho^n x_1{}^n + a^n z_1{}^n, \tag{138}$$

which are to be solved with the boundary conditions

$$x_1{}^n(0) = \alpha^{0n} a_1{}^{0n} + \sum_{\nu=1}^{N} \alpha^{\nu n} x_1{}^\nu(L^\nu) \tag{120}$$

and

$$z_1{}^n(L^n) = \sum_{\nu=1}^{N} \alpha^{n\nu} z_1{}^\nu(0). \tag{131}$$

The general solutions are

$$x_1{}^n(\xi) = A_1{}^n e^{\lambda^n \xi} + A_2{}^n e^{-\lambda^n \xi}, \tag{139}$$

$$z_1{}^n(\xi) = A_3{}^n e^{\lambda^n \xi} + A_4{}^n e^{-\lambda^n \xi}, \tag{140}$$

where

$$\lambda^n = \sqrt{(a^n)^2 + (b^n)^2},$$

$$A_3{}^n = \frac{\rho^n}{(a^n - \lambda^n)} A_1{}^n \quad \text{and} \quad A_4{}^n = \frac{\rho^n}{(a^n + \lambda^n)} A_2{}^n.$$

The $2N$ coefficients $A_1{}^n$ and $A_2{}^n$, $n = 1, 2, \ldots, N$ can be uniquely determined by substituting the general solution into the $2N$ boundary conditions, equations (120) and (131). Since the optimal decisions are given by equation (136), we have

$$\bar{\theta}^n(\xi) = -\frac{b^n}{a^n - \lambda^n} A_1{}^n e^{\lambda^n \xi} - \frac{b^n}{a^n + \lambda^n} A_2{}^n e^{-\lambda^n \xi} \tag{141}$$

for all $n$, $n = 1, 2, \ldots, N$, and $0 \leq \xi \leq L^n$.

**Example 2.** In this example we consider a continuous complex process consisting, of three tubular reactors of length $L^1$, $L^2$, and $L^3$, respectively, with a portion of product recycled to the inlet of each reactor as shown in Fig. 10.4. As before, we consider a first-order consecutive irreversible reaction of the type

$$A \xrightarrow{k_1} B \xrightarrow{k_2} C.$$

According to Section 4.2, part b, the unit equations for each reactor can be written as

$$f_1{}^n = \frac{dx_1{}^n}{d\xi} = -k_{10}e^{(-E_1/R\theta^n)}x_1{}^n, \tag{142}$$

$$f_2{}^n = \frac{dx_2{}^n}{d\xi} = k_{10}e^{(-E_1/R\theta^n)}x_1{}^n - k_{20}e^{(-E_2/R\theta^n)}x_2{}^n, \qquad n = 1, 2, 3, \tag{143}$$

where $x_1$ and $x_2$ are the molar concentrations of $A$ and $B$, respectively; $\xi$ is the space coordinate measured on the holding-time basis; that is $0 \leq \xi \leq T^n$, where $T^n$ is the holding time for the $n$th reactor defined as

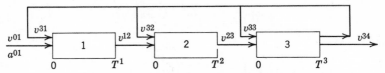

**Fig. 10.4**  Schematic diagram of a process consisting of three tubular reactors connected in series with product recycled to the initial point of each reactor.

$T^n = L^n/(v^n/A^n)$, $n = 1, 2, 3$, in which $A^n$ is the cross-sectional area of the $n$th reactor and $v^n$ is the total volumetric flow rate in the $n$th reactor.

We wish to maximize the intermediate product $B$ at the outlet of unit 3 by adjusting the temperature profiles along each reactor.

To establish the boundary conditions for each unit we consider the material balance for each unit. The total input of reactants into the units 1, 2, and 3 are, respectively, according to equation (116),

$$x^1(0) = \Gamma^{01}a^{01} + \Gamma^{31}x^3(T^3)$$

or

$$\begin{bmatrix} x_1{}^1(0) \\ x_2{}^1(0) \end{bmatrix} = \begin{bmatrix} \alpha^{01} & 0 \\ 0 & \alpha^{01} \end{bmatrix} \begin{bmatrix} a_1{}^{01} \\ a_2{}^{01} \end{bmatrix} + \begin{bmatrix} \alpha^{31} & 0 \\ 0 & \alpha^{31} \end{bmatrix} \begin{bmatrix} x_1{}^3(T^3) \\ x_2{}^3(T^3) \end{bmatrix},$$

that is,

$$x_1{}^1(0) = \alpha^{01}a_1{}^{01} + \alpha^{31}x_1{}^3(T^3), \tag{144}$$

$$x_2{}^1(0) = \alpha^{01}a_2{}^{01} + \alpha^{31}x_2{}^3(T^3), \tag{145}$$

where

$$\alpha^{01} = \frac{v^{01}}{v^1}, \qquad \alpha^{31} = \frac{v^{31}}{v^1}, \qquad v^{01} + v^{31} = v^1,$$

and

$$x^2(0) = \Gamma^{12}x^1(T^1) + \Gamma^{32}x^3(T^3);$$

or

$$\begin{bmatrix} x_1{}^2(0) \\ x_2{}^2(0) \end{bmatrix} = \begin{bmatrix} \alpha^{12} & 0 \\ 0 & \alpha^{12} \end{bmatrix} \begin{bmatrix} x_1{}^1(T^1) \\ x_2{}^1(T^1) \end{bmatrix} + \begin{bmatrix} \alpha^{32} & 0 \\ 0 & \alpha^{32} \end{bmatrix} \begin{bmatrix} x_1{}^3(T^3) \\ x_2{}^3(T^3) \end{bmatrix},$$

that is,

$$x_1{}^2(0) = \alpha^{12} x_1{}^1(T^1) + \alpha^{32} x_1{}^3(T^3), \tag{146}$$

$$x_2{}^2(0) = \alpha^{12} x_2{}^1(T^1) + \alpha^{32} x_2{}^3(T^3), \tag{147}$$

where

$$\alpha^{12} = \frac{v^{12}}{v^2}, \qquad \alpha^{32} = \frac{v^{32}}{v^2}, \qquad v^{12} + v^{32} = v^2$$

and

$$x^3(0) = \Gamma^{23} x^2(T^2) + \Gamma^{33} x^3(T^3);$$

or

$$\begin{bmatrix} x_1{}^3(0) \\ x_2{}^3(0) \end{bmatrix} = \begin{bmatrix} \alpha^{23} & 0 \\ 0 & \alpha^{23} \end{bmatrix} \begin{bmatrix} x_1{}^2(T^2) \\ x_2{}^2(T^2) \end{bmatrix} + \begin{bmatrix} \alpha^{33} & 0 \\ 0 & \alpha^{33} \end{bmatrix} \begin{bmatrix} x_1{}^3(T^3) \\ x_2{}^3(T^3) \end{bmatrix},$$

that is,

$$x_1{}^3(0) = \alpha^{23} x_1{}^2(T^2) + \alpha^{33} x_1{}^3(T^3), \tag{148}$$

$$x_2{}^3(0) = \alpha^{23} x_2{}^2(T^2) + \alpha^{33} x_2{}^3(T^3), \tag{149}$$

where

$$\alpha^{23} = \frac{v^{23}}{v^3}, \qquad \alpha^{33} = \frac{v^{33}}{v^3}, \quad \text{and} \quad v^{23} + v^{33} = v^3.$$

Since we are going to maximize the intermediate product at the end of unit 3, the objective function is

$$S = x_2{}^3(T^3). \tag{150}$$

Consequently we have, according to equation (118),

$$c^{34} = \begin{bmatrix} c_1{}^{34} \\ c_2{}^{34} \end{bmatrix} = \begin{bmatrix} 0 \\ 1 \end{bmatrix} \quad \text{and} \quad c^{14} = c^{24} = \begin{bmatrix} 0 \\ 0 \end{bmatrix}. \tag{151}$$

The adjoint system is obtained from equation (98) as

$$\frac{d}{d\xi}\begin{bmatrix} z_1{}^n \\ z_2{}^n \end{bmatrix} = \begin{bmatrix} k_{10}\, e^{-E_1/R\theta^n} & -k_{10}\, e^{-E_1/R\theta^n} \\ 0 & k_{20}\, e^{-E_2/R\theta^n} \end{bmatrix} \begin{bmatrix} z_1{}^n \\ z_2{}^n \end{bmatrix}$$

or

$$\frac{dz_1{}^n}{d\xi} = k_{10}\, e^{-E_1/R\theta^n}(z_1{}^n - z_2{}^n), \qquad n = 1, 2, 3, \tag{152}$$

$$\frac{dz_2{}^n}{d\xi} = k_{20}\, e^{-E_2/R\theta^n} z_2{}^n, \qquad n = 1, 2, 3. \tag{153}$$

The three boundary conditions for the adjoint system which are evaluated by the use of equation (117) are given as follows:

$$z^1(T^1) = \Gamma^{12} z^2(0) = \begin{bmatrix} \alpha^{12} & 0 \\ 0 & \alpha^{12} \end{bmatrix} \begin{bmatrix} z_1{}^2(0) \\ z_2{}^2(0) \end{bmatrix},$$

that is

$$z_1{}^1(T^1) = \alpha^{12} z_1{}^2(0), \tag{154}$$

$$z_2{}^1(T^1) = \alpha^{12} z_2{}^2(0), \tag{155}$$

$$z^2(T^2) = \Gamma^{23} z^3(0) = \begin{bmatrix} \alpha^{23} & 0 \\ 0 & \alpha^{23} \end{bmatrix} \begin{bmatrix} z_1{}^3(0) \\ z_2{}^3(0) \end{bmatrix},$$

that is,

$$z_1{}^2(T^2) = \alpha^{23} z_1{}^3(0), \tag{156}$$

$$z_2{}^2(T^2) = \alpha^{23} z_2{}^3(0), \tag{157}$$

and

$$z^3(T^3) = c^{34} + \Gamma^{31} z^1(0) + \Gamma^{32} z^2(0) + \Gamma^{33} z^3(0)$$

$$= \begin{bmatrix} c_1{}^{34} \\ c_2{}^{34} \end{bmatrix} + \begin{bmatrix} \alpha^{31} & 0 \\ 0 & \alpha^{31} \end{bmatrix} \begin{bmatrix} z_1{}^1(0) \\ z_2{}^1(0) \end{bmatrix}$$

$$+ \begin{bmatrix} \alpha^{32} & 0 \\ 0 & \alpha^{32} \end{bmatrix} \begin{bmatrix} z_1{}^2(0) \\ z_2{}^2(0) \end{bmatrix} + \begin{bmatrix} \alpha^{33} & 0 \\ 0 & \alpha^{33} \end{bmatrix} \begin{bmatrix} z_1{}^3(0) \\ z_2{}^3(0) \end{bmatrix},$$

that is

$$z_1{}^3(T^3) = \alpha^{31} z_1{}^1(0) + \alpha^{32} z_1{}^2(0) + \alpha^{33} z_1{}^3(0), \tag{158}$$

$$z_2{}^3(T^3) = 1 + \alpha^{31} z_2{}^1(0) + \alpha^{32} z_2{}^2(0) + \alpha^{33} z_2{}^3(0) \tag{159}$$

because of equation (151).

The Hamiltonian function for each unit is

$$H^n = -z_1{}^n k_{10} e^{-E_1/R\theta^n} x_1{}^n + z_2{}^n (k_{10} e^{-E_1/R\theta^n} x_1{}^n - k_{20} e^{-E_2/R\theta^n} x_2{}^n),$$

$$n = 1, 2, 3. \tag{160}$$

By partial differentiating the preceding equation with respect to $\theta^n$ and setting it equal to zero we obtain the optimal decision for each unit as [see equation (4.33)]

$$\bar\theta^n = \frac{E_1 - E_2}{R} \left\{ \ln \left[ \eta \frac{x_1{}^n(z_2{}^n - z_1{}^n)}{x_2{}^n z_2{}^n} \right] \right\}^{-1}, \qquad n = 1, 2, 3, \tag{161}$$

where

$$\eta = \frac{k_{10}E_1}{k_{20}E_2}.$$

Substitution of equation (161) into (142), (143), (152), and (153) [see equations (4.34) through (4.37)] gives

$$\frac{dx_1{}^n}{d\xi} = -k_{10}\left[\eta\,\frac{x_1{}^n}{x_2{}^n}\left(\frac{z_2{}^n - z_1{}^n}{z_2{}^n}\right)\right]^{\lambda_1} x_1{}^n, \tag{162}$$

$$\frac{dx_2{}^n}{d\xi} = k_{10}\left[\eta\,\frac{x_1{}^n}{x_2{}^n}\left(\frac{z_2{}^n - z_1{}^n}{z_2{}^n}\right)\right]^{\lambda_1} x_1{}^n - k_{20}\left[\eta\,\frac{x_1{}^n}{x_2{}^n}\left(\frac{z_2{}^n - z_1{}^n}{z_2{}^n}\right)\right]^{\lambda_2} x_2{}^n, \tag{163}$$

$$\frac{dz_1{}^n}{d\xi} = k_{10}\left[\eta\,\frac{x_1{}^n}{x_2{}^n}\left(\frac{z_2{}^n - z_1{}^n}{z_2{}^n}\right)\right]^{\lambda_1}(z_1{}^n - z_2{}^n), \tag{164}$$

$$\frac{dz_2{}^n}{d\xi} = k_{20}\left[\eta\,\frac{x_1{}^n}{x_2{}^n}\left(\frac{z_2{}^n - z_1{}^n}{z_2{}^n}\right)\right]^{\lambda_2} z_2{}^n, \qquad n = 1, 2, 3, \tag{165}$$

where

$$\lambda_1 = \frac{E_1}{E_2 - E_1}, \qquad \lambda_2 = \frac{E_2}{E_2 - E_1}.$$

Thus we have 12 differential equations to be solved by the use of 12 boundary conditions, equations (144) through (149) and equations (154) through (159).

## 7. THE OPTIMIZATION OF COMPOSITE SYSTEMS

First we define a composite system as consisting of the discrete and continuous type units already discussed. These units may be so mutually interconnected that we may no longer be able to identify easily a branch as discrete or continuous. We assume that there are $N$ continuous units and $M$ discrete units in the system. As in the preceding sections, each unit is assigned a number. Each of the $N$ continuous units is identified by $n = 1, 2, \ldots, N$, and each of the $M$ discrete units, by $i = N + 1$, $N + 2, \ldots, N + M$. Other definitions are not altered. For example, the boundary input and output of the $n$th continuous unit are designated by $y^{0n}$ and $y^{n,N+M+1}$, respectively. Similarly, $y^{0i}$ and $y^{i,N+M+1}$ denote respectively the boundary input and output of the $i$th discrete unit.

The optimization problem of such a system may be stated as follows: let the continuous part of the system be described by

$$\frac{dx^n(\xi)}{d\xi} = f^n(x^n(\xi), \theta^n(\xi)), \qquad 0 \le \xi \le L^n,$$

$$y^{nm} = v^{nm}(x^n(L^n)), \qquad n = 1, 2, \ldots, N, \tag{166}$$

$$m = 1, 2, \ldots, N + M + 1,$$

$$x^n(0) = w^n(y^{\mu n}), \qquad \mu = 0, 1, \ldots, N + M,$$

and the discrete part by

$$x^i = f^i(y^i, \theta^i), \qquad i = N + 1, N + 2, \ldots, N + M,$$

$$y^{im} = v^{im}(x^i), \qquad m = 1, 2, \ldots, N + M + 1, \tag{167}$$

$$y^i = w^i(y^{\mu i}), \qquad \mu = 0, 1, \ldots, N + M.$$

We are to choose a set of $\theta^n(\xi)$, $n = 1, 2, \ldots, N$, and $\theta^i$, $i = N + 1$, $N + 2, \ldots, N + M$, such that the objective function

$$S = \sum_{n=1}^{N} (c^{n, N+M+1})^T y^{n, N+M+1} + \sum_{i=N+1}^{N+M} (c^{i, N+M+1})^T y^{i, N+M+1} \tag{168}$$

attains its maximum for some preassigned boundary inputs

$$y^{0n} = a^{0n} \quad \text{and} \quad y^{0i} = a^{0i}.$$

The construction of the optimization algorithm for this problem is analogous to those preceding. To avoid repetition we shall describe the development briefly.

Let the system that has been in an optimal state be slightly perturbed away from it. The variational equations are then

$$\delta \frac{dx^n(\xi)}{d\xi} = \frac{\partial f^n}{\partial x^n} \delta x^n(\xi) + \frac{\partial f^n}{\partial \theta^n} \delta \theta^n(\xi), \qquad 0 \le \xi \le L^n,$$

$$\delta y^{nm} = \frac{\partial v^{nm}}{\partial x^n} \delta x^n(L^n),$$

$$\delta x^n(0) = \sum_{\mu=0}^{N+M} \frac{\partial w^n}{\partial y^{\mu n}} \delta y^{\mu n}, \tag{169}$$

$$\delta y^{0n} = 0, \qquad n = 1, 2, \ldots, N,$$

$$\mu = 0, 1, \ldots, N + M,$$

$$m = 1, 2, \ldots, N + M + 1,$$

for the continuous part and

$$\delta x^i = \frac{\partial f^i}{\partial y^i}\,\delta y^i + \frac{\partial f^i}{\partial \theta^i}\,\delta \theta^i,$$

$$\delta y^{im} = \frac{\partial v^{im}}{\partial x^i}\,\delta x^i,$$

$$\delta y^i = \sum_{\mu=0}^{N+M} \frac{\partial w^i}{\partial y^{\mu i}}\,\delta y^{\mu i}, \tag{170}$$

$$\delta y^{0i} = 0, \qquad i = N+1, N+2, \ldots, N+M,$$

$$\mu = 0, 1, \ldots, N+M,$$

$$m = 1, 2, \ldots, N+M+1,$$

for the discrete part. These equations are identical in form to the variational equations in the preceding sections except that now $m$ must run from 1 to $(N+M+1)$ and $\mu$ must run from 0 to $(N+M)$. The corresponding adjoint vectors are defined analogously by

$$\frac{dz^n(\xi)}{d\xi} = -\left(\frac{\partial f^n}{\partial x^n}\right)^T z^n(\xi), \qquad 0 \le \xi \le L^n,$$

$$z^n(L^n) = \sum_{m=1}^{N+M+1} \left(\frac{\partial v^{nm}}{\partial x^n}\right)^T z^{nm},$$

$$z^{\mu n} = \left(\frac{\partial w^n}{\partial y^{\mu n}}\right)^T z^n(0), \tag{171}$$

$$z^{n,N+M+1} = c^{n,N+M+1}, \qquad n = 1, 2, \ldots, N,$$

$$m = 1, 2, \ldots, N+M+1,$$

$$\mu = 0, 1, \ldots, N+M,$$

and

$$u^i = \left(\frac{\partial f^i}{\partial y^i}\right)^T z^i,$$

$$z^i = \sum_{m=1}^{N+M+1} \left(\frac{\partial v^{im}}{\partial x^i}\right)^T z^{im},$$

$$z^{\mu i} = \left(\frac{\partial w^i}{\partial y^{\mu i}}\right)^T u^i, \tag{172}$$

$$z^{i,N+M+1} = c^{i,N+M+1}, \qquad i = N+1, N+2, \ldots, N+M,$$

$$m = 1, 2, \ldots, N+M+1,$$

$$\mu = 0, 1, \ldots, N+M.$$

Then, from equations (102), (169), and (171), we can see that

$$
\sum_{n=1}^{N} \int_{0}^{L^n} (z^n)^T \frac{\partial f^n}{\partial \theta^n} \, \delta\theta^n \, d\xi
$$

$$
= \sum_{n=1}^{N} \int_{0}^{L^n} \frac{d[(z^n)^T \, \delta x^n]}{d\xi} \, d\xi
$$

$$
= \sum_{n=1}^{N} [(z^n(L^n))^T \, \delta x^n(L^n) - (z^n(0))^T \, \delta x^n(0)]
$$

$$
= \sum_{n=1}^{N} \sum_{m=1}^{N+M+1} (z^{nm})^T \frac{\partial v^{nm}}{\partial x^n} \, \delta x^n(L^n) - \sum_{n=1}^{N} \sum_{\mu=0}^{N+M} (z^n(0))^T \frac{\partial w^n}{\partial y^{\mu n}} \, \delta y^{\mu n}
$$

$$
= \sum_{n=1}^{N} \sum_{m=1}^{N+M+1} (z^{nm})^T \, \delta y^{nm} - \sum_{n=1}^{N} \sum_{\mu=0}^{N+M} (z^{\mu n})^T \, \delta y^{\mu n}
$$

$$
= \sum_{n=1}^{N} \sum_{j=1}^{N+M} (z^{nj})^T \, \delta y^{nj} + \sum_{n=1}^{N} (z^{n,N+M+1})^T \, \delta y^{n,N+M+1}
$$
$$
- \sum_{n=1}^{N} \sum_{j=1}^{N+M} (z^{jn})^T \, \delta y^{jn} - \sum_{n=1}^{N} (z^{0n})^T \, \delta y^{0n}
$$

$$
= \sum_{n=1}^{N} \sum_{j=N+1}^{N+M} (z^{nj})^T \, \delta y^{nj} + \sum_{n=1}^{N} (c^{n,N+M+1})^T \, \delta y^{n,N+M+1}
$$
$$
- \sum_{n=1}^{N} \sum_{j=N+1}^{N+M} (z^{jn})^T \, \delta y^{jn} \tag{173}
$$

On the other hand, from equations (170) and (172), we have

$$
\sum_{i=N+1}^{N+M} (z^i)^T \frac{\partial f^i}{\partial \theta^i} \, \delta\theta^i = \sum_{i=N+1}^{N+M} [(z^i)^T \, \delta x^i - (u^i)^T \, \delta y^i]
$$

$$
= \sum_{i=N+1}^{N+M} \left[ \sum_{m=1}^{N+M+1} (z^{im})^T \frac{\partial v^{im}}{\partial x^i} \, \delta x^i - \sum_{\mu=0}^{N+M} (u^i)^T \frac{\partial w^i}{\partial y^{\mu i}} \, \delta y^{\mu i} \right]
$$

$$
= \sum_{i=N+1}^{N+M} \sum_{m=1}^{N+M+1} (z^{im})^T \, \delta y^{im} - \sum_{i=N+1}^{N+M} \sum_{\mu=0}^{N+M} (z^{\mu i})^T \, \delta y^{\mu i}
$$

$$
= \sum_{i=N+1}^{N+M} \sum_{\nu=1}^{N} (z^{i\nu})^T \, \delta y^{i\nu} + \sum_{i=N+1}^{N+M} (z^{i,N+M+1})^T \, \delta y^{i,N+M+1}
$$
$$
- \sum_{i=N+1}^{N+M} \sum_{\nu=1}^{N} (z^{\nu i})^T \, \delta y^{\nu i} - \sum_{i=N+1}^{N+M} (z^{0i})^T \, \delta y^{0i}
$$

$$
= \sum_{i=N+1}^{N+M} \sum_{\nu=1}^{N} (z^{i\nu})^T \, \delta y^{i\nu} + \sum_{i=N+1}^{N+M} (c^{i,N+M+1})^T \, \delta y^{i,N+M+1}
$$
$$
- \sum_{i=N+1}^{N+M} \sum_{\nu=1}^{N} (z^{\nu i})^T \, \delta y^{\nu i}. \tag{174}
$$

By adding equations (173) and (174) side by side we obtain, on simplification,

$$\sum_{n=1}^{N} \int_0^{L^n} (z^n)^T \frac{\partial f^n}{\partial \theta^n} \delta\theta^n \, d\xi + \sum_{i=N+1}^{N+M} (z^i)^T \frac{\partial f^i}{\partial \theta^i} \delta\theta^i$$

$$= \sum_{n=1}^{N} (c^{n,N+M+1})^T \delta y^{n,N+M+1} + \sum_{i=N+1}^{N+M} (c^{i,N+M+1})^T \delta y^{i,N+M+1}. \quad (175)$$

The right-hand side of equation (175) is the variation of the objective function defined by (168) which must be zero for free variations and negative for all one-sided variations, $\delta\theta^n(\xi)$ and $\delta\theta^i$. These variations are also independent; hence the conditions

$$(z^n(\xi))^T \frac{\partial f^n}{\delta\theta^n} \delta\theta^n \leq 0, \qquad n = 1, 2, \ldots, N, \qquad 0 \leq \xi \leq L^n, \quad (176)$$

$$(z^i)^T \frac{\partial f^i}{\partial \theta^i} \delta\theta^i \leq 0, \qquad i = N+1, N+2, \ldots, N+M, \quad (177)$$

must hold. Thus we conclude that the local weak principle applies to every unit of the system, whether the units be discrete or continuous. For the continuous units, however, the principle can be strengthened if we consider second-order variational equations instead of first-order and take special variations of the form

$$\delta\theta^i = 0, \qquad i = N+1, N+2, \ldots, N+M,$$

$$\delta\theta^n(\xi) = \begin{cases} \epsilon\varphi^n(\xi), & 0 \leq \xi_1 \leq \xi \leq \xi_2 \leq L^n, \\ 0, & \text{otherwise}, \qquad n = 1, 2, \ldots, N. \end{cases}$$

Then we can show that the local strong principle can be applied to the continuous units. Defining

$$H^n = (z^n)^T f^n \quad \text{and} \quad H^i = (z^i)^T f^i,$$

we conclude finally that to maximize (minimize) the objective function $S$ defined by equation (168) it is necessary that

$$\bar{\theta}^n(\xi): \; H^n = \max \, (\min), \qquad 0 \leq \xi \leq L^n, \qquad n = 1, 2, \ldots, N, \quad (178)$$

$$\bar{\theta}^i: \frac{\partial H^i}{\partial \theta^i} = (z^i)^T \frac{\partial f^i}{\partial \theta^i} = 0, \qquad i = N+1, N+2, \ldots, N+M, \quad (179)$$

when no constraint is imposed on $\theta^i$, and

$$\bar{\theta}^i: \; H^i = \max \, (\min), \qquad i = N+1, N+2, \ldots, N+M, \quad (180)$$

when $\theta^i$ lies on a constraint.

The adjoint system, defined by equations (171) and (172), may be combined separately to yield

$$
\begin{aligned}
z^n(L^n) &= \sum_{m=1}^{N+M+1} \left(\frac{\partial v^{nm}}{\partial x^n}\right)^T z^{nm} \\
&= \left(\frac{\partial v^{n,N+M+1}}{\partial x^n}\right)^T z^{n,N+M+1} + \sum_{v=1}^{N} \left(\frac{\partial v^{nv}}{\partial x^n}\right)^T z^{nv} + \sum_{j=N+1}^{N+M} \left(\frac{\partial v^{nj}}{\partial x^n}\right)^T z^{nj} \\
&= \left(\frac{\partial v^{n,N+M+1}}{\partial x^n}\right)^T c^{n,N+M+1} + \sum_{v=1}^{N} \left(\frac{\partial v^{nv}}{\partial x^v}\right)^T \left(\frac{\partial w^v}{\partial y^{nv}}\right)^T z^v(0) \\
&\quad + \sum_{j=N+1}^{N+M} \left(\frac{\partial v^{nj}}{\partial x^n}\right)^T \left(\frac{\partial w^j}{\partial y^{nj}}\right)^T u^j, \qquad n = 1, 2, \dots, N,
\end{aligned}
\tag{181}
$$

and

$$
\begin{aligned}
z^i &= \sum_{m=1}^{N+M+1} \left(\frac{\partial v^{im}}{\partial x^i}\right)^T z^{im} \\
&= \left(\frac{v^{i,N+M+1}}{\partial x^i}\right)^T z^{i,N+M+1} + \sum_{v=1}^{N} \left(\frac{\partial v^{iv}}{\partial x^i}\right)^T z^{iv} + \sum_{j=N+1}^{N+M} \left(\frac{\partial v^{ij}}{\partial x^i}\right)^T z^{ij} \\
&= \left(\frac{\partial v^{i,N+M+1}}{\partial x^i}\right)^T c^{i,N+M+1} + \sum_{v=1}^{N} \left(\frac{\partial v^{iv}}{\partial x^i}\right)^T \left(\frac{\partial w^v}{\partial y^{iv}}\right)^T z^v(0) \\
&\quad + \sum_{j=N+1}^{N+M} \left(\frac{\partial v^{ij}}{\partial x^i}\right)^T \left(\frac{\partial w^j}{\partial y^{ij}}\right)^T u^j, \qquad i = N + 1, \dots, N + M.
\end{aligned}
\tag{182}
$$

Equations (181) and (182) constitute the boundary conditions to equations

$$
\frac{dz^n(\xi)}{d\xi} = -\left(\frac{\partial f^n}{\partial x^n}\right)^T z^n(\xi), \qquad 0 \le \xi \le L^n, \qquad n = 1, 2, \dots, N
\tag{183}
$$

and

$$
u^i = \left(\frac{\partial f^i}{\partial y^i}\right)^T z^i, \qquad i = N + 1, \dots, N + M.
\tag{184}
$$

Equation (184) may be substituted into (181) and (182) to eliminate $u^j$. Instead of carrying out further simplification, we shall consider equations (181) through (184) as the adjoint system of a composite system. The results in this section are obtained by a different method under more general conditions in Reference 7.

## 8. FURTHER DISCUSSION AND SOME EXAMPLES

Let us consider the case in which the topology of the system can be described by

$$
\begin{aligned}
y^{nm} &= v^{nm}(x^n(L^n)) = x^n(L^n), \\
x^n(0) &= w^n(y^{\mu n}) = \sum_{\mu=0}^{N+M} \Gamma^{\mu n} y^{\mu n},
\end{aligned}
\tag{185}
$$

and

$$y^{im} = v^{im}(x^i) = x^i, \tag{186}$$

$$y^i = w^i(y^{\mu i}) = \sum_{\mu=0}^{N+M} \Gamma^{\mu i} y^{\mu i},$$

$$n = 1, 2, \ldots, N, \qquad i = N+1, \ldots, N+M,$$

$$m = 1, 2, \ldots, N+M+1, \qquad \mu = 0, 1, \ldots, N+M.$$

As previously stated, the $\Gamma$ matrices are diagonal matrices defined as

$$\Gamma^{\mu n} = \begin{bmatrix} \alpha_1^{\mu n} & & & 0 \\ & \alpha_2^{\mu n} & & \\ & & \cdot & \\ & & & \cdot \\ 0 & & & \alpha_s^{\mu n} \end{bmatrix}, \qquad \Gamma^{\mu i} = \begin{bmatrix} \alpha_1^{\mu i} & & & 0 \\ & \alpha_2^{\mu i} & & \\ & & \cdot & \\ & & & \cdot \\ 0 & & & \alpha_s^{\mu i} \end{bmatrix},$$

and all the state input and output variables have $s$ number of components. In this special case equations (166) and (167) can be combined to give

$$\begin{aligned} x^n(0) &= \Gamma^{0n} y^{0n} + \sum_{v=1}^{N} \Gamma^{vn} y^{vn} + \sum_{j=N+1}^{N+M} \Gamma^{jn} y^{jn} \\ &= \Gamma^{0n} a^{0n} + \sum_{v=1}^{N} \Gamma^{vn} x^v(L') + \sum_{j=N+1}^{N+M} \Gamma^{jn} x^j \end{aligned} \tag{187}$$

and

$$\begin{aligned} y^i &= \Gamma^{0i} y^{0i} + \sum_{v=1}^{N} \Gamma^{vi} y^{vi} + \sum_{j=N+1}^{N+M} \Gamma^{ji} y^{ji} \\ &= \Gamma^{0i} a^{0i} + \sum_{v=1}^{N} \Gamma^{vi} x^v(L') + \sum_{j=N+1}^{N+M} \Gamma^{ji} x^j, \end{aligned} \tag{188}$$

which are the boundary conditions for the system of unit equations

$$\frac{dx^n}{d\xi} = f^n(x^n, \theta^n), \qquad 0 \le \xi \le L, \qquad n = 1, 2, \ldots, N, \tag{189}$$

$$x^i = f^i(y^i, \theta^i), \qquad i = N+1, \ldots, N+M. \tag{190}$$

The corresponding adjoint system can be shown to be

$$z^n(L^n) = c^{n, N+M+1} + \sum_{v=1}^{N} \Gamma^{nv} z^v(0) + \sum_{j=N+1}^{N+M} \Gamma^{nj} u^j, \tag{191}$$

$$z^i = c^{i, N+M+1} + \sum_{v=1}^{N} \Gamma^{iv} z^v(0) + \sum_{j=N+1}^{N+M} \Gamma^{ij} u^j, \tag{192}$$

$$\frac{dz^n}{d\xi} = -\left(\frac{\partial f^n}{\partial x^n}\right)^T z^n, \tag{193}$$

$$u^i = \left(\frac{\partial f^i}{\partial y^i}\right)^T z^i, \qquad n = 1, 2, \ldots, N,$$

$$i = N+1, N+2, \ldots, N+M. \tag{194}$$

Moreover, the objective function $S$, defined by equation (168) takes the form

$$S = \sum_{n=1}^{N} (c^{n,N+M+1})^T \, x^n(L^n) + \sum_{i=N+1}^{N+M} (c^{i,N+M+1})^T x^i. \tag{195}$$

It may be pointed out that by dropping all the terms of discrete characteristics from equations (187) through (195) we obtain the equations for a complex continuous system, and, similarly, by dropping all the terms of continuous characteristics we obtain the equations for a complex discrete system.

To compute $z^n$ and $z^i$ it is convenient to combine equation (194) with equations (191) and (192), respectively:

$$z^n(L^n) = c^{n,N+M+1} + \sum_{\nu=1}^{N} \Gamma^{n\nu} z^\nu(0) + \sum_{j=N+1}^{N+M} \Gamma^{nj} \left( \frac{\partial f^j}{\partial y^j} \right)^T z^j, \tag{196}$$

$$z^i = c^{i,N+M+1} + \sum_{\nu=1}^{N} \Gamma^{i\nu} z^\nu(0) + \sum_{j=N+1}^{N+M} \Gamma^{ij} \left( \frac{\partial f^j}{\partial y^j} \right)^T z^j, \tag{197}$$

which are the boundary conditions for equation (193).

When the unit equations of the discrete units are given in the form

$$h^i(y^i, x^i, \theta^i) = 0$$

rather than in the form

$$x^i = f^i(y^i, \theta^i),$$

it is again convenient to define a new set of adjoint variables $\widetilde{z^i}$ by the transformation

$$z^i = -\left( \frac{\partial h^i}{\partial x^i} \right)^T \widetilde{z^i}, \qquad i = N+1, N+2, \ldots, N+M, \tag{198}$$

as we did in Section 3. Equations (196) and (197) corresponding to this case take the following form:

$$z^n(L^n) = c^{n,N+M+1} + \sum_{\nu=1}^{N} \Gamma^{n\nu} z^\nu(0) + \sum_{j=N+1}^{N+M} \Gamma^{nj} \left( \frac{\partial h^j}{\partial y^j} \right)^T \widetilde{z^j}, \tag{199}$$

$$-\left( \frac{\partial h^i}{\partial x^i} \right)^T \widetilde{z^i} = c^{i,N+M+1} + \sum_{\nu=1}^{N} \Gamma^{i\nu} z^\nu(0) + \sum_{j=N+1}^{N+M} \Gamma^{ij} \left( \frac{\partial h^j}{\partial y^j} \right)^T \widetilde{z^j}. \tag{200}$$

The optimal condition given by equation (179) also takes the following form whenever it is applicable:

$$\frac{\partial H^i}{\partial \theta^i} = (\widetilde{z^i})^T \frac{\partial h^i}{\partial \theta^i} = 0. \tag{201}$$

**Example 1.** For illustration and comparison, let us reconsider the problem solved in Section 9.2 by the method based on the sequential union of dynamic programming and the maximum principle. The composite system under consideration (see Fig. 10.5) is described by the following set of equations for the discrete unit:

$$x_1^1 = f_1^1(y^1, \theta^1) = y_1^1 + \theta^1,$$

$$y_1^1 = a_1^{01};$$

(202)

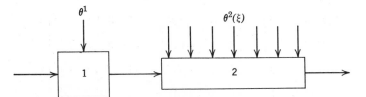

**Fig. 10.5** Schematic diagram for a composite process.

for the continuous unit:

$$\frac{dx_1^2}{d\xi} = f_1^2(x^2, \theta^2) = -ax_1^2 + \theta^2, \qquad 0 \le \xi \le L^2,$$

$$x_1^2(0) = x_1^1.$$

(203)

The object is to minimize the total cost

$$P = P^1 + P^2,$$

where

$$P^1 = x_1^1 - \mu\theta^1 = y_1^1 + \theta^1 - \mu\theta^1,$$

(204)

$$P^2 = \tfrac{1}{2} \int_0^{L^2} [(x_1^2)^2 + (\theta^2)^2] \, d\xi.$$

(205)

To choose an optimal set of $\theta^1$ and $\theta^2(\xi)$, $0 \le \xi \le L^2$, we define

$$x_2^1 = f_2^1(y^1, \theta^1) = y_2^1 + P^1 = y_1^1 + y_2^1 + (1 - \mu)\theta^1,$$

$$y_2^1 = a_2^{01} = 0,$$

(206)

and

$$\frac{dx_2^2}{d\xi} = f_2^2(x^2, \theta^2) = \tfrac{1}{2}(x_1^2)^2 + \tfrac{1}{2}(\theta^2)^2,$$

$$x_2^2(0) = a_2^{02} = 0.$$

(207)

Then the objective function $S$ is

$$S = P^1 + P^2 = x_2^1 + x_2^2(L^2),$$

which gives [see equation (195)]

$$c^{13} = \begin{bmatrix} c_1{}^{13} \\ c_2{}^{13} \end{bmatrix} = \begin{bmatrix} 0 \\ 1 \end{bmatrix} \quad \text{and} \quad c^{23} = \begin{bmatrix} c_1{}^{23} \\ c_2{}^{23} \end{bmatrix} = \begin{bmatrix} 0 \\ 1 \end{bmatrix}. \tag{208}$$

According to equations (193), (196), and (197) the adjoint system is

$$\frac{d}{d\xi}\begin{bmatrix} z_1{}^2 \\ z_2{}^2 \end{bmatrix} = -\begin{bmatrix} -a & 0 \\ x_1{}^2 & 0 \end{bmatrix}^T \begin{bmatrix} z_1{}^2 \\ z_2{}^2 \end{bmatrix},$$

$$\begin{bmatrix} z_1{}^2(L^2) \\ z_2{}^2(L^2) \end{bmatrix} = \begin{bmatrix} 0 \\ 1 \end{bmatrix} + \begin{bmatrix} 0 & 0 \\ 0 & 0 \end{bmatrix}\begin{bmatrix} z_1{}^2(0) \\ z_2{}^2(0) \end{bmatrix} + \begin{bmatrix} 0 & 0 \\ 0 & 0 \end{bmatrix}\begin{bmatrix} 1 & 0 \\ 1 & 1 \end{bmatrix}^T \begin{bmatrix} z_1{}^1 \\ z_2{}^1 \end{bmatrix},$$

$$\begin{bmatrix} z_1{}^1 \\ z_2{}^1 \end{bmatrix} = \begin{bmatrix} 0 \\ 1 \end{bmatrix} + \begin{bmatrix} 1 & 0 \\ 0 & 0 \end{bmatrix}\begin{bmatrix} z_1{}^2(0) \\ z_2{}^2(0) \end{bmatrix} + \begin{bmatrix} 0 & 0 \\ 0 & 0 \end{bmatrix}\begin{bmatrix} 1 & 0 \\ 1 & 1 \end{bmatrix}^T \begin{bmatrix} z_1{}^1 \\ z_2{}^1 \end{bmatrix},$$

or simply

$$\frac{dz_1{}^2}{d\xi} = az_1{}^2 - x_1{}^2 z_2{}^2, \quad 0 \le \xi \le L^2,$$

$$\frac{dz_2{}^2}{d\xi} = 0,$$

$$z_1{}^1 = z_1{}^2(0), \tag{209}$$

$$z_1{}^2(L^2) = 0,$$

$$z_2{}^1 = 1,$$

$$z_2{}^2(L^2) = 1,$$

which gives $z_2{}^2(\xi) = 1$.  Hence

$$H^2 = z_1{}^2(-ax_1{}^2 + \theta^2) + [\tfrac{1}{2}(x_1{}^2)^2 + \tfrac{1}{2}(\theta^2)^2] \tag{210}$$

and $H^2$ attains its minimum at

$$\theta^2 = -z_1{}^2, \quad 0 \le \xi \le L^2. \tag{211}$$

To determine $z_1{}^2$ as a function of $\xi$ we are required to solve the simultaneous equations

$$\frac{dz_1{}^2}{d\xi} = -x_1{}^2 + az_1{}^2,$$

$$\frac{dx_1{}^2}{d\xi} = -ax_1{}^2 - z_1{}^2, \tag{212}$$

with the boundary conditions

$$x_1^2(0) = x_1^1 \quad \text{and} \quad z_1^2(L^2) = 0. \tag{213}$$

The general solution of equation (212) has the form

$$x_1^2(\xi) = x_1^1(A_1 e^{\lambda\xi} + A_2 e^{-\lambda\xi}), \tag{214}$$
$$z_1^2(\xi) = x_1^1(A_3 e^{\lambda\xi} + A_4 e^{-\lambda\xi}),$$

where $\lambda = \sqrt{a^2 + 1}$ and $A_1$, $A_2$, $A_3$, and $A_4$ are constants that can be determined from the boundary conditions given in equation (213). From equations (211) and (214) we have

$$\bar{\theta}^2(\xi) = -x_1^1(A_3 e^{\lambda\xi} + A_4 e^{-\lambda\xi}), \qquad 0 \le \xi \le L^2. \tag{215}$$

To determine the optimal decision for the discrete unit we must make the Hamiltonian

$$\begin{aligned} H^1 &= z_1^1(y_1^1 + \theta^1) + z_2^1[y_1^1 + y_2^1 + (1 - \mu)\theta^1] \\ &= z_1^2(0)(y_1^1 + \theta^1) + [y_1^1 + y_2^1 + (1 - \mu)\theta^1] \end{aligned} \tag{216}$$

stationary with respect to $\theta^1$. Hence from the condition

$$\frac{\partial H^1}{\partial \theta^1} = 0$$

we have

$$z_1^2(0) = -(1 - \mu). \tag{217}$$

From equation (214) we have

$$\begin{aligned} z_1^2(0) &= x_1^1(A_3 + A_4) \\ &= (y_1^1 + \theta^1)(A_3 + A_4) \\ &= (a_1^{01} + \theta^1)(A_3 + A_4). \end{aligned} \tag{218}$$

Hence, from equations (217) and (218) we have

$$\bar{\theta}^1 = \frac{\mu - 1}{(A_3 + A_4)} - a_1^{01}, \tag{219}$$

which is the decision that makes $H^1$ stationary. It can be seen that the optimal decision $\bar{\theta}^1$ obtained here is the same as that given in (8.87). To show that a choice of $\theta^1$ is indeed the minimizing decision we shall also show that $\partial P/\partial \theta^1$ is zero and $\partial^2 P/\partial \theta^1 \partial \theta^1$ is positive-definite. The total cost $P$ is

$$\begin{aligned} P = P^1 + P^2 &= \int_0^{L^2} \tfrac{1}{2}[(x_1^2)^2 + (\theta^2)^2] \, d\xi + (x_1^1 - \mu\theta^1) \\ &= (x_1^1)^2 \int_0^{L^2} \tfrac{1}{2}[(A_1 e^{\lambda\xi} + A_2 e^{-\lambda\xi})^2 \\ &\quad + (-A_3 e^{\lambda\xi} - A_4 e^{-\lambda\xi})^2] \, d\xi + (x_1^1 - \mu\theta^1). \end{aligned} \tag{220}$$

It can be shown that the integral is equal to $\tfrac{1}{2}(A_3 + A_4)$ and is non-negative.

It follows that

$$P = \tfrac{1}{2}(A_3 + A_4)(x_1{}^1)^2 + (x_1{}^1 - \mu\theta^1)$$
$$= \tfrac{1}{2}(A_3 + A_4)(a_1{}^{01} + \theta^1)^2 + (1 - \mu)\theta^1 + a_1{}^{01}.$$

Hence

$$\left.\frac{\partial P}{\partial \theta^1}\right|_{\theta^1 = \bar{\theta}^1} = [(A_3 + A_4)(a_1{}^{01} + \theta^1) + (1 - \mu)]_{\theta^1 = \bar{\theta}^1} = 0,$$

$$\left.\frac{\partial^2 P}{\partial \theta^1\, \partial \theta^1}\right|_{\theta^1 = \bar{\theta}^1} = (A_3 + A_4)\bigg|_{\theta^1 = \bar{\theta}^1} > 0,$$

which implies that the choice of $\bar{\theta}^1$, represented by equation (219), indeed makes $P$ minimum.

**Example 2.**    In this example we consider a composite process consisting of one tubular reactor of length $L^1$ and cross-sectional area $A'$ followed by two stirred tanks of equal volume $V$ in series with a portion of the product

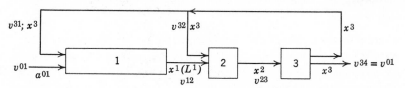

**Fig. 10.6**  Schematic diagram for a composite process for the reaction $A \rightarrow B \rightarrow C$.

recycled into the inlet of the tubular reactor and into the inlet of the first stirred tank, as shown in Fig. 10.6, in which $v$ is the volumetric flow rate. We shall, as before, consider a first-order liquid-phase consecutive irreversible reaction:

$$A \xrightarrow{k_1} B \xrightarrow{k_2} C. \tag{221}$$

According to Section 4.2, part b, we have the following unit equation for the tubular reactor:

$$f_1{}^1(x^1, \theta^1) = \frac{dx_1{}^1}{d\xi} = -k_{10}e^{-E_1/R\theta^1}x_1{}^1, \tag{222}$$

$$f_2{}^1(x^1, x^1, \theta^1) = \frac{dx_2{}^1}{d\xi} = k_{10}e^{-E_1/R\theta^1}x_1{}^1 - k_{20}e^{-E_2/R\theta^1}x_2{}^1, \tag{223}$$

where $x_1$ and $x_2$ are the molar concentration of $A$ and $B$, respectively; $\xi$ is the space coordnate measured on the holding-time basis; that is, $0 \le \xi \le T^1$, where $T^1$ is the total holding time of the tubular reactor defined as $A'L^1/(v^{31} + v^{01}) = A'L^1/v^1$, where $A'$ is the cross-sectional area.

The total input of reactants into the tubular reactor unit, according to equation (187), is

$$x^1(0) = \Gamma^{01}a^{01} + \Gamma^{31}x^3, \qquad (224)$$

where $\Gamma^{vn}$ are the diagonal matrices of the $vn$th stream defined in equation (39) and $a^{01}$ is the initial concentration of reactant fed into the tubular reactor unit.

The unit equation for units 2 and 3 are derived from the material balance as

{rate of input of component $j$ into the stirred tank}

      − {rate of output of component $j$ from the stirred tank}

      + {rate of production of component $j$ in the stirred tank}

      = 0

or

$$v^i y_j{}^i - v^i x_j{}^i + V^i(R_j{}^i) = 0, \qquad i = 2, 3, \qquad j = 1, 2, \qquad (225)$$

where $v^i$ is the constant volumetric flow rate at the $i$th discrete unit, $V^i$ is the volume of $i$th discrete unit, and $y_j{}^i$ is the molar concentration of the $j$th component in the total input to the $i$th unit. The rates of production of components 1 and 2 can be written as

$$R_1{}^i = -k_{10}e^{-E_1/R\theta^i}x_1{}^i, \qquad (226)$$

$$R_2{}^i = k_{10}e^{-E_1/R\theta^i}x_1{}^i - k_{20}e^{-E_2/R\theta^i}x_2{}^i, \qquad i = 2, 3. \qquad (227)$$

By substituting equations (226) and (227) into (225) we obtain

$$v^i y_1{}^i - v^i x_1{}^i + V^i(-k_{10}e^{-E_1/R\theta^i}x_1{}^i) = 0, \qquad i = 2, 3, \qquad (228)$$

$$v^i y_2{}^i - v^i x_2{}^i + V^i(k_{10}e^{-E_1/R\theta^i}x_1{}^i - k_{20}e^{-E_2/R\theta^i}x_2{}^i) = 0, \qquad i = 2, 3, \quad (229)$$

$$y^2 = \Gamma^{12}x^1(L^1) + \Gamma^{32}x^3, \qquad (230)$$

$$y^3 = \Gamma^{23}x^2. \qquad (231)$$

Equations (228) and (229) can be written

$$h_1{}^i(y^i, x^i, \theta^i) = y_1{}^i - x_1{}^i + t^i(-k_{10}e^{-E_1/R\theta^i})x_1{}^i = 0, \qquad (232)$$

$$h_2{}^i(y^i, x^i, \theta^i) = y_2{}^i - x_2{}^i + t^i[(k_{10}e^{-E_1/R\theta^i})x_1{}^i - (k_{20}e^{-E_2/R\theta^i})x_2{}^i] = 0,$$

$$i = 2, 3 \qquad (233)$$

where $t^i = V^i/v^i$.

We wish to maximize the intermediate product $B$ from the outlet of unit 3 or $x_2{}^3$. The objective function, therefore, is

$$S = x_2{}^3. \tag{234}$$

Consequently, we have from equation (195)

$$c^{34} = \begin{bmatrix} c_1{}^{34} \\ c_2{}^{34} \end{bmatrix} = \begin{bmatrix} 0 \\ 1 \end{bmatrix} \quad \text{and} \quad c^{14} = c^{24} = \begin{bmatrix} 0 \\ 0 \end{bmatrix}. \tag{235}$$

For the adjoint system for the continuous unit we have from equations (222) and (223)

$$\frac{\partial f^1}{\partial x^1} = \begin{bmatrix} -k_{10}e^{-E_1/R\theta^1} & 0 \\ k_{10}e^{-E_1 R\theta^1} & -k_{20}e^{-E_1/R\theta^1} \end{bmatrix}. \tag{236}$$

Substituting equation (236) into (193), we have

$$\frac{d}{d\xi}\begin{bmatrix} z_1{}^1 \\ z_2{}^1 \end{bmatrix} = \begin{bmatrix} +k_{10}e^{-E_1/R\theta^1} & -k_{10}e^{-E_2/R\theta^1} \\ 0 & +k_{20}e^{-E_2/R\theta^1} \end{bmatrix}\begin{bmatrix} z_1{}^1 \\ z_2{}^1 \end{bmatrix}. \tag{237}$$

The boundary condition for use with equation (237) can be obtained from (199) as

$$z^1(L^1) = \Gamma^{12}\left(\frac{\partial h^2}{\partial y^2}\right)^T \widetilde{z}^2. \tag{238}$$

From equations (232) and (233) we have

$$\left(\frac{\partial h^i}{\partial y^i}\right) = \begin{bmatrix} 1 & 0 \\ 0 & 1 \end{bmatrix}, \quad i = 2, 3. \tag{239}$$

By substituting equation (239) into (238) we obtain

$$\begin{bmatrix} z_1{}^1(L^1) \\ z_2{}^1(L^1) \end{bmatrix} = \begin{bmatrix} \alpha^{12} & 0 \\ 0 & \alpha^{12} \end{bmatrix}\begin{bmatrix} \widetilde{z}_1{}^2 \\ \widetilde{z}_2{}^2 \end{bmatrix}, \tag{240}$$

where

$$\alpha^{12} = \frac{v^{12}}{v^2}.$$

The adjoint system for the discrete units can be written from equation (200) as

$$-\begin{bmatrix} \dfrac{\partial h_1{}^2}{\partial x_1{}^2} & \dfrac{\partial h_2{}^2}{\partial x_1{}^2} \\ \dfrac{\partial h_1{}^2}{\partial x_2{}^2} & \dfrac{\partial h_2{}^2}{\partial x_2{}^2} \end{bmatrix}\begin{bmatrix} \widetilde{z}_1{}^2 \\ \widetilde{z}_2{}^2 \end{bmatrix} = \begin{bmatrix} \alpha^{23} & 0 \\ 0 & \alpha^{23} \end{bmatrix}\begin{bmatrix} \dfrac{\partial h_1{}^3}{\partial y_1{}^3} & \dfrac{\partial h_2{}^3}{\partial y_1{}^3} \\ \dfrac{\partial h_1{}^3}{\partial y_2{}^3} & \dfrac{\partial h_2{}^3}{\partial y_2{}^3} \end{bmatrix}\begin{bmatrix} \widetilde{z}_1{}^3 \\ \widetilde{z}_2{}^3 \end{bmatrix} \tag{241}$$

and

$$-\begin{bmatrix} \dfrac{\partial h_1{}^3}{\partial x_1{}^3} & \dfrac{\partial h_2{}^3}{\partial x_1{}^3} \\[2ex] \dfrac{\partial h_1{}^3}{\partial x_2{}^3} & \dfrac{\partial h_2{}^3}{\partial x_2{}^3} \end{bmatrix} \begin{bmatrix} \widetilde{z}_1^3 \\[1ex] \widetilde{z}_2^3 \end{bmatrix} = \begin{bmatrix} 0 \\ 1 \end{bmatrix} + \begin{bmatrix} \alpha^{31} & 0 \\ 0 & \alpha^{31} \end{bmatrix} \begin{bmatrix} z_1{}^1(0) \\ z_2{}^1(0) \end{bmatrix}$$

$$+ \begin{bmatrix} \alpha^{32} & 0 \\ 0 & \alpha^{32} \end{bmatrix} \begin{bmatrix} \dfrac{\partial h_1{}^2}{\partial y_1{}^2} & \dfrac{\partial h_2{}^2}{\partial y_1{}^2} \\[2ex] \dfrac{\partial h_1{}^2}{\partial y_2{}^2} & \dfrac{\partial h_2{}^2}{\partial y_2{}^2} \end{bmatrix} \begin{bmatrix} \widetilde{z}_1^2 \\[1ex] \widetilde{z}_2^2 \end{bmatrix}, \quad (242)$$

where

$$\alpha^{23} = \frac{v^{23}}{v^3} = 1, \qquad \alpha^{31} = \frac{v^{31}}{v^1}, \quad \text{and} \quad \alpha^{32} = \frac{v^{32}}{v^2}.$$

Partial differentiation of equations (232) and (233) with respect to $x_i$ yields

$$\left(\frac{\partial h^i}{\partial x^i}\right)^T = \begin{bmatrix} -1 - t^i k_{10} e^{-E_1/R\theta^i} & t^i k_{10} e^{-E_1/R\theta^i} \\ 0 & -1 - t^i k_{20} e^{-E_2/R\theta^i} \end{bmatrix}, \quad i = 2, 3. \quad (243)$$

By substituting equations (239) and (243) for $i = 2, 3$, into (241) and (242) we obtain

$$\begin{bmatrix} 1 + t^2 k_{10} e^{-E_1/R\theta^2} & -t^2 k_{10} e^{-E_1/R\theta^2} \\ 0 & 1 + t^2 k_{20} e^{-E_2/R\theta^2} \end{bmatrix} \begin{bmatrix} \widetilde{z}_1^2 \\[1ex] \widetilde{z}_2^2 \end{bmatrix} = \begin{bmatrix} \widetilde{z}_1^3 \\[1ex] \widetilde{z}_2^3 \end{bmatrix}, \quad (244)$$

$$\begin{bmatrix} 1 + t^3 k_{10} e^{-E_1/R\theta^3} & -t^3 k_{10} e^{-E_1/R\theta^3} \\ 0 & 1 + t^3 k_{20} e^{-E_2/R\theta^3} \end{bmatrix} \begin{bmatrix} \widetilde{z}_1^3 \\[1ex] \widetilde{z}_2^3 \end{bmatrix}$$

$$= \begin{bmatrix} 0 \\ 1 \end{bmatrix} + \begin{bmatrix} \alpha^{31} & 0 \\ 0 & \alpha^{31} \end{bmatrix} \begin{bmatrix} z_1{}^1(0) \\ z_2{}^1(0) \end{bmatrix} + \begin{bmatrix} \alpha^{32} & 0 \\ 0 & \alpha^{32} \end{bmatrix} \begin{bmatrix} \widetilde{z}_1^2 \\[1ex] \widetilde{z}_2^2 \end{bmatrix}. \quad (245)$$

The optimal decisions for discrete units can be obtained from equation (201) as

$$\frac{\partial H^i}{\partial \theta^i} = (\widetilde{z}^i)^T \frac{\partial h^i}{\partial \theta^i} = 0,$$

$$[\widetilde{z}_1^i \ \widetilde{z}_2^i] \begin{bmatrix} \dfrac{\partial h_1{}^i}{\partial \theta^i} \\[2ex] \dfrac{\partial h_2{}^i}{\partial \theta^i} \end{bmatrix} = 0,$$

or

$$z_1{}^i\left[-t^ik_{10}\left(\frac{E_1}{R(\theta^i)^2}\right)e^{-E^1/R\theta^i}x_1{}^i\right] + z_2{}^i\left[t^ik_{10}\left(\frac{E_1}{R(\theta^i)^2}\right)e^{-E_1/R\theta^i}x_1{}^i\right.$$

$$\left. - t^ik_{20}\left(\frac{E_2}{R(\theta^i)^2}\right)e^{-E_2/R\theta^i}x_2{}^i\right] = 0. \quad (246)$$

Solving this equation for $\theta^i$, $i = 2, 3$, we have

$$\bar{\theta}^i = \left(\frac{E_1 - E_2}{R}\right)\left\{\ln\left[\eta\,\frac{x_1{}^i(\widetilde{z_2{}^i} - \widetilde{z_1{}^i})}{x_2{}^i z_2{}^i}\right]\right\}^{-1}, \quad (247)$$

where

$$\eta = \frac{k_{10}E_1}{k_{20}E_2}.$$

The optimal decision for the tubular reactor unit can be obtained by assuming that the Hamiltonian is a maximum at the stationary point:

$$\frac{\partial H^1}{\partial\theta^1} = z_1{}^1\frac{\partial f_1{}^1}{\partial\theta^1} + z_2{}^1\frac{\partial f_2{}^1}{\partial\theta^1} = 0$$

or

$$-z_1{}^1k_{10}x_1{}^1\left(\frac{E_1}{R(\theta^1)^2}\right)e^{-E_1/R\theta^1} + z_2{}^1k_{10}x_1{}^1\left(\frac{E_1}{R(\theta^1)^2}\right)e^{-E_1/R\theta^1}$$

$$- z_2{}^1k_{20}x_2{}^1\left(\frac{E_2}{R(\theta^1)^2}\right)e^{-E_2/R\theta^1} = 0.$$

Solving this equation for $\theta^1$, we have

$$\bar{\theta}^1 = \left(\frac{E_1 - E_2}{R}\right)\left\{\ln\left[\eta\,\frac{x_1{}^1(z_2{}^1 - z_1{}^1)}{x_2{}^1 z_2{}^1}\right]\right\}^{-1}. \quad (248)$$

Substituting equation (248) into (222) and (223), we have

$$\frac{dx_1{}^1}{d\xi} = -k_{10}\left[\eta\,\frac{x_1{}^1}{x_2{}^1}\left(\frac{z_2{}^1 - z_1{}^1}{z_2{}^1}\right)\right]^{\lambda_1}x_1{}^1, \quad (249)$$

$$\frac{dx_2{}^1}{d\xi} = k_{10}\left[\eta\,\frac{x_1{}^1}{x_2{}^1}\left(\frac{z_2{}^1 - z_1{}^1}{z_2{}^1}\right)\right]^{\lambda_1}x_1{}^1 - k_{20}\left[\eta\,\frac{x_1{}^1}{x_2{}^1}\left(\frac{z_2{}^1 - z_1{}^1}{z_2{}^1}\right)\right]^{\lambda_2}x_2{}^1, \quad (250)$$

where

$$\lambda_1 = \frac{E_1}{E_2 - E_1} \quad \text{and} \quad \lambda_2 = \frac{E_2}{E_2 - E_1}.$$

The boundary conditions for use with equations (249) and (250) are obtained from (224):

$$\begin{bmatrix} x_1{}^1(0) \\ x_2{}^1(0) \end{bmatrix} = \begin{bmatrix} \alpha^{01} & 0 \\ 0 & \alpha^{01} \end{bmatrix}\begin{bmatrix} a_1{}^{01} \\ a_2{}^{01} \end{bmatrix} + \begin{bmatrix} \alpha^{31} & 0 \\ 0 & \alpha^{31} \end{bmatrix}\begin{bmatrix} x_1{}^3 \\ x_2{}^3 \end{bmatrix}. \quad (251)$$

By substituting equation (247) into (232) and (233) we obtain

$$y_1^i - x_1^i - t^i x_1^i k_{10}\left[\eta\,\frac{x_1^i(\widetilde{z_2^i} - \widetilde{z_1^i})}{\widetilde{x_2^i}\,\widetilde{z_2^i}}\right]^{\lambda_1} = 0, \qquad (252)$$

$$y_2^i - x_2^i + t^i x_1^i k_{10}\left[\eta\,\frac{x_1^i(\widetilde{z_2^i} - \widetilde{z_1^i})}{\widetilde{x_2^i}\,\widetilde{z_2^i}}\right]^{\lambda_1} - t^i x_2^i k_{20}\left[\eta\,\frac{x_1^i(\widetilde{z_2^i} - \widetilde{z_1^i})}{\widetilde{x_2^i}\,\widetilde{z_2^i}}\right]^{\lambda_2} = 0. \quad (253)$$

or, simplifying the preceding equations, we have

$$y_1^i = \left\{1 + t^i k_{10}\left[\eta\,\frac{x_1^i(\widetilde{z_2^i} - \widetilde{z_1^i})}{\widetilde{x_2^i}\,\widetilde{z_2^i}}\right]^{\lambda_1}\right\}x_1^i, \qquad i = 2, 3, \qquad (254)$$

$$y_2^i = t^i k_{20} x_2^i\left[\eta\,\frac{x_1^i(\widetilde{z_2^i} - \widetilde{z_1^i})}{\widetilde{x_2^i}\,\widetilde{z_2^i}}\right]^{\lambda_2}$$

$$\times \left\{1 - \left(\frac{k_{10}x_1^i}{k_{20}x_2^i}\right)\left[\eta\,\frac{x_1^i(\widetilde{z_2^i} - \widetilde{z_1^i})}{\widetilde{x_2^i}\,\widetilde{z_2^i}}\right]^{\lambda_1 - \lambda_2}\right\} + x_2^i, \qquad i = 2, 3. \quad (255)$$

The boundary conditions for use with equations (254) and (255) are obtained from (230) and (231):

$$\begin{bmatrix} y_1^2 \\ y_2^2 \end{bmatrix} = \begin{bmatrix} \alpha^{12} & 0 \\ 0 & \alpha^{12} \end{bmatrix}\begin{bmatrix} x_1^1(L^1) \\ x_2^1(L^1) \end{bmatrix} + \begin{bmatrix} \alpha^{32} & 0 \\ 0 & \alpha^{32} \end{bmatrix}\begin{bmatrix} x_1^3 \\ x_2^3 \end{bmatrix}, \qquad (256)$$

$$\begin{bmatrix} y_1^3 \\ y_2^3 \end{bmatrix} = \begin{bmatrix} \alpha^{23} & 0 \\ 0 & \alpha^{23} \end{bmatrix}\begin{bmatrix} x_1^2 \\ x_2^2 \end{bmatrix} = \begin{bmatrix} x_1^2 \\ x_2^2 \end{bmatrix}. \qquad (257)$$

The adjoint system for the tubular reactor unit is obtained by substituting equation (248) into (237):

$$\frac{dz_1^1}{d\xi} = k_{10}\left[\eta\,\frac{x_1^1}{x_2^1}\,\frac{(z_2^1 - z_1^1)}{z_2^1}\right]^{\lambda_1}(z_1^1 - z_2^1), \qquad (258)$$

$$\frac{dz_2^1}{d\xi} = k_{20}\left[\eta\,\frac{x_1}{x_2^1}\,\frac{(z_2^1 - z_1^1)}{z_2^1}\right]^{\lambda_2}z_2^1. \qquad (259)$$

The boundary conditions for use with equations (258) and (259) are given in (240). The adjoint systems for units 2 and 3 are obtained from equations

(244) and (245), respectively, after which (247) is substituted:

$$\left\{ 1 + t^2 k_{10} \left[ \eta \frac{x_1^2}{x_2^2} \frac{(\widetilde{z_2^2} - \widetilde{z_1^2})}{\widetilde{z_2^2}} \right]^{\lambda_1} \right\} \widetilde{z_1^2} - t^2 k_{10} \left[ \eta \frac{x_1^2}{x_2^2} \frac{(\widetilde{z_2^2} - \widetilde{z_1^2})}{\widetilde{z_2^2}} \right]^{\lambda_1} \widetilde{z_2^2} = z_1^3, \quad (260)$$

$$\left\{ 1 + t^2 k_{20} \left[ \eta \frac{x_1^2}{x_2^2} \frac{(\widetilde{z_2^2} - \widetilde{z_1^2})}{\widetilde{z_2^2}} \right]^{\lambda_2} \right\} \widetilde{z_2^2} = \widetilde{z_2^3}, \quad (261)$$

$$\left\{ 1 + t^3 k_{10} \left[ \eta \frac{x_1^3}{x_2^3} \frac{(\widetilde{z_2^3} - \widetilde{z_1^3})}{\widetilde{z_2^3}} \right]^{\lambda_1} \right\} \widetilde{\phantom{z}}^3 - t^3 k_{10} \left[ \eta \frac{x_1^3}{x_2^3} \frac{(\widetilde{z_2^3} - \widetilde{z_1^3})}{\widetilde{z_2^3}} \right]^{\lambda_1} z_2^3$$

$$= \alpha^{31} z_1^1(0) + \alpha^{32} \widetilde{z_1^2}, \quad (262)$$

$$\left\{ 1 + t^3 k_{20} \left[ \eta \frac{x_1^3}{x_2^3} \frac{(\widetilde{z_2^3} - \widetilde{z_1^3})}{\widetilde{z_2^3}} \right]^{\lambda_2} \right\} \widetilde{z_2^3} = 1 + \alpha^{31} z_2^1(0) + \alpha^{32} \widetilde{z_2^2}. \quad (263)$$

It should be noted, however, that equations (249) through (263) must be solved simultaneously. Once this system has been solved, the equations should be substituted into equations (247) and (248) to obtain the optimal decisions for this problem.

## REFERENCES

1. Fan, L. T., and C. S. Wang, The Discrete Maximum Principle: *A Study in Multistage Systems Optimization*, J. Wiley, New York, 1964.
2. Denn, M. M., and R. Aris, "Green's Function and Optimal System I: Necessary Conditions and an Iterative Technique," *Ind. Eng. Chem., Fundamentals*, **4,** 7 (1965).
3. Denn, M. M., and R. Aris, "Second-Order Variational Equations and The Strong Maximum Principle," *Chem. Eng. Sci.*, **20,** 373 (1965).
4. Jordan, B. W., and E. Polak, "Theory of A Class of Discrete Optimal Control System," Technical Report, Electronics Research Laboratory, University of California, Berkeley (1964).
5. Jackson, R., and F. Horn, "On Discrete Analogues of Pontryagin's Maximum Principle," *Int. J. Control*, **1,** 389 (1965).
6. Horn, F., and R. Jackson, "On the Discrete Maximum Principle," *Ind. Eng. Chem., Fundamentals*, **4,** 110 (1965).
7. Denn, M. M., and R. Aris, "Green's Function and Optimal Systems III: Complex Interconnected Systems," *Ind. Eng. Chem., Fundamentals*, **4,** 248 (1965).
8. Elsgolc, L. E., *Calculus of Variations*, Pergamon Press, London, 1962.

# 11

# The Maximum Principle and the Variational Techniques

In the preceding chapters the variational principle has been used frequently to derive various forms of the maximum principle. Several other optimization methods and techniques are based on the variational principle and its related techniques. Two of the better known among them are the calculus of variations and dynamic programming.

In this chapter we discuss the interrelationships between the various methods and some of the general aspects of the variational principle.

## 1. THE MAXIMUM PRINCIPLE AND THE CALCULUS OF VARIATIONS [1]

In this section we show that the necessary conditions in the calculus of variations can be derived from the maximum principle when the decision vector is not constrained. Conversely, by using the techniques of the calculus of variations the weakened form of the maximum principle can be derived. It is worth noting that the user of the calculus of variations is often frustrated in the solution of problems in which (a) there is linearity in the decision variables, (b) there are two-point boundary value problems, (c) there are unusual functions, (d) there are inequality constraints on the decision variables [2].*

---

* Some successful attempts have been made to extend the classical calculus of variations to the case where the decision variables are constrained [3, 4, 13, 23].

*a. The Fundamental Problem of the Calculus of Variations.*    The problem may be formulated as follows [5]: A real function

$$F(t, x_1(t), x_2(t), \ldots, x_s(t); \dot{x}_1(t), \dot{x}_2(t), \ldots, \dot{x}_s(t)) = F(t, x(t), \dot{x}(t))$$

is defined in some region $R$ of the space of the real variables $t$, $x_1$, $x_2, \ldots, x_s$ for arbitrary real finite values $\dot{x}_1, \dot{x}_2, \ldots, \dot{x}_s$. The function $F$ is continuous in all its arguments. We shall consider the collection of all piecewise smooth curves

$$\bar{x}_i = \bar{x}_i(t), \qquad i = 1, 2, \ldots, s, \qquad t_0 \leq t \leq T, \tag{1}$$

lying in the region $R$ and joining the points

$$(t_0, x(0)) = (t_0, \alpha_1, \alpha_2, \ldots, \alpha_s) = (t_0, \alpha) \tag{2}$$

and

$$(T, x(T)) = (T, \beta_1, \beta_2, \ldots, \beta_s) = (T, \beta). \tag{3}$$

Along each such admissible comparison curve the objective function in the form

$$S = \int_{t_0}^{T} F(t, x(t), \dot{x}(t)) \, dt \tag{4}$$

has a well-defined value.

The problem is to find the curve (or the extremal) such that the objective function has an extremum.

We assume that the functions

$$x_i(t), \qquad i = 1, 2, \ldots, s,$$

are absolutely continuous and have bounded derivatives; that is, at every point at which the derivative exists

$$\left| \frac{dx_i(t)}{dt} \right| \leq M \text{ (constant)}, \qquad i = 1, 2, \ldots, s, \qquad t_0 \leq t \leq T. \tag{5}$$

The set of all absolutely continuous curves

$$x = (x_1(t), x_2(t), \ldots, x_s(t)), \qquad t_0 \leq t \leq T,$$

are in a $\delta$-neighborhood of $\bar{x}_i(t)$ if

$$|x_i(t) - \bar{x}_i(t)| < \delta, \qquad \text{for} \quad t_0 \leq t \leq T, \qquad i = 1, 2, \ldots, s.$$

*b. Euler-Lagrange Equation and Legendre's Necessary Condition.*    Consider the following specific set of differential equations

$$\dot{x}_i(t) = \frac{dx_i(t)}{dt} = \theta_i(t), \qquad i = 1, 2, \ldots, s, \tag{6}$$

and the objective function

$$S = \int_{t_0}^{T} F(t, x_1(t), x_2(t), \ldots, x_s(t); \theta_1(t), \theta_2(t), \ldots, \theta_s(t))\, dt$$

$$= \int_{t_0}^{T} F(t, x(t), \theta(t))\, dt,$$

which is to be minimized or maximized.

Using equation (6), we have

$$S = \int_{t_0}^{T} F(t, x(t), \dot{x}(t))\, dt. \qquad (7)$$

The decision vector $\theta(t)$, $t_0 \leq t \leq T$, which is assumed to be piecewise continuous, and the corresponding absolutely continuous trajectory $x(t)$ of the system represented by equation (6), together with the boundary conditions given by equations (2) and (3), are called optimal if there exists a $\delta > 0$ such that

$$S[x(t), \theta(t)] \geq S[\bar{x}(t), \bar{\theta}(t)]$$

or

$$S[x(t), \theta(t)] \leq S[\bar{x}(t), \bar{\theta}(t)]$$

for every decision $\theta(t)$ for which the corresponding trajectory $x(t)$ lies in the $\delta$-neighborhood of the curve $\bar{x}(t)$. In the first case the objective function attains its minimum and in the second, its maximum.

Since the maximum principle is a necessary condition for optimality, it is at the same time a necessary condition for the curve $\bar{x}(t)$ to be an extremal of the objective function represented by equation (7).

The fundamental problem is that in which final time is specified and both end points are fixed. As we have done in problems in preceding chapters, we introduce an additional state variable $x_{s+1}$ such that

$$\dot{x}_{s+1}(t) = \frac{dx_{s+1}}{dt} = F(t, x(t), \theta(t)), \qquad x_{s+1}(0) = 0. \qquad (8)$$

Thus the Hamiltonian and the adjoint system take the form

$$H = \sum_{i=1}^{s+1} z_i \dot{x}_i$$

$$= z_1 \theta_1 + z_2 \theta_2 + \cdots + z_s \theta_s + z_{s+1} F, \qquad (9)$$

$$\frac{dz_i}{dt} = -\frac{\partial H}{\partial x_i} = -z_{s+1} \frac{\partial F(t, x, \theta)}{\partial x_i}, \qquad i = 1, 2, \ldots, s, \qquad (10)$$

$$\frac{dz_{s+1}}{dt} = 0. \qquad (11)$$

Assuming that the optimum lies at an interior point of the admissible region of $\theta(t)$, the optimal condition is determined from the following:

$$\frac{\partial H}{\partial \theta_i} = 0 = z_i + z_{s+1} \frac{\partial F(t, x, \theta)}{\partial \theta_i}, \qquad i = 1, 2, \ldots, s. \qquad (12)$$

Since

$$z_{s+1}(T) = 1,$$

from equation (11) we thus have

$$z_{s+1}(t) = 1. \qquad (13)$$

Hence equation (12) is reduced to

$$z_i(t) = -\frac{\partial F(t, x, \theta)}{\partial \theta_i} = -\frac{\partial F(t, x, \dot{x})}{\partial \dot{x}_i}. \qquad (14)$$

By substituting equation (13) into (10) and integrating the result we obtain

$$z_i(t) = z_i(t_0) - \int_{t_0}^{t} \frac{\partial F(t, x, \theta)}{\partial x_i} dt, \qquad i = 1, 2, \ldots, s. \qquad (15)$$

By combining equations (14) and (15) we obtain

$$\frac{\partial F(t, x, \theta)}{\partial \dot{x}_i} = \int_{t_0}^{t} \frac{\partial F(t, x, \theta)}{\partial x_i} dt - z_i(t_0), \qquad i = 1, 2, \ldots, s, \qquad (16)$$

which are the Euler-Lagrange equations in integral form. Differentiation of equation (16) with respect to $t$ yields

$$\frac{\partial F(t, x, \theta)}{\partial x_i} - \frac{d}{dt}\left(\frac{\partial F(t, x, \theta)}{\partial \dot{x}_i}\right) = 0, \qquad i = 1, 2, \ldots, s, \qquad (17)$$

which are the Euler-Lagrange equations in the usual form.

In solving problems by using the calculus of variations, we assume the existence and continuity of all partial derivatives of $F(t, x, \dot{x})$ up to the fourth order [6]. Then, if the Hamiltonian attains its minimum as a function of $\theta(t)$ at an interior point $\theta(t) = \bar{\theta}(t)$, the quadratic form will be

$$\sum_{i=1}^{s} \sum_{j=1}^{s} \frac{\partial^2 H(t, z(t), x(t), \theta(t))}{\partial \theta_i \, \partial \theta_j}\bigg|_{\theta=\bar{\theta}} \xi_i \xi_j \geq 0.$$

It follows from equations (9) and (13) that

$$\sum_{i=1}^{s} \sum_{j=1}^{s} \frac{\partial^2 F(t, x(t), \theta(t))}{\partial \theta_i \, \partial \theta_j}\bigg|_{\theta=\bar{\theta}} \xi_i \xi_j \geq 0 \quad \text{for all} \quad t, \ t_0 \leq t \leq T, \qquad (18)$$

where $\xi$ is an arbitrary constant vector. This condition, which is necessary for the curve $x(t)$ to be an extremal for the minimum objective function, is called Legendre's necessary condition.

*c. Weierstrass Necessary Condition.*  The necessary condition for a minimum objective function is that

$$H(t, x(t), z(t), \theta(t)) \geq H(t, x(t), z(t), \bar{\theta}(t)). \tag{19}$$

Using equation (9), we consider

$$H(t, x(t), z(t), \theta(t)) - H(t, x(t), z(t), \bar{\theta}(t))$$

$$- \sum_{i=1}^{s} (\theta_i - \bar{\theta}_i) \frac{\partial H(t, x(t), z(t), \bar{\theta}(t))}{\partial \bar{\theta}_i}$$

$$= z_{s+1}[F(t, x, \theta) - F(t, x, \bar{\theta})] + \sum_{i=1}^{s} z_i(\theta_i - \bar{\theta}_i)$$

$$- \sum_{i=1}^{s} (\theta_i - \bar{\theta}_i) \left[ \frac{\partial F(t, x, \bar{\theta})}{\partial \bar{\theta}_i} z_{s+1} + z_i \right]$$

$$= z_{s+1} \left\{ [F(t, x, \theta) - F(t, x, \bar{\theta})] - \sum_{i=1}^{s} (\theta_i - \bar{\theta}_i) \frac{\partial F(t, x, \bar{\theta})}{\partial \bar{\theta}_i} \right\}. \tag{20}$$

By substituting equation (13) into (20) we obtain

$$H(t, x, z, \theta) - H(t, x, z, \bar{\theta}) - \sum_{i=1}^{s} (\theta_i - \bar{\theta}_i) \frac{\partial H(t, x, z, \bar{\theta})}{\partial \bar{\theta}_i}$$

$$= \left\{ [F(t, x, \theta) - F(t, x, \bar{\theta})] - \sum_{i=1}^{s} (\theta_i - \bar{\theta}_i) \frac{\partial F(t, x, \bar{\theta})}{\partial \bar{\theta}_i} \right\}. \tag{21}$$

In the calculus of variations the Weierstrass $E$-function is defined as

$$E = F(t, x, \theta) - F(t, x, \bar{\theta}) - \sum_{i=1}^{s} (\theta_i - \bar{\theta}_i) \frac{\partial F(t, x, \bar{\theta})}{\partial \bar{\theta}_i}. \tag{22}$$

If the Hamiltonian function attains its minimum at an interior point of the region in which the decision vector $\theta(t)$ [or $\dot{x}(t)$] is defined, we have

$$\frac{\partial H(t, x, z, \bar{\theta})}{\partial \bar{\theta}_i} = 0, \qquad i = 1, 2, \ldots, s. \tag{23}$$

Combining equations (19), (21), (22), and (23) yields

$$E \geq 0, \tag{24}$$

which is the Weierstrass necessary condition for a minimum objective function.  It is worth noting that equation (24) is not applicable if the decision vector $\theta(t)$ lies on the boundary of the region defined.  However, the maximum principle lacks this deficiency [1].

*d. The Problem of Bolza.*  The problem of Bolza, as formulated by Bliss [6], is stated as follows: we wish to find in a class of curves

$$x_i(t), \qquad i = 1, 2, \ldots, s, \qquad t_0 \leq t \leq T$$

which satisfy the differential equations

$$\Phi_j(t, x(t), \dot{x}(t)) = 0, \qquad j = 1, 2, \ldots, m < s, \tag{25}$$

and the end conditions

$$\psi_k(t_0, x(t_0), T, x(T)) = 0, \qquad k = 1, 2, \ldots, p \leq 2s + 2, \tag{26}$$

a curve that minimizes an objective function of the form

$$S = g[t_0, x(t_0), T, x(T)] + \int_{t_0}^{T} F(t, x(t), \dot{x}(t)) \, dt. \tag{27}$$

We shall show that the optimization problem we have treated so far is equivalent to the problem of Bolza in which $g \equiv 0$ or $F \equiv 0$; that is, it is equivalent to the problem of Lagrange or the problem of Mayer.

Consider the following system of differential equations:

$$\frac{dx_i}{dt} = f_i\left(t, x_1(t), x_2(t), \ldots, x_s(t), \frac{dx_{m+1}}{dt}, \ldots, \frac{dx_s}{dt}\right),$$
$$i = 1, 2, \ldots, m < s, \tag{28}$$

and

$$\frac{dx_{m+j}}{dt} = \theta_j, \qquad j = 1, 2, \ldots, s - m. \tag{29}$$

Equation (28) can be rewritten as

$$\frac{dx_i}{dt} - f_i\left(t, x_1(t), x_2(t), \ldots, x_s(t), \frac{dx_{m+1}}{dt}, \ldots, \frac{dx_s}{dt}\right)$$
$$= \Phi_i\left(t, x_1(t), \ldots, x_s(t), \frac{dx_{m+1}}{dt}, \ldots, \frac{dx_s}{dt}\right) = 0,$$
$$i = 1, 2, \ldots, m < s. \tag{30}$$

This is equivalent to equation (25).

The boundary conditions of the optimization problem are usually of the form

$$x(t_0) = \alpha, \qquad x(T) = \beta, \tag{31}$$

which is equivalent to (26). The problem is to find an admissible optimal control (or the optimal decision) $\theta(t)$ such that the corresponding trajectory of the system can satisfy equations (30) and (31) and that the objective function

$$S = \int_{t_0}^{T} F(t, x(t), \theta(t)) \, dt,$$

which can be obtained from equation (27) by setting

$$g \equiv 0,$$

can attain its minimum. It may be noted that the problem in which the objective function is of the form

$$S = \sum_{i=1}^{s} c_i \, x_i(T)$$

has also been treated before.  This is equivalent to

$$F \equiv 0$$

in equation (27).  The values of $t_0$ and $x(t_0)$ are usually given; $x(T)$ is to be determined and $T$ may be fixed or unspecified.  It may also be noted that problems in which the objective function is in an integral form can be reduced to the form of a linear combination of the final state variables by introducing an additional state variable.

*e. From the Calculus of Variations to the Maximum Principle.*   We shall show how the maximum principle can be derived by using the classical calculus of variations if the decision variables are not constrained.

Suppose that a piecewise smooth curve

$$x = \bar{x}(t), \qquad t_0 \leq t \leq T,$$

lies entirely in the space of the real variables $t, x_1, x_2, \ldots, x_s$ and gives the objective function $S$ a weak relative extremum.  A piecewise smooth vector function

$$y(t) = (y_1(t), y_2(t), \ldots, y_s(t))$$

is chosen to satisfy the boundary conditions

$$y_i(t_0) = 0, \qquad i = 1, 2, \ldots, s. \tag{32}$$

Consider the equation

$$x(t) = \bar{x}(t) + \epsilon y(t). \tag{33}$$

If $|\epsilon|$ is small enough, the function $x(t)$ will lie in a weak neighborhood* of the extremal $\bar{x}(t)$.  The corresponding equation for $\theta(t)$ is

$$\theta(t) = \bar{\theta}(t) + \epsilon \varphi(t).$$

---

* By a weak neighborhood (or a neighborhood of the first order) we mean the collection of all piecewise smooth vector functions $x(t)$ which satisfy the relations

$$|x(t) - \bar{x}(t)| \leq \epsilon \tag{34}$$

and

$$|\dot{x}(t) - \bar{\dot{x}}(t)| \leq \epsilon. \tag{35}$$

A neighborhood of order $n$ is defined as the collection of all the piecewise smooth curves which satisfy the relations

$$\left| \frac{d^n x}{dt^n} - \frac{d^n \bar{x}}{dt^n} \right| \leq \epsilon, \qquad n = 0, 1, 2, \ldots, n \tag{36}$$

when $n = 0$; that is

$$|x(t) - \bar{x}(t)| \leq \epsilon. \tag{37}$$

The curves that satisfy this condition are called a strong neighborhood (or the neighborhood of order zero) of the extremal $\bar{x}(t)$.  An extremum is called strong or weak according to the strong or weak neighborhood in which it lies [5, 7].

Then the objective function has an extremum for $x(t)$ when $\epsilon = 0$; but

$$S(\bar{x}(t) + \epsilon y(t)) = \psi(\epsilon).$$

Consequently, the condition

$$\psi'(0) = \frac{d\psi}{d\epsilon}\bigg|_{\epsilon=0} = 0 \tag{38}$$

provides the necessary condition for an extremum.

Let us consider the objective function

$$S = \sum_{i=1}^{s} c_i \, x_i(T), \tag{39}$$

which is to be minimized. It can be written in the form

$$S = \int_{t_0}^{T} \sum_{i=1}^{s} c_i \dot{x}_i \, dt + \sum_{i=1}^{s} c_i \, x_i(t_0). \tag{40}$$

The performance equations are defined in preceding chapters as

$$\frac{dx_i}{dt} = \dot{x}_i(t) = f_i(t, x(t), \theta(t)), \qquad i = 1, 2, \ldots, s, \tag{41}$$

or

$$\dot{x}_i(t) - f_i(t, x(t), \theta(t)) = 0, \qquad i = 1, 2, \ldots, s. \tag{42}$$

Employing the $z_i(t)$ as Lagrange multipliers, we have

$$S = \int_{t_0}^{T} \left\{ \sum_{i=1}^{s} c_i \dot{x}_i - \sum_{i=1}^{s} z_i(t) \left[ \dot{x}_i(t) - f_i(t, x(t), \theta(t)) \right] \right\} dt + \sum_{i=1}^{s} c_i \, x_i(t_0). \tag{43}$$

Application of equation (38) gives

$$\psi'(0) = 0 = \int_{t_0}^{T} \left[ \sum_{i=1}^{s} (c_i - z_i(t)) \frac{dy_i(t)}{dt} + \sum_{i=1}^{s} \sum_{j=1}^{s} z_i(t) \frac{\partial f_i(t, \bar{x}, \bar{\theta})}{\partial \bar{x}_j} y_j(t) \right] dt$$

$$+ \int_{t_0}^{T} \left[ \sum_{i=1}^{s} \sum_{j=1}^{r} z_i(t) \frac{\partial f_i(t, \bar{x}, \bar{\theta})}{\partial \bar{\theta}_j} \varphi_j(t) \right] dt = 0, \tag{44}$$

where $r$ is the number of components of the decision vector.

By integrating the first term in the first bracketed quantity on the right-hand side by parts, equation (44) becomes

$$-\left[ \sum_{i=1}^{s} (c_i - z_i(t)) \, y_i(t) \right]_{t_0}^{T} = \int_{t_0}^{T} \left[ \sum_{i=1}^{s} \frac{dz_i(t)}{dt} + \sum_{i=1}^{s} \sum_{j=1}^{s} z_j(t) \frac{\partial f_j(t, \bar{x}, \bar{\theta})}{\partial \bar{x}_i} \right] y_i(t) \, dt$$

$$+ \int_{t_0}^{T} \sum_{i=1}^{s} \sum_{j=1}^{r} z_i(t) \frac{\partial f_i(t, \bar{x}, \bar{\theta})}{\partial \bar{\theta}_j} \varphi_j(t) \, dt. \tag{45}$$

By applying the boundary conditions, equation (32), to equation (45) we obtain

$$-\left[\sum_{i=1}^{s}(c_i - z_i(T))\, y_i(T)\right]$$

$$= \int_{t_0}^{T}\left[\sum_{i=1}^{s}\frac{dz_i(t)}{dt} + \sum_{i=1}^{s}\sum_{j=1}^{s}z_j(t)\frac{\partial f_j(t,\,\bar{x}(t),\,\bar{\theta}(t))}{\partial \bar{x}_i}\right] y_i(t)\,dt$$

$$+ \int_{t_0}^{T}\sum_{i=1}^{s}\sum_{j=1}^{r}z_i(t)\frac{\partial f_i(t,\,\bar{x}(t),\,\bar{\theta}(t))}{\partial \bar{\theta}_j}\,\varphi_j(t)\,dt. \qquad (46)$$

Since $y_i(t)$ and $\varphi_j(t)$ are arbitrary on the interval $t_0 \leq t \leq T$, in order that equation (46) may hold the following conditions must be satisfied:

$$c_i - z_i(T) = 0,$$

$$\frac{dz_i(t)}{dt} + \sum_{j=1}^{s}z_j(t)\frac{\partial f_j(t,\,\bar{x}(t),\,\bar{\theta}(t))}{\partial \bar{x}_i} = 0, \qquad i = 1, 2, \ldots, s,$$

and

$$\sum_{i=1}^{s}z_i(t)\frac{\partial f_i(t,\,\bar{x}(t),\,\bar{\theta}(t))}{\partial \bar{\theta}_j} = 0, \qquad j = 1, 2, \ldots, r,$$

or

$$z_i(T) = c_i, \qquad i = 1, 2, \ldots, s, \qquad (47)$$

$$\frac{dz_i}{dt} = -\sum_{j=1}^{s}z_j(t)\frac{\partial f_j(t,\,\bar{x}(t),\,\bar{\theta}(t))}{\partial \bar{x}_i}, \qquad i = 1, 2, \ldots, s, \qquad (48)$$

and

$$\sum_{i=1}^{s}z_i\frac{\partial f_i(t,\,\bar{x}(t),\,\bar{\theta}(t))}{\partial \bar{\theta}_j} = 0, \qquad j = 1, 2, \ldots, r. \qquad (49)$$

Equations (47) and (48) are the adjoint system in the maximum principle and equation (49) is the necessary condition for the extremum. We note that the derivation used in this section leads only to the stationary condition of the maximum principle [8].

*f. The Canonical Equations and Transformations.* There are many different ways in which we can transform coordinates. In general, the objective of a transformation is to change an original system of equations to a new system of equivalent equations which is easier to handle and clearer to visualize than the original form. The transformation that we have been using is equivalent to the one frequently applied in classical mechanics. In this section we present a transformation that leads to the algorithm of the maximum principle.

Suppose that we are to minimize the objective function of the form

$$S = \int_{t_0}^{T} F(t, x(t), \theta(t)) \, dt,$$

where

$$\theta_i(t) = \frac{dx_i}{dt} = \dot{x}_i(t), \qquad i = 1, 2, \ldots, s.$$

Define the Hamiltonian function and the adjoint variables as follows [9]:

$$H = \sum_{i=1}^{s} z_i \dot{x}_i + z_{s+1} F(t, x(t), \theta(t))$$

$$= \sum_{i=1}^{s} z_i \dot{x}_i + F(t, x(t), \theta(t)) \tag{50}$$

and

$$z_i(t) = -\frac{\partial F}{\partial \dot{x}_i}, \qquad i = 1, 2, \ldots, s. \tag{51}$$

Assuming that the Jacobian

$$\frac{\partial(z_1, z_2, \ldots, z_s)}{\partial(\dot{x}_1, \dot{x}_2, \ldots, \dot{x}_s)} \neq 0,$$

we can make a local transformation from the variables $t$, $x_1$, $x_2$, ..., $x_s$, $\dot{x}_1$, $\dot{x}_2$, ..., $\dot{x}_s$, $F$, to the variables $t$, $x_1$, $x_2$, ..., $x_s$, $z_1$, $z_2$, ..., $z_s$, $H$, which are called canonical variables.

Hence the Hamiltonian and adjoint system of the maximum principle can be derived by using the definitions of equations (50) and (51). From equation (50) we have

$$dH = \sum_{i=1}^{s} z_i \, d\dot{x}_i + \sum_{i=1}^{s} \dot{x}_i \, dz_i + \frac{\partial F}{\partial t} dt + \sum_{i=1}^{s} \frac{\partial F}{\partial x_i} dx_i + \sum_{i=1}^{s} \frac{\partial F}{\partial \dot{x}_i} d\dot{x}_i. \tag{52}$$

By substituting equation (51) into (52) we obtain

$$dH = \sum_{i=1}^{s} \dot{x}_i \, dz_i + \frac{\partial F}{\partial t} dt + \sum_{i=1}^{s} \frac{\partial F}{\partial x_i} dx_i. \tag{53}$$

It follows from equation (53) that

$$\frac{\partial H}{\partial t} = \frac{\partial F}{t \partial}, \tag{54}$$

$$\frac{\partial H}{\partial x_i} = \frac{\partial F}{\partial x_i}, \tag{55}$$

$$\frac{\partial H}{\partial z_i} = \dot{x}_i = \frac{dx_i}{dt}, \tag{56}$$

$$i = 1, 2, \ldots, s.$$

The Euler-Lagrange equations for the objective function $S$ are

$$\frac{\partial F}{\partial x_i} - \frac{d}{dt}\frac{\partial F}{\partial \dot{x}_i} = 0, \qquad i = 1, 2, \ldots, s. \tag{57}$$

A combination of equations (51), (55), (56), and (57) gives the following set of canonical Euler equations [9]:

$$\frac{dz_i}{dt} = -\frac{\partial H}{\partial x_i}, \tag{58}$$

$$i = 1, 2, \ldots, s.$$

$$\frac{dx_i}{dt} = \frac{\partial H}{\partial z_i}, \tag{59}$$

If the Hamiltonian function does not depend on $t$ explicitly, we have

$$\frac{dH}{dt} = \sum_{i=1}^{s}\left(\frac{\partial H}{\partial x_i}\frac{dx_i}{dt} + \frac{\partial H}{\partial z_i}\frac{dz_i}{dt}\right). \tag{60}$$

Substitution of equations (58) and (59) into (60) yields

$$\frac{dH}{dt} = \sum_{i=1}^{s}\left(\frac{\partial H}{\partial x_i}\frac{\partial H}{\partial z_i} - \frac{\partial H}{\partial z_i}\frac{\partial H}{\partial x_i}\right) = 0. \tag{61}$$

Therefore it follows that $H$ is constant along the extremal, as stated in the theorem in Chapter 2.

The transformation from the variables $t$, $x$, $\dot{x}$ and the function $F(t, x, \dot{x})$ to those of $t$, $x$, $z$ and $H(t, x, z)$, respectively, is called the Legendre transformation [9]. If $H(t, x, z)$ is subjected to the Legendre transformation, the function $F$ is recovered as follows: using equations (50) and (56), we have

$$H - \sum_{i=1}^{s} z_i \frac{\partial H}{\partial z_i} = \sum_{i=1}^{s} z_i \dot{x}_i + F(t, x(t), \dot{x}(t)) - \sum_{i=1}^{s} z_i \dot{x}_i$$

$$= F(t, x(t), \dot{x}(t)),$$

which indicates that the Legendre transformation is its own inverse.

**g. The Transversality Conditions.** Suppose that the objective function has the form

$$S = \int_{t_0}^{T} F(t, x(t), \dot{x}(t))\, dt, \tag{62}$$

that the initial point is fixed at

$$x(t_0) = \alpha,$$

and that the final point lies on the given hypersurface

$$h(x(T)) = 0. \tag{63}$$

Let $\bar{T}$ be the final time at which the optimal trajectory hits the given surface. We then have

$$T = \bar{T} + \delta T,$$

and the variational equation is

$$x(t) = \bar{x}(t) + \epsilon y(t). \tag{64}$$

The difference of the objective function is

$$
\begin{aligned}
\Delta S &= \int_{t_0}^{\bar{T}+\delta T} F(t, x + \epsilon y, \dot{x} + \epsilon \dot{y}) \, dt - \int_{t_0}^{\bar{T}} F(t, x, \dot{x}) \, dt \\
&= \int_{t_0}^{\bar{T}} [F(t, x + \epsilon y, \dot{x} + \epsilon \dot{y}) - F(t, x, \dot{x})] \, dt \\
&\quad + \int_{\bar{T}}^{\bar{T}+\delta T} F(t, x + \epsilon y, \dot{x} + \epsilon \dot{y}) \, dt.
\end{aligned} \tag{65}
$$

Hence the variation of the objective function becomes

$$\delta S = \int_{t_0}^{\bar{T}} \sum_{i=1}^{s} (F_{x_i} \epsilon y_i + F_{\dot{x}_i} \epsilon \dot{y}_i) \, dt + F \Big|_{t=\bar{T}} \delta T. \tag{66*}$$

Integration of the second member of the first term in equation (66) gives

$$\delta S = \int_{t_0}^{\bar{T}} \sum_{i=1}^{s} \left( F_{x_i} - \frac{d}{dt} F_{\dot{x}_i} \right) \epsilon y_i(t) \, dt + \sum_{i=1}^{s} F_{\dot{x}_i} \epsilon y_i(t) \Big|_{t_0}^{\bar{T}} + F \Big|_{t=\bar{T}} \delta T. \tag{67}$$

It can be seen from Fig. 11.1 that

$$\epsilon y_i(t) \Big|_{t=\bar{T}} \doteq \delta x_i(\bar{T}) - \dot{x}_i(\bar{T}) \, \delta T. \tag{68}$$

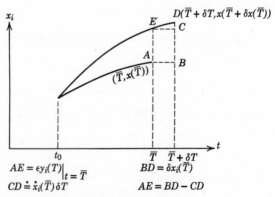

$$AE = \epsilon y_i(T) \Big|_{t=\bar{T}}$$
$$CD \doteq \dot{x}_i(\bar{T}) \delta T$$
$$BD = \delta x_i(\bar{T})$$
$$AE = BD - CD$$

**Fig. 11.1**  Variation of the trajectory.

---

* $(d/dt)[\epsilon y(t)] = \epsilon \dot{y}(t)$; that is, the derivative of a variation is the variation of a derivative [7].

Substitution of equation (68) into (67) yields

$$\delta S = \int_{t_0}^{T} \sum_{i=1}^{s} \left( F_{x_i} - \frac{d}{dt} F_{\dot{x}_i} \right) \epsilon y_i(t) \, dt$$
$$+ \left( F - \sum_{i=1}^{s} \dot{x}_i F_{\dot{x}_i} \right) \delta t \Big|_{t=T} + \sum_{i=1}^{s} F_{\dot{x}_i} \delta x_i \Big|_{t=T}. \quad (69)$$

Since the objective function $S$ has an extremum along the extremal $\bar{x}(t)$, the Euler-Lagrange equation must be satisfied; that is

$$F_{x_i} - \frac{d}{dt} F_{\dot{x}_i} = 0, \qquad i = 1, 2, \ldots, s.$$

It follows that

$$\delta S = \left( F - \sum_{i=1}^{s} \dot{x} F_{\dot{x}_i} \right) \delta t \Big|_{t=T} + \sum_{i=1}^{s} F_{\dot{x}_i} \delta x_i \Big|_{t=T}. \quad (70)$$

By substituting equations (50) and (51) into (70), we obtain

$$\delta S = \left( -\sum_{i=1}^{s} z_i \, \delta x_i + H \, \delta t \right) \Big|_{t=T}. \quad (71)$$

Thus the necessary condition for an extremum

$$\delta S = 0$$

takes the form

$$-\sum_{i=1}^{s} z_i \, \delta x_i + H \, \delta t = 0 \quad (72)$$

at $t = \bar{T}$. According to the theorem in Chapter 3, if $S$ attains a minimum

$$H_{min} = 0$$

when the final time is unspecified. Equation (72) then becomes

$$\sum_{i=1}^{s} z_i \, \delta x_i = 0 \quad (73)$$

at $t = \bar{T}$.

If the vector $a = (a_1, a_2, \ldots, a_s)$ belongs to the tangent plane of $h(x) = 0$ at $t = \bar{T}$, equation (73) can be written as

$$\sum_{i=1}^{s} z_i a_i = 0. \quad (74)$$

Similarly, if the initial point $x(t_0)$ lies on the hypersurface

$$h(x(t_0)) = 0,$$

we can obtain the similar transversality condition

$$\sum_{i=1}^{s} z_i \, \delta x_i = 0$$

at $t = t_0$.

*h. The Hamilton-Jacobi Equation* [9].  Let us define

$$dW = \sum_{i=1}^{s} z_i \, dx_i - H \, dt \tag{75}$$

at $t = \bar{T}$.  It follows that

$$\frac{\partial W}{\partial x_i} = z_i, \qquad i = 1, 2, \ldots, s, \tag{76}$$

$$\frac{\partial W}{\partial t} = -H. \tag{77}$$

From equation (77) we have

$$\frac{\partial W}{\partial t} + H\left(t, x(t), \frac{\partial W}{\partial x_i}\right) = 0 \tag{78}$$

at $t = \bar{T}$.  Equation (78) is known as the Hamilton-Jacobi equation.  Let

$$W = W(t, x(t), \eta) \tag{79}$$

be a solution of the Hamilton-Jacobi equation, in which $\eta = (\eta_1, \eta_2, \ldots, \eta_m)$, $m \leq s$ is a parameter.  Then

$$\frac{d}{dt}\left(\frac{\partial W}{\partial \eta_i}\right) = 0, \qquad i = 1, 2, \ldots, m. \tag{80}$$

This can be shown as follows:  since we have

$$\frac{d}{dt}\left(\frac{\partial W}{\partial \eta_i}\right) = \frac{\partial^2 W}{\partial t \, \partial \eta_i} + \sum_{j=1}^{s} \frac{\partial^2 W}{\partial x_j \, \partial \eta_i} \frac{dx_j}{dt}, \tag{81}$$

we substitute equation (79) into equation (78), differentiate it with respect to $\eta_i$, and employ equation (76) to obtain

$$\frac{\partial^2 W}{\partial t \, \partial \eta_i} + \sum_{j=1}^{s} \frac{\partial H}{\partial z_j} \frac{\partial^2 W}{\partial x_j \, \partial \eta_i} = 0. \tag{82}$$

From equations (81) and (82) we thus have

$$-\frac{d}{dt}\left(\frac{\partial W}{\partial \eta_i}\right) = \sum_{j=1}^{s} \frac{\partial H}{\partial z_j} \frac{\partial^2 W}{\partial x_j \, \partial \eta_i} - \sum_{j=1}^{s} \frac{\partial^2 W}{\partial x_j \, \partial \eta_i} \frac{dx_j}{dt}$$

$$= \sum_{j=1}^{s} \frac{\partial^2 W}{\partial x_j \, \partial \eta_i}\left[\frac{\partial H}{\partial z_j} - \frac{dx_j}{dt}\right] = 0 \tag{83}$$

along each extremal.  Comparing equation (61) with equation (83), we see that both $H$ and $\partial W/\partial \eta_i$ are the first integrals of the canonical Euler equations.

## 2.   THE MAXIMUM PRINCIPLE AND DYNAMIC PROGRAMMING

We show in this section that a close relation exists between the maximum principle and the method of dynamic programming, which is based on the principle of optimality stated by Bellman [10]:

An optimal policy has the property that whatever the initial state and initial decision are the remaining decisions must constitute an optimal policy with regard to the state resulting from the first decision.

Let us consider the problem of minimizing the objective function

$$S = \sum_{i=1}^{s} c_i \, x_i(T)$$

with the initial condition

$$x(t_0) = \alpha$$

and the final time $T$ fixed.

The principle of optimality implicitly states that the minimum value of $S$ is a function of the initial state $x(t_0) = \alpha$ and the initial time $t_0$. Introducing the function [11]

$$S(x(t_0), t_0) = \min_{\theta(t)} S = \min_{\theta(t)} \sum_{i=1}^{s} c_i \, x_i(T), \qquad t_0 \le t \le T, \qquad (84)$$

and denoting the optimal trajectory at $t = t_0 + \Delta t$ by $\bar{x}(t)$, where $\Delta t$ is sufficiently small, we have

$$S(x(t_0),t_0) = S(\bar{x}, t). \qquad (85)$$

Assume that the trajectory from $t_0 + \Delta t$ to $T$ is optimal. Then for any other trajectory $x(t)$ at $t_0 + \Delta t$ we have $S(x, t)$. From the definition of equation (84) it follows that

$$S(x(t_0), t_0) = \min_{\theta(t)} S(x, t), \qquad t_0 \le t \le t_0 + \Delta t. \qquad (86)$$

Assuming the existence and continuity of the partial derivatives of $S(x, t)$, we expand it in a Taylor series as follows:

$$S(x, t) = S(x(t_0), t_0) + \sum_{i=1}^{s} \frac{\partial S}{\partial x_i} (x_i - x_i(t_0)) + \frac{\partial S}{\partial t} (t - t_0) + 0(\epsilon^2), \qquad (87)^*$$

where the partial derivatives are evaluated at $(x(t_0), t_0)$ and $0(\epsilon^2)$ represents the terms of $\epsilon^2$ and those of higher orders than $\epsilon^2$. $0(\epsilon^2)$ should satisfy the condition that

$$\lim_{\Delta t \to 0} \frac{0(\epsilon^2)}{\Delta t} = 0.$$

---

* It should be noted that the differentiability assumption is generally not valid.

As before, the performance equations are

$$\dot{x}_i(t) = \frac{dx_i}{dt} = f_i(t, x(t), \theta(t)), \qquad i = 1, 2, \ldots, s. \tag{88}$$

Hence

$$x_i(t) = x_i(t_0) + f_i(t_0, x(t_0), \theta(t_0)) \, \Delta t + 0(\epsilon^2). \tag{89}$$

Substitution of equations (87) and (89) into (86) gives

$$S(x(t_0), t_0) = \min_{\theta(t)} \left[ S(x(t_0), t_0) + \sum_{i=1}^{s} \frac{\partial S}{\partial x_i} f_i \, \Delta t \right.$$
$$\left. + \frac{\partial S}{\partial t} \Delta t + 0(\epsilon^2) \right], \qquad t_0 \le t \le t_0 + \Delta t. \tag{90}$$

The decision vector is that term containing $f_i$. By simplifying equation (90) and dividing it by $\Delta t$ we obtain

$$\frac{\partial S(x(t_0), t_0)}{\partial t_0} = -\min_{\theta(t)} \left[ \sum_{i=1}^{s} \frac{\partial S}{\partial x_i} f_i + \frac{0(\epsilon^2)}{\Delta t} \right], \qquad t_0 \le t \le t_0 + \Delta t.$$

Letting $\Delta t$ approach zero yields

$$\frac{\partial S(x(t_0), t_0)}{\partial t_0} = -\min_{\theta(t)} \sum_{i=1}^{s} \frac{\partial S}{\partial x_i} f_i(t_0, x(t_0), \theta(t_0)) \tag{91}$$

at $t = t_0$. This determines the choice of $\theta(t)$ at $t = t_0$. Because $t_0$ can be chosen at any point in the interval $[t_0, T]$, equation (91) is written in general as

$$\frac{\partial S(x(t), t)}{\partial t} = -\min_{\theta(t)} \sum_{i=1}^{s} \frac{\partial S}{\partial x_i} f_i(t, x(t), \theta(t)). \tag{92}$$

It will be shown that this is equivalent to the optimal condition given by the maximum principle. We let

$$z_i(t) = \frac{\partial S(x(t), t)}{\partial x_i}, \qquad z(T) = c_i, \qquad i = 1, 2, \ldots, s, \tag{93}$$

and

$$\frac{\partial S(x(t), t)}{\partial t} = -H(t, \bar{x}(t), \bar{\theta}(t), z(t))$$
$$= -\sum_{i=1}^{s} z_i(t) f_i(t, \bar{x}(t), \bar{\theta}(t)). \tag{94}$$

From equations (93) and (94) we have

$$\frac{dz_i}{dt} = -\sum_{j=1}^{s} z_j \frac{\partial f_j}{\partial \bar{x}_i}. \tag{95}$$

By combining equations (92), (93), and (94) we obtain

$$H(t, \bar{x}(t), \bar{\theta}(t), z(t)) = \min_{\theta(t)} H(t, x(t), \theta(t), z(t)). \qquad (96)$$

The relationship between the maximum principle and dynamic programming is analogous to that between the Hamiltonian system and the Hamilton-Jacobi equation [compare (93), (94), and (96) with (76), (77), and (78)].

Generally, to find the optimal trajectory the method of dynamic programming requires an exhaustive stepwise calculation by means of equations (88) and (91) and the objective function

$$S = \sum_{i=1}^{s} c_i\, x_i(T).$$

However, when using the technique of the maximum principle, we need the solutions of the differential equations (88) and (95), and the optimal condition equation (96). The advantages and the shortcomings of each method have been broadly discussed elsewhere [1, 2, 12, 13].

It is worthwhile to mention that dynamic programming produces a set of partial differential equations, whereas the maximum principle gives a set of ordinary differential equations. The method of characteristics, however, can be used to transform the set of partial differential equations to a set of ordinary differential equations [2].

## 3. DYNAMIC PROGRAMMING AND THE CALCULUS OF VARIATIONS

In the calculus of variations we consider the properties of the admissible curves lying in the $\delta$-neighborhood of the optimal curve and obtain all the necessary conditions. By using dynamic programming we shall evaluate the optimal derivative point by point along the extremal, instead of finding the entire extremal, and in this way we shall show how the working equations of the calculus of variations are derived.

Consider

$$\frac{dx_i}{dt} = \dot{x}_i(t) = \theta_i(t), \qquad i = 1, 2, \ldots, s. \qquad (97)$$

We wish to minimize the objective function $S$ of the form

$$S = \int_{t_0}^{T} F(t, x(t), \dot{x}(t))\, dt.$$

The boundary conditions are

$$x(t_0) = \alpha,$$
$$x(T) = \beta.$$

We define the function

$$S(t, x(t)) = \min_{\theta(t)} \int_t^T F(t, x(t), \theta(t)) \, dt, \tag{98}$$

where $S(t, x(t))$ is the minimum value of the integral of $F(t, x(t), \theta(t))$ from the point $(t, x(t))$ to the fixed point $(T, x(T))$. It is clear that

$$S(T, x(T)) = 0.$$

Breaking up the time interval $[t, T]$ into two parts, $[t, t + \Delta t]$ and $[t + \Delta t, T]$, equation (98) can be written as

$$
\begin{aligned}
S(t, x(t)) = \min_{\substack{\theta(t) \\ t \le t' \le t+\Delta t}} \min_{\substack{\theta(t) \\ t+\Delta t \le t' \le T}} & \left[ \int_t^{t+\Delta t} F(t', x(t'), \theta(t')) \, dt' \right. \\
& \left. + \int_{t+\Delta t}^T F(t', x(t'), \theta(t')) \right] dt' \\
= \min_{\substack{\theta(t) \\ t \le t' \le t+\Delta t}} & \left[ \int_t^{t+\Delta t} F(t', x(t'), \theta(t')) \, dt' \right. \\
& \left. + \min_{\substack{\theta(t) \\ t+\Delta t \le t' \le T}} \int_{t+\Delta t}^T F(t', x(t'), \theta(t')) \, dt' \right].
\end{aligned}
\tag{99}
$$

According to the definition given by equation (98), we have

$$S(t + \Delta t, x + \dot{x} \, \Delta t) = \min_{\substack{\theta(t) \\ t+\Delta t \le t' \le T}} \int_{t+\Delta t}^T F(t', x(t'), \theta(t')) \, dt'.$$

Substituting this equation into equation (99), we have

$$S(t, x(t)) = \min_{\substack{\theta(t) \\ t \le t' \le t+\Delta t}} \int_t^{t+\Delta t} F(t', x(t'), \theta(t')) \, dt' + S(t + \Delta t, x + \dot{x} \, \Delta t). \tag{100}$$

For sufficiently small $\Delta t$ equation (100) becomes

$$S(t, x(t)) = \min_{\theta(t)} \left[ F(t, x(t), \theta(t)) \, \Delta t + S(t + \Delta t, x + \dot{x} \, \Delta t) \right] + [0((\Delta t)^2)], \tag{101}$$

which is the functional formulation of the principle of optimality.

A Taylor series expansion of equation (101) yields

$$
\begin{aligned}
S(t, x(t)) = \min_{\theta(t)} \Big[ & F(t, x(t), \theta(t)) \, \Delta t + S(t, x(t)) \\
& + \frac{\partial S}{\partial t} \Delta t + \sum_{i=1}^s \frac{\partial S}{\partial x_i} \dot{x}_i \, \Delta t \Big] + 0((\Delta t)^2).
\end{aligned}
\tag{102}
$$

By letting $\Delta t$ approach zero we obtain the nonlinear partial differential equation [14]

$$0 = \min_{\theta(t)} \left[ F(t, x(t), \theta(t)) + \frac{\partial S}{\partial t} + \sum_{i=1}^{s} \dot{x}_i \frac{\partial S}{\partial x_i} \right], \tag{103}$$

which is of the Hamilton-Jacobi type and called the Bellman equation.

Equation (103) is equivalent to the following two equations:

$$F_{\dot{x}_i} + \frac{\partial S}{\partial x_i} = 0, \qquad i = 1, 2, \ldots, s, \tag{104}$$

which are obtained by taking the derivative of equation (103) with respect to $\dot{x}_i$ (or $\theta_i$) and

$$F + \frac{\partial S}{\partial t} + \sum_{i=1}^{s} \dot{x}_i \frac{\partial S}{\partial x_i} = 0, \tag{105}$$

which is the minimum value of equation (101). Differentiation of equation (104) with respect to $t$ gives

$$\frac{d}{dt} F_{\dot{x}_i} + \frac{\partial^2 S}{\partial x_i\, \partial t} + \sum_{j=1}^{s} \frac{\partial^2 S}{\partial x_i\, \partial x_j} \dot{x}_j = 0, \qquad i = 1, 2, \ldots, s. \tag{106}$$

Partial differentiation of equation (105) with respect to $x_i(t)$ yields

$$F_{x_i} + \sum_{j=1}^{s} \frac{\partial F}{\partial \dot{x}_j} \frac{\partial \dot{x}_j}{\partial x_i} + \frac{\partial^2 S}{\partial t\, \partial x_i} + \sum_{j=1}^{s} \dot{x}_j \frac{\partial^2 S}{\partial x_j\, \partial x_i} + \sum_{j=1}^{s} \frac{\partial S}{\partial x_j} \frac{\partial \dot{x}_j}{\partial x_i} = 0,$$

$$i = 1, 2, \ldots, s,$$

which is reduced to

$$F_{x_i} + \frac{\partial^2 S}{\partial t\, \partial x_i} + \sum_{j=1}^{s} \frac{\partial^2 S}{\partial x_j\, \partial x_i} \dot{x}_j = 0, \qquad i = 1, 2, \ldots, s, \tag{107}$$

by using equation (104). By subtracting equation (106) from (107) we obtain the set of Euler-Lagrange equations

$$F_{x_i} - \frac{d}{dt} F_{\dot{x}_i} = 0, \qquad i = 1, 2, \ldots, s. \tag{108}$$

In deriving equation (104) we have used the fact that the first derivative must be zero at a minimum point. Meanwhile, at the minimum point the second derivative must be

$$F_{\dot{x}_i \dot{x}_j} \geq 0, \tag{109}$$

which is the Legendre necessary condition for a minimum.

It follows from equation (103) that for the optimal decision $\bar{x}(t)$ [or $\bar{\theta}(t)$] we have the following inequality:

$$F(t, x(t), \theta(t)) + \frac{\partial S}{\partial t} + \sum_{i=1}^{s} \frac{\partial S}{\partial x_i} \theta_i(t) \geq F(t, x(t), \bar{\theta}(t)) + \frac{\partial S}{\partial t} + \sum_{i=1}^{s} \frac{\partial S}{\partial x_i} \bar{\theta}_i(t),$$

or

$$F(t, x(t), (t)) - F(t, x(t), \bar{\theta}(t)) + \sum_{i=1}^{s} (\theta_i(t) - \bar{\theta}_i(t)) \frac{\partial S}{\partial x_i} \geq 0. \qquad (110)$$

Because of equation (104), equation (110) becomes

$$F(t, x(t), \theta(t)) - F(t, x(t), \bar{\theta}(t)) - \sum_{i=1}^{s} (\theta_i(t) - \bar{\theta}_i(t)) \frac{\partial F}{\partial \theta_i} \geq 0. \qquad (111)$$

This is the Weierstrass necessary condition for a minimum.

Let us now consider the final point of a trajectory which lies on the curve

$$x = g(T). \qquad (112)$$

Since the change in $S$ accompanying the change of the final point of the trajectory along the curve given by this equation is zero for the optimal trajectory, we have

$$\frac{\partial S}{\partial t} + \sum_{i=1}^{s} \frac{\partial S}{\partial x_i} \frac{dg_i}{dt} = 0 \qquad (113)$$

at $t = \bar{T}$. By combining equations (104), (105), and (113) we obtain

$$F + \sum_{i=1}^{s} \left( \frac{dg_i}{dt} - \dot{x}_i \right) F_{\dot{x}_i} = 0, \qquad (114)$$

which is equivalent to equation (70), the transversality condition at the final point.

So far we have discussed the relationship between the maximum principle, dynamic programming, and the calculus of variations. It is recognized that there is no single optimization technique superior to other techniques in handling every type of problem. How to choose an appropriate technique to solve a specific problem is an important step. The selection of a technique depends on the characteristics of the problem, the computing facilities, such as an analog or digital computer, and other influencing factors.

The application of dynamic programming to complex systems and its equivalence to the discrete maximum principle [12] is presented in Appendix 2.

## 4.   THE  MAXIMUM  PRINCIPLE  AND  THE  ADJOINT  SYSTEM

In this section we present another approach which uses Green's functions to derive the algorithm [15, 16].  A numerical iterative technique which also employs Green's functions is briefly described.

Without loss of generality, we shall consider the autonomous system

$$\frac{dx_i}{dt} = \dot{x}_i = f_i(x(t), \theta(t)), \qquad i = 1, 2, \ldots, s, \tag{113}$$

and the objective function

$$S = \sum_{i=1}^{s} c_i \, x_i(T).$$

Let $(\bar{x}(t); \bar{\theta}(t))$ be the optimal point.  Then we have the variational equations

$$x(t) = \bar{x}(t) + \delta x(t), \tag{114}*$$

$$\theta(t) = \bar{\theta}(t) + \delta\theta(t). \tag{115}*$$

By considering the variations of $f_i$ simultaneously both in $x_i$ and $\theta_i$ and linearizing we obtain

$$\delta\dot{x}_i = \sum_{j=1}^{s} \frac{\partial f_i}{\partial x_j} \, \delta x_j + \sum_{k=1}^{r} \frac{\partial f_i}{\partial \theta_k} \, \delta\theta_k, \qquad i = 1, 2, \ldots, s. \tag{116}$$

The partial derivatives are evaluated along the optimal path.  For the fixed initial point we have

$$\delta x_i(t_0) = 0, \qquad i = 1, 2, \ldots, s.$$

The so-called adjoint system of equation (116) is defined by

$$\frac{dz_i}{dt} = \dot{z}_i(t) = -\sum_{j=1}^{s} \frac{\partial f_j}{\partial x_i} \, z_j, \qquad i = 1, 2, \ldots, s. \tag{117}$$

It is obtained by deleting the control terms, transposing the matrix of coefficients, and changing the sign in equation (116); $z(t)$ is also called Green's vector [16].

By substituting equations (116) and (117) into

$$\frac{d}{dt} \sum_{i=1}^{s} z_i \, \delta x_i = \sum_{i=1}^{s} \dot{z}_i \, \delta x_i + \sum_{i=1}^{s} z_i \, \delta\dot{x}_i$$

---

* Equations (114) and (115) are the same as those used previously.  Here $\delta x(t)$ includes the terms $\epsilon y$ and $0(\epsilon^2)$ and $\delta\theta(t)$ includes $\epsilon\varphi$ and $0(\epsilon^2)$.

we obtain

$$\frac{d}{dt}\sum_{i=1}^{s} z_i\, \delta x_i = \sum_{i=1}^{s}\sum_{j=1}^{r} z_i \frac{\partial f_i}{\partial \theta_j}\, \delta\theta_j. \tag{118}$$

Equation (118) is equivalent to equation (2.39). By integrating equation (118) from $t = t_0$ to $t = T$ we obtain

$$\sum_{i=1}^{s} [z_i(T)\, \delta x_i(T) - z_i(t_0)\, \delta x_i(t_0)] = \int_{t_0}^{T}\sum_{i=1}^{s}\sum_{j=1}^{r} z_i \frac{\partial f_i}{\partial \theta_j}\, \delta\theta_j\, dt. \tag{119}$$

Suppose that the boundary conditions of $z_i$ are defined as

$$z_i(T) = c_i, \qquad i = 1, 2, \ldots, s.$$

Since

$$\delta x_i(t_0) = 0, \qquad i = 1, 2, \ldots, s,$$

and the variation of the objective function is zero along the optimal trajectory, that is

$$\delta S = \sum_{i=1}^{s} c_i\, \delta x_i(T) = 0, \tag{120}$$

equation (119) becomes

$$\sum_{i=1}^{s} c_i\, \delta x_i(T) = \int_{t_0}^{T}\sum_{i=1}^{s}\sum_{j=1}^{r} z_i \frac{\partial f_i}{\partial \theta_j}\, \delta\theta_j\, dt = 0 \tag{121}$$

or

$$\sum_{i=1}^{s} z_i \frac{\partial f_i}{\partial \theta_j} = \frac{\partial H}{\partial \theta_j} = 0, \qquad j = 1, 2, \ldots, r.$$

This is the stationary necessary condition for the weak form of the maximum principle [8].

It has been shown also that it is convenient to use Green's function to derive the above conditions [15, 16, 17].

The solution of equation (116) may be written in the form

$$\delta x_i(t) = \sum_{j=1}^{s} G_{ij}(t, t_0)\, \delta x_j(t_0) + \int_{t_0}^{t}\sum_{j=1}^{s} G_{ij}(t, \tau) \sum_{k=1}^{r} \frac{\partial f_j}{\partial \theta_k}\, \delta\theta_k\, d\tau,$$

$$i = 1, 2, \ldots, s, \tag{122}$$

where the $G_{ij}(t, \tau)$ are called Green's functions (or influence functions). The first term on the right-hand side of equation (122) represents solutions of the homogeneous system of equations. Green's functions transmit the influence on a unit impulse (or Dirac delta function) in the decision variables at time $\tau$, or unit change in $x_i(t_0)$, to the output $x_i(t)$.

We shall relate Green's functions to the solutions of an adjoint system of equations by using equation (119).

Comparison of equation (119) with equation (122) suggests that if

$$z_{ij}(T) = \delta_{ij}, \tag{123}$$

where $\delta_{ij}$ is the Kronecker delta, we then obtain

$$G_{ij}(T, t) = z_{ij}(t) \tag{124}$$

and

$$\delta x_i(T) = \sum_{j=1}^{s} z_{ij}(t_0)\, \delta x_j(t_0) + \int_{t_0}^{T} \sum_{j=1}^{s} z_{ij}(\tau) \sum_{k=1}^{r} \frac{\partial f_j}{\partial \theta_k}\, \delta \theta_k\, d\tau,$$
$$i = 1, 2, \ldots, s. \tag{125}$$

Green's vector can also be related to the adjoint vector in the following way:

$$z_i(T) = c_i = \sum_{j=1}^{s} c_j \delta_{ji} = \sum_{j=1}^{s} c_j z_{ji}(T). \tag{126}$$

Because equation (117) is linear and homogeneous, we have at any point in the interval $[t_0, T]$

$$z_i(t) = \sum_{j=1}^{s} c_j z_{ji}(t). \tag{127}$$

By taking the inner product of both sides of equation (125) and $z(T)$ we obtain

$$\sum_{i=1}^{s} z_i(T)\, \delta x_i(T) = \sum_{j=1}^{s} z_j(t_0)\, \delta x_j(t_0) + \int_{t_0}^{T} \sum_{j=1}^{s} z_j(\tau) \sum_{k=1}^{r} \frac{\partial f_j}{\partial \theta_k}\, \delta \theta_k\, d\tau$$
$$= \sum_{i=1}^{s} z_i(t_0)\, \delta x_i(t_0) + \int_{t_0}^{T} \sum_{i=1}^{s} \sum_{j=1}^{r} z_i \frac{\partial f_i}{\partial \theta_j}\, \delta \theta_j\, d\tau, \tag{128}$$

which is the same as equation (119) and equivalent to equation (2.40). It is also called Green's identity.

Whenever the variational equation (116) is written, a formal solution, equation (122), can be obtained by using Green's functions. Green's identity, equation (128), follows immediately by taking the inner product.

Green's functions also lead to computational schemes for the problems of optimization. Solution of these problems by means of the maximum principle results in two-point boundary value problems. Usually we have problems in which the initial conditions are given for the system equations and final conditions for the adjoint system equations. An iterative technique must be used to treat them.

Assume that $\theta(t)$ lies in the $\delta$-neighborhood of $\bar{\theta}(t)$; we may assume that $\delta\theta(t)$ is approximately zero. Equation (125), then, is approximated by

$$\delta x_i(T) = \sum_{j=1}^{s} z_{ij}(t_0)\, \delta x_j(t_0). \tag{129}$$

Let $x'(T)$ be the guessed final value of the state vector. If it corresponds to an initial value $x'(t_0)$, instead of the given initial value $x(t_0)$, we can obtain a better guess of $x(T)$ by using the following iterative equation obtained from equation (129):

$$x_i(T) = x_i'(T) + \sum_{j=1}^{s} z_{ij}(t_0)[x_j(t_0) - x_j'(t_0)]. \tag{130}$$

This scheme is based on the work of Bliss [18] and Goodman and Lance [19]. The unique use of the result was first described by Denn and Aris [16].

Green's functions can also be associated with the method of gradients (or method of steepest descent) to solve the optimization problems computationally [15, 20, 21].

## 5.  PHASE SPACE CONSTRAINTS

The problems already treated are those with no constraints imposed on the state variables. Therefore the state vector $x(t)$ might deviate far from the initial state $x(t_0)$ and the final state $x(T)$. It is often not desirable in physical and engineering problems that a system behave in such a manner.

Theoretically, the problems could be solved, for the theorems are already proved [1]. However, application of these theorems has been difficult. The constraints of the form $g(x(t); \theta(t))$ are mentioned in Section 2.4, part j. Other attempts to use penalty functions, method of gradients, and some other methods have been made to treat the problems [15, 20, 22, 23, 24, 25].

## 6.  THE WEAK AND STRONG FORMS OF THE MAXIMUM PRINCIPLE

We have derived the algorithm for the weak form of the maximum principle for both the simple and complex discrete [12] as well as the continuous systems by using the first-order variational equations. When the objective function is to be maximized (or minimized), the Hamiltonian function is made stationary with respect to the optimal decisions which lie in the interior of an admissible region; when they lie at the boundary of the admissible region, $H$ is made maximum (or minimum).

It has been pointed out that there is no exact analogue of the discrete maximum principle to the continuous one. In the discrete system it is shown that only the weak form of the maximum principle exists [26, 27, 28, 29]. For continuous systems the algorithm for the strong maximum principle can be obtained by considering the second-order terms in the variational equations [29].

In the following we describe how the strong form of the maximum principle is obtained for simple continuous systems. Taking into account the second-order terms, equation (2.33) can be written as

$$\epsilon \frac{dy_i}{dt} = f_i(x; \theta) - f_i(\bar{x}; \bar{\theta}) + 0(\epsilon^2)$$

$$= \sum_j \frac{\partial f_i}{\partial x_j} \epsilon y_j + \frac{1}{2} \sum_{j,k} \frac{\partial^2 f_i}{\partial x_j \, \partial x_k} (\epsilon y_j)(\epsilon y_k) + \frac{1}{2} \sum_{j,k} \frac{\partial^2 f_i}{\partial x_j \, \partial \theta_k} (\epsilon y_j)(\epsilon \varphi_k)$$

$$+ \sum_j \frac{\partial f_i}{\partial \theta_j} \epsilon \varphi_j + \frac{1}{2} \sum_{j,k} \frac{\partial^2 f_i}{\partial \theta_j \, \partial \theta_k} (\epsilon \varphi_j)(\epsilon \varphi_k) + 0(\epsilon^3), \qquad t_0 \le t \le T,$$

$$i = 1, 2, \ldots, s, \quad (131)*$$

where the partial derivatives are evaluated along the optimal trajectory and $0(\epsilon^3)$ represents the terms of the order $\epsilon^3$ and those of orders higher than $\epsilon^3$ such that

$$\lim_{\epsilon \to 0} \frac{0(\epsilon^3)}{\epsilon^2} = 0.$$

Using Green's functions, we obtain a solution for equation (131) [compare equations (116) and (122)]:

$$\epsilon y_i(t) = \sum_j G_{ij}(t, t_0) \, \epsilon y_j(t_0) + \int_{t_0}^t \sum_{j,k} G_{ij}(t, \tau) \frac{\partial f_j}{\partial \theta_k} \epsilon \varphi_k \, d\tau$$

$$+ \frac{1}{2} \int_{t_0}^t \sum_{j,k,m} G_{ij}(t, \tau) \frac{\partial^2 f_j}{\partial \theta_k \, \partial \theta_m} (\epsilon \varphi_k)(\epsilon \varphi_m) \, d\tau$$

$$+ \frac{1}{2} \int_{t_0}^t \sum_{j,k,m} G_{ij}(t, \tau) \frac{\partial^2 f_j}{\partial x_k \, \partial \theta_m} (\epsilon y_k)(\epsilon \varphi_m) \, d\tau$$

$$+ \frac{1}{2} \int_{t_0}^t \sum_{j,k,m} G_{ij}(t, \tau) \frac{\partial^2 f_j}{\partial x_k \, \partial x_m} (\epsilon y_k)(\epsilon y_m) + 0(\epsilon^3),$$

$$t_0 \le t \le T, \qquad i = 1, 2, \ldots, s. \quad (132)$$

Assume that the initial state is fixed; that is

$$\epsilon y(t_0) = 0.$$

---

* $\displaystyle\sum_{j,k}$ denotes the summation over the $j$ and $k$ subscripts; $j$ and $k$ range from one to $s$ for $x$ and one to $r$ for $\theta$.

Successive approximation by substituting $\epsilon y_i(t)$ into equation (132) itself then gives

$$\epsilon y_i(T) = \int_{t_0}^{T} \sum_{j,k} G_{ij}(T, \tau) \frac{\partial f_j}{\partial \theta_k} \epsilon \varphi_k \, d\tau$$

$$+ \frac{1}{2} \int_{t_0}^{T} \sum_{j,k\,m} G_{ij}(T, \tau) \frac{\partial^2 f_j}{\partial \theta_k \, \partial \theta_m} (\epsilon \varphi_k)(\epsilon \varphi_m) \, d\tau$$

$$+ \frac{1}{2} \int_{t_0}^{T} \sum_{j,k,m} G_{ij}(T, \tau) \frac{\partial^2 f_j}{\partial x_k \, \partial \theta_m} \epsilon \varphi_m \left( \int_{t_0}^{T} \sum_{j,m} G_{kj} \frac{\partial f_j}{\partial \theta_m} \epsilon \varphi_m \, dt \right) d\tau$$

$$+ \frac{1}{2} \int_{t_0}^{T} \sum_{j,k,m} G_{ij}(T, \tau) \frac{\partial^2 f_j}{\partial x_k \, \partial x_m} \left( \int_{t_0}^{T} \sum_{j,m} G_{kj} \frac{\partial f_j}{\partial \theta_m} \epsilon \varphi_m \, dt \right)$$

$$\times \left( \int_{t_0}^{T} \sum_{j,k} G_{mj} \frac{\partial f_j}{\partial \theta_k} \epsilon \varphi_k \, dt \right) d\tau + 0(\epsilon^3), \qquad i = 1, 2, \ldots, s,$$

$$t_0 \leq t \leq T. \quad (133)$$

Now let us consider the special variation [29]

$$\epsilon \varphi(t) = \begin{cases} \epsilon \bar{\varphi}(t), & t_1 \leq t \leq t_1 + \Delta t, \\ 0, & \text{otherwise.} \end{cases} \quad (134)$$

The first two terms on the right-hand side of equation (133) are of the order $\Delta t$; the remaining terms are of the order $(\Delta t)^2$ and those of higher orders. By letting $\Delta t$ be sufficiently small we obtain

$$\epsilon y_i(T) = \int_{t_1}^{t_1+\Delta t} \sum_{j,k} G_{ij}(T, \tau) \frac{\partial f_j}{\partial \theta_k} \epsilon \bar{\varphi}_k \, d\tau$$

$$+ \frac{1}{2} \int_{t_1}^{t_1+\Delta t} \sum_{j,k,m} G_{ij}(T, \tau) \frac{\partial^2 f_j}{\partial \theta_k \, \partial \theta_m} (\epsilon \bar{\varphi}_k)(\epsilon \bar{\varphi}_m) \, d\tau$$

$$+ 0(\epsilon^3) + 0[(\Delta t)^2], \quad (135)$$

where $0[(\Delta t)]^2$ represents second- and higher-order terms. Let the objective function be of the form

$$S = \sum_i c_i x_i(T), \qquad i = 1, 2, \ldots, s,$$

and let

$$z_i(T) = c_i, \qquad i = 1, 2, \ldots, s. \quad (136)$$

As in equation (128), we take the inner product of equation (135) and $z(T)$ and employ equations (124) and (127) to obtain

$$
\begin{aligned}
\sum_i \epsilon y_i(T) c_i &= \int_{t_1}^{t_1+\Delta t} \sum_{j,k} z_j(\tau) \frac{\partial f_j}{\partial \theta_k} \epsilon \bar{\varphi}_k \, d\tau \\
&\quad + \frac{1}{2} \int_{t_1}^{t_1+\Delta t} \sum_{j,k,m} z_j(\tau) \frac{\partial^2 f_j}{\partial \theta_k \, \partial \theta_m} (\epsilon \bar{\varphi}_k)(\epsilon \bar{\varphi}_m) \, d\tau \\
&\quad + 0(\epsilon^3) + 0[(\Delta t)^2] \\
&= \int_{t_1}^{t_1+\Delta t} \sum_k \frac{\partial H}{\partial \theta_k} \epsilon \bar{\varphi}_k \, d\tau \\
&\quad + \frac{1}{2} \int_{t_1}^{t_1+\Delta t} \sum_{k,m} \frac{\partial^2 H}{\partial \theta_k \, \partial \theta_m} (\epsilon \bar{\varphi}_k)(\epsilon \bar{\varphi}_m) \, d\tau \\
&\quad + 0(\epsilon^3) + 0[(\Delta t)^2].
\end{aligned}
\tag{137}
$$

Expanding the objective function $S$ in a Taylor series around the maximum value of $S$, we obtain

$$
\Delta S = \sum_i \frac{\partial S}{\partial x_i} \epsilon y_i \bigg|_{t=T} + \frac{1}{2} \sum_{i,j} \frac{\partial^2 S}{\partial x_i \, \partial x_j} \epsilon y_i \epsilon y_j \bigg|_{t=T} + 0(\epsilon^3).
\tag{138}
$$

But from equation (135) we know that $\epsilon y_i \epsilon y_j$ is of order $0(\epsilon^3) + 0[(\Delta t)^2]$; and we also have

$$
\frac{\partial S}{\partial x_i} \bigg|_{t=T} = c_i.
$$

Substituting this equation into equation (138), we obtain from equation (137)

$$
\Delta S = \int_{t_1}^{t_1+\Delta t} \sum_k \frac{\partial H}{\partial \theta_k} \epsilon \bar{\varphi}_k \, d\tau + \frac{1}{2} \int_{t_1}^{t_1+\Delta t} \sum_{k,m} \frac{\partial^2 H}{\partial \theta_k \, \partial \theta_m} (\epsilon \bar{\varphi}_k)(\epsilon \bar{\varphi}_m) \, d\tau \\
+ 0(\epsilon^3) + 0[(\Delta t)^2].
$$

For the objective function to be a maximum, we must have

$$
\Delta S < 0.
\tag{139}
$$

The weak form of the maximum principle requires that

$$
\frac{\partial H}{\partial \theta_k} = 0, \qquad k = 1, 2, \dots, r, \qquad t_1 \le t \le t_1 + \Delta t.
\tag{140}
$$

Since $t_1$ and $\epsilon \bar{\varphi}$ are arbitrary and $\Delta t$ may be chosen as small as we want, we have

$$
\int_{t_1}^{t_1+\Delta t} \sum_{k,m} \frac{\partial^2 H}{\partial \theta_k \, \partial \theta_m} (\epsilon \bar{\varphi}_k)(\epsilon \bar{\varphi}_m) \, d\tau < 0,
\tag{141}
$$

and the Hessian matrix whose *km*th element is

$$\frac{\partial^2 H}{\partial \theta_k \, \partial \theta_m}$$

must be negative definite at all but a finite number of points [27, 28]. Hence we can conclude that in maximizing (minimizing) an objective function the Hamiltonian function must be a maximum (or minimum) at all but a finite number of points. If the Hessian matrix is semipositive definite, we can derive the same result by considering higher order terms.

These derivations were obtained by Denn and Aris [29] and Jackson and Horn [27, 28] using tensor and matrix notation.

The basic difference between the continuous and discrete cases, as Polak, Jackson, and Horn have noted, is that in the continuous we can use a sufficiently small interval of time $\Delta t$ to simplify the result, whereas in the discrete no small interval can be adjusted.

The strong maximum principle for different cases was considered by Jackson and Horn [27, 28] and Denn and Aris [29].

As far as applications to the solution of problems are concerned, both the strong and weak forms of the maximum principle lead to the same result for continuous processes.

## REFERENCES

1. Pontryagin, L. S., V. G. Boltyanski, R. V. Gamkrelidze, and E. F. Mischenko, *The Mathematical Theory of Optimal Processes* (English translation by K. N. Trirogoff), Interscience, New York, 1962.
2. Roberts, S. M., *Dynamic Programming in Chemical Engineering and Process Control*, Academic Press, New York, 1964.
3. Valentine, F. A., "The Problem of Lagrange with Differential Inequalities as Added Side Conditions," in *Contributions to the Calculus of Variations*, 1933–1937, University of Chicago Press, Chicago, 1937.
4. Leitmann, G., *Optimization Techniques with Applications to Aerospace Systems*, Academic Press, New York, 1962.
5. Akhiezer, N. I., *The Calculus of Variations* (English translation by A. H. Fink), Blaisdell, New York, 1962.
6. Bliss, G. A., *Lectures on the Calculus of Variations*, University of Chicago Press, Chicago, 1946.
7. Elsgolc, L. E., *Calculus of Variations*, Addison-Wesley, Reading, Massachusetts, 1962.
8. Kopp, R. E., "Pontryagin's Maximum Principle" in *Optimization Techniques*, edited by G. Leitmann, Academic Press, New York, 1962.
9. Gelfand, I. M., and S. V. Fomin, *Calculus of Variations* (English translation by R. A. Silverman), Prentice-Hall, Englewood Cliffs, New Jersey, 1963.
10. Bellman, R., *Dynamic Programming*, Princeton University Press, Princeton, New Jersey, 1957.

11. Rozonoer, L. I., "L. S. Pontryagin's Maximum Principle in the Theory of Optimum System III," *Automation and Remote Control*, **20**, 1517 (1959).
12. Fan, L. T., and C. S. Wang, *The Discrete Maximum Principle: A Study of Multistage Systems Optimization*, Wiley, New York, 1964.
13. Bellman, R., "Review of the Mathematical Theory of Optimal Processes by L. S. Pontryagin et al.," *Quart. Appl. Math.*, **22**, No. 1 (1964).
14. Bellman, R., and S. E. Dreyfus, *Applied Dynamic Programming*, Princeton University Press, Princeton, New Jersey, 1962.
15. Kelley, H. J., "Methods of Gradients," in *Optimization Techniques*, edited by G. Leitmann, Academic Press, New York, 1962.
16. Denn, M. M., and R. Aris, "Green's Functions and Optimal System I: Necessary Conditions and an Iterative Technique," *Ind. Eng. Chem., Fundamentals*, **4**, 7 (1965).
17. Zadeh, L. A., and C. A. Desoer, *Linear System Theory*, McGraw-Hill, New York, 1963.
18. Bliss, G. A., *Mathematics for Exterior Ballistics*, Wiley, New York, 1944.
19. Goodman, T. R., and G. M. Lance, "The Numerical Integration of Two-Point Boundary Value Problems," *Math. Tables and Other Aids to Computation*, **10**, 82–86 (1956).
20. Denn, M. M., and R. Aris, "Green's Functions and Optimal Systems II: The Gradient Direction in Decision Space," *Ind. Eng. Chem. Fundamentals*, **4**, 213 (1965).
21. Bryson, A. E., F. J. Carroll, K. Mikand, and W. F. Denham, "Determination of the Lift of Drag Program That Minimizes Re-entry Heating with Acceleration or Range Constraints Using a Steepest Descent Computation Procedure," presented at IAS 29th Annual Meeting, New York, New York (1961).
22. Bryson, A. E., W. F. Denham, and S. E. Dreyfus, "Optimal Programming Problems with Inequality Constraints I, II," *AIAA J.*, **1**, 11 (1963); **2**, 1 (1964).
23. Berkovitz, L. D., "On Control Problems with Bounded State Variables," Rand Corp., RM-3207-PR, July (1962).
24. Chang, S. S. L., "Optimal Control in Bounded Phase Space," Technical Report 400-37, New York University, August (1961).
25. Dreyfus, S. E., "Variational Problems with State Variables Inequality Constraints," Rand Corp., p-2605-1, August (1963).
26. Jordan, B. W., and E. Polak, "Theory of a Class of Discrete Optimal Control Systems," Technical Report, Electronics Research Laboratory, University of California, January (1964).
27. Horn, F., and R. Jackson, "On Discrete Analogues of Pontryagin's Maximum Principle," *Int. J. Control*, **1**, 389 (1965).
28. Horn, F., and R. Jackson, "Discrete Maximum Principle," *Ind. Eng. Chem., Fundamentals*, **4**, 110 (1965); see also *Ind. Eng. Chem. Fundamentals*, **4**, 239 (1965).
29. Denn, M. M. and R. Aris, "Second Order Variational Equations and the Strong Maximum Principle," *Chem. Eng. Sci.*, **20**, 373 (1965); see also M. M. Denn's Ph.D. dissertation, University of Minnesota.

# Computational Procedures for Simple Continuous Processes

In this appendix some of the computational procedures used in Chapters 4 and 7 together with general background materials for the solution of two-point boundary value problems are presented. Theoretically, these problems may be solved on both analog and digital computers. We shall consider first some of the numerical techniques that require a digital computer and then some of the solution methods that employ the analog computer. In the final section several other methods are outlined.

## 1. NUMERICAL SOLUTIONS OF DIFFERENTIAL EQUATIONS

Two numerical methods which may be used to integrate differential equations of the form

$$\frac{dy}{dx} = f(x, y) \tag{1}$$

are the Euler method [1] and the Runge-Kutta method [1, 2]. Both methods require an initial value

$$y(x_0) = y_0, \tag{2}$$

from which we may begin the numerical integration.

The Euler method [1] is based on the idea that the derivative at a point is approximately equal to the ratio of corresponding small increments of the dependent and independent variables at that point; that is,

$$\frac{y_1 - y_0}{x_1 - x_0} = \frac{dy}{dx}\bigg|_{x=x_0}. \tag{3}$$

This equation may be put in the form

$$y_1 = y_0 + \frac{dy}{dx}\bigg|_{x=x_0} (x_1 - x_0) \qquad (4)$$

or finally

$$y_1 = y_0 + f(x_0, y_0)h, \qquad (5)$$

where

$$h = (x_1 - x_0) = \Delta x \qquad (6)$$

is a small increment along the $x$ axis.

Equation (5) may be used to obtain the value of $y_1 = y(x_1)$ from equations (1) and (2). This is the first step of the integration process. The general step is

$$y_{n+1} = y_n + f(x_n, y_n)h, \qquad (7)$$

and it may be used repeatedly to obtain the desired values of $y$.

The Runge-Kutta method [1, 2] applies the following formulas to obtain $y_{n+1}$ from $y_n$:

$$q_1 = f(x_n, y_n)h,$$

$$q_2 = f\left(x_n + \frac{h}{2}, y_n + \frac{q_1}{2}\right)h,$$

$$q_3 = f\left(x_n + \frac{h}{2}, y_n + \frac{q_2}{2}\right)h, \qquad (8)$$

$$q_4 = f(x_n + h, y_n + q_3)h,$$

$$y_{n+1} = y_n + \tfrac{1}{6}(q_1 + 2q_2 + 2q_3 + q_4),$$

where $h = x_{n+1} - x_n$.

## 2. NUMERICAL SOLUTION METHODS FOR TWO-POINT BOUNDARY VALUE PROBLEMS

Consider the system of differential equations that we encounter when the maximum principle is employed. After eliminating the decision variable $\theta(t)$, these equations have the form

$$\frac{dx}{dt} = f(x, z), \qquad (9)$$

$$\frac{dz}{dt} = F(x, z), \qquad (10)$$

with boundary conditions of the form

$$x(t_0) = \alpha \quad \text{at} \quad t = t_0, \tag{11}$$

$$z(T) = c \quad \text{at} \quad t = T; \tag{12}$$

that is, initial values are given for equation (9) and final values are given for equation (10).

If values are assumed for $z(t_0)$, the Runge-Kutta method may be used to integrate (9) and (10). The iterative Runge-Kutta method, which employs additional equations to predict the next trial values for $z(t_0)$, may often be used to obtain the solution of equations (9) and (10).

Let us consider first the iterative Runge-Kutta method for the case in which $x$ and $z$ are one-dimensional vectors. If equations (9) and (10) are differentiated with respect to $z_1(t_0)$, we obtain

$$\frac{d(dx_1/dt)}{dz_1(t_0)} = \frac{\partial f}{\partial x_1}\frac{dx_1}{dz_1(t_0)} + \frac{\partial f}{\partial z_1}\frac{dz_1}{dz_1(t_0)}, \tag{13}$$

$$\frac{d(dz_1/dt)}{dz_1(t_0)} = \frac{\partial F}{\partial x_1}\frac{dx_1}{dz_1(t_0)} + \frac{\partial F}{\partial z_1}\frac{dz_1}{dz_1(t_0)}. \tag{14}$$

If we let

$$g = \frac{dx_1}{dz_1(t_0)}$$

and

$$G = \frac{dz_1}{dz_1(t_0)},$$

equations (13) and (14) become

$$\frac{dg}{dt} = \frac{\partial f}{\partial x_1}g + \frac{\partial f}{\partial z_1}G, \tag{15}$$

$$\frac{dG}{dt} = \frac{\partial F}{\partial x_1}g + \frac{\partial F}{\partial z_1}G. \tag{16}$$

The initial conditions for these two equations are

$$g(t_0) = 0 \quad \text{at} \quad t = t_0 \tag{17}$$

and

$$G(t_0) = 1 \quad \text{at} \quad t = t_0. \tag{18}$$

If we assume a value for $z_1(t_0)$ and then integrate equations (9), (10), (15), and (16) from $t_0$ to $T$, using the Runge-Kutta method, we obtain values for $x_1(T)$, $z_1(T)$, $g(T)$, and $G(T)$.

The following approximation for the derivative

$$G(T) = \frac{dz_1(T)}{dz_1(t_0)} = \frac{z_1(T) - c_1}{z_1(t_0) - \xi_1} \tag{19}$$

may be solved for $\xi_1$ to give

$$\xi_1 = \frac{z_1(t_0)\, G(T) - z_1(T) + c_1}{G(T)}, \tag{20}$$

where $\xi_1$ is the new approximation for $z_1(t_0)$. We may repeat this computational procedure until equation (12) is satisfied or a result of the desired accuracy is obtained.

The iterative Runge-Kutta method for the case in which $x$ and $z$ are two-dimensional vectors is similar. Differentiation of the following equations

$$\frac{dx_1}{dt} = f_1(x_1, x_2, z_1, z_2), \tag{21}$$

$$\frac{dx_2}{dt} = f_2(x_1, x_2, z_1, z_2), \tag{22}$$

$$\frac{dz_1}{dt} = F_1(x_1, x_2, z_1, z_2), \tag{23}$$

$$\frac{dz_2}{dt} = F_2(x_1, x_2, z_1, z_2), \tag{24}$$

with respect to $z_1(t_0)$ and $z_2(t_0)$, gives

$$\frac{dg_{11}}{dt} = \frac{\partial f_1}{\partial x_1}\, g_{11} + \frac{\partial f_1}{\partial x_2}\, g_{21} + \frac{\partial f_1}{\partial z_1}\, G_{11} + \frac{\partial f_1}{\partial z_2}\, G_{21}, \tag{25}$$

$$\frac{dg_{21}}{dt} = \frac{\partial f_2}{\partial x_1}\, g_{11} + \frac{\partial f_2}{\partial x_2}\, g_{21} + \frac{\partial f_2}{\partial z_1}\, G_{11} + \frac{\partial f_2}{\partial z_2}\, G_{21}, \tag{26}$$

$$\frac{dG_{11}}{dt} = \frac{\partial F_1}{\partial x_1}\, g_{11} + \frac{\partial F_1}{\partial x_2}\, g_{21} + \frac{\partial F_1}{\partial z_1}\, G_{11} + \frac{\partial F_1}{\partial z_2}\, G_{21}, \tag{27}$$

$$\frac{dG_{21}}{dt} = \frac{\partial F_2}{\partial x_1}\, g_{11} + \frac{\partial F_2}{\partial x_2}\, g_{21} + \frac{\partial F_2}{\partial z_1}\, G_{11} + \frac{\partial F_2}{\partial z_2}\, G_{21}, \tag{28}$$

$$\frac{dg_{12}}{dt} = \frac{\partial f_1}{\partial x_1}\, g_{12} + \frac{\partial f_1}{\partial x_2}\, g_{22} + \frac{\partial f_1}{\partial z_1}\, G_{12} + \frac{\partial f_1}{\partial z_2}\, G_{22}, \tag{29}$$

$$\frac{dg_{22}}{dt} = \frac{\partial f_2}{\partial x_1}\, g_{12} + \frac{\partial f_2}{\partial x_2}\, g_{22} + \frac{\partial f_2}{\partial z_1}\, G_{12} + \frac{\partial f_2}{\partial z_2}\, G_{22}, \tag{30}$$

$$\frac{dG_{12}}{dt} = \frac{\partial F_1}{\partial x_1}\, g_{12} + \frac{\partial F_1}{\partial x_2}\, g_{22} + \frac{\partial F_1}{\partial z_1}\, G_{12} + \frac{\partial F_1}{\partial z_2}\, G_{22}, \tag{31}$$

$$\frac{dG_{22}}{dt} = \frac{\partial F_2}{\partial x_1}\, g_{12} + \frac{\partial F_2}{\partial x_2}\, g_{22} + \frac{\partial F_2}{\partial z_1}\, G_{12} + \frac{\partial F_2}{\partial z_2}\, G_{22}, \tag{32}$$

where

$$g_{11} = \frac{dx_1}{dz_1(t_0)}, \qquad g_{12} = \frac{dx_1}{dz_2(t_0)},$$

$$g_{21} = \frac{dx_2}{dz_1(t_0)}, \qquad g_{22} = \frac{dx_2}{dz_2(t_0)},$$

$$G_{11} = \frac{dz_1}{dz_1(t_0)}, \qquad G_{12} = \frac{dz_1}{dz_2(t_0)}, \tag{33}$$

$$G_{21} = \frac{dz_2}{dz_1(t_0)}, \qquad G_{22} = \frac{dz_2}{dz_2(t_0)}.$$

The boundary conditions for these eight equations are

$$g_{11}(t_0) = 0, \qquad g_{12}(t_0) = 0,$$

$$g_{21}(t_0) = 0, \qquad g_{22}(t_0) = 0,$$

$$G_{11}(t_0) = 1, \qquad G_{12}(T) = 0, \tag{34}$$

$$G_{21}(T) = 0, \qquad G_{22}(t_0) = 1.$$

If values are assumed for $z_1(t_0)$, $z_2(t_0)$, $G_{12}(t_0)$, and $G_{21}(t_0)$ and the integration of equations (21) through (32) is carried out, values of $x_1(T)$, $x_2(T)$, $z_1(T)$, $z_2(T)$, $G_{11}(T)$, and $G_{22}(T)$ will be obtained.

The derivative approximations

$$G_{11}(T) = \frac{z_1(T) - c_1}{z_1(t_0) - \xi_1}, \tag{35}$$

$$G_{22}(T) = \frac{z_2(T) - c_2}{z_2(t_0) - \xi_2} \tag{36}$$

may now be employed to compute $\xi_1$ and $\xi_2$, which are the new approximations for $z_1(t_0)$ and $z_2(t_0)$, respectively. From the given and computed values of $G_{12}(T)$ and $G_{21}(T)$ and the relation

$$G_{12}(t_0) = \frac{1}{G_{21}(t_0)}, \tag{37}$$

new approximations for $G_{12}(t_0)$ and $G_{21}(t_0)$ may be obtained. The integration may now be repeated and new trial values calculated until results of the desired accuracy are obtained.

It should be pointed out that approximations to this procedure may be obtained by deleting certain equations and certain terms of equations rather than by using equations (25) through (32) in total. For example, equations (28) and (31) may be deleted along with all terms involving

$G_{21}$ and $G_{12}$. Another approximation would be to use only equations (27) and (32) and to delete in these equations all terms that do not contain either $G_{11}$ or $G_{22}$. This approximation procedure is referred to as the approximate iterative Runge-Kutta method in Chapters 4 and 7.

It may sometimes be of advantage to use a backward integration and to start with the final rather than the initial conditions. The range of the final conditions is often known.

If final values are assumed for $x(T)$, the backward numerical integration of (9) and (10) may be executed by either the Euler or the Runge-Kutta method. The result of this integration is an optimal solution for those values of $x(t_0)$ computed by the backward integration. If this process is repeated many times, a table of optimal solutions is obtained.

This method is especially useful if we are interested also in the optimal solutions that correspond to other initial conditions in the neighborhood of the desired optimal solution.

Backward integration with the Runge-Kutta method is employed in Section 2b of Chapter 4 to treat a first-order irreversible consecutive reaction problem. In Section 3a of Chapter 4 backward integration by Euler's method is applied to obtain a table of optimal solutions for a batch distillation problem.

## 3.  SOLUTIONS OF TWO-POINT BOUNDARY VALUE PROBLEMS ON AN ANALOG COMPUTER

If initial values of $z(t_0)$ are assumed, equations (9) and (10) may be integrated on an analog computer. Since the integration may be accomplished in a short time, various values of $z(t_0)$ may be assumed until the correct values are achieved.

A feature of modern analog computation, called repetitive operation, allows the solution of two-point-boundary value problems to be determined quickly. In repetitive operation the computer essentially solves a problem many times per second. If these solutions are displayed on an oscilloscope, they appear to be continuous, and a graphic picture of the effect of parameter changes is obtained. With a repetitive analog computer the adjoint vector surface $z(t_0)$ may be searched rapidly until the desired solution to equations (9) and (10) is found.

Backward integration may also be used on the analog computer to compile a table of optimal profiles. Each backward integration computes an optimal profile for the values of $x(t_0)$ which are obtained as a part of the backward integration.

Lee [3] has considered how the maximum principle might be adapted to an analog computer to obtain optimal solutions of problems in which several decision variables must be considered. The equations associated with the maximum principle, which may be written as

$$\frac{dx_i}{dt} = f_i(x(t); \theta(t)), \qquad i = 1, 2, \ldots, s, \tag{38}$$

$$H = \sum_{i=1}^{s} z_i f_i(x(t); \theta(t)), \tag{39}$$

$$\frac{dz_i}{dt} = -\frac{\partial H}{\partial x_i}, \qquad i = 1, 2, \ldots, s, \tag{40}$$

$$x_i(t_0) = \alpha_i, z_i(T) = c_i, \qquad i = 1, 2, \ldots, s, \tag{41}$$

may be combined with a random search technique to obtain optimal solutions on the analog computer.

As already stated, the solution of equations (38), (39), and (40) leads to a two-point boundary value problem; that is, we know only the initial values of the state variables (functions), $x_i$, whereas only the final values of the adjoint variables (impulse functions), $z_i$, are given. A trial-and-error or other search procedure has to be used to fit the solution into the final values of $z$. Another problem is the interrelationship between equations (38), (39), and (40). To integrate equations (38) and (40) we must know the values of $\theta$ as a function of $t$; but this value is exactly what we hope to find from our solution. Thus another trial-and-error procedure is needed.

To obtain the values of $\theta$ as a function of $t$ some approximations are required. Clearly, we cannot make the calculations at every point along the coordinate of the independent variable $t$ for this would require an infinite number of calculations. Thus we shall divide the independent variable $t$ into $n$ intervals. The values of $\theta$ as a function of $t$ are assumed to be composed of $n$ straight-line segments. Now we need only to calculate the problem at $n + 1$ points along the $t$-coordinate.

For simplicity let us consider a system with only one decision variable, $\theta_1$. To find the maximum value of $S$ for this system we must determine the values of $\theta$ at $t = 0, t_1, t_2, \ldots, T$, such that the continuous function $\theta_1(t)$ [formed by the straight-line connections between the points $\theta_1(0)$, $\theta_1(t_1), \theta_1(t_2), \ldots, \theta_1(T)$] will make $S$ a maximum. This is accomplished by determining the values of $\theta_1, x_1, \ldots, x_s$, and $z_1, \ldots, z_s$ at $t = 0, t_1$, $t_2, \ldots, T$, which will make $H$ a maximum.

The procedure for this computational method is as follows:

1. Assume a set of initial values for the adjoint vector, say $z(0)$.
2. At $t = t_0 = 0$ the value of $\theta_1$, called $\theta_1(0)$, is obtained by maximizing (or minimizing) $H$ with the known initial conditions for $x$ and the assumed initial conditions for $z$.

3. At $t = t_1$ assume a value for $\theta$, say $\theta_1(t_1)$.

4. Connect $\theta_1(0)$ and $\theta_1(t_1)$ by a straight line. Integrate equations (38) and (40) along this straight line. A set of values for $x$ and $z$ is thus obtained at time $t_1$. We call these values $x(t_1)$ and $z(t_1)$.

5. Substitute the set of values $x(t_1)$ and $z(t_1)$ into equation (39); an improved $\theta_1(t_1)$ is obtained by maximizing (or minimizing) $H$.

6. Using this improved $\theta_1(t_1)$, repeat Steps 4 and 5 until no further change occurs in the improved $\theta_1(t_1)$.

7. At $t = t_2$ assume a value for $\theta_1$, say $\theta_1(t_2)$, and repeat Steps 4 to 6. However, the integration must be performed along the two line segments $\theta_1(t_0) - \theta_1(t_1)$ and $\theta_1(t_1) - \theta_1(t_2)$; the sets of values obtained for $x$ and $z$ are $x(t_2)$ and $z(t_2)$, respectively.

8. Similarly, we can obtain $\theta_1(t_3), \ldots, \theta_1(T)$.

9. At $t = T$ the calculated values for $z$ are compared with the given final values for $z(T)$. If they are different, appropriate adjustments are made to obtain a new set of initial values for $z$ and Steps 2 to 8 are repeated until the given values for $z$ are the same as the calculated final values for $z$.

Figure AI.1 illustrates the procedure just described. It has been found that Point 1 makes $H$ a maximum (or minimum) with the assumed initial conditions $z(0)$ and the given initial conditions $x(0) = \alpha$. It should be noted that once the initial conditions for $z$ are assumed these points are fixed. Now we can go to the next point on the $t$-coordinate. At $t = t_1$ assume $\theta_1$ is at Point 2. By integrating equations (38) and (40) along the

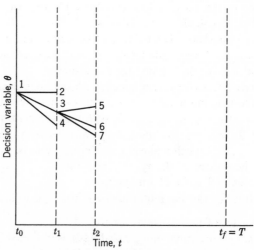

*Fig. AI.1* Schematic representation of optimization procedure by means of the maximum principle and random search using an analog computer [3].

straight line between Points 1 and 2 we obtain the values $z(t_1)$ and $x(t_1)$. Substituting this set of values into equation (39), we find $H$ is maximum (or minimum) if $\theta_1$ is at Point 3. Repeat this process until there is no further significant change in $\theta_1$. Let us assume that Point 3 is the correct value for $\theta_1$ at $t_1$ with the assumed initial conditions for $z$. We can proceed to $t_2$ and repeat the same procedure, except that the integration is along the line between Points 1, 3, and $\theta_1(t_2)$. This process is repeated until the values of $\theta_1(T)$, $x(T)$, and $z(T)$ have been computed. If the computed values of $z(T)$ are different from the given values for $z(T)$, proper adjustments are made for the assumed initial values of $z$ and the process is repeated.

For the optimization of a system with more than one decision variable this procedure is essentially valid, except that we have to find a set of values of $\theta$ at each point of the independent variable $t$.

It is worth noting that in the preceding discussion a forward integration procedure was assumed. For certain problems, however, it is advantageous to use backward integration. The procedure is the same as the forward one, except for the boundary conditions. The unknown boundary conditions at the onset of computation are the final conditions for the state variables $x$. Thus the object is to adjust the assumed final values for $x$ until the calculated initial conditions are the same as the given ones. For certain problems the backward integration procedure has been found to be more stable and less sensitive to errors [3]. Another advantage of this procedure, mentioned in the preceding section, is that in most of the design problems we are interested not only in a specified set of initial conditions but also in this vicinity. This vicinity is investigated while we are adjusting final conditions for the state variables.

The computer circuit for the method described consists essentially of three parts, shown in Fig. AI.2. We designate them as optimization circuit, integration circuit, and control circuit. The optimization circuit is used to find the values of $\theta$ such that the function $H$ is maximum (or minimum) at all time of $t$, for $0 \leq t \leq T$, with given values of $z$ and $x$. The integration circuit integrates equations (38) and (40) and obtains numerical values for $x$ and $z$ at specified values of $t$ with the given or assumed initial conditions. The control circuit performs the following functions:

1. It controls the sequence of the alternate integration and optimization process.
2. It controls and adjusts the curve of $\theta$ against $t$.
3. It adjusts the initial conditions $z(0)$ so that the calculated final conditions agree with the given final conditions of $z$.

If the optimization procedure is carried out manually on an analog computer, the control circuit is not needed. The curves of $\theta$ against $t$, which are composed of straight-line segments, can be set up manually on the diode function generators of the computer. The initial conditions $z(0)$ can also be adjusted manually by linear interpolation from the given and calculated final conditions of $z$.

If the optimization calculations are carried out automatically by the computer, several storage circuits are needed for storing the straight-line

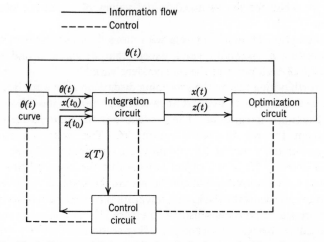

**Fig. AI.2**    Block diagram of the numerical optimization method based on the maximum principle random search technique [3].

segments of the $\theta$ against $t$ curves. Since these curves have to be changed constantly during the calculation, some easy method must be provided to change and adjust them automatically. A combined digital-analog computer (hybrid computer) is also suggested for this purpose.

So far no mention has been made of the methods that can be used to find the maximum (or minimum) of $H$ at any instant $t$. For systems with only one or two decision variables to be investigated there are numerous techniques for determining the system optimum, such as the various versions of the gradient method, factorial design, and random search technique. The random search technique is very useful when several decision variables must be considered because the computation time does not increase rapidly with an increase in the number of decision variables.

In the following a brief explanation of the random search technique on an analog computer is given. For detailed discussions readers are referred to the papers by Favreau and Franks [4] and Munson and Rubin [5]. Basically, the method consists of specifying each of the variables to be investigated in a random manner within the region of interest. Each variable is assumed to be completely independent of the others. A block diagram of the components and the information flow required of the random search method on the analog computer is shown in Fig. AI.3. The random noise generated by the noise generator is sampled frequently

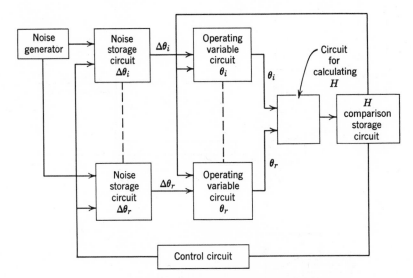

**Fig. AI.3**  Block diagram for random search method [3].

but at specified intervals and is stored in the noise storage circuit. We call this noise $\Delta\theta_i$. In the operating (decision) variable circuit this stored noise $\Delta\theta_i$ is added to the stored random variables $\theta_{is}$ to obtain $\theta_i$. The random variable (decision variable) $\theta_i$ is first passed through a limiting circuit which restricts this variable to the allowed range, and is then used to calculate $H$. The calculated $H$ is compared with the stored $H_s$. If $H$ is better than $H_s$, it is stored and $H_s$ is discarded. At the same time $\theta_i$ is stored and $\theta_{is}$ is discarded in the operating variable circuit. This process is repeated until the optimum is obtained.

The circuit used for the random search method is composed mainly of the comparison storage circuit, which is shown in Fig. AI.4, and the decision (operating) variable circuit, which is shown in Fig. AI.5. Any suitable control method can be used for the control circuit of the random search process.

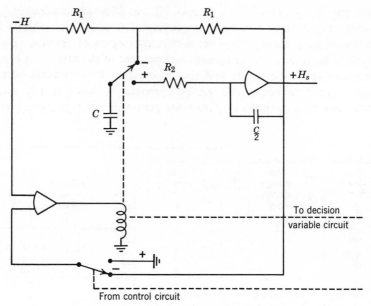

**Fig. AI.4**    Comparison-storage circuit [3].

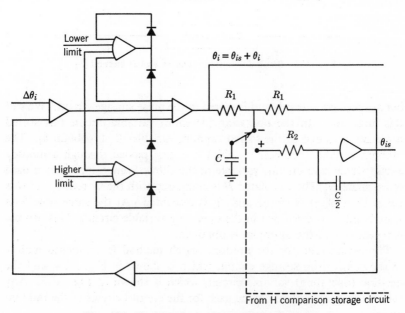

**Fig. AI.5**    Decision (operating) variable circuit [3].

This computational scheme can be used to handle most types of constraint on the decision variables (controlling or operating variables) and the objective functions (performance index) encountered in ordinary optimum design problems in which the maximum principle is employed. As already mentioned, this technique has the advantage of being able to investigate a large number of decision variables. It may not, however, be suited to investigating systems with a large number of state variables. This restriction probably stems from the very nature of the maximum principle which gives rise to a two-point (split) boundary value problem. Since the initial conditions of the adjoint variables (impulse functions) $z_i$ are usually unknown, a search method must be used to determine these initial conditions from the given final conditions. If the number of adjoint variables, which depend on the number of the state variables, is large, this search procedure may become prohibitively tedious.

Lee [3] used the computational scheme presented here to obtain numerical solutions of the problems considered in Sections 2b and 2c of Chapter 4.

## 4. OTHER METHODS

In this section we shall consider some other methods which may be used to treat two-point boundary value problems. Three methods are briefly summarized and several additional references are given.

*a. Steepest Ascent of the Hamiltonian.* This method, which is also referred to as the gradient method in function space [6], the relaxation method [7], and a successive approximation scheme employing the min operation [8], is described in detail by Noton [9].

Consider the system of differential equations that is encountered when the maximum principle is employed; that is, the performance equations

$$\frac{dx}{dt} = f(x; \theta), \tag{42}$$

the adjoint equations,

$$\frac{dz}{dt} = F(x, z, \theta), \tag{43}$$

the Hamiltonian equation

$$H = \sum_{i=1}^{s} z_i f_i(x; \theta), \tag{44}$$

and the boundary conditions given in equations (11) and (12).

If we are seeking to maximize a certain objective function, we wish to choose the decision vector $\theta(t)$ in such a way that the Hamiltonian is a maximum. The method described in this section accomplishes this by using an iterative procedure to find $\bar{\theta}(t)$, the optimal decision vector. An initial estimate of $\bar{\theta}(t)$ is obtained and $\theta(t)$ is corrected during each iteration so that the value of $H(\theta(t))$ is increased. For the $i$th component of the decision vector the following rule may be used for proceeding from the $n$th to the $(n + 1)$th approximation [9],

$$\theta_i'(t) = \theta_i(t) + k\frac{\partial H}{\partial \theta_i}, \qquad i = 1, 2, \ldots, r, \tag{45}$$

where the prime denotes the $(n + 1)$th iteration and the unprimed quantities, the $n$th iteration, and where $k$ is a suitable positive constant. The following sequence of computations for one iteration may be used [9]:

1. With $\theta(t)$ stored in the computer, the performance equations, equation (42), may be integrated from $t = t_0$ to $t = T$. The boundary conditions given in equation (11) are used to begin the integration. The values of $x(t)$ are stored in the computer.

2. Using the boundary conditions given in equation (12) and the stored values of $x(t)$ and $\theta(t)$, equation (43) is integrated from $t = T$ to $t = t_0$, using backward integration.

3. As soon as the values of $z(t)$ are computed, equation (45) is used to compute $\theta'(t)$; that is, at each step of the backward integration the values of the decision vector needed for the $(n + 1)$th iteration are obtained and stored in the computer.

This iterative method is used until there is no further change in $\theta(t)$. The values of $k$ should be small enough so that no instability will result, yet large enough so that the convergence will not be too slow.

Noton [9], Storey and Rosenbrock [6], and Merriam [7] have used this method and a digital computer to obtain numerical solutions to optimization problems.

Since it is necessary to integrate sets of differential equations repeatedly with this method, it would be better to use a hybrid computer for certain types of problem.

For more detailed discussion of this and closely related methods, readers are referred to References 6, 7, 8 and 9.

***b.  The Method of Finite Difference.***  Consider the system of differential equations given by equations (9) and (10) with the boundary conditions given in equations (11) and (12). A finite difference solution of this system of equations and boundary conditions can be used to obtain useful numerical results.

The interval of time $T$ is subdivided into $N$ equally spaced intervals of width $h$; this leads to $N + 1$ points $y^0, y^1, \ldots, y^N$, in which $y$ is any of the variables $(x_1, \ldots, x_s, z_1, \ldots, z_s)$; then $y^0 = y(t_0)$, $y^N = y(T)$, and $y^i$ refers to that variable at the end of the $i$th interval. A difference equation representation may then be substituted for the differential equation at each of the points for $x$ from $x^1$ to $x^N$ and for $z$ from $z^0$ to $z^{N-1}$. This leads to $N$ equations with $N$ unknowns ($x^1, x^2, \ldots, x^N$ for $x$ and $z^0, z^1, \ldots, z^{N-1}$ for $z$) for each component of the $x$-vector and $z$-vector, respectively, with the boundary values $x(t_0)$ and $z(T)$ included explicitly. Therefore we will obtain $2sN$ simultaneous equations with $2sN$ unknowns, in which $s$ is the dimension of the $x$-vector and $z$-vector.

If the functions $f(x, z)$ and $F(x, z)$ in equations (9) and (10) are linear, so are the simultaneous difference equations; then the Gaussian elimination method, matrix inversion method, or iteration method can be used to obtain the solution of the simultaneous equations [10, 11]. However, in most of the cases $f(x, z)$ and $F(x, z)$ are nonlinear; therefore the following relaxation method [7, 9, 11, 12] may be applied to obtain the solutions to the set of nonlinear simultaneous difference equations.

Consider the set of $n$ simultaneous difference equations,

$$
\begin{aligned}
a_{11}y_1 + a_{12}y_2 + \cdots + a_{1n}y_n &= C_1 \\
a_{21}y_1 + a_{22}y_2 + \cdots + a_{2n}y_n &= C_2 \\
&\vdots \\
a_{n1}y_1 + a_{n2}y_2 + \cdots + a_{nn}y_n &= C_n,
\end{aligned}
\tag{46}
$$

which, rewritten in the residual form, becomes

$$
\begin{aligned}
a_{11}y_1 + a_{12}y_2 + \cdots + a_{1n}y_n - C_1 &= R_1 \\
a_{21}y_1 + a_{22}y_2 + \cdots + a_{2n}y_n - C_2 &= R_2 \\
&\vdots \\
a_{n1}y_1 + a_{n2}y_2 + \cdots + a_{nn}y_n - C_n &= R_n,
\end{aligned}
\tag{47}
$$

where the $a_{ij}, i = 1, 2, \ldots, n, j = 1, 2, \ldots, n$, are all constants or functions of $y_i$.

Equation (47) may be regarded as a set of residual operators. For any set of chosen values of the unknowns, or variables, $y_1, y_2, \ldots, y_n$, they allow the residuals $R_1, R_2, \ldots, R_n$ to be immediately written down. As each of the residuals is a function of an unknown, that is to say,

$$R_i = R_i(y_1, y_2, \ldots, y_n), \quad i = 1, 2, \ldots, n,$$

the first differentials are given by

$$dR_1 = \frac{\partial R_1}{\partial y_1} dy_1 + \frac{\partial R_1}{\partial y_2} dy_2 + \cdots + \frac{\partial R_1}{\partial y_n} dy_n$$

$$dR_2 = \frac{\partial R_2}{\partial y_1} dy_1 + \frac{\partial R_2}{\partial y_2} dy_2 + \cdots + \frac{\partial R_2}{\partial y_n} dy_n$$

$$\vdots \tag{48}$$

$$dR_n = \frac{\partial R_n}{\partial y_1} dy_1 + \frac{\partial R_n}{\partial y_2} dy_2 + \cdots + \frac{\partial R_n}{\partial y_n} dy_n,$$

which can be written in matrix form as

$$
\begin{bmatrix} \Delta R_1 \\ \Delta R_2 \\ \vdots \\ \Delta R_n \end{bmatrix}
=
\begin{bmatrix}
\dfrac{\partial R_1}{\partial y_1} & \dfrac{\partial R_1}{\partial y_2} & \cdots & \dfrac{\partial R_1}{\partial y_n} \\[2mm]
\dfrac{\partial R_2}{\partial y_1} & \dfrac{\partial R_2}{\partial y_2} & \cdots & \dfrac{\partial R_2}{\partial y_n} \\[2mm]
\vdots & & & \\[2mm]
\dfrac{\partial R_n}{\partial y_1} & \dfrac{\partial R_n}{\partial y_2} & \cdots & \dfrac{\partial R_n}{\partial y_n}
\end{bmatrix}
\begin{bmatrix} \Delta y_1 \\ \Delta y_2 \\ \vdots \\ \Delta y_n \end{bmatrix}, \tag{49}
$$

where $\Delta R_i$ and $\Delta y_i$ are written for $dR_i$ and $dy_i$, respectively.

A successive iteration method is the following. Let $\Delta R_1 = -R_1$, $\Delta R_2 = -R_2, \ldots, \Delta R_n = -R_n$. Then, if $y_1, y_2, \ldots, y_n$ gives rise to residuals $R_1, R_2, \ldots, R_n$, the corrections to the variables are given by

$$
\begin{bmatrix} \Delta y_1 \\ \Delta y_2 \\ \vdots \\ \Delta y_n \end{bmatrix}
= -M^{-1}
\begin{bmatrix} R_1 \\ R_2 \\ \vdots \\ R_n \end{bmatrix}, \tag{50}
$$

where $M^{-1}$ is the inverse of the matrix $M$ where

$$
M = \begin{bmatrix}
\dfrac{\partial R_1}{\partial y_1} & \dfrac{\partial R_1}{\partial y_2} & \cdots & \dfrac{\partial R_1}{\partial y_n} \\[2ex]
\dfrac{\partial R_2}{\partial y_1} & \dfrac{\partial R_2}{\partial y_2} & \cdots & \dfrac{\partial R_2}{\partial y_n} \\[2ex]
\cdot & & & \\
\cdot & & & \\
\cdot & & & \\
\dfrac{\partial R_n}{\partial y_1} & \dfrac{\partial R_n}{\partial y_2} & \cdots & \dfrac{\partial R_n}{\partial y_n}
\end{bmatrix}.
\tag{51}
$$

Thus at each step of the iterative process a matrix of order $n$ must be inverted.

In order to minimize the truncation error in this finite difference method, the value of $h$ required may be quite small. This means that $N$ will be quite large. The storage and computational time requirements for solving such large systems of simultaneous equations ($2sN$ equations) may become completely impractical for some systems.

This method has been combined with an extrapolation formula by Noton [9] to obtain numerical solutions for a system with three state variables.

It should be pointed out that this method is similar to using a discrete version of the maximum principle to solve a continuous problem; that is, the continuous problem involving differential equations is replaced by a discrete problem involving difference equations. Once this is done, any of the methods used to treat discrete problems of this type may be selected [6, 13].

*c. Sequences of Linearized Solutions.* Sequences of linearized solutions have been used by Noton [9] to obtain numerical solutions of nonlinear differential equations of the type considered here. Noton's work is briefly summarized.

Consider equations (9) and (10) and the boundary conditions given in equations (11) and (12). Let $x(t)$ and $z(t)$ be approximate solutions of the system of equations. Better approximate solutions may be obtained by using the relations

$$
\frac{dx'}{dt} = f(x, z) + \frac{\partial f}{\partial x}(x' - x) + \frac{\partial f}{\partial z}(z' - z),
\tag{52}
$$

$$
\frac{dz'}{dt} = F(x, z) + \frac{\partial F}{\partial x}(x' - x) + \frac{\partial F}{\partial z}(z' - z),
\tag{53}
$$

where the primed quantities refer to the $(n + 1)$th solution and the unprimed quantities refer to the $n$th approximate solution. Equations (52) and (53) may be considered as a set of differential equations involving $x'$ and $z'$; that is,

$$\frac{dx'}{dt} + A(x, z)x' + B(x, z)z' = g(x, z), \tag{54}$$

$$\frac{dz'}{dt} + C(x, z)x' + D(x, z)z' = G(x, z), \tag{55}$$

where $A$, $B$, $C$, and $D$ are matrices of order $s$.

For each iteration in this sequence of solutions it is necessary to use $(s + 1)$ separate numerical integrations. On the first $s$ integrations only the homogeneous terms of equations (54) and (55) are included. For the $i$th integration the boundary condition $z_i(t_0) = 1$ is used for the $i$th component of the adjoint system. All other initial conditions are set equal to zero. The first $s$ integrations are accomplished in this manner. Let the solutions to these $s$ integrations be $X^i$ and $Z^i$, $i = 1, 2, \ldots, s$. For the $(s + 1)$th integration equations (54) and (55) are integrated by using the boundary conditions given in equation (11) and the boundary condition $z(t_0) = 0$. The full equations are used for the integration in this case. Let the solutions obtained be $X^{s+1}$ and $Z^{s+1}$, respectively. The following approximate solutions may now be written

$$x'(t) = X^{s+1}(t) + \sum_{i=1}^{s} z_i(t_0) X^i(t), \tag{56}$$

$$z'(t) = Z^{s+1}(t) + \sum_{i=1}^{s} z_i(t_0) Z^i(t), \tag{57}$$

where the $z_i(t_0)$ are the undetermined initial values of $z$. Equation (57) consists of a set of $s$ equations. The boundary conditions given in equation (12), $z(T) = 0$, may now be employed in equation (57) at $t = T$ and the values of $z(t_0)$ may be determined by solving this set of algebraic equations.

Equations (56) and (57) may now be used to determine the $(n + 1)$th solution, which is a better approximation of the desired solution.

In order to integrate equations (54) and (55) numerically, it is necessary to have the $n$th solution stored in the computer. Hence this method requires a moderate amount of computer storage. Noton [9] has described a more detailed treatment of this method and has given a specific example.

The best method of solution for a two-point boundary value problem depends on several factors. Often the analyst is limited to certain specific computing facilities which may eliminate or reduce the power of certain methods. His own background and experience may affect the relative usefulness of a given method for solving a given problem. The problem itself will also influence the choice of methods. Storey and Rosenbrock [6] and Noton [9] have used several methods on the same problem and their comments may be very helpful to someone solving a similar problem with a similar facility.

The use of hybrid computers to solve two-point boundary value problems of the type studied here will no doubt receive more attention as more of these facilities become available. Dahlin and Nelson [14] have used a hybrid computer and the maximum principle and they state that hybrid computation is often of great value for treating the split boundary value problems that arise.

## REFERENCES

1. Sangren, W. C., *Digital Computers and Nuclear Reactor Calculations*, Wiley, New York, 1960.
2. Stanton, R. G., *Numerical Methods for Science and Engineering*, Prentice-Hall, Englewood Cliffs, New Jersey, 1961.
3. Lee, E. S., "Optimization by Pontryagin's Maximum Principle on the Analog Computer," A.I.Ch.E. *J.*, **10**, 3, 309–315 (1964).
4. Favreau, R. R., and R. Franks, "Random Optimization by Analog Techniques," presented at the Second International Conference for Analog Computation, Strasbourg, September (1958).
5. Munson, J. E., and A. I. Rubin, "Optimization by Random Search on the Analog Computer," presented at the National Simulation Conference, Dallas, Texas (1958).
6. Storey, C., and H. H. Rosenbrock, in *Computing Methods in Optimization Problems*, A. V. Balakrishnan and L. W. Neustadt Eds., Academic Press, New York, 1964.
7. Merriam, C. W., III, *Optimization Theory and the Design of Feedback Control Systems*, McGraw-Hill, New York, 1964.
8. Kelly, H. J., in *Optimization Techniques with Applications to Aerospace Systems*, G. Leitmann, Ed., Academic Press, New York, 1962.
9. Noton, A. R. M., "Optimal Control and the Two-Point Boundary Problem," Advances in Automatic Control Symposium sponsored by the Institution of Mechanical Engineers, Nottingham, Britain, paper 21, 172–179 (April 1965); see also *Introduction to Variational Methods in Control Engineering*, Pergamon Press, Oxford, to be published.
10. Lapidus, L., *Digital Computation for Chemical Engineers*, McGraw-Hill, New York, 1962.
11. Varga, R. S., *Matrix Iterative Analysis*, Prentice-Hall, Englewood Cliffs, New Jersey, 1962.
12. Shaw, F. S., *Relaxation Methods*, Dover, New York, 1953.
13. Fan, L. T., and C. S. Wang, *The Discrete Maximum Principle*, Wiley, New York, 1964.
14. Dahlin, E. B., and J. M. Nelson, "Simulation and Optimal Control of Chemical Processes," *Chem. Eng. Prog.*, **60**, 49–56 (1964).

# Optimization of Complex Multistage Processes by the Dynamic Programming Technique

In this appendix a scheme based on dynamic programming for decomposing and optimizing topologically complex multistage processes is presented.

Based on the dynamic programming technique, Mitten and Nemhauser [1], Aris [2], and Chien [3] have described several schemes for the optimization of certain types of topologically complex processes. Aris, Nemhauser, and Wilde [4] have devised a method for formulating cyclic and branching processes as initial value, final value, or two-point boundary value problems. The relation between the proposed algorithm and the discrete maximum principle [5, 6] is also discussed. Comparative advantages and disadvantages of both methods are covered in Reference 5.

For convenience, some of the basic notions and definitions employed in multistage optimization are briefly reviewed. Notations slightly different from those in the main part of this book are used here to facilitate reading and to conform to the conventional usage of the dynamic programming technique.

## 1. COMPLEX MULTISTAGE PROCESSES

Since a multistage process is made up from a certain number of stages, its characteristics are completely determined by the types of stages of which it is composed and the ways in which they are connected [5].

A stage is a unit consisting of at least one input and one output stream. The characteristics of an input or output stream of a deterministic process are completely and uniquely described by a state vector $x_n$ whose subscript

$n$ is the label of the stream. Each stage is associated with a decision vector $\theta_n$ whose subscript $n$ is the label of the stage. The state vectors of the output streams from a stage are functions of the state vectors of its input streams and its decision vector. These functional relations can be expressed in vector form as [5]

$$x_n = T_n(x_{n-1}, \theta_n), \tag{1}$$

where $T_n(x_{n-1}, \theta_n)$ is the transformation function, $x_{n-1}$ is the input state vector, and $x_n$, the output state vector.

Stages can be conveniently classified according to the numbers of input and output streams associated with them. A stage with $\mu$ input

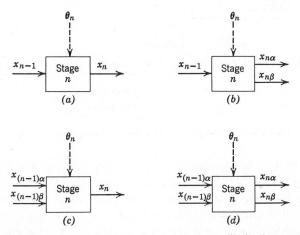

*Fig. AII.1* Four basic types of stages: (*a*) (1, 1) stage; (*b*) (1, 2) stage; (*c*) (2, 1) stage; (*d*) (2, 2) stage.

streams and $\nu$ output streams is called a $(\mu, \nu)$ stage. Figure AII.1 shows four basic types of stages, that is, (1, 1) stage, (1, 2) stage, (2, 1) stage, and (2, 2) stage, which are also given the names of linking stage, separating stage, combining stage, and complex stage, respectively [5].

A topologically complex process can be decomposed into a primary main process and one or more primary side processes. The primary main process can be any group of stages with the following four properties:

1. All of the stages are connected in series.
2. All of the streams connecting these stages flow in the same direction.
3. The initial stage of this group must be one of the initial stages of the whole process, called the global initial stages.
4. The final stage of this group must be one of the final stages of the whole process, called the global final stages.

In selecting a primary main process of any process, it is desirable to include in it as many stages as possible. Stages outside the primary main process may be conveniently grouped into several primary side processes, which may have one or more connections with the main process. A side process connected to the main process by its final stream only is called a parallel side process. A side process with at least one of its initial streams linked to the main process is a subordinate side process or simply a subprocess.

Both the main and side processes are denoted by the labels of their initial and final streams. For example, the complex process shown in

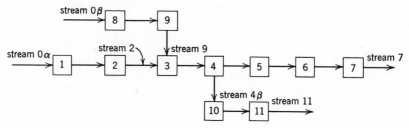

*Fig. AII.2*   A complex process with two simple side processes.

Fig. AII.2 may be decomposed into a main process ($0\alpha$, 9, $4\beta$, 7), a parallel side process ($0\beta$, 9), and a subprocess ($4\beta$, 11).

It may be noted that a main or side process can have several initial and/or final streams. An initial stream of a main or side process is called a global initial stream if it is also an initial stream of the whole process or a local initial stream if it is not an initial stream of the whole process. Similarly, a final stream is called a global final stream if it is also a final stream of the entire process. Otherwise, it is a local final stream.

The process shown in Fig. AII.2 consists of two primary side processes which are themselves a type of simple process, that is, a process solely composed of (1, 1) stages. A primary side process may also be a topologically complex process. Such a complex primary side process can be further decomposed into a secondary main process and one or several secondary side processes. A secondary main process is chosen to be a serial process. A secondary main process selected from a primary parallel side process should have a global initial stream as its initial stream and one of the local initial streams of the primary main process as its final stream. A secondary main process selected from a primary subprocess should have one of the local final streams of the primary main process as its initial stream and a global final stream, if it has one, as its final stream. For instance, the process given in Fig. AII.3 has a complex primary

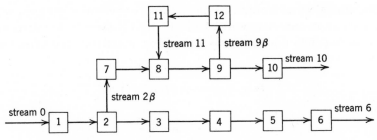

***Fig. AII.3***    A complex process with a complex side process.

subprocess $(2\beta, 10)$ which can be decomposed into a secondary main process $(2\beta, 11, 9\beta, 10)$ and a secondary subprocess $(9\beta, 11)$.

It can be seen that any complex process can be decomposed eventually into several main processes and side processes of different ranks, all of which are serial processes.

## 2. A MULTISTAGE OPTIMIZATION PROBLEM

When a process is to be optimized, each stage is associated with a return function which is a function of the input state vectors and the decision vector. The sum of the return functions over all stages is called the objective function; that is, if the return function of stage $n$ is $r(x_{n-1}, \theta_n)$, the objective function of the process is $\sum_n r(x_{n-1}, \theta_n)$. It can be seen that when all of the transformation functions are given the objective function of the process can be expressed as a function of the global initial states and the decision vector at each stage.

The optimization problem is to find the value of the decision vector at each stage which maximizes the objective function. All of the transformation functions are given, whereas the global initial states and final states may be fixed (given) or free (not given).

Since the global initial and final states play an important role in the optimization problem, it is convenient to define a "maximum return function" (abbreviated as MRF), which represents the total return of a process as a function of its global initial and final states. For example, if a process of $N$ stages has an initial state $x_0$ and a final state $x_N$, its MRF is represented by

$$f(x_0, x_N) = \max_{\theta_n} \left[ \sum_{n=1}^{N} r(x_{n-1}, \theta_n) \right], \qquad n = 1, 2, \ldots, N, \qquad (2)$$

with (a) initial state $= x_0$, (b) final state $= x_N$, where $x_0$ and $x_N$ are considered as parameters.

Once the MRF of a process is obtained, an optimization problem with any kind of boundary conditions can be readily solved. For instance, the maximum return for a process with a given initial state and a free final state can be obtained as

$$f(\bar{\bar{x}}_0, \bar{x}_N) = \max_{x_N} f(x_0, x_N)$$

with

$$x_0 = \text{the given value,}$$

where the single bar over $x_N$ indicates that this particular value of $x_N$ is obtained by maximizing the MRF with respect to the parameter $x_N$; the double bar over $\bar{\bar{x}}_0$ indicates that it is equal to the given value.

It is important to check the degree of freedom of an optimization problem. When both the global initial and final states are free, the degrees of freedom are equal to the numbers of the global initial variables plus the sum of the number of decision variables over all stages. When some or all of the initial and final states are fixed, the degree of freedom is decreased by the number of the fixed state variables.

If a process has $D_n$ decision variables at stage $n$, $S_I$ global initial state variables, and $S_F$ final state variables, the highest degree of freedom it can have is $(\sum_n D_n + S_I)$, and the MRF is a function of $(S_I + S_F)$ variables. It may happen that the number $(\sum_n D_n + S_I)$ is smaller than the number $(S_I + S_F)$. For such cases the MRF can only be a function of $(\sum_n D_n + S_I)$ variables; hence we must arbitrarily assign $(S_F - \sum_n D_n)$ final state variables as dependent variables. The MRF will then be written as $f(x_I, x_F \mid x_F)$, in which $x_I$ represent the initial state variables, $x_F$ represent those final state variables considered independent, and $x_F$, separated from $x_I$ and $x_F$ by a vertical bar, those that are considered dependent. For example, a one-stage process with $D_I = 1$, $S_I = S_F = 2$, will have its MRF written as $f(x_{0,1}, x_{0,2}, x_{1,1} \mid x_{1,2})$, in which the first subscript of $x$ represents the label of the stream and the second denotes the label of a component of a state vector.

## 3. PRINCIPLE OF OPTIMALITY AND FUNCTIONAL EQUATIONS

Since this work is for the purpose of extending the principle of optimality to deal with topologically complex processes, a careful consideration of its original version will be helpful.

The principle was formulated by Bellman in the following terms [7].

An optimal policy has the property that whatever the initial state and initial decision are, the remaining decisions must constitute an optimal policy with regard to the state resulting from the first decision.

The principle of optimality is based on an implicit assumption that the maximum return of a process is a function of its initial state only. It is important to note that it was originally formulated for a simple sequential process. The final state of such a process is either specified in the problem or can be readily determined by maximizing the return of the final stage with regard to the state of the input stream of this stage, since the final state has no effect on other stages. Utilizing this property, Bellman formulated a dynamic programming algorithm which can be represented by the following functional equation:

$$f(x_{n-1}) = \max_{\theta_n} \, [r(x_{n-1}, \theta_n) + f(x_n)], \tag{3}$$

where $x_{n-1}$ and $x_n$ represent the input and output of stage $n$, respectively, $\theta_n$ represents the decision of stage $n$, and $f(x_n)$ is the MRF of the downstream subprocess $(n, N)$, that is, the subprocess consisting of all the stages downstream to stage $n$, whereas $f(x_{n-1})$ is the MRF of the resulting process $(n - 1, N)$. As already explained, the MRF for a simple process can be expressed as a function of its initial state only.

Equation (3) can be interpreted as absorbing (imbedding) the MRF of the downstream subprocess $(n, N)$ into the MRF of the resulting process $(n - 1, N)$. The variable $x_n$ is an intermediate state variable of the resulting process $(n - 1, N)$, hence must be matched when $f(x_n)$ is absorbed into $f(x_{n-1})$. The decision variable $\theta_n$ is an independent variable and must be chosen so that $f(x_{n-1})$ will be maximum with regard to $x_{n-1}$. Thus during the process of absorbing all the intermediate state variables must be matched, whereas all the independent variables, except those that are used as parameters in the resulting MRF, must be chosen so that the resulting MRF is maximum. When the functional equation is interpreted in this way, its extension to deal with a complex process will be a straightforward matter.

Now let us consider any serial process obtained from the decomposition of a complex process. If the serial process has a local final stream, the value of this local state will affect the return of its downstream subprocesses. Such a local final state cannot be determined in the same way as that of the global final state of a simple process but must be chosen so that the sum of the return from this serial process and the return from its downstream subprocess will be maximum. A convenient way to overcome this difficulty is to express the MRF as a function of both the initial and final states. Since the final state is considered as a variable, its effect on the return of its downstream subprocess can be taken into consideration when its value is to be fixed.

Equation (3) can then be modified to the following forms for different types of stage:

(a) for (1, 1) stages (see Fig. AII.1$a$)

$$f(x_{n-1}, x_F) = \max_{\theta_n} [r(x_{n-1}, \theta_n) + f(x_n, x_F)], \qquad (4)$$

where $x_F$ represents the local final state;

(b) for (1, 2) stages (see Fig. AII.1$b$)

$$f(x_{n-1}, x_{F\alpha}, x_{F\beta}) = \max_{\theta_n} [r(x_{n-1}, \theta_n) + f(x_{n\alpha}, x_{F\alpha}) + f(x_{n\beta}, x_{F\beta})], \qquad (5)$$

where $x_{F\alpha}$ and $x_{F\beta}$ are the local final states of the downstream sub-processes $(n\alpha, F\alpha)$ and $(n\beta, F\beta)$, respectively;

(c) for (2, 1) stages (see Fig. AII.1$c$)

  (1) if none of the input streams of stage $n$ are from the local final stream of the downstream subprocess,

$$f(x_{(n-1)\alpha}, x_{(n-1)\beta}, x_F) = \max_{\theta_n} [r(x_{(n-1)\alpha}, x_{(n-1)\beta}, \theta_n) + f(x_n, x_F)], \qquad (6)$$

  (2) if one of the input streams of stage $n$, say stream $(n - 1)\beta$, is one of the local final streams of the downstream subprocess,

$$f(x_{(n-1)\alpha}, x_F) = \max_{\theta_n, x_{(n-1)\beta}} [r(x_{(n-1)\alpha}, x_{(n-1)\beta}, \theta_n) + f(x_n, x_{(n-1)\beta}, x_F)], \qquad (7)$$

where the downstream subprocess is labeled by $(n, (n - 1)\beta, F')$;

(d) for (2, 2) stages (see Fig. AII.1$d$),

  (1) if none of the input streams of stage $n$ are from the local final streams of the downstream subprocess,

$$f(x_{(n-1)\alpha}, x_{(n-1)\beta}, x_{F\alpha}, x_{F\beta}) = \max_{\theta_n} [r(x_{(n-1)\alpha}, x_{(n-1)\beta}, \theta_n) \\ + f(x_{n,\alpha}, x_{F\alpha}) + f(x_{n\beta}, x_{F\beta})], \qquad (8)$$

  (2) if one of the input streams of stage $n$, say $x_{(n-1)\beta}$, is one of the local final streams of a downstream subprocess, say subprocess $(n\beta, (n - 1)\beta, F'\beta)$,

$$f(x_{(n-1)\alpha}, x_{F\alpha}, x_{F'\beta}) = \max_{\theta_n, x_{(n-1)\beta}} [r(x_{(n-1)\alpha}, x_{(n-1)\beta}, \theta_n) + f(x_{n\alpha}, x_{F\alpha}) \\ + f(x_{n\beta}, x_{(n-1)\beta}, x_{F'\beta})]. \qquad (9)$$

It can be seen that the functional equation is nothing more than absorbing (imbedding) the MRF's of the downstream subprocesses into the MRF of the process resulting from connecting the stage $n$ under consideration to all of its downstream stages. During the process of absorption, the decision variable and the input states of the stage under consideration are considered as independent variables, which, except for those that are used as parameters, must be chosen so that the resulting MRF will be maximum.

Those initial and final states of the downstream subprocesses that become the intermediate states of the resulting process must be matched.

When the functional equation is applied to a global final stage of the type $(1, 1)$ stage, it reduces to

(a) if the output $x_n$ is free,

$$f(x_{n-1}, \bar{x}_n) = \max_{\theta_n} [r(x_{n-1}, \theta_n)], \tag{10}$$

(b) if the output $x_n$ is fixed,

$$f(x_{n-1}, \bar{\bar{x}}_n) = \max_{\theta_n} [r(x_{n-1}, \theta_n)], \tag{11}$$

with $\bar{\bar{x}}$ specified.

When the functional equation is applied to local final states, it reduces to a form similar to equation (11), except that the outputs must be considered as parameters. It is implicitly assumed in equations (10) and (11) that the number of the decision variables at stage $n$ is larger than the number of its output state variables. If this is not true, the degree of freedom must be checked carefully as already discussed, and equations (10) and (11) must be changed accordingly.

Relations similar to equations (10) and (11) can also be written for the final stages that are not of the $(1, 1)$ type.

## 4. PROCEDURES FOR OPTIMIZING COMPLEX PROCESSES

The optimal policy for a topologically complex process may be obtained by the following procedures:

1. Decompose the process into several main processes and side processes of different ranks, as discussed in Section 1.

2. Apply the functional equations given in the Section 3 to each stage to obtain the optimal decisions as functions of the initial and final states. The order of obtaining the MRF's for the side and main processes is in reverse to that of decomposing the process. In other words, the side process of the highest rank is considered first. The MRF of a subprocess is absorbed by the main process of the same rank, and the MRF of a main process is absorbed by the side process of the next lower rank. For example, the MRF of a secondary main process is absorbed by a primary side process. It may be noted that the MRF of a parallel side process is not absorbed by the abovementioned functional equations but is combined into the MRF of the main process by

$$f(x_{I\alpha}, x_{I\beta}, x_{F\alpha}, x_{F\beta}) = \max_{x_n} [f(x_{I\alpha}, x_{F\alpha}, x_n) + f(x_{I\beta}, x_{F\beta}, x_n)], \tag{12}$$

where $(I\alpha, F\alpha, n)$ is the main process and $(I\beta, F\beta, n)$ is a parallel side process.

A parallel side process with a global initial stream as its initial stream can be converted into a subordinate side process if it is a simple process and its inverse transformation function can be obtained [4]. This procedure will reduce the labor of computation.

If a main or a side process has a section that is itself a simple process, the labor of computation may be reduced by obtaining the MRF for this section first and then determining its end conditions by an equation similar to equation (12). For example, the MRF for the subprocess $(0\alpha, 2)$ in Fig. AII.2 can be obtained first and then combined with the MRF of subprocess $(2, 9, 7, 11)$ to obtain the MRF of subprocess $(0\alpha, 9, 7, 11)$ as

$$f(x_{0\alpha}, x_9, x_7, x_{11}) = \max_{x_2} \left[ f(x_{0\alpha}, x_2) + f(x_2, x_9, x_7, x_{11}) \right]. \qquad (13)$$

3. Eventually we obtain the MRF for the entire process at some fixed or chosen values of the global final states, depending on whether the final states are specified in the problem. The initial states can then be chosen so that the total return is maximum. These values of the initial states are used to obtain the optimal decisions which have been expressed as functions of the global initial states. If the global initial states are specified in the problem, the decisions of the global initial states are determined by

$$f(\bar{x}_I, \bar{x}_F) = \max_{\theta_I} \left[ r(x_I, \theta_I) + f(x_I, \bar{x}_F) \right],$$

in which $x_I = \bar{x}_I =$ the specified value.

## 5. AN EXAMPLE

Let us consider the process with two staggered feedback loops shown in Fig. AII.4. For simplicity we shall assume that all of the state and decision vectors are one-dimensional. The process can be decomposed into a main process $(0, b, d, 8\beta, 11\beta, 12)$ and two subprocesses $(8\beta, b)$ and $(11\beta, d)$.

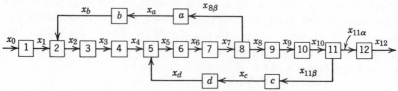

*Fig. AII.4* A process with two staggered feedback loop.

The MRF for the subprocess $(11\beta, d)$ can be obtained by the following equations:

$$f(x_c, x_d) = r(x_c, \theta_d),\tag{14}$$

$$f(x_{11\beta}, x_d) = \max_{\theta_c} [r(x_{11\beta}, \theta_c) + f(x_c, x_d)].\tag{15}$$

Similarly, we may find $f(x_{8\alpha}, x_{10}), f(x_{8\beta}, x_b), f(x_5, x_7),$ and $f(x_2, x_4)$. If the global final state is free, we have

$$f(x_{11\alpha}, \bar{x}_{12}) = \max_{\theta_{12}} [r(x_{11\alpha}, \theta_{12})].\tag{16}$$

The MRF for the entire process can then be obtained by the following equations:

$$f(x_{10}, x_d, \bar{x}_{12}) = \max_{\theta_{11}} [r(x_{10}, \theta_{11}) + f(x_{11\alpha}, \bar{x}_{12}) + f(x_{11\beta}, x_d)],\tag{17}$$

$$f(x_{8\alpha}, x_d, \bar{x}_{12}) = \max_{x_{10}} [f(x_{8\alpha}, x_{10}) + f(x_{10}, x_d, \bar{x}_{12})],\tag{18}$$

$$f(x_7, x_b, x_d, \bar{x}_{12}) = \max_{\theta_8} [r(x_7, \theta_8) + f(x_{8\beta}, x_b) + f(x_{8\alpha}, x_d, \bar{x}_{12})],\tag{19}$$

$$f(x_5, x_b, x_d, \bar{x}_{12}) = \max_{x_7} [f(x_5, x_7) + f(x_7, x_b, x_d, \bar{x}_{12})],\tag{20}$$

$$f(x_4, x_b, \bar{x}_{12}) = \max_{\theta_5, x_d} [r(x_4, x_d, \theta_5) + f(x_5, x_b, x_d, \bar{x}_{12})],\tag{21}$$

$$f(x_2, x_b, \bar{x}_{12}) = \max_{x_4} [f(x_2, x_4) + f(x_4, x_b, \bar{x}_{12})],\tag{22}$$

$$f(x_1, \bar{x}_{12}) = \max_{\theta_2, x_b} [r(x_1, x_b, \theta_2) + f(x_2, x_b, \bar{x}_{12})],\tag{23}$$

$$f(x_0, \bar{x}_{12}) = \max_{\theta_1} [r(x_0, \theta_1) + f(x_1, \bar{x}_{12})].\tag{24}$$

## 6. RELATION TO THE DISCRETE MAXIMUM PRINCIPLE

It is of interest to relate the proposed optimization scheme to a local and weak version of the discrete maximum principle [5, 6].

Let us consider the optimization problem posed in Section 2. To apply the discrete maximum principle we define a new state variable $x_{n,r}$ which satisfies the following equations:

(1) for a $(1, 1)$ stage

$$x_{n,r} = x_{n-1,r} + r(x_{n-1}, \theta_n),\tag{25}$$

where the first subscript of $x$ is the label of the stream and the second subscript is the label of this new state variable as a component of the enlarged state vector;

(2) for a $(1, 2)$ stage

$$x_{n\alpha,r} = x_{n-1,r} + r(x_{n-1}, \theta_n), \tag{26}$$

$$x_{n\beta,r} = 0, \tag{27}$$

where stream $n\alpha$ is in the main process and stream $n\beta$ is in the initial stream of a subprocess;

(3) for a $(2, 1)$ stage

$$x_{n,r} = x_{(n-1)\alpha,r} + x_{(n-1)\beta,r} + r(x_{(n-1)\alpha}, x_{(n-1)\beta}, \theta_n); \tag{28}$$

(4) for a $(2, 2)$ stage

$$x_{n\alpha,r} = x_{(n-1)\alpha,r} + x_{(n-1)\beta,r} + r(x_{(n-1)\alpha}, x_{(n-1)\beta}, \theta_n), \tag{29}$$

$$x_{n\beta,r} = 0, \tag{30}$$

where stream $n\alpha$ is in the main process and stream $n\beta$ is the initial stream of a subprocess;

(5) for a global initial stream

$$x_{0,r} = 0. \tag{31}$$

Equations (25) through (31) simply represent the summation of the return functions over all stages. It may be noted that the value of this new state variable at an initial stream is always zero. By introducing this new state variable the optimization problem becomes that of maximizing the sum of $x_{F,r}$ over all global final streams.

The technique of the discrete maximum principle is to introduce an adjoint vector $z$ and a Hamiltonian function $H$ to satisfy the following relations [5]:

(1) for a $(1, 1)$ stage

$$z_{n-1} = \frac{\partial H_n}{\partial x_{n-1}}, \tag{32}$$

$$H_n = \sum_i z_{n,i} T_{n,i}(x_{n-1}, \theta_n), \tag{33}$$

where $\sum_i$ represents summation over all components of the state vector of stream $n$;

(2) for a $(1, 2)$ stage

$$z_{n-1} = \frac{\partial H_n}{\partial x_{n-1}}, \tag{34}$$

$$H_n = \sum_i z_{n\alpha,i} T_{n\alpha,i}(x_{n-1}, \theta_n) + \sum_i z_{n\beta,i} T_{n\beta,i}(x_{n-1}, \theta_n); \tag{35}$$

(3) for a (2, 1) stage

$$z_{(n-1)\alpha} = \frac{\partial H_n}{\partial x_{(n-1)\alpha}}, \tag{36}$$

$$z_{(n-1)\beta} = \frac{\partial H_n}{\partial x_{(n-1)\beta}}, \tag{37}$$

$$H_n = \sum_i z_{n,i} T_{n,i}(x_{(n-1)\alpha}, x_{(n-1)\beta}, \theta_n); \tag{38}$$

(4) for a (2, 2) stage

$$z_{(n-1)\alpha} = \frac{\partial H_n}{\partial x_{(n-1)\alpha}}, \tag{39}$$

$$z_{(n-1)\beta} = \frac{\partial H_n}{\partial x_{(n-1)\beta}}, \tag{40}$$

$$H_n = \sum_i z_{n\alpha,i} T_{n\alpha,i}(x_{(n-1)\alpha}, x_{(n-1)\beta}, \theta_n)$$
$$+ \sum_i z_{n\beta,i} T_{n\beta,i}(x_{(n-1)\alpha}, x_{(n-1)\beta}, \theta_n). \tag{41}$$

The optimal decisions at these stages are then determined by the following conditions [5]:

$$\frac{\partial H_n}{\partial \theta_{n,k}} = 0, \qquad k = 1, 2 \ldots, r, \tag{42}$$

where $\theta_{n,k}$ is the $k$th component of the decision vector $\theta_n$.

If the global initial and final states are free, the values of the adjoint variables at the global initial and final streams are specified as

$$z_{I,i} = 0, \qquad i \neq r, \tag{43}$$

$$z_{F,i} = \delta_{ri}, \tag{44}$$

where the subscripts $I$ and $F$ denote the initial and final streams respectively, $\delta_{ri}$ is the Kronecker delta, and $r$ is the label of the new state variable as already stated.

If some of the initial or final state variables are fixed, the conditions given in equations (43) and (44) for the corresponding adjoint variables should be deleted.

We now relate the discrete maximum principle to the optimization scheme presented in Sections 3 and 4. Let us consider first the problem with free final states.

For the global final stages equations (33), (42), and (44) imply that

$$\frac{\partial H_F}{\partial \theta_{F,k}} = \frac{\partial T_{F,r}(x_{F-1}, \theta_F)}{\partial \theta_{F,k}} = \frac{\partial r(x_{F-1}, \theta_F)}{\partial \theta_{F,k}} = 0, \tag{45}$$

which is equivalent to equation (10) if we assume that the maximum of $r(x_{F-1}, \theta_F)$ lies on a stationary point. It may be noted that the vector $x_{F-1}$ in $r(x_{F-1}, \theta_F)$ does not include the component $x_{F-1,r}$.

If we let $f(x_{F-1}, \bar{x}_F)$ denote the maximum of $r(x_{F-1}, \theta_F)$, equation (32) gives

$$z_{F-1,i} = \frac{\partial f(x_{F-1}, \bar{x}_F)}{\partial x_{F-1,i}}, \quad \text{for } i \neq r, \tag{46}$$

$$z_{F-1,r} = 1. \tag{47}$$

By applying equation (42) to the preceding stage we obtain

$$\frac{\partial H_{F-1}}{\partial \theta_{F-1,k}} = \sum_{\substack{i \\ (i \neq r)}} \frac{\partial f(x_{F-1}, \bar{x}_F)}{\partial x_{F-1\,i}} \frac{\partial T_{F-1,i}(x_{F-2}, \theta_{F-1})}{\partial \theta_{F-1,k}} + \frac{\partial T_{F-1,r}(x_{F-2}, \theta_{F-1})}{\partial \theta_{F-1,k}}$$

$$= \sum_{\substack{i \\ (i \neq r)}} \frac{\partial f(x_{F-1}, \bar{x}_F)}{\partial x_{F-1,i}} \frac{\partial x_{F-1,i}}{\partial \theta_{F-1,k}} + \frac{\partial r(x_{F-2}, \theta_{F-1})}{\partial \theta_{F-1,k}} = 0, \tag{48}$$

which is equivalent to equation (4) if the maximum of $[r(x_{F-2}, \theta_{F-1}) + f(x_{F-1}, \bar{x}_F)]$ lies on a stationary point.

Again, if we let $f(x_{F-2}, \bar{x}_F)$ represent the maximum of $[f(x_{F-1}, \bar{x}_F) + r(x_{F-2}, \theta_{F-1})]$, equation (32) gives

$$z_{F-2,i} = \frac{\partial f(x_{F-2}, \bar{x}_F)}{\partial x_{F-2,i}} \quad \text{for } i \neq r, \tag{49}$$

$$z_{F-2,r} = 1. \tag{50}$$

Thus it follows that for a $(1, 1)$ stage, equation (42) corresponds to equation (4) precisely if the maximum of $[r(x_{n-1}, \theta_n) + f(x_n, x_F)]$ lies on a stationary point.

For problems with fixed final states the preceding argument still holds except that the $z_{F,i}$, $i \neq r$, play the role of Lagrangian multipliers and equation (42) becomes

$$\frac{\partial H_F}{\partial \theta_{F,k}} = \sum_{\substack{i \\ i \neq r}} z_{F,i} \frac{\partial T_{F,i}(x_{F-1}, \theta_F)}{\partial \theta_{F,k}} + \frac{\partial T_{F,r}(x_{F-1}, \theta_F)}{\partial \theta_{F,k}}$$

$$= \sum_{\substack{i \\ (i \neq r)}} z_{F,i} \frac{\partial}{\partial \theta_{F,k}}(x_{F,i} - \bar{x}_{F,i}) + \frac{\partial r(x_{F-1}, \theta_F)}{\partial \theta_{F,k}} = 0, \tag{51}$$

where $\bar{x}_{F,i}$ is the specified value of $x_{F,i}$.

Equation (51) is precisely equivalent to the Lagrangian multiplier technique of maximizing the function $r(x_{F-1}, \theta_F)$ with respect to $\theta_F$ with constraints $x_{F,i} = \bar{x}_{F,i}$.

For a $(1, 2)$ stage, if we let $f(x_{n\alpha}, \bar{x}_{F\alpha})$ and $f(x_{n\beta}, \bar{x}_{F\beta})$ represent the MRF's of subprocess $(n\alpha, F\alpha)$ and $(n\beta, F\beta)$, respectively, it can be shown that

$$z_{n\alpha,i} = \frac{\partial f(x_{n\alpha}, \bar{x}_{F\alpha})}{\partial x_{n\alpha,i}} \quad \text{for} \quad i \neq r, \tag{52}$$

$$z_{n\alpha,r} = 1, \tag{53}$$

$$z_{n\beta,i} = \frac{\partial f(x_{n\beta}, \bar{x}_{F\beta})}{\partial x_{n\beta,i}} \quad \text{for} \quad i \neq r \tag{54}$$

$$z_{n\beta,r} = 1. \tag{55}$$

Equations (26), (27), (35), and (42) then show that

$$\frac{\partial H_n}{\partial \theta_n} = \sum_{\substack{i \\ (i \neq r)}} \frac{\partial f(x_{n\alpha}, \bar{x}_{F\alpha})}{\partial x_{n\alpha,i}} \frac{\partial x_{n\alpha,i}}{\partial \theta_{n,k}} + \frac{\partial r(x_{n-1}, \theta_n)}{\partial \theta_{n,k}}$$

$$+ \sum_{\substack{i \\ (i \neq r)}} \frac{\partial f(x_{n\beta}, \bar{x}_{F\beta})}{\partial x_{n\beta,i}} \frac{\partial x_{n\beta,i}}{\partial \theta_{n,k}} = 0, \quad (56)$$

which is equivalent to equation (5).

If we let $f(x_{n-1}, \bar{x}_{F\alpha}, \bar{x}_{F\beta})$ represent the maximum of $[f(x_{n\alpha}, \bar{x}_{F\alpha}) + f(x_{n\beta}, \bar{x}_{F\beta}) + r(x_{n-1}, \theta_n)]$, it can be shown that

$$z_{n-1,i} = \frac{\partial f(x_{n-1}, \bar{x}_{F\alpha}, \bar{x}_{F\beta})}{\partial x_{n-1,i}}, \quad i \neq r, \tag{57}$$

$$z_{n-1,r} = 1. \tag{58}$$

If we let $f(x_n, x_F)$ represent the MRF of subprocess $(n, F)$ for a $(2, 1)$ stage, it follows from equations (38) and (42) that

$$\frac{\partial H_n}{\partial \theta_n} = \sum_{\substack{i \\ (i \neq r)}} \frac{\partial f(x_n, x_F)}{\partial x_{n,i}} \frac{\partial x_{n,i}}{\partial \theta_{n,k}} + \frac{\partial r(x_{(n-1)\alpha}, x_{(n-1)\beta}, \theta_n)}{\partial \theta_{n,k}}, \tag{59}$$

which is equivalent to the part of maximization with respect to $\theta_n$ in equation (7).

Equations (28), (36), and (37) show that

$$z_{(n-1)\alpha,i} = \frac{\partial f(x_{(n-1)\alpha}, x_{(n-1)\beta}, x_F)}{\partial x_{(n-1)\alpha,i}}, \quad i \neq r, \tag{60}$$

$$z_{(n-1)\alpha,r} = 1, \tag{61}$$

$$z_{(n-1)\beta,i} = \frac{\partial f(x_{(n-1)\alpha}, x_{(n-1)\beta}, x_F)}{\partial x_{(n-1)\beta,i}}, \quad i \neq r, \tag{62}$$

$$z_{(n-1)\beta,r} = 1. \tag{63}$$

Equation (62) is equivalent to the part of maximization with respect to $x_{(n-1)\beta}$ in equation (7) with the constraints

$$x_{(n-1)\beta,i} = T_{(n-1)\beta,i}(x_{(n-2)\beta}, \theta_{(n-1)\beta}).$$

Similarly, the relations between the dynamic programming algorithm and the discrete maximum principle for a $(2, 2)$ stage can be obtained. For a free global initial state it follows from equation (43) that

$$z_{I,i} = \frac{\partial f(x_I, \bar{x}_F)}{\partial x_{I,i}} = 0, \tag{64}$$

which is simply the maximization of $f(x_I, \bar{x}_F)$ with respect to $x_I$.

For a fixed global initial state the conditions $z_{I,i} = 0$ are deleted. It follows from the first equality of equation (64) that

$$\frac{\partial f(x_I, \bar{x}_F)}{\partial x_{I,i}} = z_{I,i} \frac{\partial}{\partial x_{I,i}} (x_{I,i} - \bar{\bar{x}}_{I,i}) = 0, \tag{65}$$

where $\bar{\bar{x}}_{I,i}$ is the specified value of $x_{I,i}$. Equation (65) is equivalent to the maximization of $f(x_I, \bar{x}_F)$ with respect to $x_{I,i}$ satisfying the constraints $x_{I,i} = \bar{\bar{x}}_{I,i}$.

## REFERENCES

1. Mitten, L. G., and G. L. Nemhauser, "Multistage Optimization," Chem. Eng. Prog., **59**, No. 1, 52 (1963).
2. Aris, R., *Discrete Dynamic Programming*, Blaisdell, New York, 1964.
3. Chien, H. H., private communication, July 1964.
4. Aris, R., G. L. Nemhauser, and D. Wilde, "Optimization of Cyclic and Branching Systems by Serial Procedures," a paper presented at A.I.Ch.E. Meeting, Houston, December 5, 1963.
5. Fan, L. T. and C. S. Wang, *The Discrete Maximum Principle: A Study of Multistage Systems Optimization*, Wiley, New York, 1964.
6. Fan, L. T. and C. S. Wang, "Multi-stage Optimization by the Generalized Discrete Maximum Principle," *J. Electron Control*, **16**, 441 (1964).
7. Bellman, R., *Dynamic Programming*, Princeton University Press, Princeton, New Jersey, 1957.

# Nomenclature

## CHAPTER 1

| | |
|---|---|
| $a$ | constant in objective function |
| $B$ | constant |
| $C$ | constant |
| $f$ | objective function |
| $F$ | composite function |
| $g$ | constrained function |
| $I_0$ | initial interval of search |
| $I_n$ | interval at the $n$th trial |
| $n$ | $n$th state variable or total number of state variables |
| $x$ | state vector |

**Greek Letters**

| | |
|---|---|
| $\lambda$ | Lagrange multiplier |

## CHAPTER 2

| | |
|---|---|
| $a$ | constant |
| $A_i$ | an integration constant |
| $b$ | constant |
| $c_i$ | constant in objective function |
| $g$ | constrained function |

| | |
|---|---|
| $G$ | $\dfrac{e^{-\lambda T} - e^{\lambda T}}{(\lambda + a)e^{\lambda T} - (\lambda - a)e^{-\lambda T}}$ , constant |
| $h$ | an arbitrary continuous function of $x(T)$ |
| $H$ | the Hamiltonian function |
| $\bar{H}$ | the optimal value of $H$ |
| $r$ | total number of decision variables |
| $s$ | total number of state variables |
| $S$ | objective function |
| $t$ | independent variable, time or space |
| $t_0$ | initial value of $t$ |
| $T$ | final value of $t$ |
| $x$ | state vector |
| $\bar{x}$ | the optimal value of $x$ |
| $x(0)$ | initial value of $x$ |
| $x(t_0)$ | initial condition of $x$ |
| $\underline{x}$ | a $(s + 1)$- or $(s + r)$-dimensional state vector |
| $y$ | perturbation of state vector |
| $z$ | $s$-dimensional adjoint vector |
| $\bar{z}$ | the optimal value of $z$ |
| $z(0)$ | initial value of $z$ |

## Greek Letters

| | |
|---|---|
| $\alpha$ | constant vector |
| $\beta$ | constant |
| $\epsilon$ | a small number |
| $\eta$ | constant |
| $\theta$ | decision vector |
| $\bar{\theta}$ | the optimal value of $\theta$ |
| $\theta(t_0)$ | initial value of $\theta$ |
| $\lambda$ | $\sqrt{a^2 + 1}$ |
| $\lambda_\alpha$ | unknown multipliers |
| $\sigma$ | parameter in the performance equation |
| $\Phi$ | perturbation of decision vector |
| $\psi$ | constrained function on decision vector |
| $\omega$ | new decision vector |

## CHAPTER 3

| | |
|---|---|
| $a_i$ | $i$th component of the tangent vector to the circle |
| $A$ | integration constant |
| $c_i$ | constant in objective function |
| $D$ | differential operator |

| | |
|---|---|
| $e(t)$ | error signal |
| $f$ | friction coefficient |
| $F$ | amount of effort |
| $Fm$ | maximum amount of effort |
| $g$ | load disturbance function |
| $h$ | proportionality function |
| $H$ | the Hamiltonian function |
| $H^*$ | the Hamiltonian function in which $\theta$ appears explicitly |
| $j$ | moment of inertia |
| $k$ | constant |
| $K$ | constant |
| $M$ | magnitude of control |
| $p$ | constant |
| $q(t)$ | control action |
| $r$ | total number of decision variables |
| $r(t)$ | response signal |
| $s$ | total number of state variables |
| $S$ | objective function |
| $t$ | time |
| $t_1$ | time on which saturation period ends |
| $t_0$ | initial time |
| $t_s$ | time for switching from $\theta = 0$ to $\theta = 1$ |
| $T$ | final time |
| $\bar{T}$ | the optimal value of $T$ |
| $w$ | positive constant |
| $x$ | state vector |
| $\bar{x}$ | the optimal value of $x$ |
| $x(t_0)$ | initial value of $x$ |
| $x(T)$ | final value of $x$ |
| $y$ | output of the system |
| $z$ | adjoint vector |

## Greek Letters

| | |
|---|---|
| $\alpha$ | initial values of state vector |
| $\beta$ | final values of state vector |
| $\gamma$ | locus of curves given in Fig. 3.9 |
| $\delta$ | damping ratio |
| $\Delta$ | conventional symbol for $\theta$ |
| $\eta$ | damping constant, $\delta\omega$ |
| $\eta_i$ | given constant |
| $\theta$ | decision vector |
| $\bar{\theta}$ | the optimal value of $\theta$ |

$\xi$         given constant
$\Phi$        constrained function on decision vector
$\omega$        natural frequency

## CHAPTER 4

| | |
|---|---|
| $a$ | given constant |
| $A$ | chemical specie; cross-sectional area of tubular reactor in equation (22b) |
| $B$ | chemical specie |
| $B_0$ | Bodenstein number |
| $c$ | precursor concentration |
| $c_i$ | constant in objective function |
| $c_0$ | initial precursor concentration |
| $C$ | chemical specie |
| $D$ | mass diffusion coefficient |
| $D_A$ | Damkohler number |
| $E$ | error in Section 2, part d |
| $E_i$ | activation energy |
| $F_i$ | $\dfrac{2k_{i0}L}{(G/\rho)}$ |
| $G$ | mass flow rate |
| $G_i$ | $\dfrac{dx_i(1)}{x_i(1)}$ |
| $h$ | increment in the finite difference calculation |
| $H$ | the Hamiltonian function |
| $k$ | specific reaction rate |
| $k_{i0}$ | frequency factor |
| $l$ | axial position in tubular reactor |
| $L$ | length of tubular reactor |
| $m$ | $k_{i0}T$ |
| $M$ | $\dfrac{(G/\rho)L}{2D}$ |
| $n$ | mole of reactant in Section 2c; point of decision in the finite difference calculation in Section 2d; neutron density in Section 4 |
| $n_0$ | initial neutron density |
| $N$ | total number of moles |
| $p_i$ | partial pressure of component $i$ |
| $P$ | total pressure |
| $R$ | gas constant |

| | |
|---|---|
| $R_i$ | mass reaction rate of component $i$ |
| $S$ | objective function |
| $t$ | temperature in Section 1; holding time in Section 2b; $l/G$, the length parameter in Section 2c; time of operation in Section 3a |
| $T$ | temperature of reaction in Sections 2a and 2d; total holding time in Section 2b; total length of reactor in Section 2c; duration of operation in Section 3a |
| $T$ | temperature |
| $u$ | average bulk flow velocity |
| $x$ | state vector |
| $x_e$ | equilibrium conversion |
| $x_i$ | fractional mass concentration of component $i$ in Sections 2a and 2d; molar concentration of component $i$ in Section 2b |
| $x_1$ | quantity of charge remaining in still in Section 2d |
| $x_2$ | composition of more volatile component in Section 2d |
| $\bar{x}$ | the optimal value of $x$ |
| $y$ | overhead composition in batch distillation in Section 3a; control-rod position in Section 4 |
| $z$ | adjoint vector |
| $\bar{z}$ | the optimal value of $z$ |

## Greek Letters

| | |
|---|---|
| $\alpha$ | initial value of $x$ in Section 2a; the value of $x$ corresponding to $M = \infty$ in Section 2d; power coefficient of reactivity in Section 4 |
| $\beta$ | constant in Section 2b; the value of $x$ corresponding to $M = 0$ in Section 2d; fraction of the neutrons given off in the fusion which is delayed and not emitted instantaneously, in Section 4 |
| $\eta$ | dimensionless holding time in Section 2b; dimensionless length in Section 2d |
| $\theta$ | decision vector |
| $\bar{\theta}$ | the optimal value of $\theta$ |
| $\lambda$ | Lagrange multiplier in Section 3a; equivalent decay constant for the one delay group case in Section 4 |
| $\lambda_1$ | $\dfrac{E_1}{E_2 - E_1}$ |
| $\lambda_2$ | $\dfrac{E_2}{E_2 - E_1}$ |
| $\Lambda$ | neutron generation time |

$\xi$    $\dfrac{k_{20}E_2}{k_{10}E_1}$ in Section 2a;

$\dfrac{k_{10}E_1}{k_{20}E_2}$ in Section 2b;

$\dfrac{F_1E_1}{F_2E_2}$ in Section 2d

$\rho$    density of fluid in Section 2a; reactivity in Section 4

$\rho_n$    maximum available reactivity

## CHAPTER 5

$a$    positive constant

$A$    constant defined by equation (18) in Section 1; constant defined by equation (25) in Section 2; thrust level of the vehicle in Section 3; $\alpha C$ in Section 4

$B$    constant defined by equation (19) in Section 1; constant defined by equations (41) and (42) in Section 2

$C$    constant

$f$    switching function

$g$    acceleration of the gravity of the moon in Section 1; functional representation of covariant variables defined by equation (58) in Section 2

$H$    the Hamiltonian function

$H^*$    the portion of Hamiltonian function which involves the decision variables

$I_i$    moment of inertia

$k$    velocity of the exhausted gas with respect to the vehicle

$m$    total mass of vehicle

$M$    positive constant in Section 2; maximum thrust value per gram of the initial orbit in Section 3

$n$    orbital angular frequency

$N$    exhaust velocity

$P$    amplitude

$r$    central range angle

$r_f$    final value of $r$

$s$    dummy variable; Laplacian variable given in equation (43)

$S$    objective function

$t$    time

$t_1$    time from the initiation of full thrust to touchdown

$t'$    time between 0 and $t_1$

$T$    terminal time

| | |
|---|---|
| $Tc\Phi$ | roll component of the control torque |
| $Tc\psi$ | yaw component of the control torque |
| $w$ | root of equation (43) |
| $We$ | effective outflow velocity |
| $x_1$ | altitude of vehicle in Section 1; distance from the center of attraction in Section 3; horizontal velocity component in Section 4 |
| $x_2$ | angular momentum in Section 3; vertical velocity component in Section 4 |
| $x_3$ | radial velocity in Section 3; dimensionless mass of rocket in Section 4 |
| $x_4$ | mass of vehicle in Section 3; range in Section 4 |
| $x_5$ | height |
| $y_i$ | variables defined by equation (28) |
| $z$ | adjoint vector |

**Greek Letters**

| | |
|---|---|
| $\alpha$ | initial altitude of the vehicle in Section 4; initial condition in Section 2; $$\frac{M_{\max}}{[m(0)c]}$$ in Section 4 |
| $\beta$ | initial altitude rate in Section 1; final conditions in Section 2; constant in Section 4 |
| $\delta$ | phase angle |
| $\epsilon$ | small number |
| $\theta$ | decision vector |
| $\theta_1$ | throttle settling in Section 3; dimensionless thrust based on the maximum thrust level in Section 4 |
| $\theta_2$ | steering angle in Section 3; inclination of the thrust to the horizontal |
| $\xi$ | switching position |
| $\tau$ | normalized time, nt |
| $\tau_f$ | final value of $\tau$ |
| $\varphi$ | phase shift defined by equation (91) |
| $\Phi$ | roll angle |
| $\psi$ | yaw angle |

**CHAPTER 6**

| | |
|---|---|
| $a$ | constant |
| $A$ | integration constant |

| | |
|---|---|
| $b$ | number of initial points |
| $c_i$ | constant in objective function |
| $f$ | number of final points |
| $g$ | function of state variables |
| $H$ | the Hamiltonian function |
| $k$ | branch number |
| $m$ | $m$th branch |
| $n$ | $n$th branch |
| $N$ | total number of branches |
| $r$ | total number of decision variables |
| $r^{(k)}$ | total number of decision variables in $k$th branch |
| $s$ | total number of state variables |
| $s^{(k)}$ | total number of state variables in $k$th branch |
| $t$ | independent variable, time or position |
| $T$ | final value of $t$ |
| $x$ | state vector |
| $\bar{x}$ | the optimal value of $x$ |
| $y$ | perturbation of state vector |
| $z$ | adjoint vector |

## Greek Letters

| | |
|---|---|
| $\alpha$ | constant |
| $\beta$ | constant |
| $\gamma$ | constant |
| $\epsilon$ | small number |
| $\theta$ | decision vector |
| $\bar{\theta}$ | the optimal value of $\theta$ |
| $\lambda$ | $\sqrt{a^2 + 1}$ |
| $\varphi$ | perturbation of the decision vector |

## CHAPTER 7

| | |
|---|---|
| $a$ | constant in Sections 1a and 2a; order of reaction in Section 3a |
| $A$ | chemical specie |
| $A_i$ | integration constants |
| $A^{(k)}$ | cross sectional area for $k$th branch tubular reactor |
| $B$ | chemical specie |
| $B_i$ | integration constants |
| $c$ | constant in objective function |
| $C$ | chemical specie |
| $C_i$ | integration constants; molar concentration of component $i$ in Sections 3a and 3b |

| | |
|---|---|
| $C_0$ | initial molar concentration |
| $D$ | axial diffusivity |
| $E$ | activation energy |
| $f$ | constant |
| $F_i^{(k)}$ | $\dfrac{2k_{i0}L_k}{v^{(k)}}$ |
| $g$ | functional representation of state variables in Section 1a; constant in Section 2a |
| $G$ | mass flow rate |
| $h$ | constant |
| $H$ | the Hamiltonian function |
| $k$ | specific reaction rate constant |
| $k_{i0}$ | frequency factor |
| $l$ | axial distance along a tubular reactor |
| $L$ | length of a reactor |
| $m_i$ | constants |
| $M^{(k)}$ | $\dfrac{v^{(k)}L_{(k)}}{2D}$ |
| $n$ | number of branches |
| $n_i$ | constants |
| $r$ | order of reaction |
| $R$ | gas law constant in Sections 1b and 2b; a chemical specie in Section 3a |
| $R_i$ | rate of production of component $i$ |
| $s$ | order of reaction |
| $S$ | objective function in Section 1; cross-sectional area in Section 3b |
| $t$ | independent variable, time or position in Section 1a, 2a, and 4; holding time in Sections 1b and 2b |
| $T$ | final value of $t$ in Sections 1a, 2a, and 4; total holding time in Sections 1b and 2b |
| $v$ | total volumetric flow rate |
| $x$ | state vector; molar concentration of reactant in Sections 1b and 2b; fractional molar concentration in Section 3 |
| $z$ | adjoint vector |

### Greek Letters

| | |
|---|---|
| $\alpha$ | constant in Sections 1, 2, and 4; fraction of feed fed in Section 3 |
| $\beta$ | constant in Sections 2 and 4; fraction of product recycled in Section 3 |
| $\gamma$ | constant |

$\gamma_k$     $\dfrac{v^{(k)}}{v^{(3)}}$

$\eta_i$     dimensionless time, $t/T_i$ in Sections 1b and 2b; $l/L_i$ in Section 3b

$\theta$     decision vector

$\bar{\theta}$     the optimal value of $\theta$

$\lambda$     $\sqrt{a^2 + 1}$

$\lambda_1$     $\dfrac{E_1}{E_2 - E_1}$

$\lambda_2$     $\dfrac{E_2}{E_2 - E_1}$

$\xi$     $k_{10}E_1/k_{20}E_2$ in Sections 1b and 2b; $F_1^{(2)}E_1/F_2^{(2)}E_2$ in Section 3b; $k_{20}E_2/k_{10}E_1$ in Section 3c; constant in Section 4

$\xi_i^{(k)}$     better approximate value of $x_i^{(k)}(T_k)$ in Runge-Kutta method

## CHAPTER 8

$b$     number of initial points

$c$     number of continuous branches

$c'$     number of entering streams which are continuous

$c''$     number of leaving streams which are continuous

$c_i$     constant in objective function

$d$     number of discrete branches

$d'$     number of entering streams which are discrete

$d''$     number of leaving streams which are discrete

$H$     the Hamiltonian function

$k$     $k$th branch

$m$     $m$th branch

$n$     $n$th stage

$N$     total number of branches or total number of discrete stages or the $N$th discrete stage

$r$     total number of decision variables

$s$     total number of state variables

$S$     objective function

$t$     independent variable, time or position

$t_0$     initial value of $t$

$T$     final value of $t$ in transformation operator

$x$     state vector

$\bar{x}$     the optimal value of $x$

$y$     perturbation of state vector

$z$     adjoint vector

## Greek Letters

$\epsilon$      small number
$\theta$      decision vector
$\bar{\theta}$      the optimal value of $\theta$
$\varphi$      perturbation of decision vector

## CHAPTER 9

| | |
|---|---|
| $a$ | constant |
| $A^{(k)}$ | cross-sectional area of a tubular reactor in the $k$th branch |
| $A_i$ | integration constant |
| $b$ | order of reaction |
| $B$ | chemical specie |
| $B_i$ | integration constant |
| $c_i$ | constant in objective function |
| $C$ | constant |
| $C'$ | constant |
| $C_i$ | mass concentration of the $i$th component |
| $E_i$ | activation energy |
| $f$ | function of state variables |
| $f_N$ | optimum value of the objective function for a $N$-stage process |
| $g_N$ | optimum value of the objective function for a $N$-stage process |
| $G_N$ | total amount of washing water supplied |
| $h$ | interval profit function |
| $H$ | the Hamiltonian function |
| $k_i$ | specific reaction constant |
| $k_{i0}$ | frequency factor |
| $l$ | independent variable, axial distance along a tubular reactor |
| $L$ | length of a tubular reactor |
| $L_k$ | final value of independent variable 1 at the $k$th branch |
| $n$ | the $n$th stage |
| $N$ | total number of stages |
| $P$ | net profit function |
| $q$ | mass flow rate |
| $Q_N$ | total amount of product $R$ extracted |
| $r$ | order of reaction |
| $R$ | chemical specie or gas constant |
| $R_i$ | rate of production of the $i$th component |
| $s$ | total number of state variables |
| $S$ | objective function |
| $S_i$ | objective function of the $i$th unit |

| $t$ | independent variable, time or position; holding time of a continuous stirred tank reactor in Example 4 |
|---|---|
| $T$ | final value of independent variable $t$ |
| $T_k$ | final value of independent variable $t$ at the $k$th branch |
| $u^n$ | $w^n/q$ |
| $v$ | volumetric flow rate |
| $v^{(k)}$ | volumetric flow rate in $k$th branch |
| $V$ | volume of a continuous stirred tank reactor |
| $w^n$ | washing water flow rate into $n$th stage |
| $x$ | state vector |
| $y$ | composition of extract at outlet of extractor |
| $\bar{y}$ | optimum value of a state variable at the end of a tubular reactor |
| $z$ | adjoint vector |

## Greek Letters

| $\alpha$ | proportionality constant of equilibrium relation in Example 1; constant in Example 3; fractional amount of feed stream in Example 4 |
|---|---|
| $\beta$ | constant in Example 3; fractional amount of recycle stream in Example 4 |
| $\gamma_i$ | initial value of state variable |
| $\theta$ | decision vector |
| $\lambda$ | Lagrange's multiplier, relative cost of washing water in Example 1; $\sqrt{a^2 + 1}$ in Examples 2 and 3 |
| $\lambda_1$ | $\dfrac{E_1}{E_2 - E_1}$ |
| $\lambda_2$ | $\dfrac{E_2}{E_2 - E_1}$ |
| $\mu$ | constant |
| $\rho_m$ | density of mixture |

## CHAPTER 10

| $a$ | constant |
|---|---|
| $a^n$ | given constant in the $n$th unit |
| $a^{0n}$ | given condition of boundary input to the $n$th unit |
| $A$ | chemical specie |
| $A^n$ | cross-sectional area of the $n$th unit tubular reactor |
| $A_i^{\,n}$ | integration constant |
| $b^n$ | given constant at the $n$th unit |
| $B$ | chemical specie |

| | |
|---|---|
| $c^{n,N+1}$ | constant vector in the objective function |
| $c^{n,N+M+1}$ | constant vector in the objective function in Section 7 |
| $c^{i,N+M+1}$ | constant vector in the objective function in Section 7 |
| $C$ | chemical specie |
| $E_i$ | activation energy |
| $f^i$ | unit equation of the $i$th discrete unit in Section 8 |
| $f^n$ | unit equation of the $n$th unit |
| $h^i$ | implicit discrete unit equation in Section 8 |
| $h^n$ | implicit unit equation of the $n$th unit |
| $H^n$ | the Hamiltonian function in the $n$th unit |
| $i$ | the $i$th component in a vector; the $i$th discrete unit in Sections 7 and 8 |
| $k_{i0}$ | frequency factor |
| $l^{0n}$ | total number of components in the vector $y^{0n}$ |
| $l^{nv}$ | total number of components in the vector $y^{nv}$ |
| $L^n$ | length of the $n$th tubular reactor; final value of the independent variable $\xi$ at the $n$th unit |
| $M$ | total number of discrete units in Sections 7 and 8 |
| $n$ | the $n$th unit |
| $nv$ | stream leaving the $n$th unit and entering the $v$th unit |
| $N$ | the $N$th unit; total number of units; total number of continuous units in Sections 7 and 8 |
| $N+M$ | total number of units in a composite process |
| $P$ | total cost function in a composite process |
| $P^i$ | cost function in the $i$th unit |
| $Q^n$ | amount of washing water added to the $n$th unit |
| $R$ | domain of real variable; gas constant |
| $R_j$ | rate of production of component $j$ |
| $s^n$ | total number of component in the state vector $x^n$ |
| $S$ | objective function |
| $S^n$ | objective function in the $n$th unit |
| $t^i$ | holding time in the $i$th continuous stirred tank reactor |
| $T$ | transpose of a matrix |
| $T^n$ | total holding time in the $n$th tubular reactor |
| $u^n$ | adjoint vector corresponding to $y^n$ |
| $v^i$ | total volumetric flow rate in the $i$th discrete unit |
| $v^{nm}$ | functional relationship between the state vector $x^n$ and the output state vector $y^{nm}$ |
| $v^{nv}$ | volumetric flow rate in the $nv$th stream |
| $V^i$ | volume of the $i$th continuous stirred tank |
| $w^n$ | functional relationship between the total input state vector $y^n$ and the component inputs state vector $y^{\mu n}$ |

$x^n$ — state vector of the $n$th unit

$\bar{x}^n$ — optimum value of $x^n$

$y^n$ — state vector of total input to the $n$th unit

$y^{0i}$ — state vector of an input crossing the boundary and entering the $i$th discrete unit

$y^{0n}$ — state vector of an input crossing the boundary and entering the $n$th unit

$y^{i,N+M+1}$ — state vector of the boundary output of the $i$th discrete unit in a composite process

$y^{nm}$ — state vector of the $nm$th stream, leaving the $n$th unit and entering the $m$th unit

$y^{n,N+1}$ — state vector leaving the $n$th unit and crossing out of boundary

$y^{n,N+M+1}$ — state vector of the boundary output of the $n$th continuous unit in a composite process

$y^{\mu n}$ — state vector of the $\mu n$th stream, input to the $n$th unit from the $\mu$th unit

$\bar{y}^n$ — optimum value of $y^n$

$\bar{y}^{0n}$ — optimum value of $y^{0n}$

$\bar{y}^{nm}$ — optimum value of $y^{nm}$

$\bar{y}^{\mu n}$ — optimum value of $y^{\mu n}$

$z^n$ — adjoint vector corresponding to $x^n$

$z^{nm}$ — adjoint vector corresponding to $y^{nm}$

$\tilde{z}^n$ — adjoint vector defined in equation (49)

## Greek Letters

$\alpha^{\mu n}$ — fraction of the $\mu n$ stream to the total input to the $n$th unit; a nonnegative constant defined in equation (39)

$\beta^{nm}$ — fraction of the $nm$th output stream to the total flow rate through the $n$th unit

$\Gamma$ — diagonal matrix defined in equation (39)

$\epsilon$ — small positive number

$\eta$ — $\dfrac{k_{10}E_1}{k_{20}E_2}$

$\theta^n$ — decision vector in the $n$th unit

$\lambda$ — given scalar constant in Example 1, Section 3; relative cost in Example 2, Section 3

$\lambda_1$ — $\dfrac{E_1}{E_2 - E_1}$

$\lambda_2$ — $\dfrac{E_2}{E_2 - E_1}$

$\lambda^n$ — constant for the $n$th unit

| | |
|---|---|
| $\mu$ | the $\mu$th unit; constant in equation (204) |
| $\nu$ | the $\nu$th unit |
| $\xi$ | independent variable |
| $\rho^n$ | total mass flow rate of the $n$th unit in Section 3; a predetermined weighting factors at the $n$th unit in Section 6 |
| $\rho^{\mu n}$ | mass flow rate of the $\mu n$th stream |
| $\varphi^n$ | variation of decision vector from its optimal one at the $n$th unit |
| $\varphi(x_1{}^n)$ | function of $x_1{}^n$ in equation (52) |

## CHAPTER 11

| | |
|---|---|
| $a$ | vector belonging to a tangent plane |
| $c_i$ | constant in the objective function |
| $E$ | Weierstrass excess function |
| $f_i$ | real function |
| $F$ | real function |
| $g$ | real function |
| $G_{ij}$ | Green's function |
| $h$ | real function |
| $H$ | the Hamiltonian function |
| $M$ | constant |
| $r$ | dimension of the decision vector $\theta$ |
| $R$ | region of the space of real variables |
| $s$ | dimension of the state vector $x$ |
| $S$ | objective function |
| $t$ | time |
| $t_0$ | initial value of time $t$ |
| $t'$ | time as a dummy variable |
| $T$ | final value of time $t$ |
| $W$ | real function |
| $x$ | state vector |
| $\bar{x}$ | optimal value of $x$ |
| $\dot{x}$ | derivative of $x$ with respect to time $t$ |
| $\epsilon y$ | perturbation of the state vector |
| $z$ | Green's vector, covariant vector, or adjoint vector |
| $z_{ij}$ | Green's tensor |

**Greek Letters**

| | |
|---|---|
| $\alpha$ | initial value of $x$ |
| $\beta$ | final value of $x$ |
| $\delta_{ij}$ | Kronecker delta |
| $\epsilon$ | small number |

| | |
|---|---|
| $\eta$ | parameter |
| $\theta$ | decision vector |
| $\bar{\theta}$ | optimal decision |
| $\xi$ | constant |
| $\tau$ | parameter |
| $\epsilon\varphi$ | perturbation of the decision vector |
| $\epsilon\bar{\varphi}$ | special variation of the decision vector |
| $\Phi$ | real function |
| $\psi$ | real function |

## APPENDIX I

| | |
|---|---|
| $c$ | constant in equation (11) |
| $c_i$ | constant in equation (41) |
| $f$ | function defined in equation (9) |
| $f_i$ | performance function defined in equation (38) |
| $F$ | function defined in equation (10) |
| $g$ | $\dfrac{dx_1}{dz_1(t_0)}$ |
| $g_{ij}$ | $\dfrac{dx_i}{dz_j(t_0)}$ |
| $G$ | $\dfrac{dz_1}{dz_1(t_0)}$ |
| $G_{ij}$ | $\dfrac{dz_i}{dz_j(t_0)}$ |
| $h$ | a small increment of state vector $x$ |
| $H$ | the Hamiltonian function |
| $i$ | the $i$th component of state vector $x$ or decision vector $\theta$ |
| $q$ | increment of ordinate in Runge-Kutta calculation |
| $s$ | total number of component of state vector |
| $t$ | independent variable coordinate |
| $T$ | final value of $t$ |
| $x$ | state vector; independent variable in Section 1 |
| $x_0$ | initial value of $x$ in Section 1 |
| $y$ | dependent variable in Section 1 |
| $y_0$ | initial value of $y$ in Section 1 |
| $y_n$ | value of $y$ in the $n$th step integration |
| $z$ | adjoint vector |

### Greek Letters

| | |
|---|---|
| $\alpha$ | initial value of $x$ |
| $\alpha_i$ | initial value of $x_i$ |

$\theta$          decision vector

$\xi_i$         new approximation for $z_i(t_0)$

## APPENDIX II

$D_n$        decision variable at the stage $n$

$H$          the Hamiltonian function

$N$          total number of stages or the $N$th stage

$r$           return function; label of the new state variable

$S_I$         global initial state variable

$S_F$        global final state variables

$T_n$        transformation operator at the $n$th stage

$x_n$        state variable for the $n$th stage

$x_I$         initial state variable

$x_F$        final state variable

$x_{Fi}$       local final state variable of downstream subprocess

$\bar{\bar{x}}$         specified value of $x$

$z$          adjoint variable

## Greek Letters

$\delta_{ri}$        the Kronecker delta

$\theta_n$        decision variable for the $n$th stage

$\mu$         number of input streams at a stage

$\nu$          number of output streams at a stage

# Author Index

# Subject Index